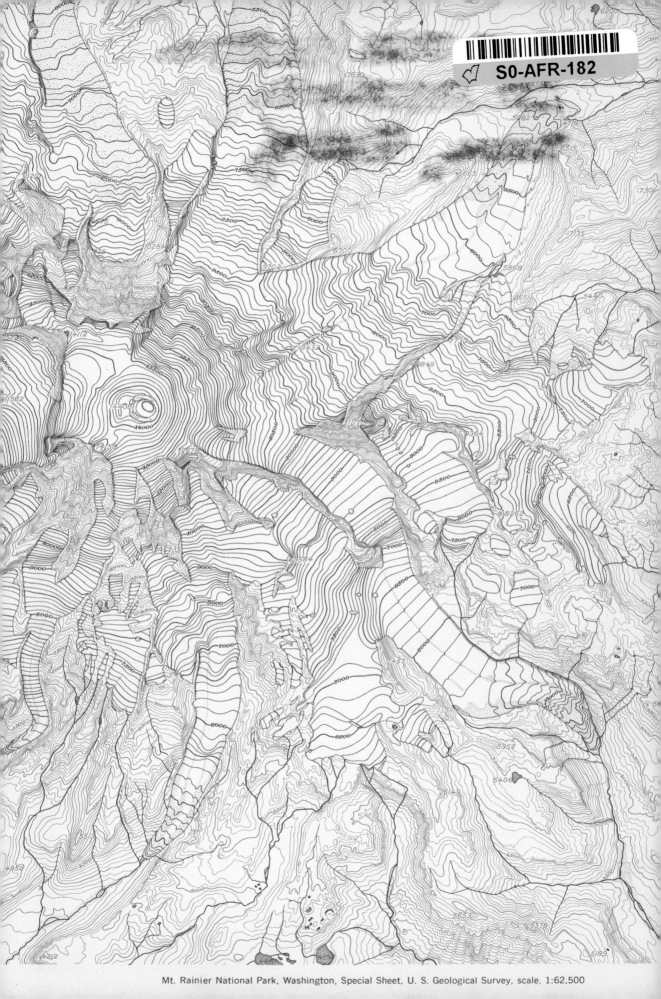

Mt. Rainier National Park, Washington, Special Sheet, U. S. Geological Survey, scale, 1:62,500

Arthur N. Strahler, *Professor of Geomorphology, Columbia University*

Physical Geography

Second Edition

John Wiley & Sons, Inc.
New York, London

Preface

A healthy resurgence of interest in physical geography as a basic, essential ingredient of the American geography curriculum has made itself felt in the near-decade elapsing between publication of the first edition of *Physical Geography* and the present revision. We may never return to the early form of environmental determinism, to which reaction was so strong, but there are unmistakable signs that a large number of geography teachers regard the elements of natural environment as strongly influencing and in some cases severely limiting the activities of mankind. With the generous encouragement of many friends in the geography profession, I have tried to improve my treatment of physical geography in order to provide a broad natural science base constructed of topics germane to those problems of regional, economic, cultural, and historical geography with which the more advanced student will later be concerned.

Perhaps the largest group of students to profit by the treatment of physical geography as presented in this book will not go on to advanced studies of geography or any of the natural sciences. Instead, they will simply observe throughout their lives the phenomena they have studied here. These students will see the sun's path in the sky day after day; they will note the changing lengths of day and night as the annual cycle progresses; they will feel the daily and annual temperature variations; they may see daily the changing tide levels and tidal currents (if they commute in a coastal metropolitan area); they will see various map projections used in newspapers and magazines; and they will watch the passage of storms and fronts, noting the representation of the pressure systems on the daily weather maps in the newspaper and on the television screen; they will see the topographic features of the landscape in their vacation and business travels; they will note the differences in appearance and productivity of the soil from place to place and the characteristic vegetative assemblages associated with certain regions. How can we question the immediate relevance of the topics in this book to the everyday experience of human beings? The student will remember the elementary principles of physical geography because he is repeatedly exposed to a demonstration of them in a way that forces the phenomena upon his attention. Therefore I urge that physical geography, as an earth science, be given a major place in our liberal arts colleges.

The explanatory-descriptive technique is generally used throughout the book. As applied by William Morris Davis to the analysis of landforms, explanatory description has provided an excellent vehicle for geographical purposes. The technique may also be applied to the presentation of elements of weather and climate. Without explanation, description is unsatisfying and sterile. On the other hand, without penetration into mechanics, thermodynamics, and higher mathematics, the degree of explanation that can be achieved by verbal description must necessarily be limited and will seem superficial to the specialist. Painfully evident as this superficiality—or oversimplification—is to me in the treatment of geomorphic processes and forms in which my own researches lie, it must be equally disconcerting to specialists in the other fields covered.

Among those teachers who have unknowingly contributed a major share to this book, three in particular should be acknowledged: Professor A. K. Lobeck, whose friendly interest provided me with a constant source of encouragement, has set the example for graphic illustrations of landforms through his publications. Many borrowed ideas in this book have their sources in *Geomorphology, an Introduction to the Study of Landscapes, The Earth in Space,* and *Panorama of Physiographic Types.* Having used Professor G. T. Trewartha's publications both as a student and teacher, it is not surprising that I have leaned heavily on his published works on weather and climate for methods of presentation as well as for many of the climate data. Users of Willis E. Johnson's *Mathematical Geography,* published over a half-century ago, will see at once the similarity of subject matter and presentation between that most useful little volume and the first chapters of my own book. It is a pleasure to perpetuate Johnson's contributions to mathematical geography.

In the treatment of climate I have tried to explain the basic varieties of climate and their origin in terms of air masses, source regions, and frontal zones, but to avoid stressing definitions and climate boundaries. Because the terminology used in the first edition proved awkward in teaching, I have been more than happy to yield to the better judgment of my colleagues and reinstate the well-known climate names. Inclusion of the Köppen system as a parallel and optional treatment may make the book more generally useful without sacrificing the explanatory-descriptive method. If the present book can lay the foundations of understanding of climates it will have fulfilled its purpose. For the vast majority of college students, any climate system of symbols and arbitrarily defined boundaries will be quickly forgotten. Only by attention to essential climate characteristics and their explanation in the dynamics of atmospheric circulation can we hope to add a permanent and useful increment to the general education of the student.

Of rapidly increasing concern to geographers is the development and conservation of water resources. Regional planning for economic development must face realistically the problem of availability of large supplies of fresh water for irrigation and power, or for industrial and domestic uses. To give the geography student some familiarity with the fundamental hydrologic and geologic principles involved, new chapters have been devoted to soil moisture, ground water, and surface runoff.

References for further study listed at the end of the book will give the serious student a sample of the original books and scientific papers, both old and new, on which physical geography is built. No attempt has been made to compile complete or even adequately representative lists. Because I have drawn heavily from the more widely distributed American journals, the lists may make up in accessibility what they lack in selectivity. Highly technical articles using mathematics or a specialized terminology have been generally avoided.

Exercises emphasize operations in which data are transformed into graphic form or interpreted from graphic form. Few long written answers are required in the exercises, and the factor of ease and rapidity of checking has been kept in mind. Where the student is asked to draw or color on a map printed in the book, he may do this work on a tracing sheet laid over the page. By superimposing the student's tracing over his own master copy, the instructor can check the work at a glance.

Over a period of years many users of the first edition have sent in suggestions for improving the content and accuracy of the text. These contributors are too numerous to acknowledge individually, but the sum of their contributions has been a major force in shaping the revised edition. Personal acknowledgment and thanks are due several specialists who read portions of the revised text: Professor Theodore G. Mehlin of Williams College examined chapters on astronomical aspects of the earth as a globe; Colonel L. E. Schick and Assistants of the Department of Military Topography & Graphics, U.S. Military Academy, West Point, reviewed the material on map reading and military grids; and Professor John C. Sherman of the University of Washington reviewed those parts dealing with cartography. The sections on weather and climate received particular attention from Professor F. Kenneth Hare of McGill University, who also added many helpful comments on other parts of the book. Professor Gerhard Neumann of New York University reviewed the oceanographic material. Professor L. E. Spock of New York University's geology department reviewed the geological chapters; Dr. Charles W. Carlston of the U.S. Geological Survey's Ground Water Branch examined particularly the chapters on ground water and runoff, and the entire section on geomorphology received careful attention from Professor Arthur D. Howard of Stanford University. The generous assistance of these reviewers led to many corrections and improvements in the text. Such errors and misconceptions as may have persisted can only be blamed on the author. To my wife, Margaret, I am deeply grateful for much help in manuscript typing and proofreading.

A. N. S.

Columbia University
March 1960

Contents

Introduction

WHAT IS PHYSICAL GEOGRAPHY? As a first step in understanding this term we might well expand it to read "the physical basis of geography," for physical geography is simply the study and unification of a number of earth sciences which give us a general insight into the nature of man's environment. Not in itself a distinct branch of science, physical geography is a body of basic principles of earth science selected with a view to including primarily the environmental influences that vary from place to place over the earth's surface.

What, then, are the individual earth sciences that comprise physical geography, and why are they selected? First and most fundamental are the form of the earth, a concern of the science of *geodesy*, and the relationship between earth and sun, a part of *astronomy*. Much of astronomy is beyond the concern of the geographer, for only two bodies, the sun and the moon, appreciably affect life on earth. Because all energy for sustaining life, all motive power for streams, winds, and ocean currents, comes by radiant emanation from the sun, and because the intensity of this energy changes through daily and annual cycles, an understanding of the motions of the earth in its orbit about the sun is a prime essential. The moon, as the body that controls ocean tides, enters into physical geography only in a minor way.

Because the data of earth science are often best represented by maps, and perhaps many are impossible to describe without maps, the science of maps, *cartography*, is an essential ingredient of physical geography. True, cartography is really a science of technique, rather than a basic earth science, but it deserves a place early in the list of topics so that it may provide a means for representing the information to follow.

1

Man, though he lives *on* the earth's solid surface, is an air-breather *in* the atmosphere and owes his very survival to favorable conditions of weather and climate. The sciences of *meteorology* and *climatology*, which treat these topics, are thus a major concern of the physical geographer. Lying between the atmosphere and the land masses of the earth is a thin layer, the soil, which reflects the influence of both climate and topography. Soil science, or *pedology*, is thus another constituent of physical geography. The distribution of natural vegetation types, though a botanical rather than a physical science subject, cannot easily be excluded from consideration in physical geography because plants are remarkably consistent indicators of climate, soils, and topography. Thus the science of *plant geography* is taken into the fold of physical geography.

In our concern for the lands of the earth we should not overlook the oceans of the globe. *Physical oceanography*, which includes a study of ocean waves, currents, and tides, finds its way into physical geography inevitably because man uses the oceans for intercontinental communication, for naval and air operations, and as a source of food as well.

The topographic features, or landforms, of the earth's surface are of prime concern to man because they influence the placement of his agricultural lands, his cities, his lines of communication. The science of *geomorphology* treats the origin and systematic development of all types of landforms and is a major part of physical geography. Very often topography is merely a surface expression of the varieties and structures of rocks under the surface, so that a certain minimum knowledge of the principles of *geology* is included. An understanding of geological principles will have the further value of explaining the origin and distribution of the principal types of mineral deposits—coal, petroleum, natural gas, metallic ores, building stones, and many others. Closely involved with geomorphology is the science of *hydrology*, which treats the earth's surface and underground waters, including rivers, lakes, springs, and marshes. Fresh water, a basic essential for man's survival, thus looms as an important element of the physical basis of geography.

The professional physical geographer will usually be a specialist in only one of the several fields involved, such as climatology, geomorphology or soil science. Besides carrying out original research in his chosen specialty, to which he may be making important scientific contributions, the physical geographer attempts to keep informed on important developments as they occur in the other fields of specialization. He is thus able to assemble and integrate pertinent fragments of knowledge into a unified picture of the natural environment of man at any place on the globe at any season of year.

Part One
The Earth as a Globe

CHAPTER ONE

Form of the earth, the geographic grid

THE spherical form of the earth is one of the facts of our physical environment, which children learn at an early age, but probably few people give much thought to some of the simple proofs of the earth's sphericity. For example, the evidence that people have repeatedly sailed or flown completely around the globe is tacitly assumed to prove the sphericity of the earth, whereas it means only that the earth is a solid body. Circumnavigation could be performed on a cubical or cylindrical earth. Sphericity of the earth might, however, be proved if it could be shown that in a large number of plane flights made around the largest circumference of the earth, each starting in a different direction, all flights were of equal distance.

A second proof of the earth's sphericity may be had from observations at sea. Most persons on shipboard have at one time or another noticed that, as a passing ship recedes farther and farther into the distance, it appears to sink slowly beneath the water level (Figure 1.1). Through binoculars or a telescope the sea level will appear to rise until the decks are awash, then gradually to submerge the funnel and the masts, leaving finally only smoke visible above the horizon. The explanation obviously lies in the fact that the sea surface is curved. To prove that this curvature is spherical

would require numerous observations in which measurements were made of the amount of apparent sinking of a vessel per unit of distance in many different directions away from the observing point. The proof would still not be satisfactory unless the experiment were repeated in many different ocean

Figure 1.1 Seen through a telescope, a distant ship seems to be partly submerged.

areas over the globe and the amount of curvature were found to remain constant.

A third proof may be had from the observation that in all lunar eclipses, at which time the earth's shadow falls on the moon, the edge of the shadow

above: Measuring the sun's altitude by sextant.
Official U.S. Navy photograph.

5

appears as an arc of a circle. It can be shown by geometrical proof that a sphere is the only body that will always cast a circular shadow upon another sphere. Because at the time of these eclipses the earth is rarely turned in just the same position, we may conclude that, no matter what earth profile is cast on the moon, the circular shadows are all alike and the earth must be spherical.

Examination of photographs taken at extremely high altitudes may show the horizon as a curved line. Should the curvature appear to be the same in many widely separated parts of the earth, a series of such photographs might provide us with a fourth proof of the earth's spherical form.

A fifth proof may be had from observation of the position of the north star (or any other star). To the observer at the equator the north star is on the horizon, but as he travels toward the north pole the star seems to be located higher and higher in the sky, until, at the north pole, it is directly overhead in the sky. It would be found that the north star rises 1° higher in the sky for every 69 miles of northward travel by the observer. A similar condition would hold for travel from the equator to the south pole if a star nearly in line with the earth's axis in the southern sky were observed. Thus we can prove that all arcs drawn from pole to pole are arcs of circles, and that the earth is spherical in form.

A sixth proof is found in surveying operations with precise telescopic instruments. Suppose that an engineer should drive two posts into the ground, one mile apart, to such a depth that when he sights from the top of the first to the top of the second, his line of sight will be perfectly horizontal according to the sensitive level bubble on the telescope (Figure 1.2). Now suppose that he drives a third post in line with the first two, but a mile beyond the second, and that he adjusts the height of the third post so that a telescopic line of sight back to the second post is a perfect horizontal, as shown by his level bubble. Were he not aware of the earth's curvature, the engineer might be surprised to find that if he now sights with his telescope from the

top of the first to the top of the third post, the top of the second projects above this new line of sight. This is explained by the fact that a telescopic line of sight does not follow the curve of the earth, but is a tangent straight line which extends out into space. Surveyors, therefore, have to make corrections for the earth's curvature, and because this correction is approximately constant for all places on the earth we may conclude the earth to be spherical.

A seventh proof of the earth's sphericity comes from the observation that an object will weigh very nearly the same amount on a spring type of scales at any place on the globe. Knowing that the weight depends upon the pull of gravity, we conclude that the object weighs the same everywhere because all points on the earth's surface are equidistant from its center, hence, the earth is spherical. Extremely precise calculations based upon this principle, however, show slight variations in gravity, which, as will be explained later, led to the discovery that the earth's true form is not a perfect sphere.

As an eighth and last proof it may be noted that modern navigation methods are based on the assumption that the earth is a sphere. When we consider that for more than a century, positions of vessels have been correctly determined innumerable times by these methods, it becomes obvious that the correctness of the assumption has been established many times over.

Eratosthenes' measurement of the earth

Although the ancient Greeks, among them Pythagoras (540 B.C.) and associates of Aristotle (384–322 B.C.), believed the earth to be spherical and had speculated upon its circumference, it remained until 200 B.C. for Eratosthenes, librarian at Alexandria, to perform a direct measurement based upon a sound principle of astronomy. He observed that at Syene, Egypt, located on the upper Nile River close to the Tropic of Cancer, 23½° N, the sun's noon rays on the date of the summer solstice (June 21) shone directly upon the floor of a deep, vertical well. In other words, the sun was then in the zenith point in the sky and its rays were perpendicular to the earth's surface at that latitude (Figure 1.3). At Alexandria, however, on this same date, the rays of the noon sun made an angle of one-fiftieth of a circumference, or 7° 12′, with respect to the vertical. As we can see from the relations between parallel sun's rays and radial lines from the earth's center, the arc of the earth's surface lying between Alexandria and Syene is also equal to 7° 12′ or one-fiftieth of the earth's circumference. Therefore, it is necessary only to determine the ground distance along the north-south line between the two places, multiply

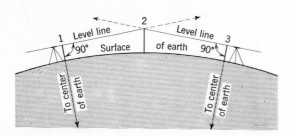

Figure 1.2 Because of the earth's surface curvature, the sight lines of surveying telescopes do not maintain a constant elevation.

this by 50, and the circumference is known.

Eratosthenes took as the distance between Alexandria and Syene 5000 stadia, but this may have been only a rough estimate. This gave 250,000 stadia for the earth's circumference. Using a stadium equivalent of 185 meters, the circumference comes out to 46,250 kilometers or about 26,660 miles, which is of the same general order of size as the true value of about 25,000 miles.

From Eratosthenes' classic experiment, it is an easy step to design an astronomical method of measuring the earth's figure. We need only to select a north-south line, whose length can be measured directly on level ground by surveying means. The line should be at least 70 miles long to give an arc of about one degree. At the ends of the line the altitude of any selected star can be measured at its highest point above the horizon or with respect to the vertical, using a level bubble or a plumb bob as a means of establishing a true horizontal or vertical reference. The difference in angular position of the star will be the arc of the earth's circumference lying between the ends of the measured line. This very procedure is believed to have been followed by Arabs of the ninth century. Their measurements were probably much more accurate than those of Eratosthenes, but because the units of measure are not known in modern equivalents, their work cannot be checked.

Amount of the earth's surface curvature

The amount of curvature of the earth's surface may be stated in terms of the actual distance between a curved line lying on the earth's surface (as on the calm ocean) and a tangent straight line originating at the same point. This distance we will call the *divergence* (Figure 1.4). Because the air decreases in density upwards, a light ray will not be a straight line but will bend earthward. The effect of this phenomenon, which is known as *refraction*, is to decrease the divergence by about one-seventh of what it would be if the earth had no atmosphere. A simple rule for finding the divergence in feet between the surface line and the light-ray line is to take three-fifths of the square of the number of miles between the two desired places (points A and B in Figure 1.4). The formula may be written as follows:

$$f = \tfrac{3}{5}M^2$$
$$(\text{Exact value: } f = 0.574M^2)$$

where f = number of feet between surface and light-ray lines, and M = distance in miles. For example, if the distance is 10 miles, the two lines have diverged to the extent of being approximately 60 feet apart.

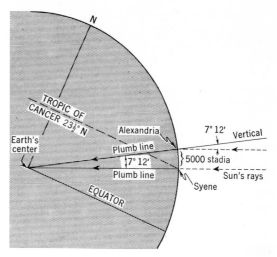

Figure 1.3 Eratosthenes' method of measuring the earth's circumference.

If we already know the divergence in feet of the surface line from the light-ray line, we may find the distance in miles separating the two points by the formula:

$$M = 1\tfrac{1}{3}\ \sqrt{f}$$
$$M = 1.317\ \sqrt{f}$$

That is to say, take the square root of the number of feet of divergence and multiply by $1\tfrac{1}{3}$. If the divergence were 81 feet, for example, the distance in miles would be $9 \times 1\tfrac{1}{3}$, or 12 miles.

In Table 1 somewhat more accurate figures are given for a variety of examples.

The amount of curvature becomes of great interest and practical importance in problems of visibility over the open ocean. The expanse of ocean visible from a single point increases greatly with rising elevation above the water surface. Table 1 shows that from a point 5 feet above the surface, as from a small boat, the radius of vision is about 3 miles, whereas from a point 150 feet above sea level, as from the mast of a ship, it increases to 16 miles.

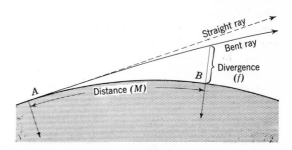

Figure 1.4 Even though a light ray is bent slightly earthward, its divergence from the earth's surface increases with distance.

Where both points lie at different elevations above sea level, as for example, a lighthouse 100 feet above sea level and the bridge of a ship 65 feet above sea level (Figure 1.5), the distance of visibility of the light is the sum of the two distances obtained by solving the curvature problem in two parts. For the observer on the ship's bridge, the radius of vision of the horizon is about 10½ miles. The light rays from the lighthouse are tangent to the sea surface at a distance of 13 miles. The total is therefore about 23½ miles. We have not taken into account other factors that might modify our calculations, such as waves, which would add to the level of the horizon and thus tend to reduce visibility.

TABLE 1

Divergence, feet	Distance, miles	Distance, miles	Divergence, feet
1	1.32	1	0.6
2	1.86	2	2.3
5	2.94	5	14.4
10	4.16	10	57.4
15	5.10	15	129.1
20	5.89	20	229.5
30	7.21	25	358.6
50	9.31	30	516.4
75	11.40	35	703.0
100	13.17	40	918.1
150	16.13	45	1162.0
200	18.63	50	1434.6
500	29.45	60	2065.8
1000	41.65	75	3228.7
5000	93.10	100	5740.0

The earth as an oblate spheroid

In 1671 a French astronomer, Jean Richer, was sent by Louis XIV to the Island of Cayenne, French Guiana, to make certain astronomical observations. His clock had been so adjusted that its pendulum, slightly over 39 inches long, beat the exact seconds in Paris. Upon arriving in Cayenne, which is near the equator, Richer found the clock to be losing about two and one-half minutes per day. This he correctly attributed to a somewhat lesser force of gravity near the equator, and it was soon realized that this phenomenon could be accounted for only by supposing that the equatorial portions of the earth's surface lie farther from the earth's center than do more northerly places. Refined

Figure 1.5 Curvature of the earth's surface limits the range of visibility from high points.

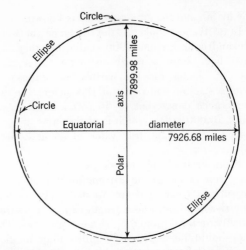

Figure 1.6 The earth is slightly elliptical in a cross section passing through its polar axis. Dimensions are those of the International Ellipsoid of Reference (Hayford, 1909).

measurements of a similar type have since revealed that the true form of the earth is like that of a spherical globe, compressed along the polar axis and bulging slightly around the equator (Figure 1.6). This form is known as an *oblate spheroid* or *ellipsoid of revolution*. A cross section through the poles gives an *ellipse* rather than a circle. The equator remains a circle and is the largest possible circumference on the spheroid. The earth's oblateness is attributed to the centrifugal force of the earth's rotation, which deforms the somewhat plastic earth into a form in equilibrium with respect to the forces of gravity and rotation.

Confirmation of the earth's oblateness was obtained in the eighteenth century by the work of two scientific expeditions sent out under the auspices of the Royal Academy of Sciences of Paris. One party went to Lapland, where, in the years 1736–1737 an arc of 57′ was measured. Finding this arc to be longer than a known equivalent arc at Paris, France, they demonstrated a flattening of the earth toward the poles. Meanwhile, the second party, which had set out for Peru in 1735, actually began measurements near the equator at Quito, Ecuador, completing the measurement of an arc of more than 3° in 1743. The length of a degree of arc there proved to be less than an equivalent arc in France and still less than in Lapland, providing conclusive evidence of the earth's resemblance to an oblate spheroid.

Rounding off the dimensions given in Figure 1.6 to the nearest whole mile, the earth's equatorial diameter is 7927 miles, whereas the length of polar axis is 7900 miles, a difference of about 27 miles (actually 26.70). The *oblateness* of the earth spheroid, or *flattening of the poles*, is the ratio of this difference to the equatorial diameter, or roughly ²⁷⁄₉₂₇, which reduces to a fraction only slightly larger than ⅓₀₀. Further details concerning the earth spheroid and various calculations of its precise dimensions are given later in this chapter.

The science of *geodesy* (from the Greek words meaning "to divide the earth"), which takes for its goal the determination of the form and dimensions of the earth, developed from the need to ascertain precisely the nature of the oblate spheroid which the earth resembles. The scientist who practices geodesy, the *geodesist,* uses extremely precise surveying methods along with delicately refined determinations of the force of gravity to achieve this goal.

The earth as a geoid

Although the oblate spheroid is a much better description of the form of the earth than is the sphere, there is need for still further refinement. The earth's figure, which geodesists are trying to measure and describe, is not the configuration of the ground surface, for this rises and falls in a highly irregular way over the sea floor and continents. The surface whose form is sought is the sea-level surface of the oceans extended in an imaginary way under the lands to form a continuous figure known as the *geoid.* If we could crisscross the continents with canals or tunnels at sea level, permitting the ocean water to seek its level in the heart of the continent, the geoid could be established.

Because of the presence of a large rock mass above sea level in a continent, the force of gravity at sea level is somewhat diminished there. Consequently the sea-level surface, or geoid surface, lies somewhat higher under the continents than the spheroid, which is used as a surface of reference (Figure 1.7). Under the deep ocean basins, where a large mass of rock is replaced by less dense water, the force of gravity at sea level is greater, depressing the surface of the geoid beneath the surface of the reference spheroid. Thus the geoid can be thought of as an undulating surface of irregular form (Figure 1.8). It can be described in terms of its position above or below the imaginary spheroid surface, but is too complex a surface to be described by a simple mathematical formula.

Much of modern research in geodesy is devoted to determining the surface of the geoid. This is important because the direction of downward pull of gravity depends on the form of the geoid surface (Figure 1.7). Because surveying and astronomical observations are based on use of the plumb line or level bubble to give true vertical and horizontal reference directions, the accuracy of such observations hinges on a knowledge of the geoid.

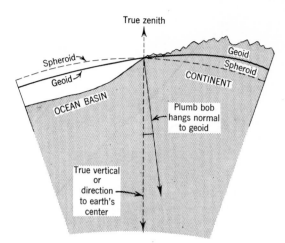

Figure 1.7 Relative positions of geoid and spheroid are reversed from ocean basin to continent.

Great and small circles

If a perfect sphere is divided exactly in half by a plane passed through the center, the intersection of the plane with the sphere is the largest circle that can be drawn on the sphere and is known as a *great circle* (Figure 1.9). Circles produced by planes passing through a sphere anywhere except through the center are smaller than great circles and are designated *small circles.*

It will be of great value to the student of physical geography to be thoroughly familiar with the properties of great circles, because they frequently

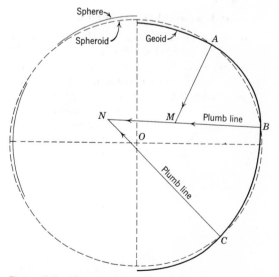

Figure 1.8 The geoid has an irregular shape, in contrast to the perfectly symmetrical spheroid. Plumb lines from A and B intersect at M, giving too small an earth radius. Plumb lines from B and C intersect at N, giving too great an earth radius. (After W. A. Heiskanen.)

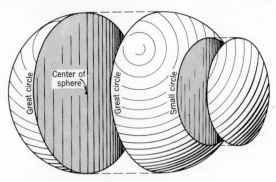

Figure 1.9 A great circle is made by a plane cutting a sphere into two equal halves; a small circle, by a plane cutting the sphere into unequal parts.

enter into such global subjects as meridians, navigation, illumination of the globe, and map projections. The following properties may be listed:

1. A great circle results when a plane passes through the center of a sphere, regardless of the attitude of the plane.

2. A great circle is the largest possible circle that can be drawn on the surface of a sphere.

3. An infinite number of great circles can be drawn on a sphere.

4. One and only one great circle can be found that will pass through two given points on the surface of the sphere (unless the two points are at the extremities of the same diameter, in which case an infinite number of great circles can be drawn through them). This follows the geometrical law that three points determine a plane, the third point in this instance being the center of the sphere.

5. An arc of a great circle is the shortest distance, following the surface, between any two points on a sphere.

6. Intersecting great circles bisect each other.

In view of the earlier discussion of the earth's form, in which it was stated that the earth is not a perfect sphere, but an oblate spheroid, the student may wonder whether the properties of great circles can be properly applied to the earth. For all ordinary purposes, including the use of great circles, the earth may be treated as a sphere without fear of appreciable error. Throughout most of the subject matter that follows in later chapters, the spherical form will be assumed. An exception is in regard to the exact values for degrees of latitude, a subject requiring use of the spheroidal form.

One use of great circles that may be elaborated on here is in navigation. Wherever ships must travel over vast expanses of open ocean between distant ports, or planes must make long flights, it is desirable in the interests of saving fuel and time to follow the great-circle arc between the two points, provided, of course, that there are no obstacles or other deterring factors preventing the use of the great-circle path. Navigators employ special types of maps which have the property of always showing great-circle arcs as straight lines. These are known as *great-circle sailing charts* and are discussed more fully under the subject of map projections. To plot the shortest course between any two points it is necessary only to draw a straight line between the two points on the chart.

Great-circle courses may easily be found by the student using only a small globe and a piece of thin string or a rubber band (Figure 1.10). The string can be held in such a way that it is stretched tightly against the surface of the globe between the two thumbnails, each of which is on one of the points between which the great-circle course is desired. If a rubber band is used, a complete great circle can be shown; it is of special value for points on opposite sides of the globe. Most globes show great-circle routes between distant ports on the Pacific, Atlantic, or Indian oceans. These may readily be checked by the stretched piece of string.

Figure 1.10 A great-circle course may be found by stretching a string between two points on a globe. (Charles Phelps Cushing.)

Meridians and Parallels

The rotational motion of the earth, spinning on its axis, provides two natural points—the poles—upon which to base the *geographic grid*, a network of intersecting lines inscribed upon the globe for

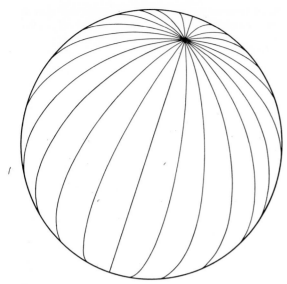

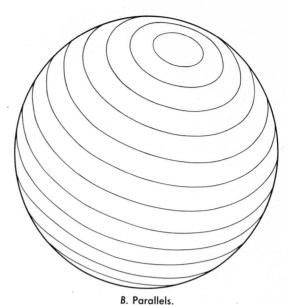

Figure 1.11   A. Meridians.   B. Parallels.

purposes of fixing the location of surface features. It consists of a set of north-south lines connecting the poles—the *meridians*—and a set of east-west lines running parallel with the equator—the *parallels* (Figure 1.11).

All meridians are halves of great circles, whose ends coincide with the earth's north and south poles. Though it is true that opposite meridians taken together comprise a complete great circle, it is well to remember that a single meridian is only half of a great circle and contains 180° of arc. Additional characteristics of meridians are:

1. All meridians run in a true north-south direction.

2. Meridians are spaced farthest apart at the equator and converge to common points at the poles.

3. An infinite number of meridians may be drawn on a globe. Thus a meridian exists for any point selected on the globe. For representation on maps and globes, however, meridians are selected at suitable equal distances apart.

Parallels are entire small circles, produced by passing planes through the earth parallel to the plane of the equator. They possess the following characteristics:

1. Parallels are always parallel to one another. Although they are circular lines, they always remain equal distances apart.

2. Parallels are always true east-west lines.

3. Parallels intersect meridians at right angles. This holds true for any place on the globe, except the two poles, despite the fact that the parallels are strongly curved near the poles.

4. All parallels except the equator are small circles; the equator is a complete great circle.

5. An infinite number of parallels may be drawn on the globe. Therefore, every point on the globe, except the north or south pole, lies on a parallel.

Longitude

The location of points on the earth's surface follows a system in which lengths of arc are measured along meridians and parallels (Figure 1.12). Tak-

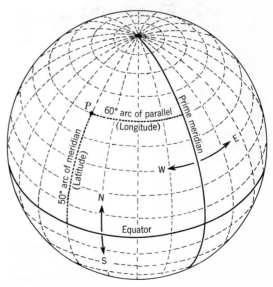

Figure 1.12   The point *P* has a latitude of 50° N, a longitude of 60° W.

ing the equator as the starting line, arcs are measured north or south to the desired points. Taking a selected meridian, or *prime meridian*, as a reference line, arcs are measured eastward or westward to the desired points.

The *longitude* of a place may be defined as the arc, measured in degrees, of a parallel between the place and the prime meridian (Figure 1.12). The prime meridian is almost universally accepted as that which passes through the Royal Observatory at Greenwich, near London, England, and is often referred to as the *meridian of Greenwich*. This meridian has the value 0° longitude. The longitude of any given point on the globe is measured eastward or westward from this meridian, whichever is the shorter arc. Longitude may thus range from 0° to 180°, either east or west. It is commonly written in the following form: *long. 77° 03′ 41″ W*, which may be read "longitude 77 degrees, 3 minutes, 41 seconds west of Greenwich."

If only the longitude of a point is stated we cannot tell its precise location because the same arc of measure applies to an entire meridian. For this reason, a meridian might be defined as a line representing all points having the same longitude. This definition explains why the expression "a meridian of longitude" is often used. Confusion may arise in the mind of the student because of the statement that longitude is measured along a parallel of latitude, but this may be clarified by the realization that in order to measure the arc between a point and the prime meridian it is necessary to follow eastward or westward along one of the parallels (Figure 1.12).

The actual length, in miles, of a degree of longitude will depend upon where it is measured. At the equator this distance may be computed by dividing the earth's circumference by 360°:

$$\frac{24{,}901.92 \text{ miles}}{360 \text{ degrees}} = 69.172 \text{ statute miles}$$
$$= 60 \text{ nautical miles (approx.)}$$

The student should memorize the value of 1° on longitude at the equator as 69 miles, because many computations of map distance and scale can be made by converting degrees of longitude into miles. Other figures that hold at the equator are:

1′ of longitude = 1.15 statute miles
            = 1 nautical mile (approx.)
1″ of longitude = 0.019 statute mile or about
            100 feet

Because of the rapid convergence of the meridians northward or southward, care should be taken not to employ these equivalents inadvertently except close to the equator. It is a further useful item of knowledge that the length of 1° of longitude is re-

duced to about one-half as much at the 60th parallels, or about 34½ miles.

Latitude

The *latitude* of a place may be defined as the arc, measured in degrees, of a meridian between that place and the equator (Figure 1.12). Latitude may thus range from 0° at the equator to 90° north or south at the poles. The latitude of a place, written as *lat. 34° 10′ 31″ N*, may be read "latitude 34 degrees, 10 minutes, 31 seconds north." When both the latitude and longitude of a place are given, it is accurately and precisely located with respect to the geographic grid.

For almost all practical purposes we consider the earth to be a sphere, and therefore the parallels of latitude are taken to be exactly equidistantly spaced if they are drawn on a globe for unit amounts of arc, as, for example, every 10°. The length of a degree of latitude is almost the same as the length of 1° of longitude at the equator, slightly over 69 miles, and so that figure may be used for ordinary purposes.

To be very precise, and take into account the oblateness of the earth, it must be recognized that a degree of latitude changes slightly in length from equator to poles. The following figures apply to the earth spheroid as computed by A. R. Clarke:

At the equator:
1° of latitude = 68.704 statute miles
            = 60 nautical miles (approx.)
1′ of latitude = 1.1 statute miles
            = 1 nautical mile (approx.)
1″ of latitude = 0.02 statute mile or about 100 feet

At latitude 89° to 90° N or S:
1° of latitude = 69.407 miles

The explanation of this variation may be had from a diagram showing how degrees of latitude are determined (Figure 1.13). Because of the earth's

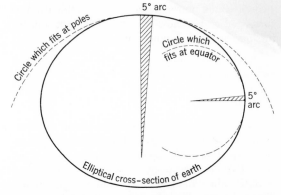

Figure 1.13 Because the earth is an ellipse in cross section, the length of a degree of latitude is very slightly greater at the poles than at the equator.

oblateness, the surface curvature is less strong near the poles than at the equator. That is to say, a smaller circle can be fitted to the curvature near the equator than at the poles, as shown in Figure 1.13. A single degree on the largest circle has a greater length of arc than a degree on the smallest circle. Hence the length of a single degree of latitude will be greatest near the poles and least near the equator. In order to obtain the correct values for specific latitudes, it is necessary to consult prepared tables. Table 2 gives the lengths of single degrees of both latitude and longitude for various latitudes.

TABLE 2*

Latitude, degrees	Length of 1° of Latitude, statute miles	Length of 1° of Longitude, statute miles
0	68.704	69.172
5	68.710	68.911
10	68.725	68.129
15	68.751	66.830
20	68.786	65.026
25	68.829	62.729
30	68.879	59.956
35	68.935	56.725
40	68.993	53.063
45	69.054	48.995
50	69.115	44.552
55	69.175	39.766
60	69.230	34.674
65	69.281	29.315
70	69.324	23.729
75	69.360	17.960
80	69.386	12.051
85	69.402	6.049
90	69.407	0.000

* Based on Clarke Spheroid of Reference, from *U.S. Geological Survey Bulletin 650*, "Geographic Tables and Formulas," by S. S. Gannett, 1916, pp. 36–37.

Statute mile and nautical mile

Both marine and air navigation use the *nautical mile* as the unit of length or distance. Meteorology (weather science) of the upper atmosphere has also adopted as the unit of wind speed the mariner's *knot*, which is a velocity of one nautical mile per hour. It is therefore worthwhile for the geographer to understand the nautical mile, which has already been stated to be approximately equivalent to the length of one minute of arc of the earth's equator.

On July 1, 1954, the U.S. Department of Defense adopted the *international nautical mile*, defined as exactly equivalent to 1852 international meters, or 6076.103333 feet (the digit 3 is repeated indefinitely). Therefore, dividing this value in feet by 5280, the number of feet per *statute mile*, we arrive at the equivalent: one international

nautical mile = 1.150777 statute miles. For ordinary calculations, then, the value of 1.15 statute miles per nautical mile is quite satisfactory.

At what place on the earth does the international nautical mile equal the length of one minute of arc of the earth spheroid? This can be computed by first multiplying 1.150777 by 60 to give 69.04663 statute miles per degree of arc. Next, consulting Table 2, this figure is seen to be very close to the length of one degree of latitude at 45°, which is given as 69.054 miles according to the Clarke spheroid of reference. Furthermore, if all of the values of the middle column of Table 2 are added and the average value computed, it will be found to be 69.055. This leads to the conclusion that the international nautical mile very closely approximates the average length of one minute of latitude, or that it is the 1/5400 part of the length of a meridian between equator and pole.

Earth spheroids

Preparation of maps of the earth's surface requires precise plotting of a network of meridians and parallels that form the framework upon which terrain details are inscribed. Exact lengths of degrees of latitude and longitude can be stated only after the dimensions of the earth spheroid are agreed upon. Unfortunately, a single set of dimensions has not been used over the entire earth. Instead, five sets of earth spheroid dimensions have been widely used: (1) the *International spheroid*, whose values were computed by J. F. Hayford of the U.S. Coast and Geodetic Survey in 1909 and adopted by the International Geodetic and Geophysical Union in 1924; (2) the *Clarke spheroid of 1866* computed by A. R. Clarke, the head of the English Ordnance Survey; (3) the *Clark spheroid of 1880*, a recomputation by General Clark; (4) the *Bessel spheroid* computed in 1841 by a Prussian astronomer of that name; and (5) the *Everest spheroid* of 1830.

For purposes of a unified system of international military mapping the world is divided up into areas, each assigned to one of the above five spheroids (Figure 1.14). Thus, military maps of North America will be based on the Clarke spheroid of 1866; those of Europe on the International spheroid; those of central Africa on the Clark spheroid of 1880; those of India on the Everest spheroid, and so forth. The reason for assignment of regions to particular spheroids is that precise surveying and mapping went forward for many decades under individual governments according to selected reference spheroids. To make use of existing map information it is practical to accept the spheroids for those regions for which mapping has been completed and to establish boundaries (heavy lines in

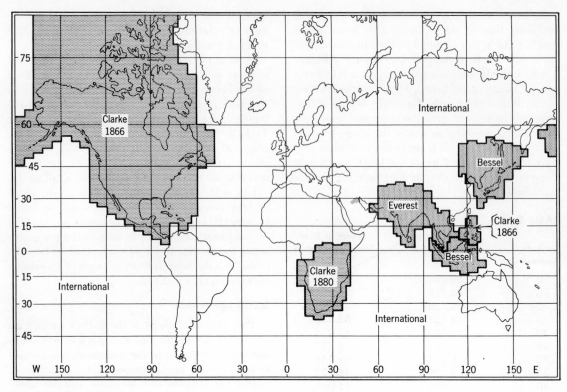

Figure 1.14 World regions are assigned to each of five spheroids of reference. (After Department of the Army, TM 5—241.)

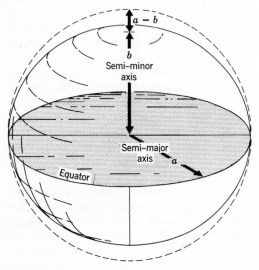

Figure 1.15 Figures of Table 3 give dimensions of semi-major and semi-minor axes of the ellipsoid as defined here. (After Department of the Army, TM 5—241.)

TABLE 3*

Spheroid	Semi-major Axis a	Semi-minor Axis b	Flattening f	Approximate Fraction
International (Hayford 1909)	6,378,388	6,356,912	0.003 367	1/297
Clarke 1866	6,378,206	6,356,584	0.003 390	1/295
Clarke 1880	6,378,249	6,356,515	0.003 408	1/293
Bessel 1841	6,377,397	6,356,079	0.003 343	1/299
Everest 1830	6,377,276	6,356,075	0.003 324	1/301

* Data from Departments of the Army and the Air Force, TM 5-241, TO 16-1-233.

Figure 1.14) for the extension of those areas so as to cover the earth.

In order that the student may compare the five spheroids, a table of dimensions is given on p. 14. The unit of length used in this table is the *international meter*, equal to 1.093611 American yards. The *semi-major axis* of the ellipsoid, designated by the letter *a*, is the radius of the equator circle (Figure 1.15). The *semi-minor axis*, designated by the letter *b*, is exactly one-half the length of the polar axis.

The oblateness, or flattening of the poles, desig-nated by the letter *f*, is defined as $f = \dfrac{a - b}{a}$.

The figures of Table 3 may seem unnecessarily elaborate to the average person, who can make no possible use of such trivial differences in the dimensions of the earth spheroid. Nevertheless, these data show something of the degree of precision practiced in geodesy and needed in many scientific applications. The five spheroids differ in semi-major axis by as much as 1100 meters, which is almost two-thirds of a mile; the semi-minor axes by about 850 meters, or half a mile.

Review Questions

1. Describe at least six proofs of the earth's approximate sphericity.

2. Explain how Eratosthenes estimated the earth's circumference.

3. How may the amount of the earth's surface curvature be expressed? What effect has the decreasing density of the earth's atmosphere on a horizontal line of sight?

4. Explain how a knowledge of earth's surface curvature can be applied to problems of visibility.

5. How did Richer discover that the earth is an oblate spheroid, rather than a true sphere? How and when was this inference confirmed by surveying methods?

6. What geometrical form has a cross section of the earth cutting through the poles? What is the oblateness of the earth? What fraction approximately expresses the oblateness?

7. What is the geoid? How does the surface of the geoid depart from the spheroid? Why?

8. What is a great circle? How is it formed? How many great circles can be drawn upon the surface of a sphere? What is a small circle?

9. List six properties of great circles. Of what practical importance are great circles?

10. What is a meridian? How are meridians formed on a globe? List the characteristics of meridians.

11. What is a parallel? How are parallels formed? List the characteristics of parallels.

12. Define and explain longitude. How is longitude written? Give an example. What is a prime meridian? Where is the Greenwich meridian? How long is a degree of longitude, in miles, at the equator? at 60° latitude? at the poles?

13. Define and explain latitude. How is latitude written? Give an example. How long is a degree of latitude, in miles? Does it vary from equator to poles? How much? Why?

14. What is a nautical mile? a knot? At what latitude is the international nautical mile most nearly equal to the length of one minute of arc of the spheroid?

15. List five earth spheroids used in international military mapping. Why is one spheroid not used for the entire earth?

Exercises

1. What is the most distant point on the sea surface visible from an eye point (**a**) 49 feet above sea level, (**b**) 121 feet above sea level, (**c**) 4900 feet above sea level?

2. A shore battery is firing shells into a floating target 25 feet high and 20 miles distant. Is any part of the target visible to an observer at the battery who is 50 feet above sea level? 400 feet above sea level?

3. At a distance of twelve miles the tips of a ship's funnels are just on the horizon as seen through a submarine periscope at sea level. How high above sea level do the ship's funnels rise?

4. (**a**) Survivors on a life raft are 18 miles from a lighthouse. Taking the light to be 100 feet above sea level, and the maximum eye level of the survivors to be 6 feet above the sea surface, can they see the rays from the lighthouse? (**b**) Calculate the distance at which light would just be visible on the horizon.

5. (**a**) Determine exactly the oblateness of the earth, using the following formula:

$$\text{Oblateness} = \frac{a - b}{a}$$

where a = equatorial diameter, 7926.68 miles; b = polar diameter, 7899.98 miles. (**b**) On a perfectly scaled globe, ten inches in equatorial diameter, how much shorter would the polar diameter be than the equatorial diameter?

6. Using a small globe and a piece of thin string or a rubber band, make great circle courses between (**a**) Seattle and Tokyo. (**b**) New York and Liverpool. (**c**) New York and Bombay. (**d**) Colombo, Ceylon, and Buenos Aires, Argentina. (**e**) Miami, Florida, and Capetown, South Africa. For each route list the principal cities or geographical features lying on or very near the route.

7. Using a small globe, give as closely as possible the latitude and longitude of the following cities: New York, Capetown, Shanghai, Honolulu, London, Rio de Janeiro.

8. What error has been made in each of the following notations: (**a**) Lat. 5° 08′ 31″ S, long. 191° 33′ 04″ W. (**b**) Lat. 89° 71′ 23″ N, long. 88° 21′ 56″ E. (**c**) Lat. 21° 43′ 59″ E, long. 177° 03′ 00″ E. (**d**) Lat. 94° 21′ 10″ N, long. 103° 42′ 51″ W. (**e**) Lat. 48° 54′ 45″ N, long. 2° 00′ 31″ N.

9. Show by a geometric construction that a degree of longitude at the 60th parallel is one-half as long as a degree of longitude at the equator. Label your diagram, and attach a full explanation.

10. From how many different starting points on the globe would it be possible to travel 100 miles north, then 100 miles east (or west), then 100 miles south and be exactly at the same starting point? (The southern-hemisphere case is simple, but can you solve this problem for the northern hemisphere?)

CHAPTER TWO

Map projections

A MAP projection is an orderly system of parallels and meridians used as a basis for drawing a map on a flat surface. The fundamental problem is to transfer the geographic grid from its actual spherical form to a flat surface in such a way as to present the earth's surface or some part of it in the most advantageous way possible for the purposes desired.

One way to avoid the map-projection problem is to use only a globe. Unfortunately a globe has shortcomings. First, we can see only one side of a globe at a time. Second, a globe is on too small a scale for many purposes. On globes ranging from a few inches to two or three feet in diameter, only the barest essentials of geography can be shown. The few large globes in existence, those several feet in diameter, may show considerable detail, but they serve also to accentuate a third shortcoming of globes—their lack of portability. Flat maps printed on paper can be folded compactly so that many may be carried in a small pocket, whereas even the smallest globe is a cumbersome and delicate object. Ease of reproduction greatly favors maps over globes. Making a quality globe requires not only that a map be printed but also that the map be trimmed and carefully pasted onto a spherical shell.

The problem of map projection must therefore be squarely faced in an endeavor to learn what types of networks of parallels and meridians are best suited to illustration of various portions of the earth's surface. It is well to point out, however, that no map projection will ever substitute fully for a globe to show general world relations, and use of a globe is to be recommended in conjunction with flat maps.

Developable geometric surfaces

Certain geometric surfaces are said to be *developable* because by cutting along certain lines they can be made to unroll or unfold to make a flat sheet. Two such forms are the *cone* and the *cylinder* (Figure 2.1). Were the earth conical or cylindrical, the map-projection problem would be solved once and for all by using the developed surface. No distortion of surface shapes or areas would occur, although it is true that the surface would be cut apart along certain lines. The earth belongs to a group of geometric forms said to be *undevelopable*, because, no matter how they are cut, they cannot be unrolled or unfolded to lie flat.

above: Plotting a bearing on the Mercator projection.
Official U.S. Navy photograph.

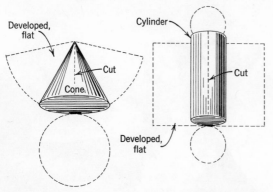

Figure 2.1 The cone and cylinder are developable geometric forms.

It is possible to draw a true straight line in one or more directions on the surface of a developable solid, but nowhere can this be done on an undevelopable form such as a spherical surface. In order to make the parts of a spherical surface lie perfectly flat, it must be stretched—more in some places than in others. Thus, it is impossible to make a perfect map projection.

When a map is made of a very small part of the earth's surface, for example, an area four miles across, the map-projection problem can be ignored. If the meridians and parallels are drawn as straight lines, intersecting at right angles and correctly spaced apart, the actual error present is probably so small as to fall within the width of the lines drawn and is not worth correcting. As the area included on the map is increased, however, the problem gains in importance. When an attempt is made to show the whole globe, very serious trouble develops. Only by some compromise can the distortion be reduced to a reasonable degree over important parts of the earth's surface. We should remember that the human eye cannot see the entire surface of a globe at once, and the marginal section within view is greatly foreshortened. Thus, map projections actually improve our ability to perceive the earth's surface.

Although for purposes of simplicity this chapter treats projections of a spherical globe upon a flat map, it is well to point out that in precise plotting of a map projection the earth spheroid is the geometrical form that is actually used. But because the earth's oblateness is slight, the earth can be assumed a true sphere for an elementary and descriptive study of map projections.

Map scale

All globes and maps depict the earth's features in much smaller size than the true features which they attempt to represent. Globes are intended in principle to be perfect models of the earth itself,

differing from the earth only in size, but not in shape. The *scale* of a globe is therefore the ratio between the size of the globe and the size of the earth, where size is expressed by some measure of length or distance (but not area or volume). Take, for example, a globe 10 inches in diameter representing the earth, whose diameter is about 8000 miles. The scale of the globe is therefore the ratio between 10 inches and 8000 miles. Dividing both figures by ten, this reduces to a scale stated as: *one inch represents 800 miles*, a relationship that holds true for distances between any two points on the globe.

Scale is more usefully stated as a simple fraction, termed the *fractional scale*, or *representative fraction* (*R.F.*), which can be obtained by reducing both map and globe distances to the same unit of measure, thus:

$$\frac{\text{1 in. on globe}}{\text{800 mi. on earth}} = \frac{\text{1 in.}}{800 \times 63,360 \text{ in. (per mi.)}}$$

$$= \frac{\text{1 in.}}{\text{50,688,000 in.}} = \frac{1}{50,688,000}$$

This fraction may be written as 1 : 50,688,000 for convenience in printing. The advantage of the representative fraction is that it is entirely free of any specified units of measure, such as the foot, mile, meter, or kilometer. Persons of any nationality understand the fraction, regardless of the language or units of measure used in their nation, provided only that the arabic numerals are understood.

A globe is a *true-scale model* of the earth, in that the representative fraction applies to any distances on the globe, regardless of the latitude or longitude, and regardless of the compass direction of the line whose distance is being considered. This is to say that the scale remains constant over the entire globe. Map projections, however, cannot have the uniform-scale property of a globe, no matter how cleverly devised. In flattening the curved surface of the sphere to conform to a flat plane, all map projections stretch the earth's surface in a non-uniform manner, so that the fractional scale changes from place to place. Thus, we cannot say about a map of the world: "the scale of this map is 1 : 50,000,000," for the statement is false for any form of projection.

It is quite possible, however, to have the fractional scale of a flat map remain true, or constant, in certain specified directions. For example, one type of projection preserves constant scale along all parallels, but not along the meridians. This condition is illustrated in Figure 2.2*B*, which is a part of the network of the polyconic projection shown complete in Figure 2.17. Another type of projection keeps scale constant along all meridians, but not along parallels. This is shown in Figure 2.2C, which is part of the polar position of azimuthal equidistant projection shown in Figure 2.12. Still other projections have changing scale along both meridians and parallels, as illustrated in Figure 2.2D, which is part of the gnomonic projection shown in Figure 2.11.

Preserving areas on map projections

Because a globe is a true-scale model of the earth, given areas of the earth's surface are shown to correct relative scale everywhere over its surface. The scale of distance is constant in all compass directions. If we should take a small wire ring, say one inch in diameter, and place it anywhere on the surface of the ten-inch globe, the area enclosed will represent an equal amount of area of the earth's surface. But a similar procedure would not enclose constant areas on all parts of most map projections, only on those having the special property of being *equal-area* projections.

At this point a good question arises. If, as stated above, no projection preserves a true, or constant, scale of distances in all directions over the projection, how can circles of equal diameter placed on the map enclose equal amounts of earth area? The answer is suggested in Figure 2.3. The square, one mile on a side, encloses one square mile between two meridians and two parallels. The square can be deformed into rectangles of different shapes, but if the dimensions are changed in an inverse manner, each will still enclose one square mile. The scale has been changed in one direction to compensate for change in another in just the right way to preserve equal areas of map between corresponding parts of intersecting meridians and parallels. Hence, any small square or circle moved about over the map surface will enclose a piece of the map representing a constant quantity of area of the earth's surface. Projections shown in Figures 2.13, 2.25 and 2.26 have the equal-area property, but it is also obvious that these networks have bad distortions of shape, particularly near the outer edges of the map.

Preserving shapes on map projections

A map projection is said to be *conformal*, or *orthomorphic*, when any small piece of the earth's surface has the same shape on the map as it does on a globe. Thus, the appearance of small islands or countries is faithfully preserved by a conformal map. One characteristic of a conformal projection is that parallels and meridians cross each other at right angles everywhere on the map, just as they do on the globe. However, not all projections whose parallels and meridians cross at right angles are conformal.

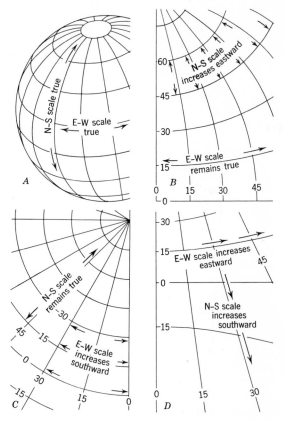

Figure 2.2 Although scale is true in all directions on a globe, **A**, scale changes must occur on all map projections. **B**. Scale is true along all parallels but not along all meridians. **C**. Scale is true along all meridians but not along all parallels. **D**. Scale changes along both parallels and meridians.

Another way of saying that parallels and meridians intersect at right angles is that *shearing* of areas does not occur. Figure 2.4 illustrates the meaning of shearing. For projections consisting of straight parallels and meridians, shearing gives parallelograms formed of acute and obtuse angles. For projections with curved meridians and parallels, straight lines are drawn tangent to the curves at the point of intersection. If these tangent lines

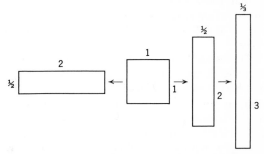

Figure 2.3 Areas can be preserved even though scales and shapes change radically.

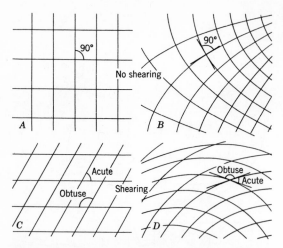

Figure 2.4 Shearing of areas is a defect of many projections.

cross at right angles, the projection is not sheared; but if the tangents form obtuse and acute angles, shearing is present. Conformal maps are not sheared, but not all maps without shearing are conformal. A conformal map cannot have equal-area properties besides, so that some areas are greatly enlarged at the expense of others. Generally speaking, areas near the margin of a conformal map have a much larger scale than central ones.

Whether a conformal or equal-area projection is to be selected depends on what is to be shown. Where the areal distribution of something, such as grain crops, or forest-covered lands, is to be shown, an equal-area projection is needed. For most general purposes a conformal type is preferable because physical features most nearly resemble their true shapes on the globe. Many map projections are neither perfectly conformal nor equal area, but represent a compromise between the two. This compromise may be desired either to achieve a map of more all-around usefulness or because the projection has some other very special property that makes its use essential for certain purposes.

Classification of map projections

Map projections may be classified according to the following groups: (1) *zenithal* (*azimuthal*), (2) *conic*, (3) *cylindric*, and (4) individual, or unique types.

The *zenithal*, or *azimuthal*, group of projections includes all types that are centered about a point and have a radial, or wheel-like, symmetry. Some zenithal projections can actually be demonstrated in the laboratory by the following method. (See Figure 2.5.) A wire replica of the earth, in which the wires represent parallels and meridians, is used. A tiny light source, such as a flashlight bulb or an arc light, is placed at the center of the wire

globe (or at any one of several prescribed positions). In a darkened room the shadow of the wire globe is cast upon a screen or upon the wall or ceiling. This shadow is a true geometric projection. All projections made with this apparatus are of the zenithal type, which are characterized by the following properties (Figure 2.6).

1. A line drawn from center point of the map to any other point gives the true compass direction taken by a great circle as it leaves the center point, headed for the outer point. This direction, or "azimuth," may be measured with respect to the central meridian of the projection. Continual readjustment of course with respect to geographic north will be needed along the route, unless it coincides with a meridian or the equator.

2. When a complete globe or hemisphere is shown, the map is circular in outline. Inasmuch as any map can be trimmed down to have a circular outline, this feature is not a reliable criterion of the azimuthal class.

3. The map possesses a center point around which all its properties are grouped. All changes of scale and distortion of shapes occur uniformly (concentrically) outward from this center.

4. All points equidistant from the center lie on a circle, known as the *horizon circle*. When the entire globe is shown by a zenithal map, the circular edge of the map represents the opposite, or *antipodal*, point on the globe. When a hemisphere is shown, the outer edge of the map represents a great circle, everywhere equidistant from the point on which the projection is centered.

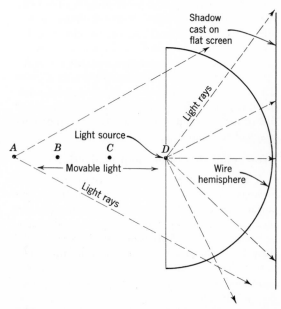

Figure 2.5 Certain zenithal projections may be made by using a light, a wire hemisphere, and a screen.

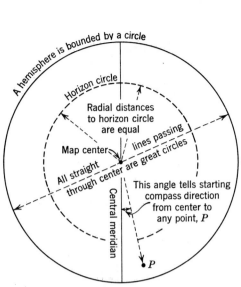

Figure 2.6 Zenithal projections have special properties that hold true regardless of where the map is centered on the globe.

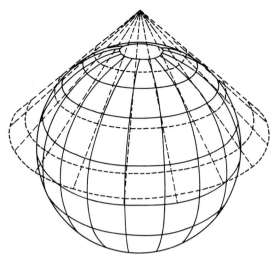

Figure 2.7 Conic projections use the principle of a cone resting on a sphere.

5. All great circles which pass through the center point of the projection appear as straight lines on the map. Likewise, all straight lines drawn through the center point of the map are true great circles.

Zenithal projections appear in three positions, or orientations: (1) *polar*, (2) *equatorial*, and (3) *oblique* or *tilted*, illustrated in Figures 2.9, 2.10, 2.11, 2.12, and 2.13. In the polar position, the center of the projection coincides with the north or south pole; in the equatorial position, the center is somewhere on the equator; in the oblique position, the center is at any desired point intermediate between the equator and poles. Although the equatorial and oblique types may not seem to be radially symmetrical, they nevertheless possess, just as truly as the polar type, the five characteristics described above.

The *conic* group of projections is based on the principle of transferring the geographic grid from a globe to a cone, then developing the cone to a flat map. This principle, too, can be demonstrated in the laboratory with the wire globe and a point source of light (Figure 2.7). Instead of a vertical flat screen, however, a translucent cone of stiff paper is seated on the wire globe, much as a lampshade is seated on a lamp. The shadow of the wires cast upon the conical shade gives a conic projection. If this shadow were traced in pencil or ink and the cone unrolled, a true conic projection would result. Simple conic projections possess the following features (Figures 2.14, 2.15). All meridians are straight lines, converging to a common point at the north (or south) pole. All parallels are arcs of concentric circles, whose common center

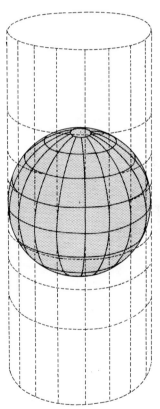

Figure 2.8 Cylindric projections use the principle of a cylinder wrapped around the globe.

lies at the north (or south) pole. A complete conic projection is a sector of a circle, never a complete circle. A conic projection cannot show the whole globe and usually shows little more than the northern (or southern) hemisphere.

Cylindric projections are based on the principle of transferring the geographic grid first onto a

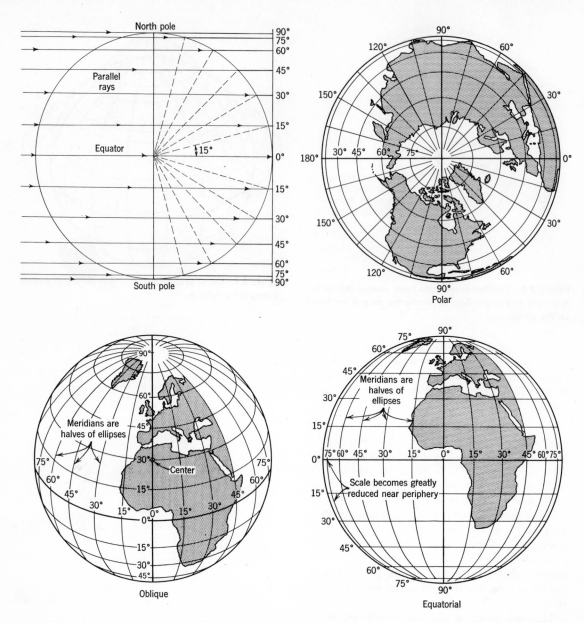

Figure 2.9 The orthographic projection gives the effect of viewing a globe from different vantage points.

cylinder wrapped about the earth, then unrolling the cylinder to make a flat map (Figure 2.8). Simple cylindric projections are easy to draw because they consist of intersecting horizontal and vertical lines. (See Figures 2.18, 2.19.) The completed map is rectangular in outline, and the whole circumference of the globe can be shown. When the cylinder is tangent to the equator, meridians are equally spaced vertical lines. Parallels are spaced in various ways, according to the particular projection desired.

Many other kinds of map projections exist, each based upon some unique principle.

Most of the particular types of projections selected for illustration here are important or useful ones, but not all the important map projections in general use are included in the list. Those selected illustrate the principles and classes already explained.

Zenithal (azimuthal) class

1. *Orthographic projection.* The *orthographic* projection employs a principle of construction illustrated in Figure 2.9. Parallel rays, or lines, are used to project the geographic grid of one hemisphere on a tangent plane. It can also be imagined as resulting when the shadow of a hemispherical wire globe is cast on a screen by light rays coming

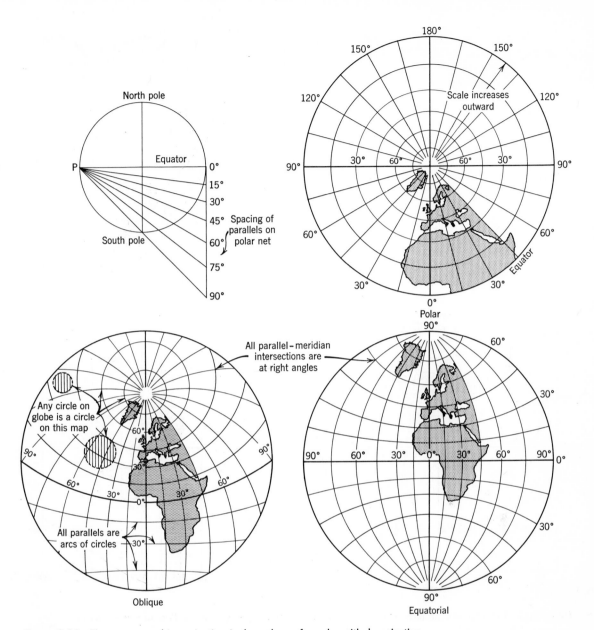

Figure 2.10 The stereographic projection is the only conformal zenithal projection.

from a very distant source, such as the sun. In the polar projection the parallels of latitude crowd close together near the outer margin. This form serves to distinguish it from other polar zenithal projections. In the equatorial projection, the meridians are parts of true ellipses and show close crowding near the outer margin, whereas the parallels are straight, horizontal lines, spaced more closely near the poles. No other zenithal projection in the equatorial position has straight, horizontal parallels. In the oblique position, the closer crowding of meridians and parallels near the outer margin is also noticeable.

The largest possible portion of a globe that can

be shown on the orthographic projection is one hemisphere. The projection is neither equal-area nor conformal. The scale of miles is much larger near the center than near the outer edges. Use of this projection is quite limited. It gives a visual effect of a globe in three dimensions and is very similar to a photograph taken of a globe. For this reason it often appears to illustrate articles or books on global political or military strategic problems. It gives a true picture of relations between countries or continents which are located near the central point of the projection. A little shading added to the map accentuates the perspective effect.

2. Stereographic projection. In the *stereo-*

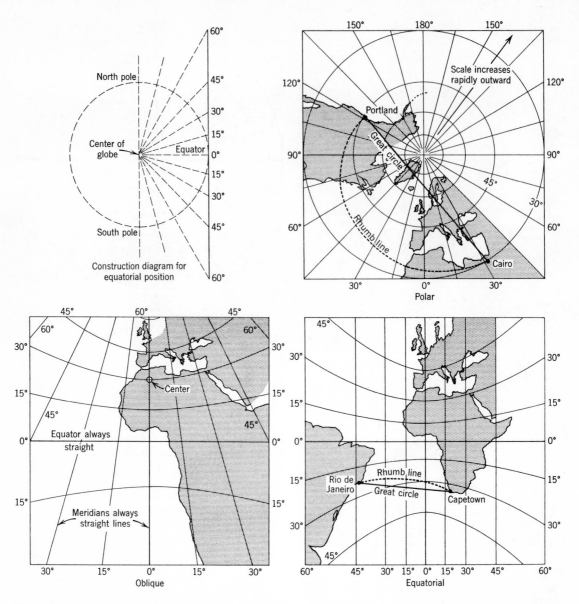

Figure 2.11 The gnomonic projection shows all great circles as straight lines, regardless of where they lie.

graphic projection the point from which construction lines, or rays, emanate is located on the globe at a point diametrically opposite to the point where the tangent plane touches the globe. Whereas the orthographic projection gives a map of exactly the same diameter as the original globe used, the stereographic projection gives a much larger map than the original globe. Furthermore, the stereographic net can show much more than one hemisphere, although it cannot show the whole globe. This is evident from inspection of the construction diagram shown in Figure 2.10. The principal distinguishing characteristic of this projection is evident in all three of its positions: parallels and meridians show close spacing near the map center

and increasingly wider spacing toward the outer margins. On any stereographic projection the parallels and meridians are either straight lines or arcs of circles. No other kinds of curved lines occur. The reason for this is that the stereographic projection is truly conformal. All lines that are circles on the globe are shown as circles on the map. The scale, however, grows greatly from the map center toward the periphery.

With the enormous growth in importance of polar regions in the age of long-range missile and aircraft operation, the polar stereographic projection has assumed great importance. It forms the base on which the Universal Polar Stereographic Military Grid System is constructed for latitudes between 80° and the poles (Chapter 3).

World Aeronautical Charts issued by the U.S. Coast and Geodetic Survey on a scale of 1:1,000,000 are based on a polar stereographic projection for latitudes 80° to 90°. The U.S. Weather Bureau's daily weather map is printed on a polar stereographic projection.

The stereographic projection also has great importance in certain branches of science. Because of its perfect conformal properties, it is used in the study of mineral crystals, where the crystal faces can be plotted on a blank stereographic net. In solving certain problems of descriptive geometry, in which the intersections of various planes and lines must be determined, this net is valuable.

3. Gnomonic projection (great-circle sailing chart). The *gnomonic* projection is made by drawing rays from a point at the center of the globe, as illustrated in Figure 2.11. The resulting network is easily distinguished because the spacing of meridians and parallels increases enormously outward from the map center and results in great distortion of shapes of land areas in the outer part of the map. Though the stereographic net also increases in scale outward from the center, the increase is much less and the true shapes of small land areas are preserved. The gnomonic projection comes out with a vastly greater size than the original construction globe. For geometrical reasons evident from the construction lines in Figure 2.11, it is impossible to show a complete hemisphere. It is even impractical to include the greater part of a hemisphere because of the enormous sheet of paper that would be required. For this reason, a gnomonic map is usually trimmed to a rectangular shape.

The gnomonic projection, with its grotesque distortions of both scale and shapes, would find little use were it not for one unique and important property. On a gnomonic map all straight lines are great circles. Conversely, all great circles appear as straight lines. Note that on all three of the projections illustrated in Figure 2.11, all meridians and the equator are straight lines, regardless of where they are located on the map. For navigational purposes the plotting of great-circle courses is accomplished by merely connecting with a straight line any two desired points. For this reason the gnomonic projection goes by the name *great-circle sailing chart* when adapted to navigational uses. Illustrations of great-circle routes plotted on a gnomonic net are shown in Figure 2.11 on the polar and equatorial maps. (Refer to Figure 2.19 to see these same routes plotted on the Mercator projection.)

4. Azimuthal equidistant projection. The *azimuthal equidistant* projection (Figure 2.12) cannot be produced optically by using a single point source for lines or rays as was possible for the previous three kinds. As the name implies, this network is made by deliberately spacing the meridians and parallels equidistantly outward from the map center. Moreover, there is nothing to stop the cartographer from extending the map to include the whole globe. The opposite pole, or *antipode*, is then shown as a circle surrounding the map. Thus constructed the map scale remains constant along all radial straight lines emanating from the map center. This gives the map a specialized use for air navigation. When centered on a particular city or airport, great-circle routes can easily be laid off and measured by drawing a line from the central point to any desired point on the map and finding the distance on a graphic scale having equally spaced units. Moreover, the correct compass direction for starting the flight can be measured from the map as the angle between the plotted route and the central meridian of the map.

The azimuthal equidistant net is often used for small-scale hemispherical maps. The polar position is easy to construct, requiring only a compass, protractor, scale, and straightedge, and makes a pleasing map to show grouping of the world's principal land areas about the North Polar Sea.

5. Azimuthal equal-area projection. This projection (Figure 2.13) was designed by J. H. Lambert in 1772 and is therefore often called the *Lambert azimuthal equal-area projection*. It is constructed according to a formula which gives it true equal-area properties, something that none of the projections thus far described possess. The geometrical method of finding spacing of parallels for the polar position is shown in Figure 2.13. Chords of arcs of a semicircle divided into equal parts are used as radii for the projection. Spacing of meridians and parallels becomes slightly closer toward the periphery of the map, but not nearly so close as in the orthographic projection.

The azimuthal equal-area projection is widely used for small-scale maps of general geographical nature.

Conic class

6. Perspective conic projection. The perspective conic projection is based on the principle that a cone can be placed over a globe in such a way as to have its apex directly over the north pole and to touch the globe along a single parallel. If the parallels and meridians are then projected upon the cone by drawing rays from the globe's center, and the cone is developed to a flat surface, a conic map results. Meridians are straight lines radiating from the pole; parallels are arcs of concentric circles, centered on the pole. The projection is easy to construct with compass, protractor, and straight-

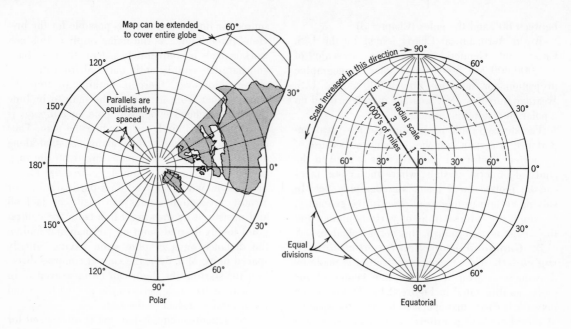

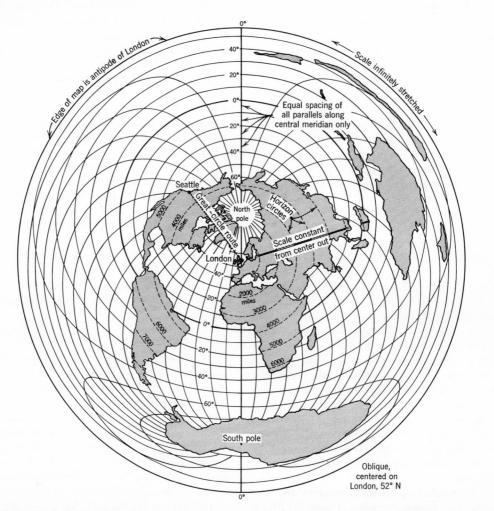

Figure 2.12 The azimuthal equidistant projection is useful in measuring distances from the center to other points.

edge. This map will always be a portion, or sector, of a circle, never a complete circle as with the zenithal projections.

The parallel that touches the globe is called the *standard parallel* (Figure 2.14). On this parallel the scale is the same as on the globe from which the projection was made, whereas the scale is larger everywhere else on the map and increases both north and south from the standard parallel. If a cone is used that touches at the 30th parallel of latitude, the resulting map is exactly half a circle. But, because any other parallel except the equator or pole could be chosen and a cone found to fit, the resulting map might be more or less than a half circle. A perspective conic projection with one standard parallel makes a fairly good global map, without shearing of areas, but can effectively show little more than the northern hemisphere. However, modified conic projections are greatly improved, so that actually the perspective type is rarely used.

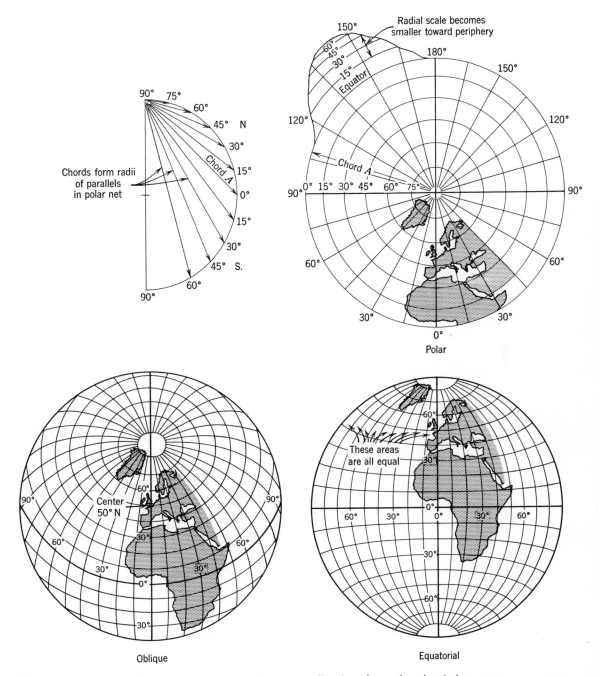

Figure 2.13 The azimuthal equal-area projection gives an excellent base for northern hemisphere maps.

One effective modification is made by passing a cone through two parallels of latitude (Figure 2.15). The cone thus cutting the surface of the globe is said to take the *secant* position, or, simply, is a *secant cone*. The resulting map now has two standard parallels along which the scale is the same. Scale increase north and south of the standard parallels is considerably reduced. Between the standard parallels the scale is less than on these parallels. By selecting the two parallels so as best to fit a particular continent or country in middle latitudes, a highly useful map with small errors of scale and shape results.

7. Lambert conformal conic projection. The perspective conic projection with two standard parallels has been further improved by adjusting

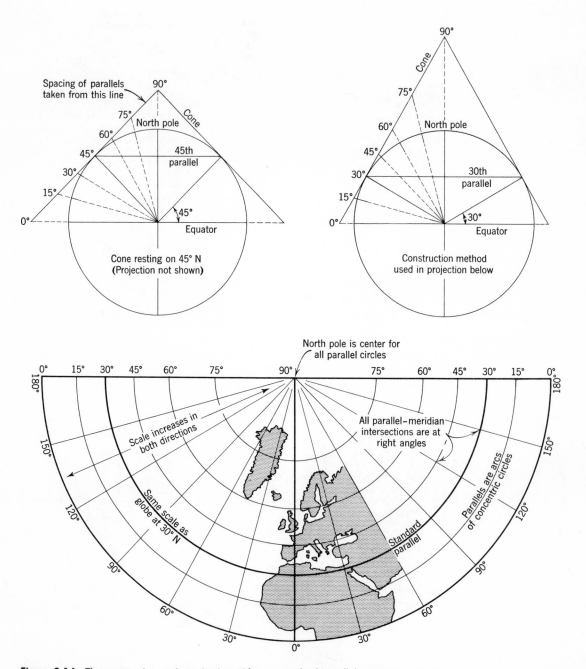

Figure 2.14 The perspective conic projection with one standard parallel is easy to construct.

the spacing of all other parallels in such a way that the map has true conformal properties. This is the *Lambert conformal conic* projection (Figure 2.16). Data for constructing the projection can be found in prepared tables. Because the meridians are straight lines converging to a common point and the parallels are arcs of concentric circles, not only is the projection easy to construct, but also, if it is used as a base of a series of large-scale maps, the individual map sheets will fit perfectly with their neighbors.

The Lambert conformal projection is a highly important type and is in widespread use. When the 33rd and 45th parallels are taken as standard parallels (Figure 2.15), the maximum scale error is about 0.5 per cent for nine-tenths of the United

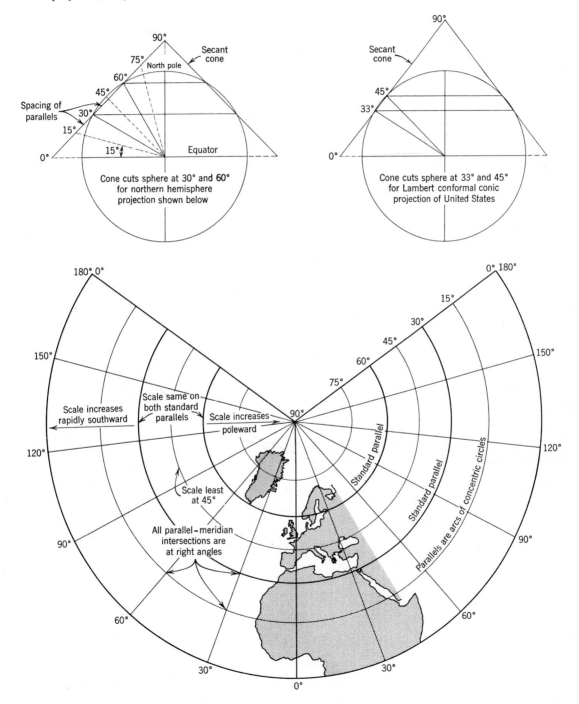

Figure 2.15 When two standard parallels are used, the perspective conic projection is improved in scale qualities.

States, and a straight line drawn on the map so closely approximates a great circle that the gnomonic chart is not needed for air navigation. The U.S. Coast and Geodetic Sectional Aeronautical charts of the United States on a scale of 1:500,000 illustrate this application (Figure 2.16).

Another important use of the Lambert conformal conic projection is for the World Aeronautical Charts, 1:1,000,000, also issued by the U.S. Coast and Geodetic Survey. From the equator to 80° latitude, 20 different cones, each with its own two standard parallels, are used in belts 4° in width.

8. Polyconic projection. If two standard parallels are better than one, why not use three or four, or more, standard parallels? Of course, the same cone cannot pass through more than two parallels, but it is feasible to have several cones, using only those parts that are near their respective standard parallels, thus obtaining a *polyconic* (from the Greek, meaning "many cones") projection. The flattened cone segments shown in Figure 2.17, left, are separated along their edges, and so it is necessary to stretch the map strips to achieve a continuous map. Furthermore, instead of imagining a specific number of standard parallels, an infinite number are imagined, so that true scale exists along the line of any parallel on the map. Only

along the central meridian, which is a vertical straight line, is the scale the same as along all parallels. Every other meridian is a curved line along which the scales become greater toward the outer margins. Note also that the equator is a straight line at right angles to the central meridian, and that all other parallels are arcs of circles (but not of concentric circles).

The polyconic projection is neither equal-area nor conformal, but, near the middle of the net, distortions of scale and shape are very small. Within 560 miles of either side of the central meridian of the map, the scale error does not exceed 1 per cent. Tables are available giving data for construction of the projection.

Many sets of large-scale maps published by various national agencies have been based on the polyconic projection or a slight modification of it. Ferdinand Hassler, first director of the U.S. Coast and Geodetic Survey, devised the polyconic projection in 1820, and it was formerly used by that organization for many of its maps. The U.S. Geological Survey uses the polyconic net as a base for its topographic maps and various other maps of the United States. The International Map of the World, on a scale of 1:1,000,000, uses a modified polyconic grid. One disadvantage of the polyconic projection is that meridians are curved. When in-

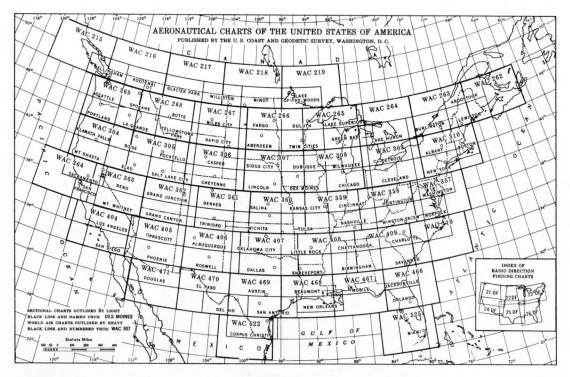

Figure 2.16 A Lambert conformal conic projection of the United States provides an excellent base for a series of large-scale maps. (From U.S. Coast and Geodetic Survey Chart 3060b.)

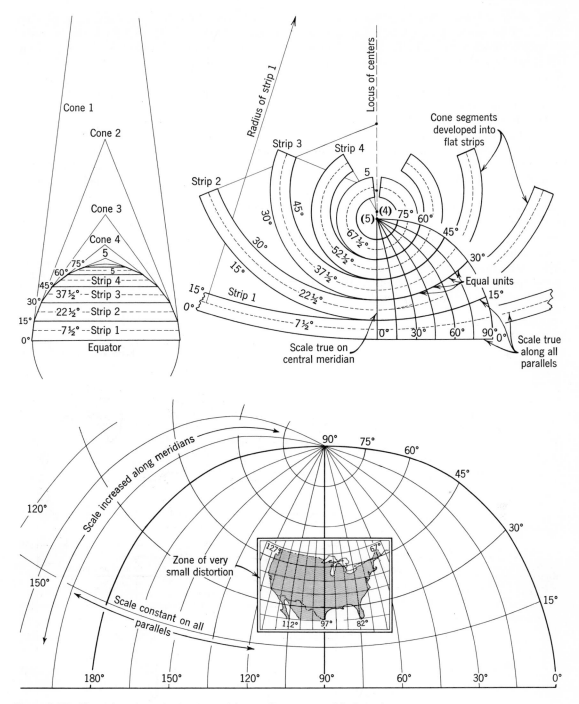

Figure 2.17 The polyconic projection is used for small areas in middle latitudes.

dividual sheets of a map series are prepared they are usually centered on a straight central meridian passing through the map center. Hence the meridians bounding the map on both the left- and right-hand margins curve in toward the top. When adjoining map sheets are trimmed to these meridians, the sheets do not fit together perfectly.

Cylindrical projections

9. Gall's stereographic cylindrical projection. One example of a simple type of cylindrical projection is *Gall's stereographic cylindrical* projection (Figure 2.18). It was invented by Gall in 1855. Instead of fitting around the outside of the globe, the cylinder passes through the 45th parallels, north and south. The map has true scale only along the two 45th parallels. Between them the scale is slightly reduced; to the north and south is it greatly increased. Polar areas are not so badly distorted in a north-south direction as in the Mercator projection, although they are very badly stretched in an east-west direction.

10. *Mercator projection.* Perhaps the best known of all map projections is the *Mercator* net, devised by Gerardus Mercator in 1569 and used by him for a world map (Figure 2.19). It cannot be made by a simple projection onto a cylinder wrapped around the globe, but instead is based upon a mathematical formula. The principle, however, can be explained without mathematical expression, as follows. On any cylindrical projection in which the meridians are straight vertical lines, equidistantly spaced, the meridians have had to be spread apart. (See right side of Figure 2.19.) Only along the equator are they the same distance apart

as on a globe of the same equatorial scale. In order to maintain them as parallel lines, the normally converging meridians have had to be spread apart in a greater and greater ratio as the poles are approached. At 60° N and S lat., the meridians are spread apart twice as far as originally, because at that place a degree of longitude is only half what it is at the equator. At the poles the spreading is infinitely greater, because the poles themselves are infinitely tiny points. Now, to maintain the map as a truly conformal map, we must space the parallels increasingly far apart toward the poles, using the same ratio of increase that resulted when the meridians were spread to make vertical lines.[1] For example, near the 60th parallel north, parallels must be spread twice as far apart as on the globe

[1] The map scale increases poleward as the secant of the latitude. The secant of 60° is 2.0; of 70° is 2.9; of 80° is 5.8; of 85° is 11.5; and of 89° is 57.3. The scale is stretched by these factors at the stated latitudes.

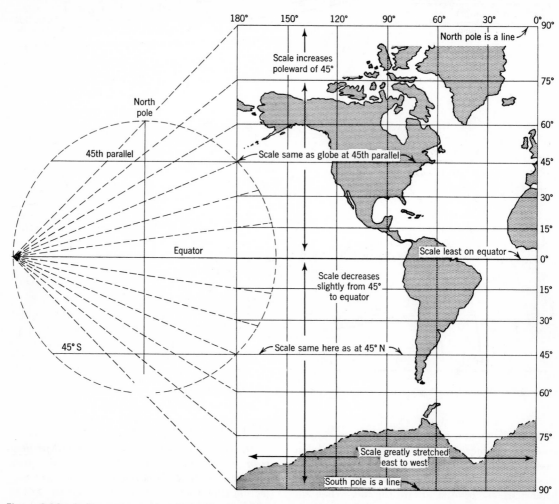

Figure 2.18 Gall's stereographic cylindrical projection uses the principle of a cylinder cutting through the globe at the 45th parallel.

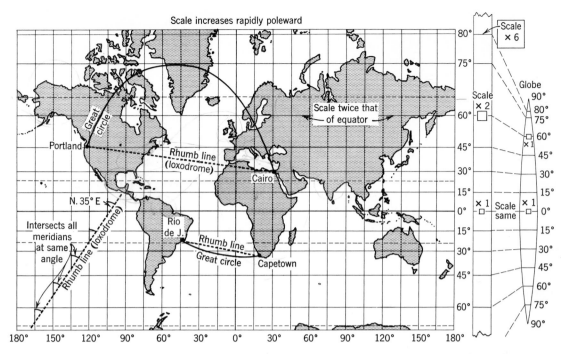

Figure 2.19 The equatorial Mercator projection shows all lines of constant compass direction as straight lines.

because, as explained above, the meridians here are also spread twice as far apart. At 80° latitude the scale is enlarged almost six times. Near the poles the spacing of parallels increases enormously and rapidly approaches infinity. Because an enormous sheet of paper would be needed to show extreme polar regions, the Mercator map is usually cut off about 80° or 85° N and S lat. The poles can never be shown.

The Mercator chart is a true conformal projection. Any small island or country is shown in its true shape. The scale of the map, however, becomes enormously greater toward the poles. The classical Mercator projection described above is in the equatorial position. That is, the cylinder is tangent to, or touches, the earth's equator, as illustrated in Figure 2.8. The earth's polar axis here coincides with the cylinder axis. Other forms of Mercator projection can be obtained by turning the globe within the cylinder so that the great circle of tangency is a pair of meridians, or any other great circle. These varieties are discussed below.

The really important, unique feature of an equatorial Mercator projection is that a straight line drawn anywhere on the map, in any direction desired, is a line of constant compass bearing. Such a line is known to navigators as a *rhumb line*, or *loxodrome* (Figure 2.19). If this line is followed, the ship's (or plane's) compass will show that the course is always at a constant angle with respect to geographic north.[2] Once the proper compass bear-

ing is determined, the ship is kept on the same bearing throughout the voyage, if the rhumb line is to be followed. The equatorial Mercator is the only one of all known projections on which all rhumb lines are true straight lines, and vice versa. A protractor can be used with reference to any meridian on the map, and the compass bearing of any straight line can be measured off directly.

The relation of great-circle routes to rhumb lines is shown by two examples on Figures 2.11 and 2.19. Note that on the gnomonic map great circles are straight and rhumb lines curved, whereas on the Mercator chart rhumb lines are straight and great circles curved. Along the equator and all meridians (but only on these lines) rhumb lines and great circles are identical and are straight lines on both charts. In navigation it is desirable to follow a great-circle course, which is the shortest distance, yet at the same time this is difficult to do because compass bearing constantly changes along the great-circle track. In practice, the course is drawn on a great-circle chart, then transferred as a series of straight segments or legs, to the Mercator chart. The navigator can now measure the compass bearing of the first leg by means of a protractor. After the ship has traveled the distance of the first leg, the ship is turned to follow the bearing of the second leg, etc. Although this is not truly a great-

[2] Correction would be necessary for changing magnetic declination, explained in Chapter 3.

Cylindrical projections | 33

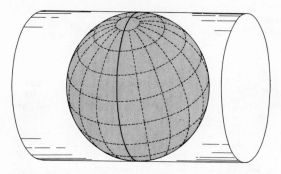

Figure 2.20 The transverse Mercator projection uses the principle of a cylinder tangent on a pair of meridians.

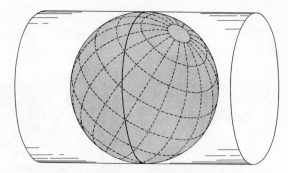

Figure 2.21 The oblique Mercator projection uses a cylinder tangent on a great circle cutting obliquely across meridians and parallels.

circle route, it fits so closely that the extra distance is negligible.

Aside from its indispensable property for navigational uses, the equatorial Mercator projection has little to recommend it for unrestricted global use. Except for equatorial regions, for which it provides an excellent grid, distortions of scale are very serious. Because of infinite stretching toward the poles, this map fails completely to show how the land areas of North America, Asia, and Europe are grouped around the polar sea. In the mind of an inexperienced user it may enhance a false sense of isolation between inhabitants of these lands. In this respect, zenithal or conic projections are preferable for study of continental regions in middle and high latitudes.

The *transverse Mercator projection* uses the principle of a cylinder tangent to the globe along a chosen pair of opposite meridians (Figure 2.20), or tangent to any great circle cutting across the equator and meridians obliquely (Figure 2.21). The second case is sometimes referred to separately as an *oblique Mercator* projection. Figure 2.22 shows a transverse Mercator projection tangent to the globe on the Greenwich (0° longitude) and 180th meridians. This particular form of transverse Mercator net is also known as the *Gauss conformal* projection. The projection extends infinitely far to left and right. Points in line with the cylinder axis, at lat. 0°, long. 90° E and lat. 0°, long. 90° W, can never be shown. Scale of the map is constant only on the central meridian. If the user selects a narrow belt extending but a few degrees of arc to the east and west of the central meridian, scale increase is very small throughout and the advantages of a true conformal projection are enjoyed.

A slight modification has brought the transverse Mercator projection to its peak of usefulness. Instead of having the enclosing cylinder tangent along a meridian, the cylinder cuts through the surface of the globe, intersecting it on two smaller

circles, taking what is described as the *secant position* (Figure 2.23). Now the map scale is constant along two straight, parallel lines on the map. These lines are equidistant from the central meridian. For purposes of the Universal Transverse Mercator military grid system, described in Chapter 3, the two lines of equal scale are separated on the map by a distance of 360,000 meters, or 360 kilometers (223.6 miles). Scale changes are extremely small within a 6° belt of longitude. The transverse Mercator projection is thus an excellent base for large-scale topographic maps, for which purpose it has been adopted since World War II by the U.S. Army Map Service. To cover the entire world, the central meridian is moved by 6° intervals, so that 60 central meridians are required in all. Regions lying poleward of 80° latitude are, however, covered by polar stereographic projections.

The transverse Mercator projection, when used in the oblique case, can be made tangent to any selected great circle. This makes it an ideal projection for showing a great circle air-navigation route between two distant airports (Figure 2.24). Being a conformal projection, all intersections of parallels and meridians are at right angles.

Other types

11. *Mollweide homolographic projection.* One projection rather widely used to show the entire globe is the *homolographic* projection, invented by Karl B. Mollweide in 1805 (Figure 2.25). "Homolographic" is a word often used to mean "equal area," a property this projection possesses. One hemisphere is outlined by a circle; the other hemisphere is divided into two parts and added with an elliptical outline to either side of the circle. All other meridians, except the straight central meridian, are halves of ellipses. The equator is twice as long as the central meridian, which is also true on a globe. Parallels are straight, horizontal lines, becoming more closely spaced toward

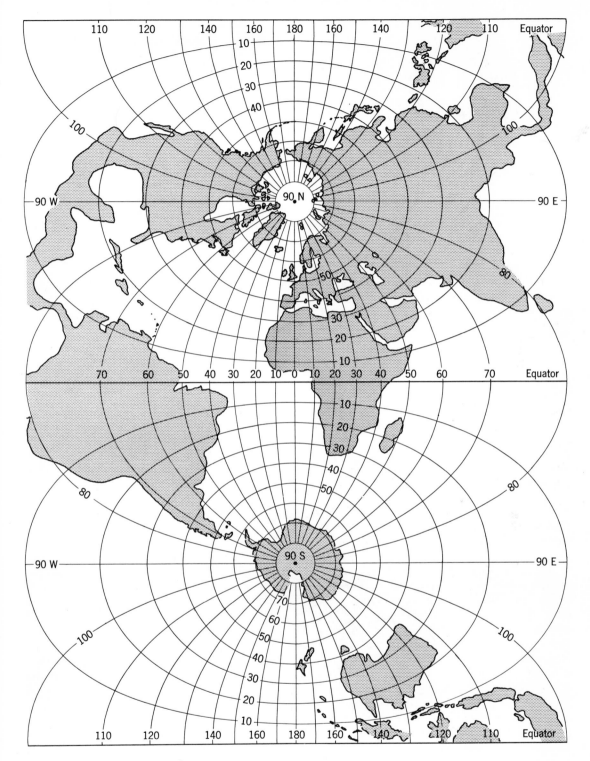

Figure 2.22 A world transverse Mercator projection.

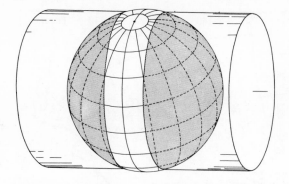

Figure 2.23 The secant position of the transverse Mercator projection minimizes scale changes in a narrow zone.

the poles. The spacing of parallels, so adjusted as to give the map equal-area properties, is obtained by an involved method. Tables are available for construction.

The Mollweide projection has distinct advantages as well as disadvantages. Its equal-area property makes it valuable for showing the global areal distribution of geographical or political entities. Severe

distortion in the polar regions, however, has hindered its wider use. It can, of course, be centered on any desired meridian so as to reduce distortion for a particular area. It makes a good base for maps of Africa and South America, either of which can be included in the central area of relatively little distortion. Interrupted and tilted forms have proved valuable as world maps.

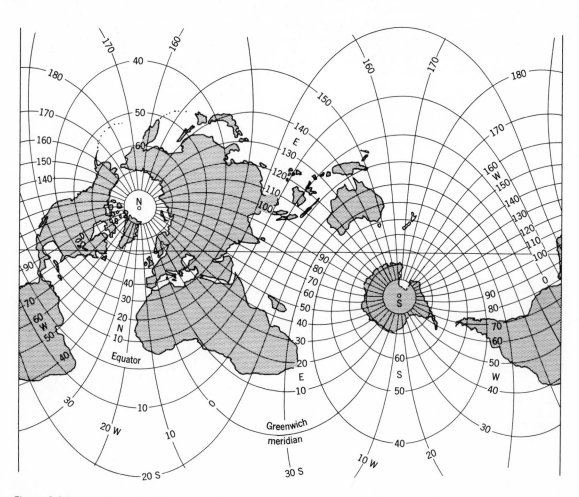

Figure 2.24 A world oblique Mercator projection. (After Hinks, *Geographical Journal*, 1941.)

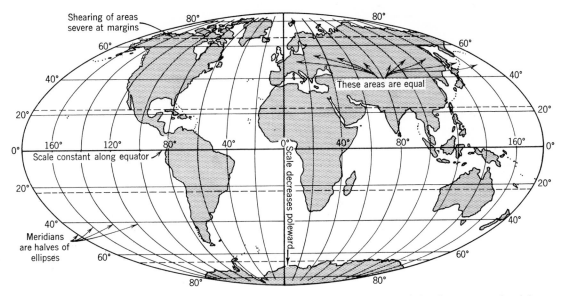

Figure 2.25 The Mollweide homolographic projection is widely used to show areal distributions over the globe.

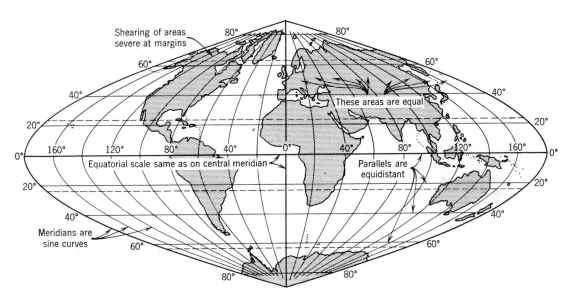

Figure 2.26 The sinusoidal projection is an excellent equal-area projection for lower latitudes.

12. Sinusoidal projection. In some ways the *sinusoidal* projection (sometimes called the Sanson-Flamsteed projection) is similar to the Mollweide homolographic projection. It is an equal-area projection with straight central meridian and horizontal straight parallels (Figure 2.26). The difference lies in the type of curve used in meridians. Whereas the homolographic net uses ellipses, the sinusoidal net uses families of *sine curves*. Figure 2.27 shows three wave crests of a sine curve superimposed. If we turn this figure sidewise and compare it with Figure 2.26, it is evident that a similar set of

curves has been used to draw the projection. Now, it is a remarkable property of the sinusoidal projection that, by spacing the parallels equidistantly from equator to poles, a true equal-area net results.

The same advantages and disadvantages apply to the sinusoidal projection as to the homolographic projection. Distortion in polar areas is not quite so great in the sinusoidal net but is nevertheless offensive. If Africa or South America is placed in the center of the projection, the continent is extremely well shown, with little distortion of scale or shape.

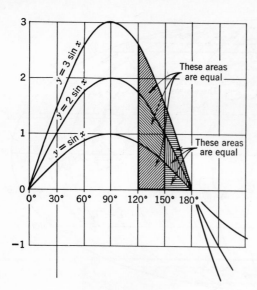

Figure 2.27 Sine curves are used as meridians in the sinusoidal projection.

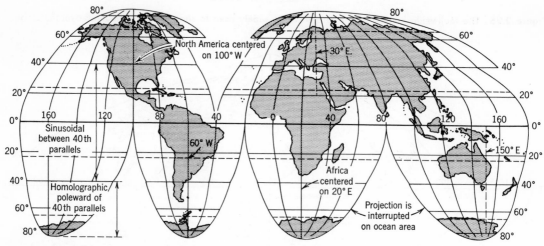

Figure 2.28 Goode's interrupted homolosine projection combines the homolographic and sinusoidal projections. (Based on Goode Base Map. Copyright by the University of Chicago. Used by permission of the University of Chicago Press.)

13. *Homolosine projection.* The *homolosine* projection, invented by Dr. Paul Goode in 1923, is a combination of the homolographic and sinusoidal types. The sinusoidal projection is used between 40° N and S lat., the homolographic for the remaining poleward parts.

In both homolographic and sinusoidal projections the shearing of polar areas is especially marked to the extreme right and left of the map. This distortion can be reduced by centering each important land area on its own straight central meridian and fitting together the parts. The *interrupted* homolosine projection (Figure 2.28) has North America, Eurasia, South America, Africa, and Australia, each based on the best-suited meridian. Because the map cannot thus fit together between the land areas, except along the equator, large gaps occur.

If our interest is in land areas only, as, for example, if we wish to show the areas under wheat cultivation, the interruption is of no special detriment. To show oceans of the world we may center the oceans on central meridians, making the interruptions occur on land areas.

Summary

Thirteen projections have been explained and illustrated. This should serve to give the geography student a good start into map-projection principles. But, because more than 200 projections have been invented, unfamiliar types will frequently be encountered. The majority of them are closely enough related to one or more of the types discussed in this chapter so that the principle is either obvious from inspection of the map or can be understood from a brief note of explanation.

The following admonitions may serve to point out some of the principles of selecting a projection:

1. Use a good globe whenever possible if points or areas are to be related in distance and direction. There is no substitute for a true-scale model of the earth's surface features.

2. Where a map is required, select the projection best suited to the need. For example, use an equal-area map to show the areal distribution of things. Use conic or azimuthal maps for high latitudes.

3. Before you begin to drawn conclusions and analyze geographical factors from a map, be sure that you know the qualities of the projection, whether equal-area, conformal, or neither. If in doubt, compare two or more projections of the same areas and see what possible erroneous concepts each might give. The more of the earth's surface a map shows, the greater should your caution become.

Review Questions

1. What is a map projection? What is the basic problem of map projection?

2. For what purposes is a globe inferior to a flat map? For what purposes is a globe preferable to a flat map?

3. What is a developable solid? an undevelopable solid? Give examples, and explain what this has to do with map projections.

4. Explain the concept of map scale. What is the representative fraction? Which varieties of map projections preserve constant scale in all places and directions over the map?

5. What is an equal-area map projection? Name three equal-area types.

6. What is a conformal map projection? Name three conformal types.

7. Are projections which are neither equal-area nor conformal of any value? Illustrate with specific examples.

8. Into what large groups may map projections be classified?

9. List the properties common to all zenithal (azimuthal) map projections.

10. List the properties common to conic projections. In what way does the polyconic projection differ from other conic types?

11. What advantages do the cylindrical projections have over other groups?

12. For each of the zenithal (azimuthal) projections which you have studied answer the following questions: (*a*) What principle of construction is used? (*b*) What conditions of scale pertain along a radial line extending outward from the center of the map? (*c*) In the equatorial position, what kind of lines are the parallels? the meridians? (Are they curved or straight; if curved, what kind of curves?) (*d*) Can the projection show an entire hemisphere? an entire globe? (*e*) Is the projection conformal, equal-area, or neither? (*f*) What special value has the projection? For what uses can it be recommended?

13. What advantage is gained by having two standard parallels instead of one on a perspective conic projection? How do scale conditions compare?

14. Explain the basic principle of the Lambert conformal conic projection. What advantages has this projection? What use is made of it? Would a world map be satisfactory on this projection?

15. Explain the principle of the polyconic projection. Along what lines is the scale constant? For what purposes is this a good projection? Name some of the map agencies that have used it. Which is better for sets of large-scale maps, the Lambert conformal conic projection or the polyconic projection? Explain.

16. Explain the construction principle and scale qualities of Gall's stereographic cylindrical projection.

17. Explain the principle of the equatorial Mercator projection. Is this an equal-area or conformal projection? What shape has a complete Mercator map showing the entire globe? How does the map scale at 60° latitude compare with the equatorial scale?

18. What is a rhumb line? What is a loxodrome? What projection shows all great circles as straight lines? What use is made of rhumb lines and great circles in navigation? Under what circumstances are these two types of lines identical on a Mercator projection?

19. Describe the transverse Mercator projection. What advantages has this projection? In what way does use of the secant position improve the scale qualities? How is this projection used as the base for the Universal Transverse Mercator Grid?

20. Compare the homolographic and sinusoidal projections as to construction principles and properties. Are these projections equal-area, conformal, or neither?

21. What advantages has Goode's interrupted homolosine projection over the homolographic and sinusoidal projections?

Exercises

1. For each of the following statements select from the thirteen projections discussed in this chapter all those to which the statement applies. (List polar, equatorial, and oblique positions of azimuthal projections as separate types.) (**a**) All are equal-area projections. (**b**) All are conformal projections. (**c**) All are neither equal-area nor conformal. (**d**) All the parallels are curved lines. (**e**) All the parallels are straight lines. (**f**) All the meridians, except the central one, are curved lines. (**g**) All the meridians are straight lines. (**h**) All the curved parallels and meridians are true arcs of circles. (**i**) All the parallels are arcs of circles, but not necessarily concentric. (**j**) All the parallels and meridians intersect at true right angles. (**k**) Neither pole can be shown. (**l**) Only one pole can be shown at a time. (**m**) Map outline is circular when exactly one hemisphere is shown. (**n**) The projection can be constructed by drawing lines or rays from a single point, through a globe, onto a flat surface or a developable surface.

2. Make a table on which are noted the physical properties of the thirteen projections you have studied. Down the left-hand side of a large sheet of paper list the thirteen projections. Make vertical columns across the paper, using each one to note a certain property of the projection. A suggested list of column headings is as follows: Class to which projection belongs. Name of projection. (If azimuthal type, subdivide into polar, equatorial, oblique.) Shape of map when showing complete globe. Shape of map when showing one hemisphere. Form of meridians (curved or straight; kind of curves). Form of parallels (curved or straight; kind of curves). Equal-area, conformal, or neither. Special properties (such as "great circles are straight lines"). Best uses (such as "large-scale maps," "small-scale maps," "navigation," "areal distribution"). Perhaps other columns could be added. A chart of this type is excellent for review purposes.

3. Using only a pencil, compass, ruler, and protractor, construct some of the simpler projections you have studied. Several easy ones are suggested below. (**a**) Polar orthographic projection. (**b**) Stereographic projection (polar position). (**c**) Azimuthal equidistant projection (polar position). (**d**) Azimuthal equal-area projection (polar position). (**e**) Perspective conic projection, one standard parallel, 45° N. (**f**) Gall's stereographic cylindrical projection.

CHAPTER THREE

Location on the globe and on maps

THIS chapter deals with the problem of determining the location of the earth's surface features, in order that they may be correctly shown on maps. Equally important to geographers is a reverse problem, that of reading from a map the location, size, or orientation of features shown on maps and of stating this information in terms of some established system. The geographer relies heavily upon maps. Not only do maps provide him with information which he uses in his studies, but much of the new information that he gathers or synthesizes must be shown on maps. The making of maps, a specialized field combining a mathematical science with a graphic art, is known simply as *cartography*. Although the actual publication of finished maps is best left to the professional cartographer, there are many things that a geographer needs to know about maps in order to gain the maximum amount of information from them and to select base maps best suited to showing the information that he wants to display.

The system of parallels and meridians described in Chapter 1 provides a network of lines to which specific points on the earth's surface are tied. It is the task of the geodesist, geologist, and surveyor to measure the position, size, and shape of the earth's natural and man-made features. The task of the cartographer is to compile this information and to draw it as precisely and effectively as possible for reproduction on printed sheets.

Maps cover a wide range both in the amount of earth's surface shown by a sheet of a given size and in the type of material represented. On a small sheet of paper may be printed a map of the entire globe or a detailed city plan showing but a few city blocks. With respect to the type of information shown we can classify maps in two large groups, *planimetric* and *topographic*. Planimetric maps show the exact location of surface features projected on a single plane, as if no differences of vertical elevation existed. A planimetric map may show such features as shorelines, rivers, lakes, boundary lines, roads, and the precise position of cities and mountain peaks, but it gives no information as to relief forms and slope of the land surface or how high above sea level or surrounding objects the various features lie. On the other hand, topographic maps, treated in Chapter 20, are intended to depict the relief features of the land surface and to indicate the degree of slope of the ground.

above: Iowa farm lands laid out on the Land Office grid.
Photograph, Fairchild Aerial Surveys, Inc.

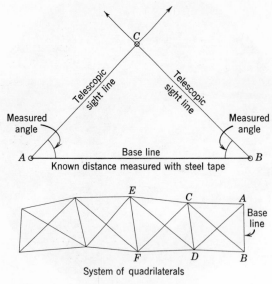

Figure 3.1 The principle of triangulation.

Relative and absolute locations

Suppose that an explorer has reached a little known land where he finds three prominent mountain peaks, A, B, and C, not previously mapped or described. With suitable surveying equipment he finds that Peak A lies five miles north of Peak B; that Peak C lies seven miles due east of Peak B.

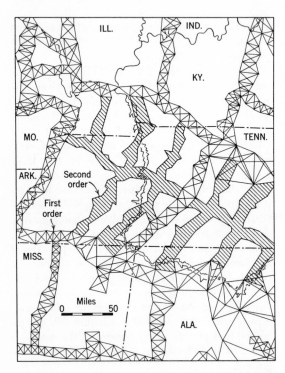

Figure 3.2 A network of triangulation quadrilaterals in the Tennessee Valley region. (After *TVA Tech. Report* 23, 1951, U.S. Govt. Printing Office.)

Taking a blank sheet of paper and letting one inch on the paper represent one mile of horizontal ground distance, he can draw a map to show the correct relative locations of the three peaks with respect to one another. A triangle connecting peaks A, B, and C is true in shape and is true in orientation with respect to north. The *relative location* of the points is thus determined with respect to one another, but not with respect to any fixed, world-wide system of reference lines, such as the parallels and meridians with a prime meridian passing through Greenwich, England.

If the explorer is equipped with suitable knowledge and instruments he can determine the approximate location of one of the peaks in terms of latitude and longitude by astronomical methods. This establishes the *absolute location* of the peak, in turn, permitting the absolute location of the remaining points. Absolute location describes the position of a point in such terms that its unique position with respect to all other points on the globe is made clear. In general, three grid systems (sets of intersecting lines) described in this chapter provide absolute location of points: the geographic grid, military grid, and U.S. Land Office grid. Triangulation surveying by itself, and designation of position by compass bearing and distance, explained below, provide relative locations.

Triangulation and base lines

Planimetric maps show the exact location of features on a map, as if all were reduced to a sea-level surface. Before any major mapping operation is begun it is essential to locate relative to one another with extreme accuracy several key points within the area. Because all additional points are located with reference to the first set, the highest order of accuracy is required for the original key points. Secondary sets of points are located with somewhat less accurate methods, which take less time and money. From these, still larger numbers of points are determined in more rapid fashion.

Surveying of points begins with the careful measurement of a long, straight *base line*, which may be several miles long. The base line usually follows a highway, railroad, or beach so as to encounter the fewest obstacles. Between points marked by permanent monuments set in the ground, the base line is measured by means of a steel tape. A special nickel-steel alloy is used for the tape, which must change length very little with temperature changes. The tape must be stretched with exactly the right force, measured by a spring balance, so that error due to its elasticity is the minimum. With extreme care and an elaborate outfit it is possible to measure the length of a base line so that the actual error will not be more than one part in 300,000. Thus, a line five miles long is measured to within one inch of its true length. Actual errors in first-order surveying are commonly very much smaller, generally about one part in two million. Once the base line has been measured, triangulation is begun.

Triangulation is the measurement of large triangles on the ground, using the geometric principle that if the length of one side of a triangle (the base line) is known, and the two angles made by the base and adjacent sides are also known, the remaining sides and angle can be calculated (Figure 3.1). Thus if a surveyor sets up a telescopic instrument, known as a *theodolite,* upon one end of the base line (point *A*), he can sight both to a flag on the other end of the base line and to a second flag on a third, unknown point (point *C*) and measure the horizontal angle between the two lines of sight. If he then takes his theodolite to the other end of the base line (point *B*) and sights back to points *A* and *C,* measuring the angle between them, he has the necessary information to determine the lengths of the other two sides of the triangle and thus to locate point *C* exactly with respect to the base line. The great advantage of triangulation over actual ground measurement is the saving in time and labor, especially where the terrain is rugged. (The Grand Canyon was mapped in this way.) Once the first triangle *ABC* is measured, either of the other two sides *AC* or *CB* can be used as base lines from which to construct more triangles. As more triangles are added, the known points are extended across country as a *system of quadrilaterals* (Figure 3.1). These, in turn, join one another to form an intersecting network (Figure 3.2).

Triangulation and measurement of base lines is described as of *first order, second order, third order,* and *fourth order,* depending upon the degree of accuracy attained. First-order and second-order triangulation in the United States is carried out by the U.S. Coast and Geodetic Survey, which achieves a degree of precision almost incredible to the ordinary person. For example, in first-order work, the sum of the three angles of a triangle must approach the theoretical value of 180° to within 1 second of arc. (There are 3600 seconds to 1 degree.) Work is done at night, using a small electric light whose pinpoint image can be picked up by telescope many miles away. During the daytime the image of a distant point shifts about incessantly in the telescope field because the light rays are bent irregularly as unequal heating of the air sets up eddies in the lower atmosphere. Fourth-order triangulation is used by mapping parties to establish a large number of points within the area, and neither requires nor uses the elaborate precision instruments and techniques of the higher orders.

Although triangulation is fundamentally a system of determining relative location of a given point with respect to other points, a triangulation system can be made one of absolute location by precise determination of the latitude and longitude of one point on the base line, then computing by trigonometry the geographic coordinates of all other points in the network.

In general, the plan of the U.S. Coast and Geodetic Survey was to span the United States with a number of first-order triangulation networks, each being a system of quadrilaterals begun at a coastal point and extended into the heart of the country. Many such traverses, following generally along parallels and meridians, now provide the United States with a control network (Figure 3.3). Triangulation points on this net serve as the reference points for all mapping and surveying operations carried out locally. Information on the precise latitude and longitude of these points is available.

Unfortunately, the most precise determinations of latitude and longitude at various coastal points do not result in exact agreement as to the position of a triangulation station where two or more traverses have met at a common point in the heart of the country. Therefore, after east-west and north-south triangulation surveys were joined in the United States, a single reference station was selected to become the absolute standard of geographical position. This is a station known as "Meades Ranch," located in central Kansas, approximately at the geographical center of the United States. Using the Clarke spheroid of 1866 as the reference spheroid, latitude and longitude were computed for Meades Ranch station. All other positions of the triangulation networks were adjusted accordingly. This set of absolute locations of control points is known as the *North American Datum of 1927* and all local mapping is tied to it. Both Canada and Mexico decided to adopt the datum based on Meades Ranch. All of North America thus has its triangulation based on the 1927 datum, and is the only continent having all of its triangulation carried out with reference to a common spheroid and a single starting point on that spheroid.

Vertical control by leveling

Triangulation establishes location of points projected upon the imaginary spheroid surface, but does not measure the precise vertical distance between a given point and a reference level. Such information, known as *vertical control,* is supplied by *precise leveling.* The instrument used is known simply as a *level,* or *spirit level.* It is a telescope mounted horizontally with a level bubble astride

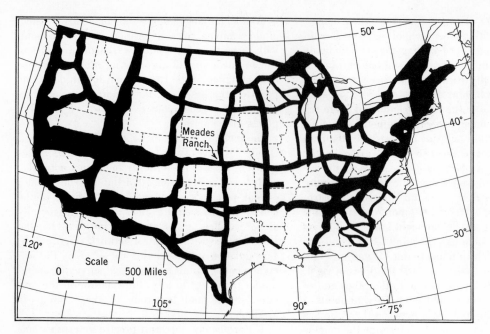

Figure 3.3 The first-order triangulation network of the United States as it was in 1929, shortly after the establishment of the North American Datum of 1927. (After C. V. Hodgson, in *Physics of the Earth,* Vol. II, "Figure of the Earth," National Research Council, 1931.)

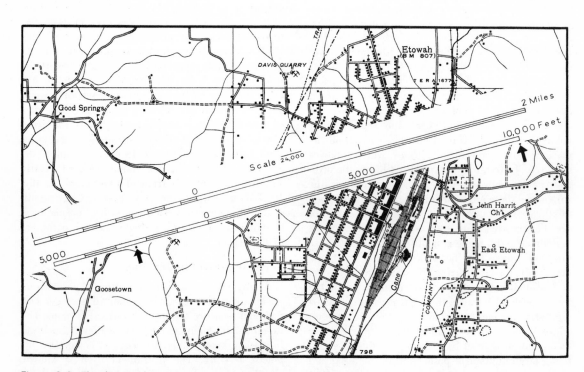

Figure 3.4 The distance between two points on a map can be read directly from a graphic scale. (Portion of U.S. Geological Survey map.)

the telescope tube. By means of thumb screws the telescope can be adjusted until brought to an exactly level sight line. Sighting horizontally to a point of known elevation, the height of instrument is read on a scaled rod held erect on that point. The telescope is then turned to another point, where the scaled rod is again read. Elevation of the second point is determined by adding and subtracting the height readings.

As with triangulation, leveling is described as of first order, second order, third order, and lower order. That of the highest precision, first-order leveling, is carried out by the U.S. Coast and Geodetic Survey in such a way as to form a fundamental level net of which several thousand miles have been completed, largely following railroads and highways. A level line starts at the coast, where the reference level, or datum, is mean sea level. Although easily determined, mean sea level varies from place to place along the coast, so that two precision level lines meeting in a common point may not agree as to elevation. All first-order level nets were adjusted in 1929 to agree with respect to the *Sea-level Datum of 1929.*

Just as triangulation stations are marked by permanent bronze discs set in bedrock or concrete, so level stations are marked by permanent *benchmarks* (Figure 18.13) for use in local mapping and surveying.

Representing distances on maps

Distance between points shown on a map depends on the scale of the map—the ratio between map distances and the actual ground distances which the map represents (Chapter 2). Given a fractional scale (representative fraction, or R.F.) on which to draw his map, the cartographer must convert this fraction to units of measurement, for he must use a ruler scaled in inches or centimeters to measure lengths of line on the map to represent ground distances in miles or kilometers.

For example, if the map scale is given as $\frac{1}{63,360}$, or $1:63,360$, as explained in Chapter 2, this fractional scale may be interpreted as "one inch on the map represents one mile on the ground." A map scale of $1:100,000$ could be read as "one centimeter represents one kilometer."

Most maps of small areas carry a fractional scale printed on the map margin. Conversion to equivalent ratios of inches to miles or centimeters to kilometers is left to the reader to compute. For practical map use, however, a *graphic scale* is printed on the map margin. This is a length of line divided off into numbered segments (Figure 3.4). The units are in conventional terms of measurement, such as feet, yards, and miles, or meters and kilometers. To use the graphic scale, a piece of

paper with a straight edge is held along the line to be measured on the map and the distance marked on the edge of the paper. The paper is then placed along the graphic scale and the length of the line read directly. Where many measurements are to be made it will save time to copy the graphic scale onto the edge of a piece of paper and apply it directly between points on the map (Figure 3.4).

In the study of map projections (Chapter 2) it was emphasized that no global map on a flat sheet of paper can have a constant scale in all parts and in all directions. Within the limits of maps of large scale, showing only a very small part of the earth's surface, the scale changes are so slight as to be dismissed. A graphic scale will be true in terms of the extent to which the eye of the user can distinguish the width of a finely printed line.

Conversion of scale from one form to another

An important skill in cartography and map reading is the conversion of scale from one form to another. These manipulations are best explained by examples.

Example A. *Fractional form to length units.* Problem: How may the scale $1:100,000$ be stated in familiar units, such as inches to the mile? To avoid any mistake, go back to the definition of scale and work by easy steps to the final answer. The following sequence is suggested:

$$\frac{\text{Distance on map}}{\text{Distance on ground}} = \frac{1 \text{ inch on map}}{100,000 \text{ inches on ground}}$$

Now, in order to have the ground distance in miles, we must divide 100,000 inches by 63,360, because there are 63,360 inches to a mile. Therefore

$$\frac{1 \text{ inch on map}}{100,000 \div 63,360} = \frac{1 \text{ inch on map}}{1.57 \text{ miles on ground}}$$

or "1 inch to 1.57 miles."

Example B. *Length units to fractional form.* Problem: How may the scale "1 inch to 1 mile" be written as a fraction? Following the general rule, write the information as follows:

$$\frac{1 \text{ inch on map}}{1 \text{ mile on ground}}$$

Convert the denominator into inches by multiplying by 63,360 (because there are 63,360 inches in a mile). Then

$$\frac{1 \text{ inch on map}}{63,360 \text{ inches on ground}} \quad \text{or} \quad \frac{1}{63,360}$$

Example C. Problem: Construct a graphic scale for the scale "1 inch to 1 mile." This is the simplest of all scale operations. Lay off a line and divide it into segments 1 inch long. Each unit represents 1 mile and can be so labeled.

Example D. Problem: Construct a graphic scale for the scale "1 inch to 11.3 miles." Here, although the line could be divided into 1-inch parts, marking them "0, 11.3, 22.6, 33.9, etc.," such a graphic scale would be of little use to anyone. The problem is to make the graphic scale consist of some even-numbered unit, preferably some power of ten, such as 1, 10, 100, or 1,000 miles or kilometers. Therefore, perform the following operation:

$$\frac{1 \text{ in.}}{11.3 \text{ mi.}} = \frac{x \text{ inches}}{10 \text{ miles}}$$

Solving for x,

$$11.3x = 10$$
$$x = \frac{10}{11.3}$$
$$x = 0.885 \text{ inch}$$

Now lay off segments 0.885 inch apart on the line. Each unit represents 10 miles.

Example E. Problem: Given the fractional scale 1:50,000, make a graphic scale using miles as units of measure. This problem can be broken down to two problems already treated. First convert the fractional scale to length units of inches and miles, as explained in Example A, then construct the graphic scale, as explained in Example D.

Example F. Problem: Given the graphic scale shown below, determine the fractional scale:

Miles

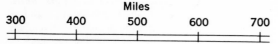

Solution of this problem requires a ruler, preferably one scaled off in tenths of inches. Measure the exact length of several units on the graphic scale, recording your results in the following form:

$$\frac{1.97 \text{ inches}}{300 \text{ miles}}$$

First reduce the 300 miles to inches by multiplying by 63,360 (because there are 63,360 inches in a mile); then reduce to a simple fraction:

$$\frac{1.97 \text{ inches}}{300 \times 63,360 \text{ inches}} = \frac{1.97}{19,008,000} = \frac{1}{9,650,000} \text{ approx.}$$

Large-scale and small-scale maps

The relative size of two different scales is determined according to which fraction is the larger and which the smaller. For example, a scale of 1:10,000 is twice as large as a scale of 1:20,000.

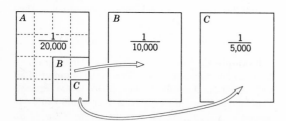

Figure 3.5 Area shown on a map decreases as scale increases.

Many students are confused about this because they unthinkingly suppose that the fraction with the larger denominator represents the larger scale. If in doubt ask yourself the question: "Which fraction is larger: ¼ or ½?"

Maps with scales ranging from 1:600,000 down to 1:100,000,000 or smaller are known as *small-scale maps*. Those of scale 1:599,999 to 1:75,000 are *medium-scale* maps; those of scale greater than 1:75,000 are *large-scale* maps. Starting at the small-scale end, the following are examples of the use of various scales: A 6-inch globe or a Mercator map of the world measuring about 12 by 18 inches has an equatorial scale of about 1:85,000,000 and is classed as a very small-scale map. A large map of the world suitable for hanging on the wall of a classroom has an equatorial scale of about 1:15,000,000 if the earth's equator is represented on the map as a line 8 feet long. One inch on this small-scale map represents a distance of 240 miles. A wall map of the United States measuring about 7 feet across has a fractional scale of 1:2,500,000. Each inch represents a distance of about 40 miles. A wall map of Wyoming measuring 3 by 4 feet is on a medium scale of 1:500,000 and represents distances on the ratio of 1 inch to about 8 miles.

For representing details of the earth's surface configuration, or *topography*, large-scale maps are needed and the area of land surface shown by an individual map sheet must necessarily be small. A topographic sheet 10 by 20 inches, on a scale of 1,63,360 (1 inch to 1 mile) would, of course, include an area 10 by 20 miles, or 200 square miles. Of the common sets of topographic maps published by national governments for general distribution, most fall within the scale range of 1:20,000 to 1:250,000.

Relation between scales and areas

Assuming that two maps, each on a different scale, have the same dimensions, what is the relation between the ground areas shown by each? In Figure 3.5 are shown three maps, each having the same dimensions, but representing scales of 1:20,000, 1:10,000, and 1:5,000, respectively, from left to right. Although map B is on twice the scale of map A, it shows a ground area only one-fourth as great. Map C is on four times as large a scale as map A, yet it covers a ground area only one-sixteenth as much. From this example can be deduced the following rule: the ground area that is represented by a map of given outside dimensions varies inversely with the square of the change in scale. Thus, if the scale is reduced to one-third its original value, the area that can be shown on a map of fixed dimensions increases to nine times the original value.

Map orientation and declination of the compass

It is a well-known convention to draw maps in such a way that north is in a direction toward the top of the map, south to the bottom of the map, and east and west to the right- and left-hand sides, respectively. There are exceptions, of course, as on polar azimuthal projections.

The geographic north pole, to which all meridians converge, forms a reference point for the *true north*, or *geographic north*, direction. There is, however, another place, the *magnetic north pole*, to which magnetic compasses point. The magnetic north pole is located in the Northwest Territories of Canada on Prince of Wales Island about lat. 73° N, long. 100° W (Figure 3.6). Most published large-scale maps have printed on the margin two arrows stemming from a common point. One arrow designates true north, the other one *magnetic north*. The angular distance between the two directions is known as the *magnetic declination*.[1] Although the

[1] Termed *variation of the compass* on nautical charts.

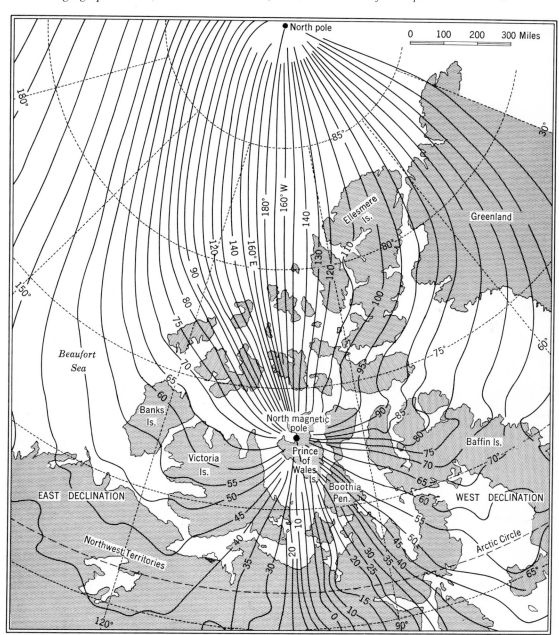

Figure 3.6 Isogonic map of the magnetic north polar area for 1948. (After a map published by Canada Department of Mines and Resources.)

magnetic declination does not need to be known in the laboratory reading of maps, it becomes extremely important when the map is used out of doors with a compass.

Magnetic declination varies greatly in different parts of the world, depending principally on one's position relative to the geographic and magnetic poles. Lines on Figure 3.6 are drawn through all places having the same compass declination and are known as *isogonic lines*. As would be expected, the compass declination is a full 180° along a line between the geographic and magnetic north poles. Here the compass directions exactly reverse the true directions.

Figure 3.7 is an isogonic map of the United States. Along the 100th meridian, which passes through the north magnetic pole, the declination is 10° to 12° east, whereas the line of zero declination line runs through the eastern United States. Anywhere along this line the compass points to true geographic north, and no adjustment is required.

Magnetic declination changes appreciably with the passage of years so that isogonic maps must be redrawn every ten to fifteen years. The amount of change in declination annually is usually stated on the margin of a good map. Isogonic maps may show a second set of lines, usually in a different color, connecting points of equal annual change.

Bearings and azimuths

In using maps it is frequently necessary to state the direction followed by a road or stream, or to describe the direction that can be taken to locate a particular object with respect to some known reference point. In air and marine navigation the direction from one point to another must be stated. For these purposes the angle that the given line makes with a north-south line is measured. The unit of angular measurement most common in map work is the *degree*, 360 of which comprise a complete circle, but other systems of angular measurement, such as the *mil* (of which there are 6400 in a complete circle), are sometimes preferable for special applications.

Two systems of stating directions with respect to north can be used (Figure 3.8). (*a*) *Compass quadrant bearings* are angles measured eastward or westward of either north or south, whichever happens

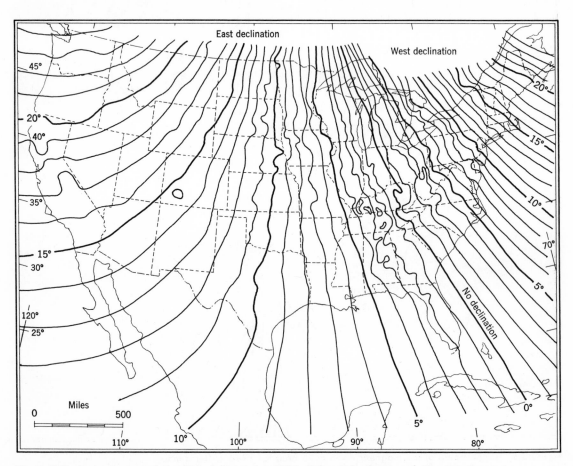

Figure 3.7 Isogonic map of the United States for 1934. (After U.S. Coast and Geodetic Survey.)

to be the closer. Examples are shown in Figure
3.8A. The direction from a given point to some
object on the map is thus written as "N 49° E" or
"S 70° W." All bearings range between 0° and
90°. Compass bearings may be magnetic bearings,
related to magnetic north, or true bearings, related
to geographic north. Unless specifically stated
otherwise, a bearing should be assumed to be a
true bearing. A disadvantage of compass quadrant
bearings is that the same number of degrees can
be repeated for four different bearings, once for
each of the four combinations of north or south,
east or west. This may cause confusion or mistakes.

(*b*) *Azimuths* are used by military services and
in air and marine navigation generally. As shown
in Figure 3.8B, all azimuths are read in a clockwise direction from north and therefore range between 0° and 360°. There is no repetition of numbers and no use of the words "north," "south,"
"east," or "west," as in the quadrant bearing system. Azimuths are usually measured from either
magnetic north or true north, referred to as *magnetic azimuth* and *true azimuth* respectively. On air
navigation charts (Exercise 3), magnetic azimuth
(called "bearing"[2]) is used. For each radio transmitter, magnetic north at the station serves as the
reference line.

With a knowledge of map scales and azimuths
(or bearings), we can describe the position of any
desired object on a map with reference to a known
point. Using the graphic scale the distance from
the known point to the object is measured; then the
azimuth or bearing of a line between the two places
is read from a protractor laid directly upon the
map. For example, a certain farmhouse might be
found to lie 512 meters from a highway intersection along a true azimuth of 224°. Although this
system accurately locates one point with respect to
a second point, the location of the second point
must still be described in some other manner.
We therefore turn next to a study of coordinate
systems for the absolute location of points on the
earth's surface.

Coordinate systems used on maps

Any system whereby points on the earth's surface are located with reference to a previously determined set of intersecting lines can be called a
coordinate system. The student is already familiar
with the system of parallels and meridians used
throughout the world, and the designation of any
point on the earth's surface in terms of latitude
and longitude (Chapter 1). This constitutes the
commonest of the coordinate systems in general

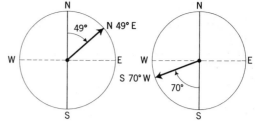

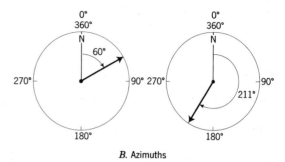

A. Compass quadrant bearings

B. Azimuths

Figure 3.8 Directions are expressed by means of bearings or azimuths.

use. Two other systems will be included in this discussion: the *military grid* and the *township grid of
U.S. Land Survey.*

The geographic grid

A geographer often speaks of the latitude and
longitude of a place as *geographic coordinates,* and
of the network of parallels and meridians on a
globe or map as the *geographic grid* (Chapter 1).
Most published sets of large-scale maps use the
geographic grid to determine the position and size
of individual map sheets in a series. A single map
sheet, or *quadrangle,* is bounded on the right- and
left-hand margins by meridians, and on the top and
bottom by parallels, which are a specified number
of minutes or degrees apart. Thus, individual
sheets may be fitted together to form unified
groups. Parallels and meridians are usually labeled
at the corners of the map. Often additional meridians and parallels are printed on the map, sub-
dividing the area into smaller rectangles. Where
the actual lines are not printed their positions are
sometimes shown by short lines, or *ticks,* at the
edges of the map; their intersections by small
crosses on the map interior.

Good examples of the geographic grid system
used on large-scale maps are found on the U.S.
Geological Survey's topographic maps of the United
States. Their relations to one another are shown in
Figures 3.9 and 3.10. Most 15-minute and 30-
minute quadrangles measure 17½ inches from top
to bottom, a figure that remains constant over the
entire country because the length of a degree of

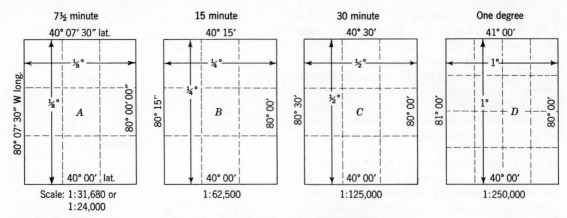

Figure 3.9 Large-scale maps of the U. S. Geological Survey are bounded by parallels and meridians to form quadrangles. The four quadrangles shown here represent the scales and areas commonly used in the United States, exclusive of Alaska.

latitude, as shown in an earlier chapter, is everywhere nearly the same. Width of these quadrangles varies from about 15 inches for Texas to about 12 inches for North Dakota because of the northward convergence of meridians.

Seven standard scales comprise the National Topographic Map Series:

Series	R.F.	Unit Equivalents
7.5 minute	1:24,000	1 inch to 2000 feet
7.5 minute	1:31,680	1 inch to one-half mile
15 minute	1:62,500	1 inch to about one mile
Alaska	1:63,360	1 inch to one mile
30 minute	1:125,000	1 inch to about 2 miles
1:250,000	1:250,000	1 inch to about 4 miles
1:1,000,000	1:1,000,000	1 inch to about 16 miles

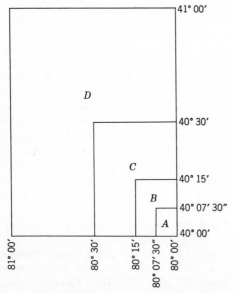

Figure 3.10 If the four quadrangles of Figure 3.9 were reduced to the same scale, their areas would compare as shown here.

Figures 3.9 and 3.10 compare the coverages and sizes of standard quadrangles on several of these series.

Alaska provides an illustration of the geographic grid applied to map quadrangles in high latitudes, where the length of a degree of longitude is much shorter than a degree of latitude (Figure 3.11). Two scales are used. The map series on 1:250,000 consists of quadrangles of one degree of latitude by three degrees of longitude. The large-scale series, 1:63,360, consists of quadrangles all covering 15 minutes of latitude, but including 20, 22½, 30, or 36 minutes of longitude according to latitude, so as to provide sheets of about equal map dimensions.

Still another example of the geographic grid applied to map sheets is the series of U.S. World Aeronautical Charts issued by the U.S. Coast and Geodetic Survey on the scale of 1:1,000,000. These maps are for use in military and civilian air navigation the world over. Figure 3.12 is a portion of the index map of World Aeronautical Charts and shows how parallels and meridians form the boundaries of individual map sheets. All sheets have a latitude coverage of 4°, but the longitude span ranges from 6°, in low latitudes, to 12° at 60° latitude. Poleward of 60° the longitude span increases rapidly.

One caution must be taken in the use of foreign maps. Although the system of latitude and longitude based on the prime meridian of Greenwich, England, is widely used, some European countries employ a reference meridian of their own choosing, such as the meridian passing through the astronomical observatory in the capital city. For some older European series, such as the German topographic maps on a scale of 1:100,000, a special prime meridian, the *meridian of Ferro*, is used. This meridian passes through Ferro, western-

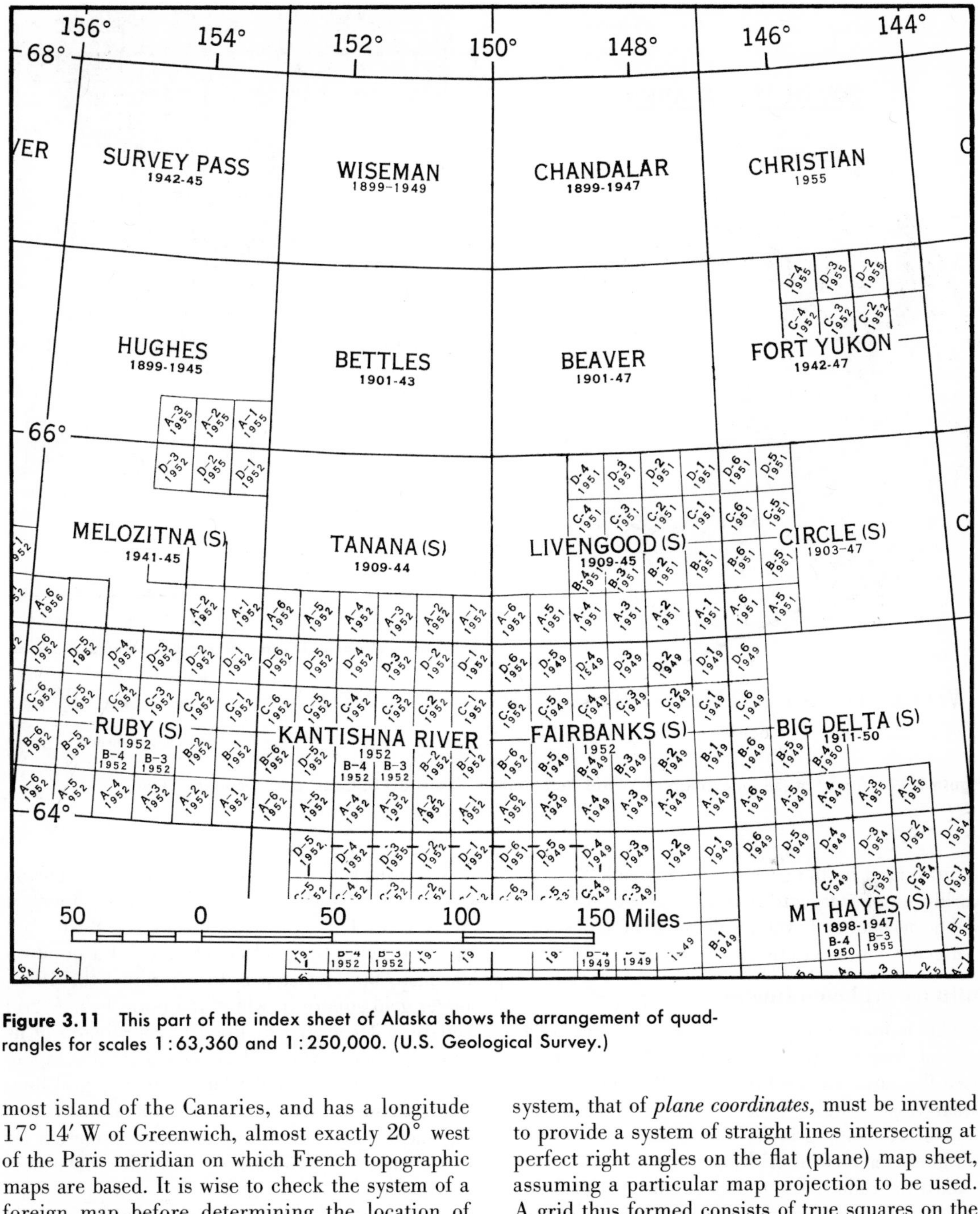

Figure 3.11 This part of the index sheet of Alaska shows the arrangement of quadrangles for scales 1:63,360 and 1:250,000. (U.S. Geological Survey.)

most island of the Canaries, and has a longitude 17° 14′ W of Greenwich, almost exactly 20° west of the Paris meridian on which French topographic maps are based. It is wise to check the system of a foreign map before determining the location of places in terms of geographic coordinates.

Spherical and plane coordinates

The geographic coordinates may be considered as *spherical coordinates,* because they designate location of points on a spherical (or spheroidal) surface. The meridians and parallels are neither straight, equidistantly spaced lines over the globe, nor can they form such a net on any of the useful map projections. Therefore, an entirely different

system, that of *plane coordinates,* must be invented to provide a system of straight lines intersecting at perfect right angles on the flat (plane) map sheet, assuming a particular map projection to be used. A grid thus formed consists of true squares on the map and is superimposed upon the geographic grid.

Plane coordinate systems have been set up by individual states of the United States, some of which use the transverse Mercator projection; others the Lambert conformal conic projection. The grid is scaled in thousands of feet. Many of the large-scale topographic maps of the U.S. Geological Survey indicate the position of 10,000-foot grid lines by ticks on the map margin. Important as these state grids are for surveying and mapping, they will

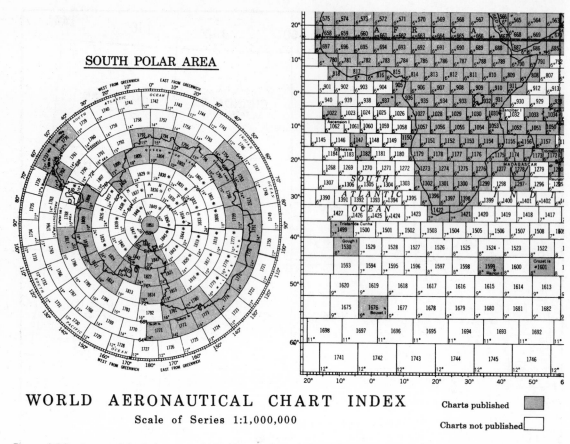

Figure 3.12 A part of the index map of World Aeronautical Charts. (U.S. Coast and Geodetic Survey.)

be little used by the geographer. Instead, a single world-wide *military grid system* of plane coordinates will be encountered over a wide range of map scales and geographical locations.

Military grid coordinates

The military grid uses the *meter* as the basic unit of length, although earlier military systems used the yard. The grid is essentially a network of squares, each square 1000 meters wide. A portion of a 1000-meter grid is shown in Figure 3.13. Numbers on vertical grid lines increase eastward, toward the right; those on horizontal grid lines increase northward, or upward. Only two digits are printed on most grid lines, those that denote thousands and tens of thousands. In the case of the 1000-meter grid, three zeros have been dropped as well as those digits that denote hundreds of thousands and millions. Full numbers are printed once near the lower left-hand corner of the map. Grid line spacing of 1000 meters is used on large-scale maps, 1:100,000 or smaller, whereas a spacing of 10,000 meters is used in the grid printed on maps of scale smaller than 1:100,000.

In stating grid coordinates, the number of meters east (right) is given first; then the number of meters north (up). This gives a simple rule. "Read right up." In giving the grid coordinates of a point on the map, the first step is to determine the 1000-meter grid square in which the point lies. A grid square is designated by the grid coordinates of its lower left-hand corner. Thus grid square *A* in Figure 3.13 is designated by the intersection of grid lines *87* east and *80* north. These numbers are written together as *8780*. This is a shorthand notation for coordinates 687,000 meters east, 3,880,000 meters north.

For a particular point within a grid square, the coordinates may be read to the tenth part of a grid square, which is 100 meters. Point *B* of Figure 3.13 lies about four-tenths of the distance from 84 to 85, so that one coordinate is *844* east. It lies about five-tenths of the distance up from 76 to 77, so that the second coordinate is *765*. These are written together as a six-digit number: *844765*. Should we need to locate the point to the nearest 10 meters, still another digit is read by more precise measurements. Thus Point *C* is found to have

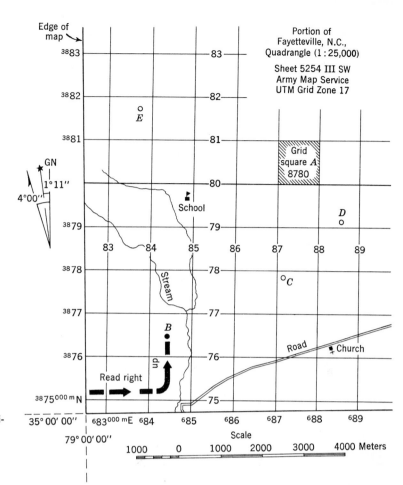

Figure 3.13 Military grid coordinates on the 1000-meter grid.

coordinates *8715* east and *7783* north; written as a single number: 87157783. In all three examples, above, an even number of digits forms the combined number. Therefore, given a coordinate designation, the number is broken in half. The first half is taken as the *easting;* the second half as the *northing.*

Grid zones

Grid coordinates of any small area belong to a particular *grid zone.* An international system provides military grid zones for the entire globe. Between lat. 80° S and 80° N the *Universal Transverse Mercator Grid System* is used; poleward of 80°, the *Universal Polar Stereographic Grid System.* These systems are named for the map projections on which they are based. (Both projections are explained in Chapter 2.)

The Universal Transverse Mercator grid system, hereafter referred to as the *UTM* grid, consists of 60 grid zones, each 6° of longitude in width (Figure 3.14). An additional one-half degree on each side provides for overlap into the adjacent zone. The *origin* of the grid zone lies at the intersection of the central meridian, which is a straight north-south line, and the equator, which is a straight east-west line. In order to have all eastings increase toward the right across the entire zone, the central meridian is given the arbitrary value of *500,000 meters east.* The equator is given the value of *0 meters north* as the reference line for northings increasing upward to the 80th parallel north. For the southern hemisphere, the equator is given the arbitrary northing of *10,000,000 meters north,* so that northings begin with their lowest value at 80° S lat. and increase northward to attain that figure at the equator.

The relationship of grid lines to parallels and meridians in various parts of a grid zone is shown in Figure 3.14. Near the equator both sets of lines are approximately parallel to one another. Toward higher latitudes the two sets of lines diverge increasingly, because the meridians converge whereas the grid lines remain equidistant. The grid zone itself narrows greatly because it is bounded by meridians. This leads to a definition of a second kind of declination, *grid declination,* which is the angle between *grid north* (the direction taken by

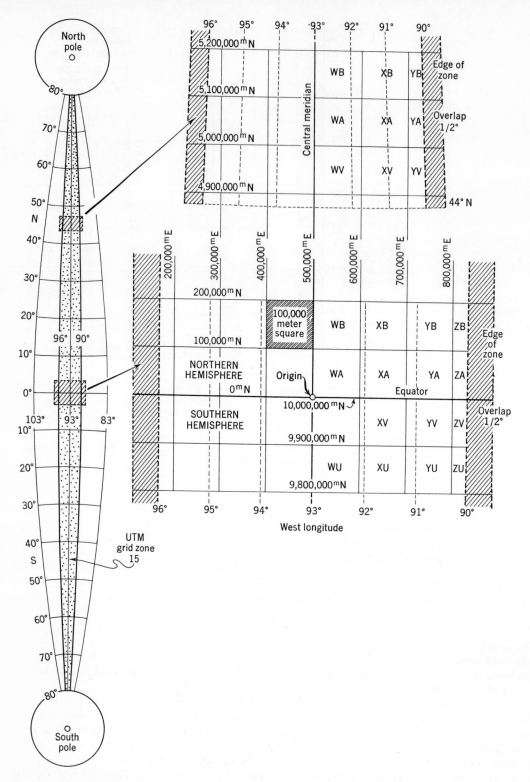

Figure 3.14 The UTM grid zone near the equator and at 45° N. (Data from U.S. Departments of the Army and Air Force, TM 5—241, 1951.)

the vertical grid lines) and true (geographic) north. Grid declination can be read directly with a protractor placed on the angle formed between a grid line and the meridian marking the edge of the map. The angle between grid north and magnetic north is termed the *grid magnetic (GM) angle*. Large-scale military maps, such as those produced by the U.S. Army Map Service, carry in the lower margin a diagram telling the relations among the three norths (Figure 3.15). Three kinds of azimuth are also possible on a military map: *grid azimuth, true azimuth*, and *magnetic azimuth* (Figure 3.16).

The Universal Polar Stereographic Grid system, hereafter designated the *UPS* grid, is superimposed upon a polar stereographic projection within the circle formed by the 80th parallel (Figure 3.17). An additional half degree of latitude is provided for overlap with the UTM grid. The vertical grid lines are parallel with meridians of 0° and 180° longitude; the horizontal grid lines are parallel with meridians of 90° E and 90° W long. Although the origin of the grid is the pole, this point is given an arbitrary easting and northing of 2,000,000 meters. Grid declination therefore ranges from 0° to 180°, depending upon location. The North Zone is shown in Figure 3.17. The South Zone, applied to the Antarctic region, is essentially the same except for a reversal in position of the 0° and 180° meridians which form the central meridian of the projection.

Scale factors and the military grids

The lines of the military grid are exactly uniform in spacing, so that the printed squares are exactly the same in dimension wherever printed on maps of a given stated scale, such as 1:100,000. In the study of map projections it was emphasized that no map printed on a flat sheet can preserve a truly constant scale in all parts of the map and in all directions. Consequently, we must reckon with the fact that the so-called "1000-meter grid square" does not everywhere represent a ground square exactly 1000 meters wide. On the UTM grid the map scale is exactly true with respect to the grid along two lines that lie parallel with the central meridian at a distance of 180,000 meters on each side (Figure 3.18). Thus the scale is true at eastings of 320,000 meters and 680,000 meters. Between these grid lines the map scale is smaller than the true scale by a *scale factor* of 0.9996. This means that a straight horizontal 1000 meter line on the ground at sea level will appear to be 999.6 meters long with respect to the grid scale. The scale factor at the outer edge of the grid zone is 1.0010, so that a 1000-meter line on the ground will appear to be 1001.0 meters long with respect to the grid scale. These scale errors are trivial in most

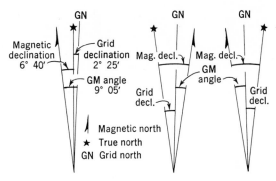

Figure 3.15 A special marginal symbol shows the relations among three kinds of north.

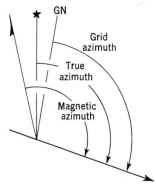

Figure 3.16 Azimuth may be measured with respect to three norths.

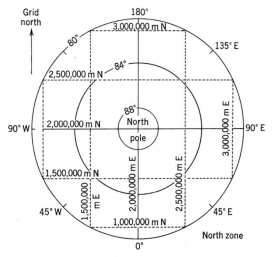

Figure 3.17 The Universal Polar Stereographic Grid, North Zone. (After U.S. Department of the Army and Air Force, TM 5–241, 1951.)

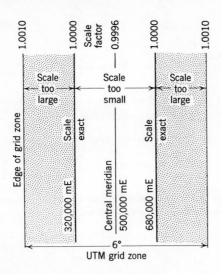

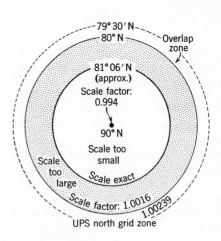

Figure 3.18 Scale factors in the UTM and UPS grids. (After U.S. Departments of the Army and Air Force, TM 5—241, 1951.)

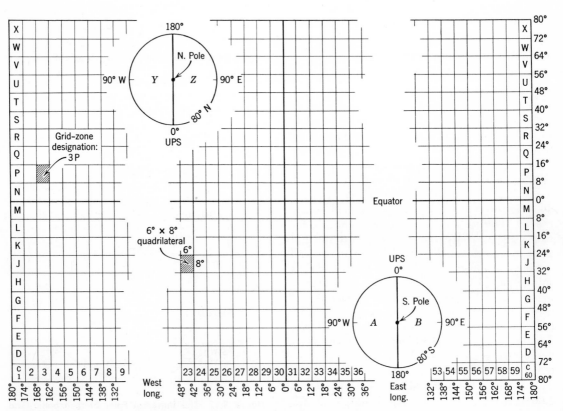

Figure 3.19 Identification of 6° × 8° quadrilaterals in the grid referencing system. (After U.S. Departments of the Army and Air Force, TM 5—241, 1951.)

practical problems of map reading, but the principle is nevertheless important.

On the UPS grid, the scale factor is set arbitrarily as 0.994 at the pole. The scale is true to the grid (scale factor 1.000) at latitude 81° 06'. At 80° latitude, the limit of the UPS system, the scale is too large by a factor of 1.0016 (Figure 3.18).

The military grid referencing system

The large number of grid zones of the UTM grid system requires that some orderly system be available to designate approximate global position, not only as to the correct grid zone, but also the part of the zone, because these are long narrow strips of great latitudinal extent. The *Military Grid Referencing System* provides such information by means of numerals and letters (Figure 3.19). The world between the 80th parallels north and south is considered divided into geographical areas, or quadrilaterals, extending 6° in longitude and 8° in latitude. The north-south boundaries of these areas conform to the 60 UTM grid zones, so that the east-west position of the area columns is designated by the grid zone number, which begins with Zone 1, 180° to 174° W, and increases eastward by integers to Zone 60. The 8° rows of areas are designated by letters, starting with *C*, 80° to 72° S, and extending to *X* at 72° to 80° N. Letters *A*, *B*, *Y*, and *Z* are reserved for the UPS grid system. The *grid zone designation* of a quadrilateral is thus given by a numeral and a letter, as for example *3P* in Figure 3.19.

To give location within a 6° by 8° quadrilateral, a secondary order of lettered columns and rows is used, applying to *100,000 meter squares* (Figure 3.20). Starting at the 180th meridian and proceeding eastward along the equator for 18°, the 100,000-meter columns are lettered consecutively *A* through *Z*, omitting *I* and *O*, including the partial columns along grid zone junctions. This alphabetical sequence is repeated at 18° intervals of longitude and at two-million meter intervals of latitude. Other details of the letter arrangement are omitted here. A particular 100,000-meter grid square shown in Figure 3.20 is designated as *3PWN*. To this may be added the grid coordinates in terms of 10,000-meter and smaller units, as described previously. Thus a complete military grid reference to the nearest 100 meters might read: *3PWN539544*.

For polar areas in the UPS grid system the letters *A*, *B*, *Y*, and *Z* designate the largest grid zones, while a system of letters by columns and rows designates the 100,000-meter grid squares (Figure 3.20). Complete details of the military grid reference system are available in manuals prepared by the Departments of the Army and Air Force and published by the U.S. Government Printing Office. The geographer will find a knowledge of the universal grid systems a valuable asset because of their global application.

The United States Land Survey

Students of American geography and history may frequently run across maps showing the division of lands in the central and western United States. The survey lines have exerted a powerful control on the size, shape, and distribution of farms, homes, townships, and counties, and on the location of roads.

In 1785, Congress authorized a survey of the territory lying north and west of the Ohio River. To avoid the irregular and unsystematic type of land subdivision that had grown up in seaboard states during colonial times, Congress specified that the new lands should be divided into six-mile squares, now called *congressional townships*, and that the grid of townships should be based upon a carefully surveyed east-west base line, designated the "geographer's line." Meridians and parallels laid off at six-mile intervals from the base line were to form the boundaries of the townships. This general plan, believed to have been proposed by Thomas Jefferson, was subsequently carried out to cover the balance of the central and western states.

The *principal meridians* and *base lines*, from which rows of townships were laid off, are shown in Figure 3.21. Principal meridians run north or south, or both, from selected points whose latitude and longitude were calculated by astronomical means. Some 32 principal meridians have been surveyed. Westward from the Ohio-Pennsylvania boundary these are numbered from 1 through 6, after which they are designated by names.

Through the initial point selected for starting the principal meridian, an east-west base line was run, corresponding to a parallel of latitude through that point. North and south from the base line, horizontal tiers of townships were laid off and numbered accordingly. Vertical rows of townships, called *ranges*, were laid off to the right and left of the principal meridians, and were numbered accordingly (Figure 3.22). The position of Township *A* in Figure 3.22 is stated as "township 2 north, range 3 east," abbreviated "T. 2 N., R. 3 E." Township *B* is designated "T. 3 S., R. 6 W." The area governed by one principal meridian and its base line is restricted to a particular section of country, usually about as large as one or two states. Where two systems of townships meet, they do not correspond, because each system was built up independently of the others. Of all the systems, that based on the 5th principal meridian covers the largest area. Its most northerly tier of townships is number 163; the most westerly range, number

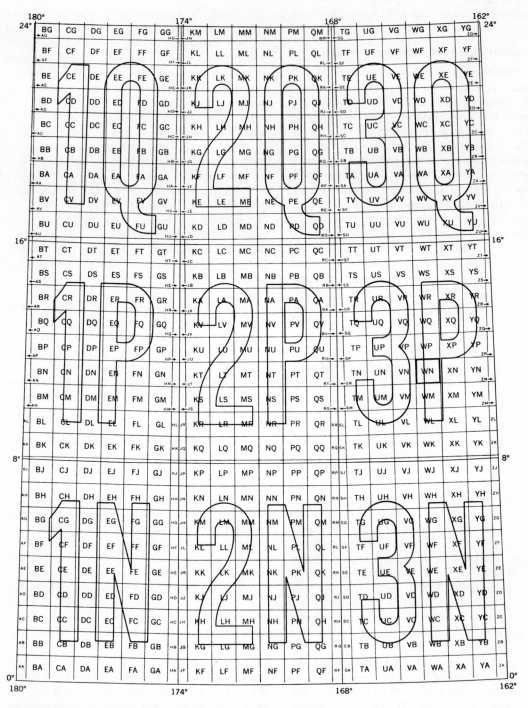

Figure 3.20 Identification of 100,000-meter squares in the grid referencing system.
(After U.S. Departments of the Army and Air Force, TM 5—241, 1951.)

100,000 METER SQUARE IDENTIFICATIONS
FOR THE
MILITARY GRID REFERENCE SYSTEM

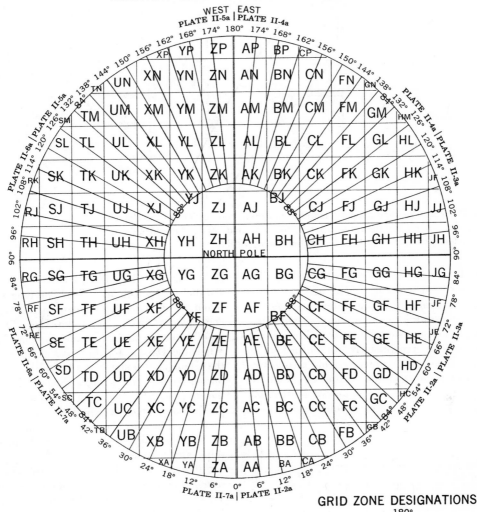

INTERNATIONAL SPHEROID

GRID ZONE DESIGNATIONS

Figure 3.20 continued

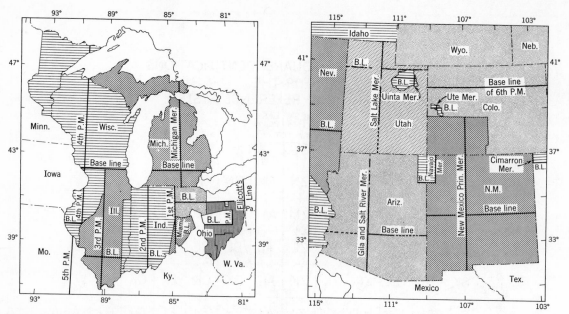

Figure 3.21 Base lines and principal meridians of these two portions of the United States are representative of the system used by the U.S. Land Office. (After U.S. Dept. Interior, General Land Office Map of the United States, 1937.)

104. In all, it has an east-west spread covering 726 miles, a north-south extent of 1122 miles.

Because the range lines, on eastern and western boundaries of townships, are meridians converging slightly as they are extended northward, the width of townships is progressively diminished in a northward direction. In order to avoid a considerable reduction in township widths in the more northerly tiers, new base-lines, known as *standard parallels*, are surveyed for every four tiers of town-

ships. They are designated 1st, 2nd, 3rd Standard Parallel N, etc. (Figure 3.23). The ranges will be found to offset at the standard parallels, and in consequence, roads which follow range lines make an offset or jog when crossing standard parallels. When the Dakota Territory was divided to enter the Union as two states, the boundary was placed on the 7th standard parallel from the base line of the 5th principal meridian in preference to the 46th parallel of latitude which lies four miles to the north of it, because the former line was already in use as a boundary between farms, sections, townships, and counties.

Subdivisions of the township are square-mile *sections*, of which there are 36 to the township. These are numbered in the manner illustrated in Figure 3.24. Each section may be subdivided into halves, quarters, and half quarters, or even smaller units. These divisions, together with the number of acres contained in each, are illustrated in Figure 3.25. Abbreviations are read as follows: "N½SW ¼" as "north half of the southwest quarter;" "SW ¼ SW ¼ SW ¼" as "southwest quarter of the southwest quarter of the southwest quarter." Abbreviation of the location of an area might read as follows: NE ¼ of SE ¼ of Sec. 24, T. 28 N., R. 6 W., 5 PM meaning "the northeast quarter of the southeast quarter of section No. 24, township 28 north, range 6 west of the 5th principal meridian."

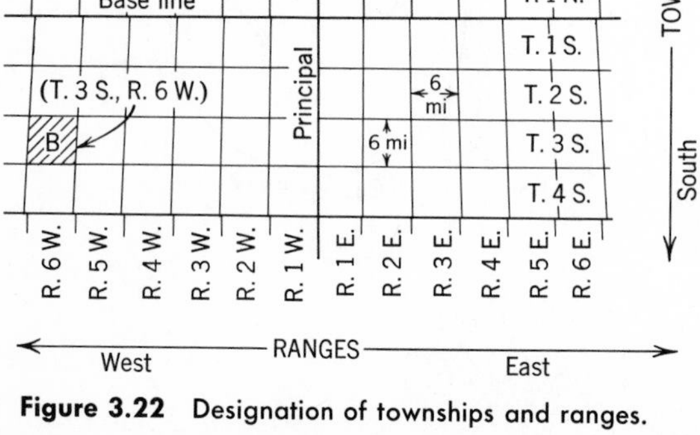

Figure 3.22 Designation of townships and ranges.

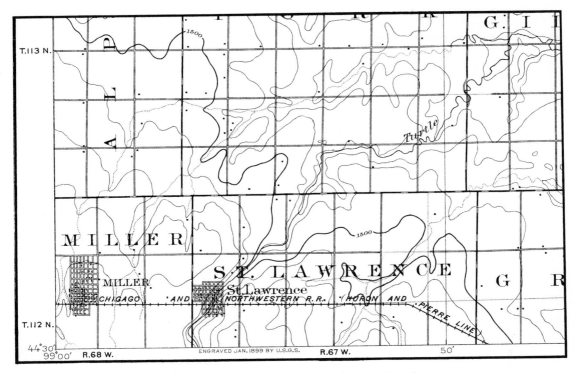

Figure 3.23 This portion of the Redfield, South Dakota, Quadrangle shows the off-setting of ranges along a standard parallel. (U.S. Geological Survey topographic map.)

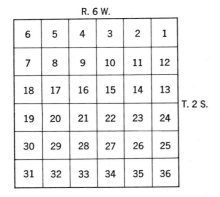

Figure 3.24 A township is divided into 36 sections, each one a square mile.

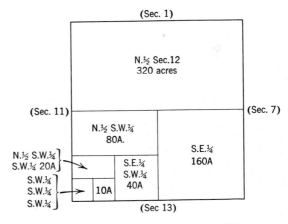

Figure 3.25 A section may be subdivided into many units. (After Willis E. Johnson.)

Review Questions

1. What is the scope of cartography? of geodesy? What role does each play in location of earth features on the globe and on maps?

2. Distinguish between relative location and absolute location of points on the earth's surface.

3. What is the principle of triangulation? How and why is a base line measured? What orders of accuracy are defined in triangulation?

4. What is the North American Datum of 1927? Why is it needed? Who uses it?

5. How is precise leveling carried out? What datum is used? How are leveling control points designated and preserved?

6. Explain the various ways of expressing map scale and the uses of each. Explain the conversion of a fractional scale to length units; of a fractional scale to a graphic scale.

7. What is the distinction between a large-scale map and a small-scale map? What rule expresses the way in which ground area shown on a map varies with map scale, assuming a map sheet of fixed dimensions?

8. Define magnetic north, magnetic declination, and isogonic lines.

9. Explain the compass quadrant bearing system of designating direction. How does it differ from azimuth, or full-circle bearing?

10. Explain the geographic coordinates and show how the geographic grid is used in limiting individual quadrangles of map systems. What is the meridian of Ferro?

11. What advantages have plane coordinates over spherical coordinates in map grids? Describe the plane coordinates used by the states.

12. How can the position of a point on a map be designated by military grid coordinates? What abbreviations are used? What units of length are used? What are northing and easting?

13. Describe in detail a grid zone in the UTM grid system. How is it related to the map projection on which it is based?

14. Define grid declination, grid north, and the grid magnetic angle. List three kinds of azimuth and define each.

15. Describe in detail the UPS grid system and its relation to the projection on which it is based.

16. How does the scale factor change on the UTM and UPS grid systems?

17. What is the military grid reference system? Tell how the location of a particular point on the earth's surface is uniquely given by this system.

18. Explain the U.S. Land Office system of subdivision of western lands. Include discussion of principal meridian, base line, township, range, standard parallel, section. How are townships designated? How are sections subdivided?

Exercises

1. See Figure 3.4. (**a**) This map was originally on a scale of 1:24,000 but has been reduced for publication. What is the fractional scale of this map as printed here? (**b**) Determine the width and length in miles of the area shown by the map. (**c**) Determine the distance in yards from Davis Quarry to John Harrit Church. (**d**) Prepare a graphic scale in kilometers for this map. (**e**) State the scale of this map in inches to miles.

2. See Figure 3.7. Estimate the magnetic declination at the following places: (**a**) Miami, Florida. (**b**) Boston, Massachusetts. (**c**) San Francisco, California. (**d**) New Orleans, Louisiana. (**e**) Chicago, Illinois. (**f**) Seattle, Washington. (**g**) Havana, Cuba.

3. Refer to the accompanying air-navigation exercise map. This is a reduced portion of Sheet 406 of the World Aeronautical Chart issued on the scale of 1:1,000,000. (**a**) Give the geographic coordinates to the nearest one minute for Artesia (town), Roswell Radio, and Carlsbad Airport. (**b**) Using a protractor, estimate the magnetic declination in this area. (**c**) What is the magnetic bearing of a line from Carlsbad Airport to Pinon Radio? (**d**) What is the magnetic bearing of a line from Fuller Ranch Airport to Roswell Radio?

4. See Figure 3.4 (**a**) Determine the bearing of a line from John Harrit Church to Davis Quarry. (**b**) State the azimuth of this same line. (**c**) Determine the azimuth and distance of a line between the two points marked by the heavy black arrows below the graphic scale.

5. On an air photograph taken from a vertical position a measured distance between two points is 7.36 inches. This represents 2.37 miles on the ground. (**a**) What is the fractional scale of the photograph? (**b**) Construct an equivalent graphic scale in units of 1000 yards.

6. See Figure 3.13. (**a**) Give the grid designation of the square in which the letter *D* is printed. (**b**) Give the grid coordinates to the nearest 100 meters of the point *E*. (**c**) Using a protractor, measure the grid declination. (**d**) Measure the grid azimuth of a line from Point *C* to the center of grid square *A*. (**e**) Measure the grid azimuth from Point *B* to a point (unmarked) located at 833794.

7. See Figure 3.23. (**a**) On a sheet of thin tracing paper laid over this map, number all sections with their correct numbers according to the system shown in Figure 3.24. (**b**) State accurately and fully the location of the letter "T" of the word "Turtle" on this map, using the Land Office system illustrated in Figures 3.22, 3.24, and 3.25.

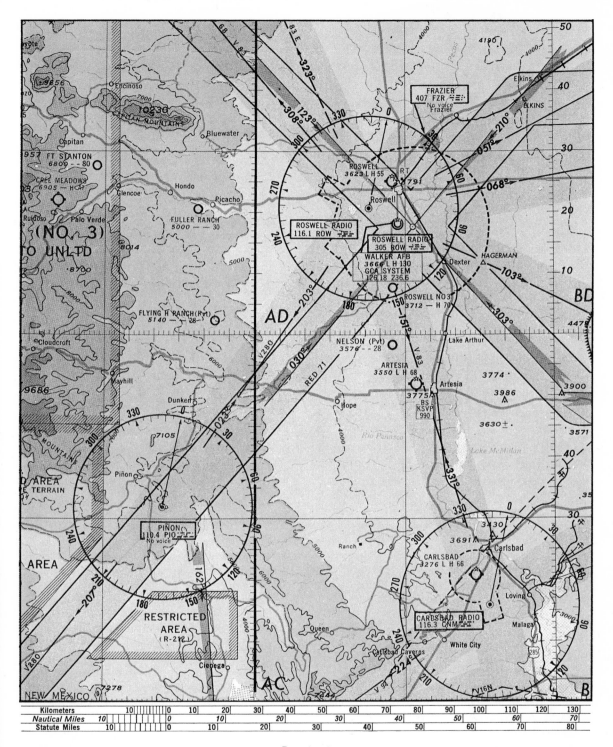

Exercise 3

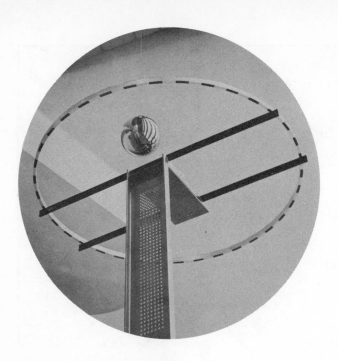

CHAPTER FOUR

Illumination of the globe

OF all astronomical phenomena, by far the most important to man is the relation between the earth and the sun's rays. The angles at which rays strike the earth at different latitudes and at different times of day and year determine the apparent path of the sun in the sky, the lengths of day and night, the measurement of time, and the occurrence of seasons. Systematic changes in amounts of solar energy received by different parts of the earth at different times act as fundamental controls of atmospheric temperatures, which in turn have a major effect on pressure variations, systems of winds, storms and precipitation, and oceanic circulation, all of which taken together make up the earth's varied climates.

It cannot be stressed too strongly that the student of physical geography must thoroughly master earth-sun relationships before proceeding to the subjects of weather and climate. Because the earth is turning on its axis, which is tilted, and at the same time moving in a path about the sun, these relationships are often difficult to understand. We must learn to think in terms of three dimensions, to imagine ourselves viewing the earth from various vantage points in space; then imagine the same situations as they would appear to an observer standing at various points on the earth.

Rotation of the earth

The spinning of the earth on its polar axis is termed *rotation*. The period of rotation, or the time required for the earth to turn through 360°, is 23 hours, 56 minutes, 4.09 seconds. The reason this period is not exactly 24 hours is discussed in Chapter 5. It will suffice here to state that the period $23^h 56^m 4.09^s$, termed the *sidereal day*, is determined by the stars, whereas the 24-hour period is the average time of one complete turn in respect to the sun. For the study of earth-sun relationships the 24-hour period of rotation is used.

The direction of rotation can be determined by adhering to one of the following rules. (*a*) If we imagine ourselves to be looking down upon the north pole of the earth, the direction of turning is counterclockwise. (*b*) If we place a finger upon a point on a globe near the equator and push the finger eastward, it will cause the globe to rotate in the correct direction (Figure 4.1). This explains the common expression "the eastward rotation of the earth." (*c*) The direction of rotation of the earth is opposite that of the apparent motion of the

above: Foucault pendulum at U. N. Headquarters, New York.
Photograph by courtesy of United Nations.

sun, moon, and stars. Because these bodies appear to travel westward across the sky the earth must be turning in an eastward direction. Although the matter of direction of the earth's rotation may seem simple and obvious, it often proves confusing, and if incorrectly determined, may upset calculations of time relationships and illumination of the globe.

The velocity of rotation, defined as rate of travel of a point on the earth's surface in a circular path due to rotation alone, may easily be computed by dividing the length of parallel at the latitude of the point in question by 24, the approximate period of rotation. Thus at the equator, where the circumference is about 25,000 miles, the velocity of an object on the surface is about 1050 miles per hour. At the 60th parallel the velocity is half this amount, or about 525 miles per hour. At the poles it is, of course, zero. We are unaware of this motion because the rotation is at an almost perfectly constant rate.

Two important physical phenomena result from the decrease in rotational velocity with increase in latitude. First, there is a *centrifugal force* generated by the earth's turning which gives surface objects a faint tendency to fly off into space. Because the force of gravity is 289 times greater than this centrifugal force at the equator, objects cannot leave the surface, but the practical effect is to reduce the weight of objects slightly. Near the equator, where the centrifugal force is strongest, this effect is most marked. For example, an object which would weigh 289 pounds at the equator if the earth were not turning actually weighs 1 pound less.

Another effect of the decreasing rotational velocity with increasing latitude is to cause objects in motion to be deflected slightly to the right or left of their paths. This effect will be more fully treated under the subject of the earth's wind systems.

How constant is the rate of the earth's rotation? Is the earth "slowing down"?

Astronomers are generally agreed that the length of day is increasing by about 0.0016 sec per century, but this can be disregarded in the study of physical geography. We may confidently assume that the earth's turning with respect to the stars provides an almost perfect timepiece. Other extremely minute variations, both irregular and seasonal, can also be detected in the earth's period of rotation, but these, too, can be disregarded.

Proof of the earth's rotation; the Foucault experiment

The several kinds of proofs offered for the earth's rotation are beyond the needs of the student

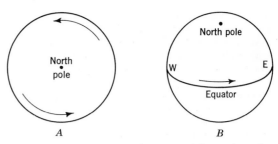

Figure 4.1 The direction of rotation of the earth can be thought of as (**A**) counterclockwise at the north pole or (**B**) eastward at the equator.

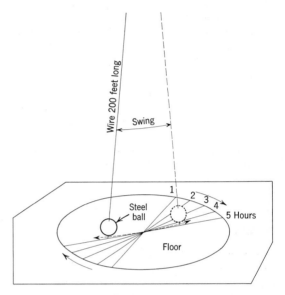

Figure 4.2 The Foucault pendulum experiment proves earth rotation.

of physical geography, but one proof in particular, the *Foucault experiment,* is so outstanding as to warrant study. It has been described as follows.[1]

In 1851, the French physicist, M. Leon Foucault, suspended from the dome of the Pantheon, in Paris, a heavy iron ball by wire 200 feet long. A pin was fastened to the lowest side of the ball so that when swinging it traced a slight mark in a layer of sand placed beneath it. Carefully the long pendulum was set swinging. It was found that the path gradually moved around toward the right. (See Figure 4.2.) Now either the pendulum changed its plane or the building was gradually turned around. By experimenting with a ball suspended from a ruler one can readily see that turning the ruler will not change the plane of the swinging pendulum. If the pendulum swings back and forth in a north and south direction, the ruler can be entirely turned around without changing the direction of the pendulum's swing. If at the north pole a pendulum was set swinging toward a fixed star, say Arcturus, it would continue swinging toward the same star and the earth would thus be seen to turn around in a day. The earth

[1] W. E. Johnson, *Mathematical Geography*, American Book Co, New York, 1907, pp. 54–57.

would not seem to turn but the pendulum would seem to deviate toward the right, or clockwise.

At first thought it might seem as though the floor would turn completely around under the pendulum in a day, regardless of the latitude. It will be readily seen, however, that it is only at the pole that the earth would make one complete rotation under the pendulum in one day, or show a deviation of 15° in an hour. At the equator the pendulum will show no deviation, and at intermediate latitudes the rate of deviation varies.

Table 1 gives the hourly change in direction of the pendulum's swing and the total time required for the direction to change through 360°.

For the student familiar with elementary trigonometry it may be explained that the amount of turning of the pendulum's direction per hour varies according to the *sine of the latitude* and may be obtained by the formula:

$$d = 15 \sin L$$

where d = number of degrees of turning per hour and L = latitude.

Another proof of the earth's rotation lies in the oblate spheroidal form of the earth. In order to explain the bulging at the equator and shortening of the polar axis, centrifugal force due to rotation on an axis is required.

Revolution of the earth

The motion of the earth in its orbit around the sun is termed *revolution*. Care should be taken to use the terms rotation and revolution correctly and not to use them interchangeably. The period of revolution, or year, is the time required for the earth to complete one circuit around the sun. This

TABLE 1

Latitude	Hourly change in pendulum direction, degrees	Total time for 360° change in direction, hours
0°	None	None
5	1.31	275
10	2.60	138
15	3.88	93
20	5.13	70
25	6.34	57
30	7.50	48
35	8.60	42
40	9.64	37
45	10.61	34
50	11.49	31
55	12.29	29
60	12.99	28
65	13.59	26.5
70	14.10	25.6
75	14.49	24.9
80	14.77	24.5
85	14.94	24.1
90	15.00	24.0

may be measured in different ways. For example, the time required for the earth to return to a given point in its orbit with reference to the fixed stars is called the *sidereal year*. The period of time from one vernal equinox to the next is the *tropical year*, which has a length of 365^d 5^h 48^m 45.68^s, or approximately 365¼ days. Every four years the extra one-fourth day difference between the tropical year and the calendar year of 365 days totals nearly one whole day. By inserting a 29th day in February every leap year we are able to correct the calendar with respect to the tropical year. Further minor corrections are necessary to perfect this system, but these are beyond the scope of the present discussion.

In its orbit the earth moves in such a direction that if we imagine ourselves in space, looking down upon the earth and sun so as to see the north pole of the earth, the earth is traveling counterclockwise around the sun (Figure 4.3). This is the same direction of turning as the earth's rotation. It is further worth noting that nearly all planets and their satellites in our solar system have the same direction of rotation and revolution, suggesting that their motions were imparted to them at a time when they and the sun were originally formed.

Earth's orbit

The earth's orbit is an ellipse, rather than a circle, although the *ellipticity*, or degree of flattening of the ellipse, is very slight. The sun occupies one *focus* of the ellipse. Ellipses of various shapes are easily constructed using only a drawing board, two pins or thumb tacks, a piece of thread or thin string, and a pencil, as illustrated in Figure 4.4. The thread is made into a loop which passes around the two pins and serves to guide the pencil point. By this device we maintain the sum of the distances from pencil point to each pin always the same. Each pin is located at one *focus* of the ellipse. The two *foci* lie on a line which is the maximum diameter of the ellipse and is called the *major axis*. The shortest diameter, drawn at right angles to the major axis, is known as the *minor axis*. The size of the ellipse may be controlled by the length of the loop of thread, whereas the ellipticity may be controlled by changing the distance between the two foci.

Perihelion and aphelion

The mean distance between earth and sun is about 93 million miles, but because of the ellipticity of the orbit the distance may be 1½ million miles greater or less than this figure (Figure 4.5). The distance is least, or about 91½ million miles, on about January 3, at which time the earth is said to be in *perihelion* (from the Greek *peri*, around or

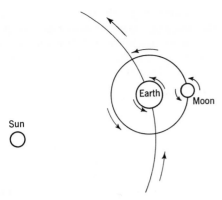

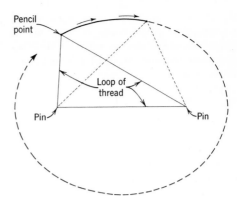

Figure 4.3 Viewed as if from a point over the earth's north pole, the earth both rotates and revolves in a counterclockwise direction.

Figure 4.4 An ellipse can be easily constructed.

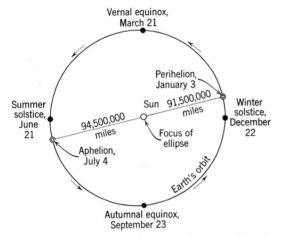

Figure 4.5 The earth's orbit is an ellipse in which the sun is located at one focus.

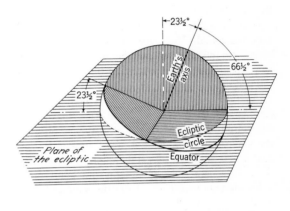

Figure 4.6 The earth's axis keeps an angle of 66½° with the plane in which its orbit lies.

near; and *helios,* the sun). On about July 4 the earth is at its farthest point from the sun, or in *aphelion* (from the Greek *ap,* away from; *helios,* sun), at a distance of 94½ million miles.

These differences in distance do cause some difference in the amount of solar energy received by the earth, but they are not the cause of summer and winter seasons. This is obvious because perihelion, when the earth should receive most heat, falls at the coldest time of year in the northern hemisphere. Moreover, opposite seasons are present simultaneously in the northern and southern hemispheres, proving that another cause exists. It is probable, however, that if all other conditions were considered to be equal, summers and winters would be slightly intensified in the southern hemisphere and slightly moderated in the northern hemisphere as a result of the relation of the dates of perihelion and aphelion to the summer and winter seasons.

The mean velocity of the earth in its orbit is about 66,000 miles per hour but varies according to the part of the orbit occupied. The velocity is greatest at perihelion, least at aphelion. The cause and importance of this variation are discussed in Chapter 5.

Inclination of the earth's axis

Most globes that are made to rotate on the polar axis are fixed in a tilted position. So accustomed are we to seeing the earth represented this way that a globe with its axis vertical seems unnatural. For tilted globes the plane in which the earth's orbit and the sun lie, or the *plane of the ecliptic,* is imagined to be horizontal and to pass through the center of the globe (Figure 4.6). The trace of the plane of the ecliptic upon the globe is a great circle. Most globes have an *ecliptic circle* drawn on them. It will be seen to cut across the equator at opposite points on the globe (from the rule that intersecting great circles bisect each other) and to run as far north as 23½° N lat., and as far south as 23½° S lat. By rotating the globe slowly, a position will be found in which the ecliptic circle lies in a horizontal plane parallel with the table top. In this position the globe may be used to illustrate the fact that the plane of the equator is inclined 23½° with the plane of the ecliptic. More exactly, this angle is 23° 27', but the difference between this value and 23½° can be disregarded. The earth's axis makes an angle of 66½° with the plane of the ecliptic, and is tilted 23½° from a line perpendicular to that plane. No other single fact connected with earth-sun relationships is so important as the inclination of the earth's axis.

The earth's axis, although always making the angle 66½° with the plane of the ecliptic, maintains a fixed orientation with respect to the stars.[2] The earth's axis continues to point to the same spot in the heavens as it makes its yearly circuit around the sun. To help in visualizing this movement hold a globe so as always to keep the axis tilted at 66½° with horizontal. Move the globe in a small horizontal circle, representing the orbit, at the same time keeping the axis pointed at the same point on the ceiling.

As a direct consequence of the facts (1) that the earth's axis keeps a fixed angle with the plane of the ecliptic and (2) that the axis always points to the same place among the stars, it will be seen that at one point in its orbit the earth's axis leans toward the sun, that at an opposite point in the orbit the axis leans away from the sun, and at the

[2] This statement does not take into account the precessional motion of the axis or other deviations of the axis.

two intermediate points the axis leans neither toward, nor away from, the sun (Figure 4.7). Here again, a globe, or, better still, four globes, may be used to aid in visualizing the facts. The four critical positions will be treated in detail.

Solstice and equinox

On June 21 or 22 the earth is so located in its orbit that the north polar end of its axis leans at the maximum angle 23½° toward the sun. The northern hemisphere is tipped toward the sun, and the southern hemisphere is tipped away from the sun. This condition is named the *summer solstice.* Six months later, on December 22 or 23, the earth is in an equivalent position on the opposite point in its orbit. At this time, known as the *winter solstice,* the axis again is at a maximum inclination with respect to a line drawn to the sun, but now it is the southern hemisphere that is tipped toward the sun.

Midway between the dates of the solstices occur the *equinoxes,* at which time the earth's axis makes a 90° angle with a line drawn to the sun, and neither the north nor south pole has any inclination toward the sun. The *vernal equinox* occurs on March 20 or 21; the *autumnal equinox* on September 22 or 23.[3] Conditions are identical on the

[3] The exact time of solstices and equinoxes ranges into two calendar days because of the one-fourth day difference in the tropical year and the calendar year, which builds up to one whole day every fourth year and is corrected by adding one day in leap year.

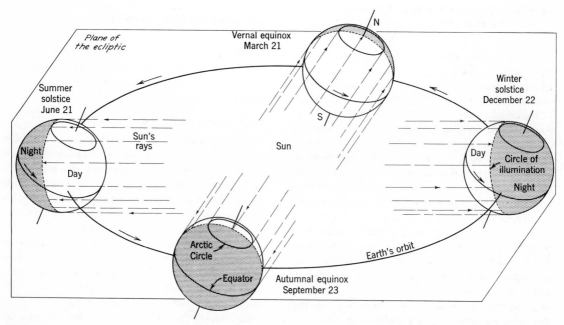

Figure 4.7 The seasons result because the tilted earth's axis keeps a constant orientation in space as the earth revolves about the sun.

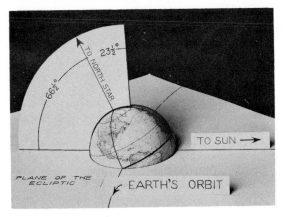

A. Winter solstice.

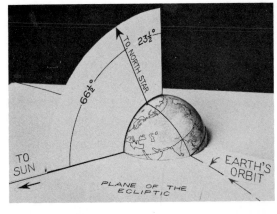

B. Summer solstice.

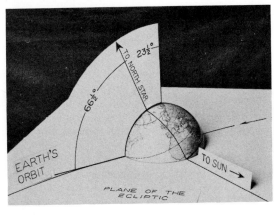

C. Equinox.

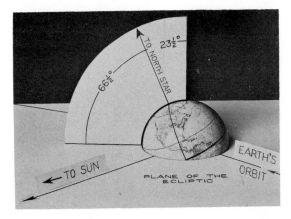

D. Intermediate date.

Figure 4.8 This three-dimensional model can show earth-sun relationships at any date of the year.

two equinoxes as far as earth-sun relationships are concerned, whereas on the two solstices, the conditions of one are the exact reverse of the other. For this reason it is necessary to consider each solstice separately, whereas the equinoxes can be treated together.

Winter solstice

Conditions at the winter solstice, December 22 or 23, are best studied with the aid of diagrams. Figure 4.8 is a three-dimensional model to illustrate the general conditions; Figure 4.9 is a more detailed cross-sectional representation to show the angles at which the sun's rays strike the earth. Keep in mind that "winter" applies only to the northern hemisphere; that the southern hemisphere is experiencing its summer season.

The great circle which marks the boundary between sunlit and shadowed halves of the earth is called the *circle of illumination*. At the winter solstice it divides all parallels of latitude which it crosses except the equator into unequal parts. The circle of illumination is tangent to the *Arctic Circle* (66½° N lat.) and the *Antarctic Circle* (66½° S lat.). This occurrence explains why the two parallels are given special designation on the globe. The circle of illumination bisects the equator in accordance with the law that any two intersecting great circles bisect each other.

Because of the position of the great circle at the winter solstice, day and night are unequal in length over most of the globe. This inequality may be estimated from Figure 4.9 by noting what proportions of a given parallel lie on either side of the

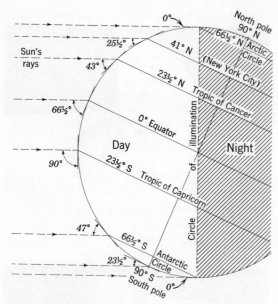

Figure 4.9 Winter solstice.

circle of illumination. The following facts are evident.

(*a*) Night is longer than day in the northern hemisphere.

(*b*) Day is longer than night in the southern hemisphere.

(*c*) The inequality between day and night increases from the equator poleward.

(*d*) At corresponding latitudes north and south of the equator the relative lengths of day and night are in exact opposite relation.

(*e*) Between the Arctic Circle, 66½° N, and the north pole, night lasts the entire 24 hours.[4] This is evident from Figure 4.9 because the entire polar area north of the Arctic Circle lies on the shaded side of the circle of illumination and hence will not come into the sun's rays even when the earth turns through 360°.

(*f*) Between the Antarctic Circle, 66½° S, and the south pole day lasts the entire 24 hours, because the earth's turning fails to bring any part of this area into the zone of darkness.

Altitude of noon sun at winter solstice

At any given instant all places on the earth where the sun is at its highest point in the sky lie on a single meridian. Thus noon occurs simultaneously at all points having the same longitude. For this reason noon is often termed the *meridian passage* of the sun. The vertical angle of the sun above the horizon at noon is designated the *altitude*.

It may be determined from Figure 4.9 by measuring the angle between a ray from the sun and a line tangent to the globe at a selected latitude. Although the earth's surface is curved, the apparent world in which we, as tiny individuals, live is a flat world. Within the limits of vision the horizon appears to make a circle on a flat plane. This explains why a straight tangent line may be used for measuring the angle on the diagram. The significant latitudes and altitudes are as follows.

(*a*) At lat. 23½° S the sun's rays at noon strike the earth at an angle of 90° above the horizon. Thus the sun is exactly in the center of the sky, or *zenith*. The parallel 23½° S has therefore been designated the *Tropic of Capricorn.*[5] It is the most southerly parallel which the sun's rays can strike vertically. The latitude at which the sun's rays strike with an angle of 90° is the same as a value termed the *sun's declination*. At the winter solstice, therefore, the sun's declination is 23½° S.

(*b*) At the equator the sun's noon altitude is 66½° above the southern horizon. Note that this altitude is equal to 90° minus 23½°.

(*c*) At the Arctic Circle, 66½° N, the sun at noon is exactly on the horizon.

(*d*) At the Antarctic Circle, 66½° S, the sun at noon has an altitude of 47° above the northern horizon.

(*e*) At the south pole, the noon sun has an altitude of 23½° above the horizon.

Careful analysis of the various altitude figures given above will show that there is a systematic relation between latitude and the sun's noon altitude. The general rule, which applies at any selected time of year for any selected latitude, may be stated as follows. *The sun's noon altitude at a place is equal to 90° minus the arc of meridian between the place and the parallel where the sun's rays strike vertically.*

In using this rule great care must be taken to determine correctly the actual number of degrees of arc separating the desired place from the parallel where the sun's rays strike vertically. This method should be used to determine the sun's noon altitude at the Tropic of Capricorn, equator, Arctic Circle, Antarctic Circle, and south pole, checking the answers against the values cited above for those latitudes. A small globe will prove useful in solving problems of the sun's noon altitude. First locate that parallel of latitude representing the sun's declination, then measure the arc north or south to the place in question.

---

[4] This statement does not take into account *twilight*, which provides considerable light near the Arctic Circle.

[5] So named because in ancient times the sun had a position among the stars of the constellation of Capricorn at the time of the winter solstice.

Path of sun in sky at winter solstice

The path of the sun in the sky at the winter solstice is illustrated for various latitudes in Figure 4.10. The horizon is drawn as a circle lying in a horizontal plane, and the sky is visualized as a hemispherical celestial dome. The sun daily completes an entire circle inscribed on the celestial sphere. On certain occasions, as on the equinoxes, these circular paths are great circles on the celestial sphere; otherwise they are small circles.

One general statement about the path of the sun in the sky holds true for any latitude at any time of year: *The plane of the sun's path at all times makes an angle with the plane of the horizon equal to 90° minus the latitude.* Checking this against the diagrams in Figure 4.10 it is seen that at the poles the sun's path lies in a plane parallel with the horizon plane, because the latitude of the poles, 90° N and S, subtracted from 90°, equals 0°. At the equator the sun's path always lies in a plane perpendicular to the horizon plane, because the latitude, 0°, subtracted from 90°, equals 90°. Do not, however, confuse this angle with the sun's noon altitude, which is measured from the center point of the horizon circle. The two angles are identical only at the equinoxes.

Solstice conditions at the poles

At the poles the path of the sun in the sky is the most extraordinary of all places on the earth (Figure 4.10). Here the sun does not rise and sink in a slanting path with respect to the horizon, as at other latitudes. Instead it follows a horizontal circle, remaining parallel with the horizon throughout the day. In actuality this path is spiral, but so low a spiral that it cannot be detected by ordinary observation. At the December solstice the sun at the north pole remains 23½° below the horizon throughout the day, while at the south pole it is constantly 23½° above the horizon. At the south pole we would have no natural way of determining when noon would occur because the sun's altitude remains constant. Moreover, all meridians converge to a point at the pole so that we could not refer the time to any local meridian.

Another curious fact is that the shadow of an object would always point due north no matter what the hour of the day, because all points of the horizon are north from the south pole. A simple sundial could be made by a perpendicular rod in the center of a horizontal disc whose circumference is divided into 24 equal parts. Selecting any particular point on the circumference as midnight, the hours could be read directly by noting the shadow of the rod on a target held above the edge of the disc.

Direction of sunrise and sunset at solstice

The compass direction of sunrise and sunset points on the horizon varies greatly with latitude, as shown in Figure 4.10. At the Antarctic Circle on the December solstice, sunrise and sunset occur at the same instant—midnight—at a point due south on the horizon. At all places between the Antarctic Circle and the Arctic Circle, the sun rises at some point between south and east, and sets at a point between south and west.

Summer solstice

In almost every way the conditions at summer solstice, June 21 or 22, are the exact reverse of winter solstice conditions. At this time the north polar end of the earth's axis is inclined directly toward the sun and the northern hemisphere enjoys the same conditions of increased sunshine that the southern hemisphere had during the winter solstice (Figure 4.11). Instead of a special diagram to show the relation of sun's rays to the earth, it is suggested that Figure 4.9 be turned upside down, exchanging north for south, Arctic for Antarctic, and Tropic of Cancer for Tropic of Capricorn. The various statements made in the previous pages concerning circle of illumination, length of day and night, and the sun's noon altitude at the winter solstice may reread, with suitable changes to fit the reversed conditions of the summer solstice.

The path of the sun in the sky on June 21 is shown in Figure 4.10. Note that the sun's noon altitude at each latitude differs from that on December 22 by 47° (23½° plus 23½°), and that conditions at the poles have been exactly reversed. For all latitudes between the Arctic and Antarctic Circles the sun rises on the northeastern horizon, rather than on the southeastern horizon, and sets on the northwestern horizon rather than on the southwestern horizon.

The equinoxes

On March 20 or 21 and September 22 or 23, the vernal and autumnal equinoxes, respectively, the relation of earth to sun's rays is identical and the two dates may be treated jointly. Figures 4.7 and 4.8C show the general situation. Although the earth's axis is, as always, inclined 66½° to the plane of the ecliptic, the inclination is so oriented that it is neither toward nor away from the sun. The sun's rays make an angle of 90° with the earth's axis. Further details of the equinoctial conditions are shown in Figure 4.12.

The circle of illumination at the equinoxes passes through the poles and hence coincides with the meridians as the earth turns.

As evident from Figure 4.12, the parallels are divided into equal halves by the circle of illumination. Hence day and night are of exactly equal length, twelve hours each, at all latitudes.[6] Conditions are the same for both northern and southern hemispheres. Sunrise occurs at 6:00 A.M. (local ap-

parent solar time), sunset at 6:00 P.M., at all places on the globe, except at the poles, where special conditions prevail.

The sun's noon altitude is found by direct measurement of the angle between the sun's parallel rays and tangent lines drawn at selected points (Figure 4.12). A few such measurements should reveal that the altitude is always the *colatitude*, or 90° minus the latitude. Thus, on the equinoxes,

[6] This explains the word *equinox*, from the Latin *aequus*, equal; and *nox*, night. We are not taking into account twilight, which extends the period of daylight before sunrise and after sunset.

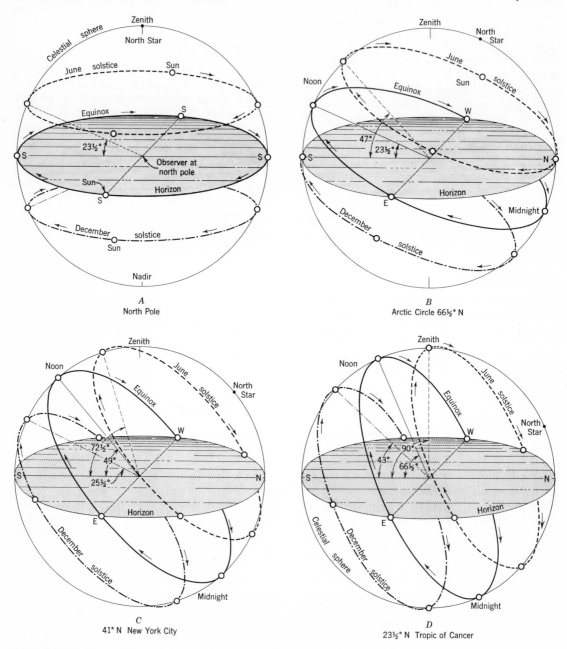

A
North Pole

B
Arctic Circle 66½° N

C
41° N New York City

D
23½° N Tropic of Cancer

Figure 4.10 To the earth-bound observer the earth's surface is a flat, horizontal disc. The sun, moon, and stars seem to travel on the inner surface of a hemispherical dome above him. The path of the sun in the sky at various latitudes is shown here for the equinox and both solstices.

but not for any other time of year, the sun's noon altitude may be computed by a single simple subtraction, if only the latitude is given. Although the altitude is the same for similar latitudes both north and south of the equator, it should be remembered that the angle is measured from the southern horizon in the northern hemisphere, from the northern horizon in the southern hemisphere.

The path of the sun in the sky at the equinoxes is illustrated in Figure 4.10. In each case the path is midway between the paths at the solstices. The sun rises at a point due east on the horizon and sets at a point due west on the horizon at all latitudes except at the two poles. At the poles, the sun remains on the horizon all day long, traveling one complete circuit of the horizon in 24 hours. Note, however, that the direction of apparent movement of the sun is opposite for the two poles.

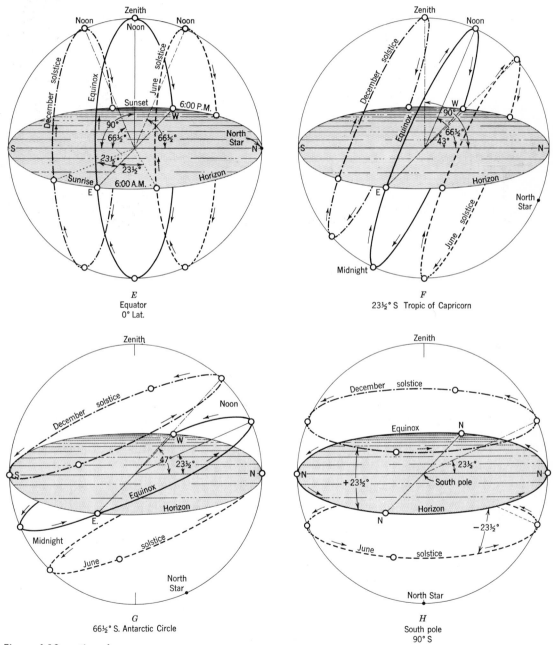

E
Equator
0° Lat.

F
23½° S Tropic of Capricorn

G
66½° S. Antarctic Circle

H
South pole
90° S

Figure 4.10 continued

Figure 4.11 This photograph of the sun was taken at midnight at Hammerfest, Norway, 70° 40' N. lat., during the summer solstice period. The sun has reached its lowest point in the sky. (Photograph by A. Kalland, Hammerfest.)

At the equator the sun has an altitude of 90° at noon; moreover, its path is in a plane perpendicular to the horizon plane. For this reason the sun changes altitude 15° per hour throughout the day at the equator on the equinoxes. Furthermore, at the equator on these dates the shadow of any vertical rod will point due west from 6:00 A.M. to noon, will disappear precisely at noon, and will point due east from noon until 6:00 P.M.

Intermediate dates

What may be said of the earth-sun relationships on the days between the equinoxes and solstices? The sun's declination changes continuously from solstice to solstice. The word "solstice" is, in fact, derived from the Latin *sol*, sun, and *stare*, to stand, referring to the fact that the sun, having reached the greatest extent of its southward or northward declination, appears to keep its position for a brief period as its declination begins to reverse. The exact amount of the sun's declination may be found for every day of the year in *The Air Almanac*, whose

contents are described in Chapter 5. The sun's noon altitude can thus be computed for every day in the year. The following facts regarding the rate of change of sun's declination may be of practical value in rough computation of sun's altitude for dates other than the solstices and equinoxes:

Amount of change in declination per month	Month
11¾°	First months before and after equinox
8½°	Second months before and after equinox
3¼°	Months adjacent to solstices

It is apparent that the declinational changes are very slow near the solstices but rapid near the equinoxes. This explains the rapid shortening and lengthening of days in the fall and spring months and the apparent persistence of the sun in the very high or very low path in the sky in June-July and December-January periods.

The path of the sun in the sky throughout the year takes intermediate positions from those drawn on Figure 4.10. If all the daily paths from one winter solstice to the next summer solstice were carefully drawn on such a figure they would be seen to form a spiral of very low pitch. Perhaps this concept will clarify the manner in which the sun behaves at the poles (Figure 4.13). Ascending day after day in this low-pitched spiral from its lowest position below the horizon at the winter solstice, the sun requires three months to attain the level of the horizon at the vernal equinox. After this, it continues to spiral upward, reaching its highest point about June 21, then starts to spiral back down, again reaching the horizon around September 23 and continuing to sink back to its winter-solstice position. This is why the sun rises and sets only once each year at the north pole. Sunrise occurs on March 21, sunset on September 23, separated by six months of sunshine and six months of twilight and total darkness. At the south pole similar, but reversed, conditions prevail.

Finding lengths of day and night and times of sunrise and sunset for all latitudes

To determine approximately the length of day and night and times of sunrise and sunset for various latitudes and at various times of a year, a small globe and a rubber band can be used (Figure 4.14). For the equinoxes, no problem exists because lengths of day and night are equal at all latitudes. For other dates proceed as follows:

1. *Winter solstice.* Place the rubber band so as to represent the circle of illumination (great circle) crossing the equator at the 90° meridians west and

east, and just tangent to the Arctic and Antarctic Circles where they cross the Greenwich and 180th meridians. Now select a particular latitude, for example 40° N. Taking the Greenwich meridian as noon, count 15° of longitude to the hour, westward along the 40th parallel, until the rubber band is reached. This number of hours subtracted from 12:00 noon gives the approximate time of sunrise (local apparent solar time), added to 12:00 noon gives the time of sunset. The lengths of day and night can be obtained by simple calculation. The shorter arc in this case gives the length of day; the longer arc, by way of the Pacific, gives length of night.

2. *Summer solstice.* Turn the globe around and use the Pacific side, leaving the rubber band in the same position as before.

3. *Other times of year.* Determine the sun's declination from the analemma, Figure 5.7. Then adjust the rubber band so that it is tangent to the parallels having the latitude 90° minus the declination. Be sure that the rubber band maintains a great circle and cuts the equator at the 90th meridians west and east, as before. Proceed with the determinations as described for the solstices.

The method explained here will, if carefully carried out, permit times of sunrise and sunset to be read correctly within one-fourth hour or less for the low and middle latitudes. It is not so satisfactory for high latitudes because of the oblique crossing of the parallels by the circle of illumination. Note that the globe gives local apparent solar time, which may disagree considerably with stand-

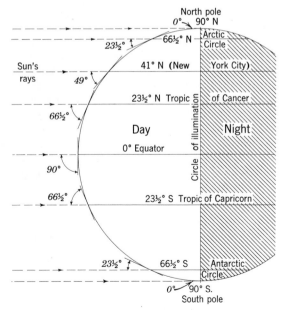

Figure 4.12 Equinox.

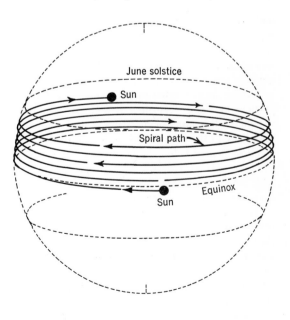

Figure 4.13 The sun's apparent path in the sky throughout the year at the north pole is a spiral of low pitch.

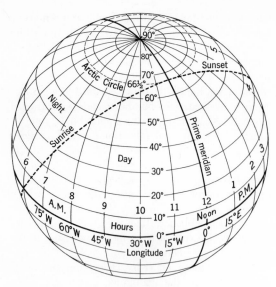

Figure 4.14 A small globe can be used as a graph for determining the lengths of day and night at any latitude.

ard time systems (Chapter 5). Time of sunrise and sunset can also be read directly from a prepared diagram (Figure 4.15).

Twilight

In order to simplify the treatment of lengths of day and night it was assumed that total darkness comes on instantaneously at setting of the sun and that sunrise is marked by immediate change from total darkness to sunlight. As everyone knows, this is not so. *Twilight,* a diffuse illumination that follows sunset and precedes sunrise, provides important additions to the period of useful daylight, especially in the higher latitudes. Because morning and evening twilight periods are of equal duration and of similar origin, no distinction will be made between them.

Twilight is attributed to the presence of minute particles of dust and moisture disseminated throughout the earth's atmosphere. They reflect the sun's rays back to the earth's surface long after the sun has disappeared below the horizon of observers on the ground (Figure 4.16). After sunset this diffuse light steadily dies out, being finally distinguished only as a faint glow in the western sky.

The duration of twilight depends on the thickness of the earth's atmosphere and the rate at which the sun sinks below the horizon. Assuming that the atmosphere is of uniform thickness and has a uniform horizontal distribution of dust, the length of twilight will depend on the path of the sun in the sky, which, in turn, depends on latitude. This is illustrated in Figure 4.17. Where the plane of the sun's path is vertical, as at the equator, the sun sinks below the horizon most rapidly, that is, at the

rate of 15° per hour. At higher latitudes the slanting path of the sun causes the sun to descend more slowly below the horizon. At 60° N, for example, the sun's path lies in a plane that makes an angle of 30° with the horizon plane (90° − 60° = 30°), and on the equinoxes twilight lasts approximately twice as long here as at the equator.[7]

Three kinds of twilight are recognized. *Astronomical twilight* is the period during which any detectable glow exists in the sky, and it is considered to last while the sun is between the horizon and a point 18° below the horizon. *Nautical twilight* endures while the sun is between the horizon and a point 12° below the horizon. At 12° the general outlines of ground objects are visible, although the horizon is probably indistinct and all of the stars used for navigation can be seen. *Civil twilight* is the period during which normal outdoor activities can be carried on without the aid of lights; it is the period during which the sun is between the horizon and a point 6° below the horizon. At 40° latitude, near the time of the equinoxes, civil twilight lasts about 30 minutes, which is the period commonly designated in legal statutes. Duration of civil twilight is given to the nearest one minute for each day of the year and for a wide range of latitudes in the *Air Almanac,* which also carries tables enabling nautical twilight to be calculated.

Figure 4.18 is a twilight diagram prepared by the Hydrographic Office of the U.S. Department of the Navy. On it may be found the length of astronomical twilight for any latitude at any time of year.

Many persons subscribe to the popular idea that near the equator twilight is lacking or is extremely short. This supposition has no basis in fact. Astronomical twilight at the equator, it is true, is shorter than anywhere else on the globe, but in order to reach a point 18° below the horizon the sun, descending at a rate of 15° per hour, requires 1 hour and 12 minutes. Civil twilight, based on the sun's being 6° below the horizon, would last one-third as long, or 24 minutes. Carefully conducted observations by scientists have confirmed these facts. S. I. Bailey, in a paper entitled "The Duration of Twilight in the Tropics" (*Harper's Weekly,* April 5, 1902), states:

Arequipa, Peru, lies within the tropics, and has an elevation of 8000 feet, and the air is especially pure and dry. Thus conditions appear to be exceptionally favorable for

[7] The sun's path at 60° N may be considered to approximate the hypotenuse of a 30° 60° 90° plane triangle, of which the short leg represents the actual distance below the horizon. In such a triangle the short leg is half the length of the hypotenuse. At the equator the sun would follow the short leg of the triangle, thus reaching the same number of degrees below the horizon in half the time required at the 60th parallel.

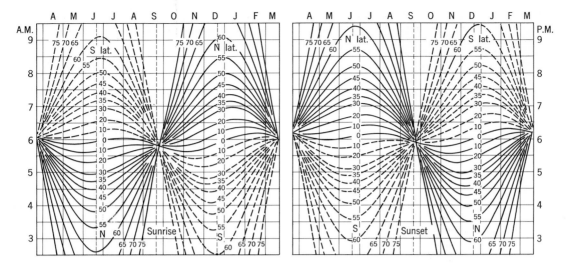

Figure 4.15 This sunrise-sunset diagram tells the time of sunrise and sunset for any latitude on any date of the year. (After U.S. Navy, Hydrographic Office No. 5175.)

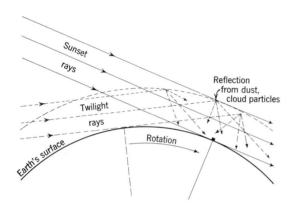

Figure 4.16 Twilight is a diffuse reflection from atmospheric dust and moisture particles.

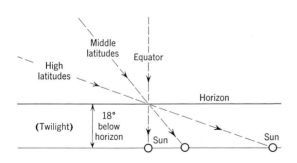

Figure 4.17 Duration of twilight depends on the slope of the sun's path below the horizon.

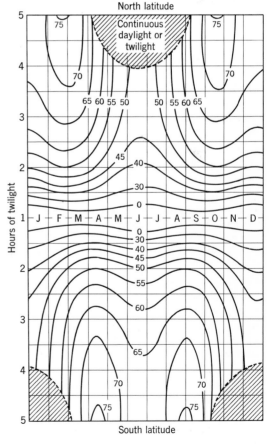

Figure 4.18 Twilight diagram. (After U.S. Navy Hydrographic Office, No. 5175.)

an extremely short twilight. On Sunday, June 25, 1899, the following observations were made at the Harvard Astronomical Station, which is situated here: The sun disappeared at 5:30 P.M. Local mean time. At 6:00 P.M., thirty minutes after sunset, I could read ordinary print with perfect ease. At 6:30 P.M. I could see the time readily by an ordinary watch. At 6:40 P.M., seventy minutes after sunset, the illuminated western sky was still bright enough to cast a faint shadow of an opaque body on a white surface. At 6:50 P.M., one hour and twenty minutes after sunset, it had disappeared.

At high latitudes, owing to the low slant of the path of the sun as it goes below the horizon, twilight is greatly lengthened. In northerly regions the twilight period, relative to length of night, is enormously lengthened during June and July; in southerly regions, during December and January. Above a certain critical latitude, which varies from about 48° to 90° throughout the year, the combined lengths of twilight before sunrise and after sunset equal or exceed the total time the sun is below the horizon and twilight lasts all night. Another way of saying this is that the sun's path never reaches a point more than 18° below the horizon. Various latitudes should be examined on the twilight diagram (Figure 4.18) in order to note the wide range in duration throughout the year.

Duration of twilight at the poles is easy to compute. Because the sun's path is a very low-pitched horizontal spiral, twilight persists throughout the whole period that the sun's declination is changing from 0° to 18°. This means that at the north pole astronomical twilight lasts from September 23 to November 14, and from January 29 to March 21, each of which is a period of seven weeks.

Review Questions

1. Why are earth-sun relationships important in the study of geography?

2. What is meant by rotation of the earth? What is the period of rotation with reference to the sun? Is this longer or shorter than the period of rotation with reference to the stars?

3. What is the direction of rotation of the earth? Does the earth's rotation have any observable effects on objects at or near the earth's surface aside from the astronomical effects? Is the earth slowing in its rate of rotation?

4. Describe and explain the Foucault pendulum experiment. What does it prove? Could you determine your latitude by means of a Foucault pendulum? How?

5. What is meant by revolution of the earth? In what two ways can the length and starting point of a year be reckoned? Which one is used in our calendar system? How long is this type of year? How must it be periodically corrected to fit our calendar?

6. What is the direction of the earth's revolution? How does this compare with directions of rotation and revolution of the moon and the other members of the solar system?

7. What form has the earth's orbit? What is perihelion? What is aphelion? On what dates do they occur? What distances separate earth and sun at perihelion and at aphelion? What effect does this have on the seasons?

8. Describe the way in which the earth's axis is tilted with respect to the plane of the earth's orbit. What is the angle of tilt? Does this angle change throughout the year?

9. Describe each of the two solstice and two equinox positions of the earth with respect to the sun, giving the dates of each in correct sequence.

10. What is the circle of illumination? Where is the circle of illumination located on the date of equinox? on December solstice? on June solstice?

11. Describe the conditions of global illumination, length of day and night, and path of sun in the sky at June solstice. Give details for the equator, Tropics of Cancer and Capricorn, Arctic and Antarctic Circles, and poles.

12. What rule or formula can be used to determine the sun's noon altitude at any selected date of the year for any desired latitude?

13. Describe the conditions of global illumination, length of day and night, and path of sun in the sky at equinox. Give details for the equator, Tropics of Cancer and Capricorn, Arctic and Antarctic Circles, and poles. How is the sun's noon altitude related to latitude on the date of equinox?

14. Describe the path of the sun in the sky throughout the year at the north pole. How do conditions differ at the south pole?

15. Describe the path of the sun in the sky at the Arctic Circle at equinox and at each solstice.

16. How rapidly does the sun's declination change between one solstice and the next equinox? Give approximate figures.

17. Describe in a general way how the compass direction of sunrise and sunset varies with season of year and with latitude.

18. How can the times of sunrise and sunset be approximated for various latitudes and dates, using only a globe and a rubber band?

19. What is twilight? What causes twilight? What factors determine the duration of twilight? What is the difference between civil and astronomical twilight? How long does astronomical twilight last at the poles? at the equator?

Exercises

1. Practice drawing ellipses of various sizes and degrees of ellipticity, using a drawing board, pins or thumb tacks, a piece of thread or thin string, and a pencil. (Directions are contained in the text, p. 66 and Figure 4.4.) On one of these ellipses draw and label the following: focus, major axis, minor axis, radius vector. Does the sum of the radius vectors always remain the same for all points on the ellipse? How do you know this?

2. Construct an ellipse to represent the earth's orbit around the sun. Label the following: earth, sun; perihelion and aphelion with their dates and distances. With arrows show the directions of the earth's rotation and revolution. Find points on the orbit that correspond to the equinoxes and solstices, and label them appropriately.

3. Arrange four small globes in a circle on the laboratory table in such a way that they represent correctly the equinoxes and solstices. Using a piece of chalk, draw on the table top the earth's orbit, and write the correct name and date of the equinox or solstice beside each globe. Indicate by an arrow the direction of earth's revolution. Take care that the axes of all four globes are parallel.

4. To what parallel (or pole) does each of the following statements apply? (**a**) Day and night are always of equal length (three answers). (**b**) The sun's noon altitude is 90° on June 21. (**c**) The sun's noon altitude is 50° on September 23 (two answers). (**d**) The sun at midnight on December 22 is exactly on the horizon at a point due south. (**e**) The path of the sun in the sky at all times of year lies in a plane perpendicular to the horizon plane. (**f**) The sun at noon on December 22 is exactly on the horizon at a point due south. (**g**) The path of the sun in the sky at all times of the year lies in a plane inclined 45° with the plane of the horizon. (**h**) On March 21 the sun's noon altitude is 66½° (two answers). (**i**) Throughout the day the shadow of a vertical rod sweeps clockwise around the rod at the rate of 15° per hour and remains the same length. (**j**) The shadow of a straight east-west wall with a straight horizontal top remains the same width from mid-morning to midafternoon and is as wide as the wall is high. (**k**) The shadow of a vertical rod points due west during the morning, then due east during the afternoon. (**l**) The circle of illumination bisects the parallel on August 9.

5. Given the following information, find the latitude of the place.

Noon sun altitude	Latitude at which sun's rays strike earth perpendicularly at noon	Date	Latitude of place
(a) 11°	Not given	Sept. 23	_____
(b) 44½°	12° N	Not given	_____
(c) 90°	Not given	March 21	_____
(d) 90°	Not given	June 21	_____
(e) 0°	20° S	Not given	_____
(f) 8½°	Not given	Dec. 22	_____
(g) 81°	9° S	Not given	_____

6. (**a**) Imagine the earth's axis to be inclined 45° to the plane of the ecliptic. Make a diagram similar to Figures 4.10*A* and 4.10*E* to show the path of the sun in the sky at the equinoxes and solstices. (**b**) Imagine the earth's axis to be inclined 90° to the plane of the ecliptic. Make a diagram similar to Figures 4.10*A* and 4.10*E* to show the path of sun in the sky at equinoxes and solstices.

7. Using a small globe and a rubber band according to directions given on p. 75 determine the time of sunrise and sunset and the length of the day for every ten-degree parallel of latitude from 0° to 60° N. Do this first for the winter solstice, then for the summer solstice. Record your results in a table as follows:

Latitude	Sunrise	Sunset	Length of day
0°	6:00 A.M.,	6:00 P.M.	12 hours
10°	etc.		
20°			

SPECIAL PROJECTS

1. Construct a three-dimensional model to show the earth, the plane of the ecliptic, and the inclination of the earth's axis for the equinoxes and solstices. Figure 4.8 shows such a device, made from a seven-inch globe and sheets of cardboard. By turning the globe in its socket and moving the vertical card showing angles, the conditions at equinoxes and solstices can be duplicated.

2. Construct a mechanical model to show the path of the sun in the sky for the equinoxes and solstices for any selected latitude. Suggested procedure: Use a circular disc for the horizon plane and three circular wire hoops for the paths of sun at the solstices and equinoxes. The hoops must be so mounted that they can be adjusted for any given latitude. With this contrivance, it should be possible to duplicate all the conditions shown in Figure 4.10, and to read the compass direction of sunrise and sunset as well as the noon altitude of the sun.

3. Construct a device to measure the altitude of the noon sun. This may be made of cardboard and a protractor and may be installed on the sill of a south-facing classroom window. It must be oriented correctly with respect to true north. Make a daily or weekly record of the altitude when the shadow points due north (or at apparent solar noon, calculated). Check the correctness of your reading at an equinox or solstice, or on any other date, by obtaining the sun's declination from the analemma (Figure 5.7).

CHAPTER FIVE

Time

THE need for understanding global time relationships and the various kinds of time in use scarcely needs emphasis in this modern day of instantaneous communication and high-speed travel. Before the coming of the telegraph, problems of time differences were of little or no concern to people who lived most of their lives in one community. Even the traveler was caused only the inconvenience of resetting his watch to the time used by local communities. The amount of time consumed in getting from one place to another was so much more than the difference in watch time between the two places that the difference was of little practical consequence. When it became possible to transmit messages instantaneously by telegraph, differences in local time resulting from differences in longitudinal position were immediately apparent. With the development of rapid means of travel it became important to correct schedules for the gain or loss of time incurred by passage across the meridians. East-to-west flight in the middle latitudes can now approximate the speed necessary to keep pace with the sun. For example, a plane leaving New York at 12:00 noon, Eastern Standard time, can by travel-

ing about 800 mph arrive in San Francisco at 12:00 noon, Pacific Standard time.

Longitude and time

To avoid confusion and make the study of time relations as simple as possible it is necessary to think of the earth as standing still and of the sun as completing one circuit about the earth every 24 hours. This is a perfectly permissible concept inasmuch as earth-sun relationships are purely relative. Imagine that a meridian is free to sweep westward around the globe and that it constantly maintains such a speed as to be located always where the sun's rays strike the earth's surface at the highest possible angle. This line we shall call the *noon meridian* (Figure 5.1). Directly opposite this meridian, on the other side of the globe, is the *midnight meridian*. It, too, sweeps westward over the globe and remains constantly 180° of longitude apart from the noon meridian. Whereas the noon meridian separates the forenoon and afternoon of the same calendar day, the midnight meridian is the dividing line between one calendar day and the next.

Because the noon meridian sweeps over 360° of longitude every 24 hours, it must cover 15° of longitude every hour, or 1° of longitude every 4

above: A marine chronometer.
Photograph by courtesy of The Hamilton Watch Company.

minutes. We therefore find it convenient to state that one hour of time is the equivalent of 15° of longitude. This equality forms the basis for all calculations concerning time belts of the globe. For example, if the noon meridian reaches one place on the globe 4 hours after it leaves another place, the two places are separated by 60° of longitude.

Enlarging this concept of time meridians still further, let it be imagined that in addition to the noon and midnight meridians there are 22 hour circles, each one a half great circle, 15° of longitude apart from its neighbor. The hour circles are equidistantly spaced between the noon and midnight meridians (Figure 5.1). Each hour circle will then represent a given hour of the day and can be labeled with a specific hour number which it keeps permanently. Together with the noon and midnight meridians, the hour circles can be imagined to form a birdcagelike net enclosing the globe and attached only at the north and south poles. As a further convenience in analyzing global time relations, it is most helpful if the globe used has meridians drawn for every 15°. If so, wherever the noon meridian of the time net coincides with the Greenwich meridian, all other hour circles coincide with true meridians on the globe.

A working model of global time relations is illustrated in Figure 5.2. If a small globe is available, make a cardboard girdle to fit about the equator and mark upon the cardboard the positions of the time meridians. If no globe is available, make two carboard discs of different radius and attach them at their centers in such a way that one disc can be turned while the other remains still. On the inner disc draw radii to represent 15° meridians of a globe seen from a point above the north pole. On the outer disc similar radii, but label them in hours to represent the time net. As a further refinement, the inner disc may consist of a hemispherical world map.

People sometimes become confused when trying to decide whether the watch time of places to the east (or west) of them is ahead or behind their own watch time. This is especially evident where the problem is to calculate when a radio or television program will be on the air in different parts of the country, or to decide whether to set one's watch ahead or behind one hour when traveling from one standard time zone to another. To avoid confusion let the time meridians be visualized as moving westward around the globe. Then consider, for example, that you are in New York City and the time there is 12:00 noon. The noon meridian which is at New York left Greenwich, England, five hours earlier. Therefore, in England five hours must have elapsed since noon and it must be 5 P.M. in that country. From this we get the general rule: *places that lie east of you have a later hour.* Again, consider that the noon meridian is at New York City. It will take that meridian about three hours to travel westward to reach San Francisco. Hence it must be 9:00 A.M. in that city. This gives a counterpart of the rule stated above, namely: *places that lie west of you have an earlier hour.* Both rules are subject to qualifications where the International Date Line lies between the places.

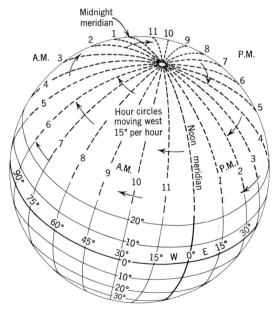

Figure 5.1 The hours may be thought of as meridians spaced 15° apart and moving westward around the globe.

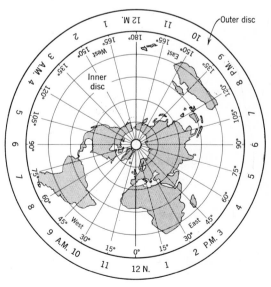

Figure 5.2 A working model helps to clarify global time relationships.

Local time

One means of establishing a time system for a small community is to take the meridian of longitude that passes through some central point in the town or city, as for example the courthouse or a cathedral. All clocks of the community are set to read 12:00 noon when the sun is directly over that meridian, that is to say, when a shadow cast by a vertical rod points due north. As will be fully explained later, the sun is an erratic timekeeper, and it would be necessary to take the mean value of the sun's noon position, but this need not concern us now. The time system thus derived is called *local time* and may be defined as mean solar time based on the local meridian. All places located on the same meridian, regardless of how far apart they may be, have the same local time, whereas all places located on different meridians have unlike local times, differing by four minutes for every degree of longitude between them.

Standard time

The undesirability of using local time systems in each community of a highly populated country in our modern day is obvious. American railroads, about 1870, introduced a standardized system covering considerable belts of territory, but this system was developed by the railroad companies for their own convenience. Consequently, if several railroads met or passed in a single town, the inhabitants might have had to contend with several different kinds of railroad time in addition to their own local time. It is said that before 1883 as many as five different time systems were used in a single town and that the railroads of the United States altogether followed 53 different systems of time.

The obvious solution to such problems is *standard time*, based on a *standard meridian*, whose local time is arbitrarily given to wide strips of country on both sides. Thus, all clocks within the belt are set to a single time. It is evident that if standard meridians are 15° apart, adjacent zones will have standard times differing by exactly one hour. Furthermore, if these meridians represent longitudes which are multiples of 15, for example, 60°, 75°, 90°, or 105°, each successive standard time zone will differ from the standard time of Greenwich, England, by whole hour units. This is the system of standard time zones employed over most of the globe.

Standard time in the United States

The present system of standard time in the United States was placed in operation on November 18, 1883, but it was not until March 19, 1918, that Congress passed legislation directing the Interstate Commerce Commission to determine time-zone boundaries. The standard meridians and boundaries are shown on Figure 5.3. The four time zones and their meridians are as follows:

Eastern Standard time	75th meridian
Central Standard time	90th meridian
Mountain Standard time	105th meridian
Pacific Standard time	120th meridian

If it had been carried out precisely, the system would have resulted in belts extending exactly 7½° east and west of each standard meridian, but a glance at the map shows that great liberties have been taken in locating the boundaries. Wherever the time-zone boundary could conveniently be located along some already existing and widely recognized line, this was done. Natural physiographic boundaries have been used. For example, the Eastern time-Central time boundary line follows Lake Michigan down its center, and the Mountain time-Pacific time boundary follows a ridge-crest line also used by the Idaho-Montana state boundary. Most frequently, the time-zone boundary follows state and county boundaries. For example, before 1941, the Eastern time-Central time boundary passed north to south through Georgia, but in that year the ICC held hearings in Georgia and officially moved the time-zone boundary westward to the Alabama-Georgia state line, thus bringing all of Georgia into the Eastern Standard zone.

The time belts are by no means equally distributed on both sides of the standard meridians, as a glance at the map will show. An extreme example is found in western Texas, where the Central time-Mountain time boundary follows the western boundary of Texas, even crossing west of the standard meridian (105° W) of the Mountain time zone. Although such deviations may seem odd, they cause little difficulty when the boundaries are once well established. The advantage gained by extreme deviations of the boundaries is in permitting entire states to operate under one kind of time. In some places the determining factor was a railroad division point junction or terminal. Where the line was drawn through such a point, as for example at Ogden or Salt Lake City, divisions east and west of the city each ran under a single time.

Daylight Saving time and War time

Because many human activities, especially in cities and manufacturing areas, start well after sunrise but continue long after sunset, it would seem desirable to set forward the hours of daylight so as to utilize them to best advantage. A considerable saving in electric power would be made if the early morning daylight period, wasted while people are still in bed and offices and factories are closed, were transferred to the early evening when the large majority of persons are awake and busy. The adjusted time system is known as Daylight Saving time and is obtained by setting ahead all timepieces by one hour. Thus, when the sun is over the standard meridian (i.e., noon by the mean sun), all clocks in that time zone read 1:00 P.M. Sunrise and sunset at the equinoxes or equator, instead of occurring at 6:00 A.M. and 6:00 P.M., would occur at 7:00 A.M. and 7:00 P.M., respectively.

In terms of the standard time system, we may describe Daylight Saving time as based on the standard meridian lying 15° of longitude east of the standard meridian normally giving the standard time to that zone. For example, Eastern Daylight Saving time is the same as standard time of the meridian 60° W long.; Central Daylight Saving time is the same as Eastern Standard time, both being based on the meridian 75° W long.

Daylight Saving time was adopted in the United States during the First World War, and by act of Congress was put into effect from the last Sunday in April to the last Sunday in September of 1918. After that war it was used locally throughout the United States where authorized by local legislation. During the Second World War, Daylight Saving time was used nationally throughout the entire period of February 1942, to October 1945, and was known as War time. England during the same war period employed a double daylight saving time in which clocks were running two hours ahead of Greenwich Civil time. This was desirable because of the unusually long summer days which England enjoys as a result of her relatively far northerly latitude. Many European countries normally use daylight saving time, which goes under the name *Summer time*, during a part of the year. Nations whose time is advanced by an hour throughout the entire year are Spain, France, the Netherlands, Belgium, and the USSR.

World time zones

In 1884 an international congress was held in Washington to consider the subject of world standard time. As a result, standard times of countries throughout the world are based on standard meridians, which are multiples of the unit 15° and thus differ from one another by whole hourly amounts. In all global time calculations, the prime meridian of Greenwich, England, is taken as the reference meridian. All time zones of the globe are described in terms of the number of hours' difference between the standard meridian of that zone and the Greenwich meridian. In order to distinguish whether the time zones lie east or west of the Greenwich meridian the time is designated *fast* for all places east of Greenwich (east longitude), and *slow* for all

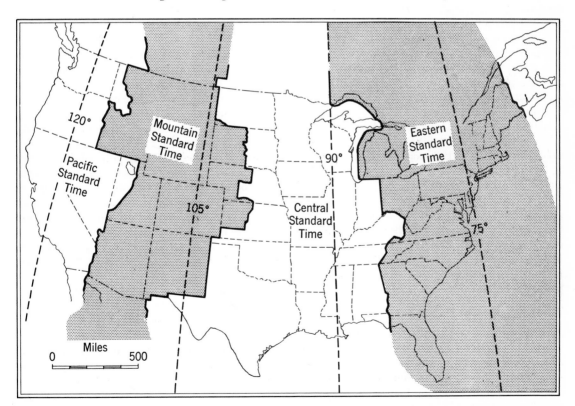

Figure 5.3 Time-zone map of the United States. (After National Bureau of Standards, U.S. Dept. Commerce.)

places west of Greenwich (west longitude). U.S. Eastern Standard time, for example, is said to be "5 hours slow."

Figure 5.4 is a world map on which the 24 principal standard time zones of the world are shown. Fifteen-degree meridians are in dashed lines; 7½° meridians, which form large elements of the zone boundaries, are indicated in heavy lines. Within each time zone is inscribed the number of hours' difference between the zone time and Greenwich time. Careful examination of this map brings out a number of interesting facts. Some small countries or islands lie about midway between 15° meridians. Under such circumstances a standard meridian is chosen which lies halfway between the two and is thus a multiple of 7½°. The standard time of the country is therefore fast or slow by some multiple of a half hour. Iran (3½ hours fast) and Venezuela (4½ hours slow) illustrate this point. India, for a large country, is unusual in having the time 5½ hours fast. The country having the greatest east-west extent is the Soviet Union, with eleven standard time zones, but these are all advanced by one hour with respect to the standard time meridians in each zone, to give a perpetual daylight saving time. The Dominion of Canada has six time zones.

Although virtually all countries today have standard times related by whole hours or half hours to Greenwich Civil time, it was not so long ago that many countries determined their standard times by meridians of the capital cities or those passing through local observatories. For example, in 1905, all of France used the local time of the meridian passing through the Paris Observatory. This gave a time which was $0^h\ 9^m\ 20.9^s$ fast. India in 1905 used the local time of the Madras Observatory, which is $5^h\ 20^m\ 59.1^s$ fast of Greenwich Civil time. Ireland in 1905 was employing the time $0^h\ 25^m\ 21.1^s$ slow, which is the local time of the Dublin meridian.

By 1957, only a few small countries or colonies persisted in the use of odd local meridians for their standard time. Among these were Liberia ($0^h\ 44\frac{1}{2}^m$ slow), British Guiana ($3^h\ 45^m$ slow), Maldive Republic ($5^h\ 05^m$ fast), and Tonga Islands ($12^h\ 20^m$ fast). An up-to-date list of world standard times will be found in *The Air Almanac*.

The International Date Line

If we were to take a world map or globe on which 15° meridians are drawn and count them in an eastward direction, starting with the Greenwich meridian as 0, we would find that the 180th meridian is number 12, and that the time of this meridian is therefore 12 hours fast. Counting in a similar manner westward from the Greenwich meridian, we find that the 180th meridian is again number 12, but that the time is 12 hours slow. Both results are, of course, correct; and the explanation becomes obvious when we note that the difference in time between 12 hours fast and 12 hours slow is 24 hours, or a full day. At the precise instant when the noon meridian coincides with the Greenwich meridian, the 180th meridian coincides with the midnight hour meridian. At this instant, and only at this instant, the same calendar day exists on both sides of the meridian. At all other times the calendar day on the west (Asiatic) side of the 180th meridian is one day ahead of that on the east (American) side. For example, if it is Monday on the Asiatic side of the 180th meridian, it is Sunday on the American side. Confusion can be avoided and the correct dates consistently obtained if it is remembered that by counting hours from the Greenwich meridian eastward around the globe by way of Asia, the 180th meridian has the time 12 hours fast, hence that the Asiatic side of the meridian must be a day ahead of the other side.

Travelers crossing the Pacific by ocean liner know that when the vessel is near the 180th meridian the ship's calendar must be set ahead or dropped back by a full day. When traveling eastward toward North America a day is repeated; for example, Tuesday is followed by another Tuesday. When traveling westward toward the Orient a day is skipped; for example, Tuesday is followed by Thursday, Wednesday simply being dropped out. It was due to the failure to make this change that the crew of Magellan's only surviving ship, reaching Seville after circumnavigating the globe in a westward direction, found that in Spain it was September 8, 1522, whereas by their own reckoning it was only September 7 of that year.

Because of these peculiar properties the 180th meridian was designated the *International Date Line* by the International Meridian Conference held in Washington, D.C., in 1884 (Figure 5.5). It is one of the fortuitous occurrences of modern civilization that after the Greenwich meridian had come into widespread use in English-speaking countries as the international basis for the reckoning of longitude, the 180th meridian should have been found to fall in an almost ideal location— squarely in the middle of the world's largest expanse of ocean. Nevertheless, the International Date Line has had to deviate both eastward and westward to permit certain land areas and groups of islands to have the same calendar day (Figure 5.5). By an eastward bulge passing through Bering Strait, the easternmost part of Siberia is included in the Asiatic side, and a westward deflection of the line allows the Aleutian Islands to be in-

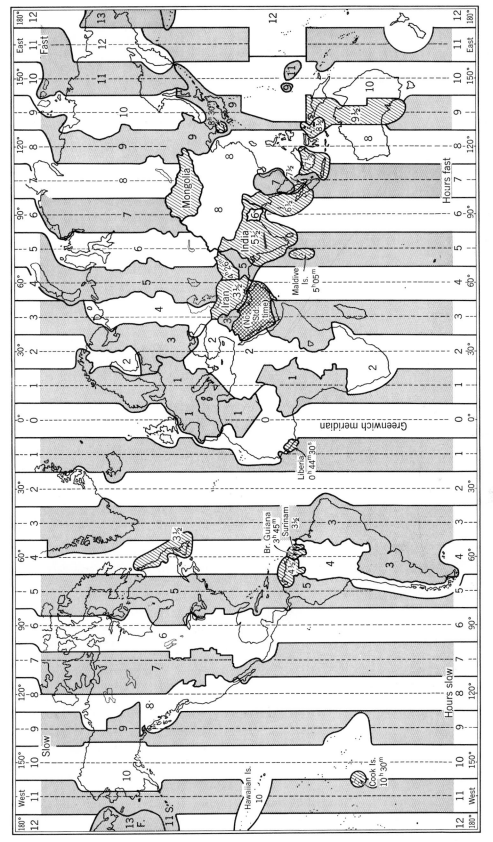

Figure 5.4 Time-zone map of the world. (After U.S. Navy, Hydrographic Office, No. 5192.)

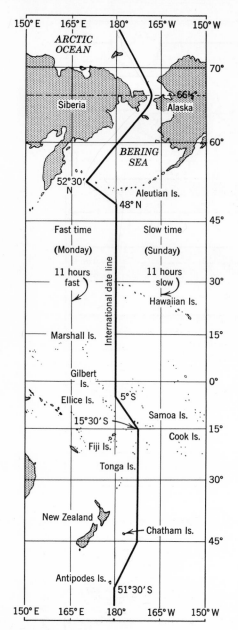

Figure 5.5 The International Date Line.

cluded with the Alaskan peninsula. A few degrees south of the equator the date line is shifted eastward 7½° and thus avoids cutting through the Ellice, Wallis, Fiji, and Tonga island groups, which have the same day as New Zealand.

Duration of days on the globe

One of the most curious aspects of global time is the manner in which calendar days appear and disappear on the globe. If a day lasts 24 hours for a specific place on the earth, and the same series of hours reaches places lying farther west at a later time, it follows that a calendar day exists more

than 24 hours for the earth as a whole. To develop this idea fully use the following visual aids:

Holding a small globe in your hands so that the Pacific Ocean is before you, imagine that the international date line is a narrow slit extending from pole to pole on the 180th meridian. (For the time being let it be assumed that the line has no deviations from the meridian.) Imagine further that calendar days—Monday, Tuesday, etc.—issue from the long slit and spread westward over the globe like a thin film. The leading edge of this film extends from pole to pole and corresponds to the midnight time meridian. The film, which is now issuing from the slit, can be designated Monday, and all global areas which it covers have the calendar day Monday. Traveling at the rate of 15° of longitude per hour, the midnight meridian, or leading edge of the film, will require twelve hours to arrive at the Greenwich meridian. At this precise moment it is midnight in England and the calendar day Monday covers the eastern hemisphere. The western hemisphere still has the calendar day Sunday, which may be pictured as retreating ahead of Monday. Twelve hours later the imaginary film which we are calling Monday has spread over the entire globe and the edge of the film has reached the slit at the 180th meridian. At this precise instant Monday envelops the entire earth and is the only calendar day present anywhere.

Because no calendar day can ever cross the date line, we will have to picture Monday as disappearing into the slit whence it had begun to issue 24 hours earlier. As it does so, the next calendar day, Tuesday, is beginning to issue from the slit and to spread across the Pacific Ocean toward Asia, just as Monday had done earlier. Now we are prepared to answer the intriguing question: what is the total number of hours that the calendar day Monday, whose progress we are observing, will exist on the globe? The answer is that Monday will exist 48 hours. It has required 24 hours for the film representing Monday to spread around and completely cover the earth, and it requires an additional 24 hours for it to disappear back into the slit. Thus Monday is present on the earth's surface for a continuous period of 48 hours, although for any specified place on the globe it can last only 24 hours.

Solar and sidereal time

Unfortunately the sun is a bad timekeeper, running sometimes slow, sometimes fast, with a total range of more than a half hour from one extreme to the other. The stars, on the other hand, provide a perfect timepiece, but they do not operate according to the conventional system of hours and days that our clocks and calendars follow. Our time system averages out the sun's errors and so is basically controlled by the sun, but the stars are used to check the accuracy of the corrected sun time. The main object of a study of sun time, or *solar time*, is to learn how and why it differs from star time, or *sidereal time*, and what causes the sun to run fast or slow at various times of year.

The interval of time required for 360° of rotation of the earth, causing a given star to return to exactly the same position in the sky, is $23^h 56^m 4.09^s$ of mean solar time and is known as the *sidereal day*. The interval of time required for successive passages of the sun over a given meridian (i.e., from noon to noon), if averaged throughout the year, is exactly 24 hours and is known as the *mean solar day*. The reason why the value is exactly 24 hours, with no odd number of minutes or seconds more or less, is that our 24-hour-day system was chosen to divide the mean solar day into equal parts.

The solar day is about four minutes longer than the sidereal day. An explanation may be found by study of Figure 5.6, in which the earth's size is enormously exaggerated. Suppose that, when the earth is at *A,* the sun and a particular star are both exactly over the same meridian at the same instant. One day later, after the earth has turned through 360°, the star is again over the meridian, but, because the earth has moved about 1° along in its orbit, a slight amount of additional turning will be required to bring the sun over the meridian again. About 1° more than the full 360° is necessary, and this requires an additional four minutes.

Apparent solar time and mean solar time

In order to determine when solar noon occurs we might set up a vertical straight rod, from the base of which is drawn a straight line pointing to true north. When the rod's shadow coincides exactly with the north line it is solar noon, and the sun is directly above the meridian passing through the rod.[1] If the time of solar noon by reference to an accurate clock were recorded day after day throughout the year, it would be found that at certain times of the year noon occurs a few minutes early, at other times a few minutes late, and that on only four days in the entire year is the sun over the meridian exactly on time.

Apparent solar time is the system of days and hours which goes strictly by the sun itself and which is therefore continually changing in value from day to day. *Mean solar time* is the system of days and hours mathematically computed so as to give the average value to every hour and day. The

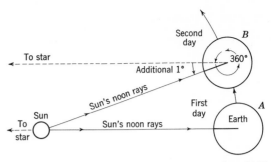

Figure 5.6 The earth must turn slightly more than 360° each day to bring the sun to noon position over a given meridian.

imaginary sun which would run on mean solar time is termed by astronomers the *mean sun*. All accurate clocks and watches in general use run on mean solar time. The difference in value between apparent and mean solar time is known as the *equation of time*. The sun is said to be *fast* when it arrives over the meridian before 12:00 noon by mean solar time, and the equation of time is said to be *positive*. When the sun is *slow*, or arrives late over the meridian, the equation of time has a *negative* value. From September through December the sun is fast; from January through March it is slow. During these two periods the equation of time reaches a value of plus 16 and minus 14 minutes respectively. During May the sun is again fast; during July and August it is again slow, but in these periods the equation of time does not exceed plus 4 and minus 6½ minutes respectively.

The analemma

Values of the equation of time for any day in the year can be estimated from a graph known as the *analemma* (Figure 5.7). Two things are shown on the analemma: (1) the equation of time, and (2) the declination of the sun. Values of the equation of time are plotted to the left or right of the vertical center line, depending on whether the sun is fast or slow. Values for the sun's declination are plotted above or below a horizontal center line, and they range from 23½° south to 23½° north. Therefore, for every calendar day there is a point on the analemma which simultaneously registers the equation of time and the sun's declination. When all these points have been plotted and connected by a curving line, the curious figure-8 graph results. A crude analemma is often found on globes, printed astride the equator in the Pacific Ocean.

A crude natural analemma can be obtained as follows. A tiny hole is made in a shade or darkened window pane on a south wall. The ray of sunlight entering this hole falls as a spot of light on the floor. If the position of the spot of light is marked

---

[1] In the southern hemisphere the shadow would point due south. The method described here would be difficult to use in low latitudes where the sun's altitude is great and the shadow short.

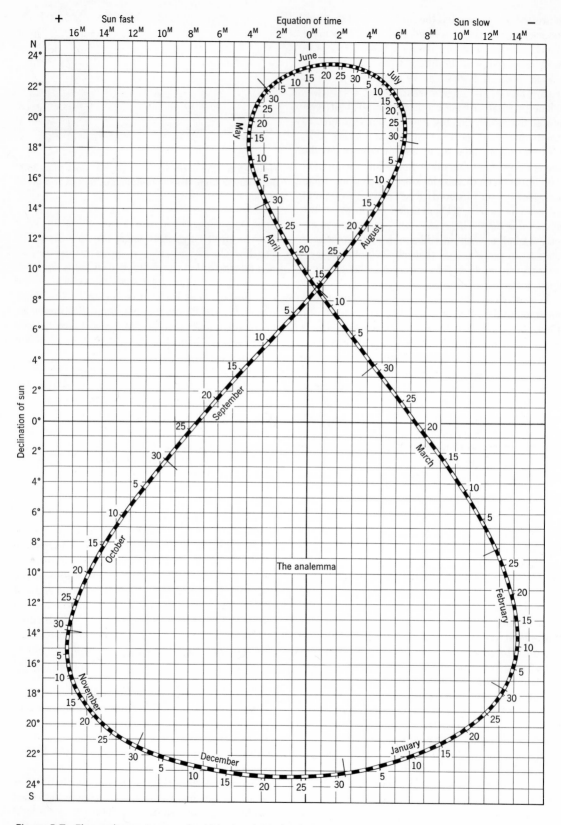

Figure 5.7 The analemma is a graph which gives both the declination of the sun and the equation of time for every day of the year.

daily at noon, mean solar time, the marks will, throughout a year, form an analemma.

A comprehensive explanation of why the sun runs fast or slow in the peculiar, but nevertheless systematic, way it does is beyond the scope of this discussion, but a partial explanation is feasible. The equation of time is determined by the combination of two influences, both of which tend to vary the interval between successive meridian passages of the sun. One influence is the varying speed of the earth in different parts of its orbit. The great astronomer Kepler discovered fundamental laws of the behavior of planets in their orbits. The first law states that the orbit of each planet is an ellipse; the second states that a planet moves at such a rate that the straight line connecting planet and sun (the radius vector) sweeps over equal areas in equal times. It is evident from Figure 5.8 that in order for the radius vector to cover the same area per unit of time when the earth is near perihelion (A), the earth must increase its speed of revolution. On the other hand, when the earth is near aphelion (B), the radius vector is relatively long and will sweep over the same area per unit time only if the earth goes more slowly in its orbit. When the earth is traveling faster it must rotate slightly farther than usual to bring the sun over the same meridian on successive days, and slightly less when it is traveling slower near aphelion. Consequently, the real sun tends to overtake the mean sun in the more distant part of the orbit and to drop behind the mean sun in the nearer part of the orbit.

The second influence helping to determine the equation of time is less easily understood. Because of the inclination of the earth's axis, the unit of time of successive meridian passages changes systematically from equinox to solstice, and back to equinox. The reason for this will not be clear unless the subject is studied from an astronomical approach, in which the yearly path of the sun among the stars (the ecliptic) is considered in relation to meridian circles on an imaginary celestial sphere. There is a tendency for the sun to run fast twice a year (from May through July and from November through January), and slow twice a year (from August through October and from January through April). Superimposing this tendency upon that due to changing velocity of revolution gives the peculiar effects shown on the analemma.

Use of the analemma

A carefully constructed analemma is a handy tool for the approximate solution of problems of the type suggested below.

1. When will the sun be over the meridian and the shadow of a vertical rod point to true north? This

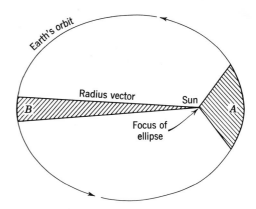

Figure 5.8 The radius vector must sweep over equal areas in equal times.

question would need to be answered if a true north-south line was to be drawn, or in order to know at what moment to read the altitude of the noon sun. A systematic solution of the problem is outlined below. Suppose that the place is New York City, long. 74° W, and the date February 25. To avoid confusion, always start your calculations with the figure *12:00 noon,* representing the apparent solar noon.

Apparent solar noon of local meridian	12:00 noon.
Equation of time for February 25 (If *slow,* add. If *fast,* subtract.)	0:13 slow
Mean solar time of local meridian	12:13 P.M.
Correction for difference between local meridian and standard time zone meridian (75° W long.) at rate of 1° = 4^m	0:04
(If standard meridian lies to west, subtract the correction; if to east, add.)	12:09 P.M.

Thus a watch, set to Eastern Standard time, will read 12:09 P.M. when the sun arrives over the local meridian on February 25.

2. What will be the altitude of the noon sun for a given place on a given date? Suppose that the place is Capetown, South Africa, lat. 34° S, and that the date is December 10. The following method may be used to solve problems of this type:

Declination of sun on December 10 (read from analemma)	23° S
Latitude of Capetown	34° S
Number of degrees difference between these two parallels	11°
Difference between 11° and 90° (*Answer*)	79°

The sun's noon altitude at Capetown on December 10 is 79° above the northern horizon.

Exact times of sunrise and sunset

Thus far, explanation of lengths of day and night and of times of sunrise and sunset have been oversimplified by assuming that the earth has no atmosphere (hence no refraction of light rays) and that the sun is a tiny pinpoint source of light. Were this so, the length of day on the equinox date would be very nearly 12 hours, with sunrise at 6:00 A.M., local time, and sunset at 6:00 P.M., local time.

Anyone who consults an almanac or newspaper will find that on the equinox date the length of day is about 12 hours and 10 minutes for places at about 40° latitude, such as New York, Chicago, and San Francisco. After correcting for both longitude and equation of time, as explained above, the time of sunrise may still prove to be, say, 5:56 A.M.; the time of sunset 6:05. Why is the length of day some 8 to 10 minutes longer than 12 hours at this latitude? Two factors contribute.

First, because of the earth's atmosphere, light rays are bent so that a sight line is slightly curved, with the convexity upward, as explained in Chapter 1. A horizontal light ray thus bends down over the curve of the earth and our visual horizon is actually lowered by a small amount, approximately 36 minutes of arc (Figure 5.9). For this reason, the sun is actually in sight for a longer time than if the earth had no atmosphere and the day is lengthened accordingly.

Second, the sun is a disc of light, whose average width is equivalent to about 32 minutes of arc as seen from the earth. Sunrise is defined as the instant of appearance of the upper rim (called *upper limb*) of the sun's disc above the horizon, and sunset is defined as the instant of total disappearance of the upper limb below the horizon. At both sunrise and sunset, then, time is added to the day—enough for the sun to rise and set through half of its diameter, or 16′ in each case. If we add the 16′ to 36′, the total is 52′. On a slanting path at 40° latitude, this is equivalent to about 4½ minutes of time (Figure 5.10). Doubling this to include both sunrise and sunset, the total is about 9 minutes, which is quite close to the value given in the almanac or newspaper as the excess over 12 hours. At higher latitudes the excess will be greater, because of the lower angle of the sun's slanting path as it passes below the horizon. For this reason, on the day of equinox the length of day at 72° N lat. is about $12^h 21^m$, which is roughly 14 minutes longer than at the equator, where the length is about $12^h 07^m$.

Figure 5.9 Atmospheric refraction lowers the apparent horizon.

The Air Almanac

One authoritative source of astronomical information required for navigation is *The Air Almanac,* produced jointly by Her Majesty's Nautical Almanac Office, Royal Greenwich Observatory, England, and the Nautical Almanac Office of the U.S. Naval Observatory, Washington, D.C. It is printed separately by the two countries, however, and can be obtained in the U.S. through the Superintendent of Documents. The *Air Almanac* is issued in three numbers yearly, covering the periods January–April, May–August, and September–December. Two other authoritative sources are the *Nautical Almanac* and the *American Ephemeris and Nautical Almanac,* also published jointly with Great Britain.

In the *Air Almanac* will be found the sun's declination, as well as time of sunrise and sunset, and duration of civil twilight for a wide range of latitudes. World standard time is given for most countries. The bulk of the almanac is devoted to tables giving the precise position of the sun, moon, and planets. Star charts and sky diagrams are also included.

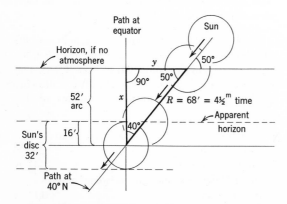

Figure 5.10 The slanting path of the setting sun in middle latitudes lengthens the time needed for it to sink out of sight below the horizon, as compared with a perpendicular path at the equator.

Review Questions

1. Explain how longitude is related to time. How many degrees of longitude are the equivalent of one hour of time?

2. How many hour meridians are there on the globe? In which direction do they travel?

3. Do places located east of you have a time that is earlier or later than your time?

4. What is local time? On what is it based? Can places that differ in longitude have the same local time? Can places that differ in latitude have the same local time?

5. What is standard time? Explain the system of standard time used in the United States. Which meridians are used?

6. How are boundaries between standard time zones determined? Give examples of various kinds of boundaries used in the United States.

7. What is daylight saving time? Why is it used? When is it used?

8. Explain the system of world time zones now in general use. On what prime meridian is it based? What is fast time? slow time? What advantages are there in conforming to the world time zone system?

9. What is the international date line? Describe its location and form. Explain the difference in calendar days on the two sides of this line. Which side has the earlier day? Is it possible for the same day to exist simultaneously on both sides of the line?

10. How long does a given calendar day exist on the globe? Describe the life history of one calendar day as it envelops the globe and then disappears.

11. What is the difference between solar time and sidereal time? Which is the more constant time? Which is the basis of our hour system?

12. Explain why the sidereal day is shorter than the mean solar day.

13. How is mean solar time different from apparent solar time? Which time is followed by our clocks? What is the mean sun?

14. What is the equation of time? How is it designated? What range of values does it have? Where can we find out the value of the equation of time?

15. Explain the analemma. What information does it give? How is it constructed? Why does the graph have such a peculiar lopsided figure-8 form? What types of problems can be solved with the aid of an analemma? Give examples.

16. Why, at the equinox date, is the sun actually seen above the horizon for more than twelve hours? Does this excess time over twelve hours change with latitude?

17. What almanacs provide authoritative data for use in navigation? By what agencies are they published? What information of interest in the study of time and global illumination is contained in the *Air Almanac?*

Exercises

1. Using a small globe having 15° meridians or, if no globe is available, the time zone map of the world (Figure 5.4), determine the standard time in use by each of the following countries. (State the time in hours and minutes fast or slow.) (*a*) Philippine Islands. (*b*) Iceland. (*c*) India. (*d*) Hawaiian Islands. (*e*) Spain. (*f*) Guam. (*g*) Italy. (*h*) New Zealand.

2. Give the exact longitude of the meridian used for the standard times of the following places: (*a*) Rocky Mountain region (7 hours slow). (*b*) Maldive Republic (5 hours 5 minutes fast). (*c*) Liberia (44 minutes 30 seconds slow). (*d*) New York City (5 hours slow). (*e*) Cook Islands (10 hours 30 minutes slow).

3. An airlines traveler, delayed at a foreign airfield, notes that the sun is setting just at the moment when his watch, set to Greenwich Civil time when he left London, reads 1:32. The date is March 21. (*a*) Assuming the sun to be on time, what is his longitude? (Two answers.) (*b*) On March 21, the sun is eight minutes slow. Correct your answers to (*a*) so as to take this fact into account. (Disregard the effects of atmospheric refration and sun's semidiameter.)

4. Construct an analemma by plotting the data of Table 1 on cross section paper. Use an 8½ by 11 inch sheet of paper ruled five squares to the inch. Allow one square for each degree of declination and one square for each minute of time fast or slow. Lay out the page similar to Figure 5.7, and label the analemma fully. After the points have been plotted, each with the date labeled beside it, connect the points with a smooth curve. Because these figures are rounded off to the nearest one-half, they will lie slightly to one side or the other of a smooth curve.

5. Using the analemma, Figure 5.7, as a source of data, solve the following problems: (*a*) At what time, according to a clock set for Central Standard time, will the noon sun be over the meridian at Amarillo, Texas (102° W long.), on October 5? (*b*) What will be the altitude of the noon sun at New York City (41° N lat.) on February 25? (*c*) At what time, according to a clock set for Indian Standard time (5½ hours fast), will the sun rise at Bombay (73° E long.) on September 23? (On the equinox the sun, if on time, would rise at 6:00 A.M. local time.)

TABLE 1

Date		Equation of time	Declination
Jan.	1	−3	23° S
	10	−7	22
	20	−11	20
	30	−13½	17½
Feb.	10	−14	15
	20	−14	11
March	1	−13	8
	10	−10½	4½
	20	−8	½
	30	−5	3½ N
April	10	−1½	7½
	20	+1	11
	30	+3	14½
May	10	+4	17
	20	+4	20
	30	+3	22
June	10	+1	23
	20	−1	23½
	30	−3½	23
July	10	−5	22½
	20	−6½	21
	30	−6½	18½
Aug.	10	−5½	16
	20	−4	12½
	30	−1	9
Sept.	10	+2½	5
	20	+6	1½
	30	+9½	2½ S
Oct.	10	+12½	6½
	20	+15	10
	30	+16	13½
Nov.	10	+16	17
	20	+14½	19½
	30	+11½	21½
Dec.	10	+7½	23
	20	+3	23½

CHAPTER SIX

Moon and tides

AN understanding of ocean tides and tidal currents is important to the geographer who is concerned with coastal geography, shoreline landforms, ocean commerce, harbor systems, reclamation of marsh lands, debarkation of armed forces, and many other topics relating to human activity at or near shorelines. Though the tide means little or nothing to inhabitants of midcontinental regions, its influence is so continuous and vital to coastal inhabitants that for them its importance needs no emphasis.

To understand ocean tides with their seemingly complex variations from time to time and place to place, a knowledge of the moon and its motions is essential. Both the sun and moon exert tide-producing forces upon the earth, but it is the moon, by reason of its closeness, that controls the timing of the tidal rise and fall of ocean level. We turn first, therefore, to a study of the moon's motions, orbit, and phases.

The moon's orbit

The moon, a satellite of the earth, is about 2160 miles in diameter and has a mass of about ⅟₈₁ that of the earth. The moon revolves in an elliptical orbit in which the mean distance between earth and moon is about 240,000 miles. The direction

of revolution is similar to the earth's direction of revolution about the sun. If we imagine ourselves to be looking down upon the solar system in such a way that the earth's north pole is below us, the moon's motion is counterclockwise (Figure 6.1). It is also worth noting that the moon rotates upon an axis more or less parallel to the earth's axis, and that both bodies rotate in the same direction, counterclockwise, if we look down upon the north polar end of the earth's axis. This high degree of uniformity in direction of revolution and rotation is found throughout the solar system and strongly suggests that the planets and their satellites originated as condensations in a slowly rotating, flattened cloud of gas and dust. Similarity in method of their formation from a single solar nebula would be expected to produce the uniformity of motion we observe today.

The moon's orbit is an ellipse, considerably more flattened than the ellipse of the earth's orbit, with the earth located at one focus (Figure 6.2). When at its nearest point to the earth, the moon is said to be in *perigee;* when farthest, in *apogee.* Distances from the earth are about 222,000 miles in perigee; about 253,000 miles in apogee. In ac-

above: Low tide at Ketchikan, Alaska.

Photograph, Ewing Galloway.

93

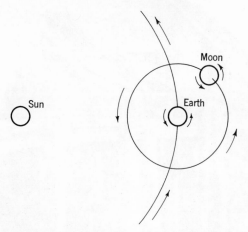

Figure 6.1 Moon and earth revolve and rotate in the same direction.

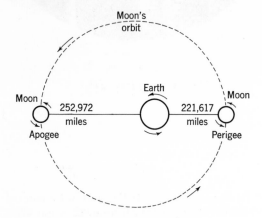

Figure 6.2 The moon's orbit is an ellipse.

cordance with Kepler's law of areas, explained previously in connection with our study of the equation of time, the moon's speed of revolution is somewhat faster near perigee and slower near apogee.

Period of moon's revolution

If we observe the moon's position with relation to a star very near it in the sky, then observe it again exactly 24 hours later, the moon will be found to be about 13° eastward of the same star. Falling back eastward at this rate, 13.2° per 24 hours, it takes about 27⅓ days for the moon to be relocated in exactly the same meridional position with respect to the stars. This period, which is 27.32166 days or 27^d 7^h 43^m $11\frac{1}{2}^s$, is called the *sidereal month*. It is the time required by the moon to complete one revolution about the earth.

With reference to the sun, however, the moon's period of revolution is somewhat longer, being about 29½ days. The explanation of this fact is much like that which accounts for the difference between solar and sidereal time. Because the earth is moving in its own orbit about the sun, the sun's position is steadily changing with reference to the stars. In order for the moon to complete one whole revolution with respect to the sun, the moon must travel an additional small angular distance beyond 360°. The extra time increases the moon's time of orbit to 29.53 days, which has been called the *synodic month*. Whereas the sidereal month is always exactly of the same duration, the synodic month may be several hours more or less than 29.53 days, which is only the mean figure. The total possible variation in length of the synodic month is about 13 hours.

It is the synodic month which is of special importance to the physical geographer because the appearance of the moon in the sky and the periods of rise and fall of tides are regulated according to this interval of time.

Inclination of the moon's orbit

The plane containing the moon's orbit is inclined at an angle of about 5° to the plane of the ecliptic (Figure 6.3). Thus, during a single revolution the moon will lie in the plane of the ecliptic only at two places, known as *nodes*. For most purposes, however, the moon may be thought of as moving almost in the plane of the ecliptic, and hence following a path in the sky very similar to that taken by the sun.

Declination of the moon

Just as the sun's declination ranges over a total of 47° from summer solstice to winter solstice, the moon's declination experiences a similar range, but with the possibility of an additional 5° 9′ both north and south, or a total possible range of 57° 18′. This maximum declination occurs only once every 18½ years.

The moon's entire cycle of declination from maximum south to maximum north, and return, is experienced in 27.2 days, a period known as the *tropical month*. This is much the same as saying that in a month the moon passes through two "equinoxes" and two "solstices" of its own as compared with a similar set of declination changes accomplished by the sun in a whole year. Should we observe the moon's path in the sky on successive nights throughout a month, we would notice that the moon's path is quite low in the sky during one part of the month but becomes fairly high in the sky approximately two weeks later.

Conjunction, opposition, quadrature, and syzygy

When both sun and moon are on the same side of the earth, so that all three bodies lie approx-

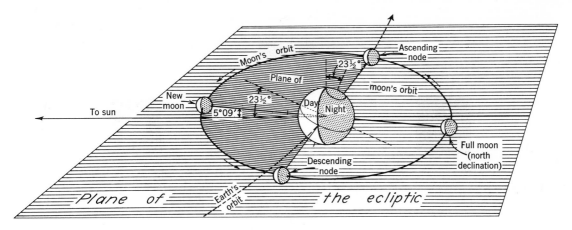

Figure 6.3 The moon's orbit is shown here as it might look at the time of the winter solstice.

imately on a straight line, the moon is said to be in *conjunction* with the sun (Figure 6.4). At this time the possibility exists for an eclipse of the sun, or *solar eclipse*, but this is a rare occurrence because the moon is so small and the plane of its orbit is tilted about 5° with respect to the plane of the ecliptic. When the moon and sun are on the opposite sides of the earth they are said to be in *opposition*. Again all three bodies are approximately in a straight line. The possibilty now exists for an eclipse of the moon, or *lunar eclipse*, in which the earth's shadow falls on the moon, partly or completely covering it for a short period. The chances of our seeing a lunar eclipse from a given place on earth are much better than for seeing a solar eclipse.

The word *syzygy* combines the meanings of conjunction and opposition. Thus, when we are told that the moon is in syzygy, we know that all three bodies are approximately in a straight line, but we do not know whether sun and moon are on the same side or opposite sides of the earth.

The word *quadrature* means that sun and moon are so situated that rays drawn from each to the earth make an angle of about 90° (Figure 6.4). The moon is thus in quadrature twice every synodic month.

Phases of the moon

Illumination of the moon and earth and the progressive changes in appearance, or *phases*, of the moon throughout the synodic month, are illustrated in Figure 6.5. At the outset it is important to make clear that one-half of the moon's surface is always illuminated by the sun's rays, just as one-half of the earth's surface is always illuminated. To the earth-bound observer, however, the amount of the illuminated half of the moon that can be seen changes throughout the month and ranges from none visible to the entire illuminated half visible.

The synodic month begins with the phase of *new moon*, when sun and moon are in conjunction. (See Figure 6.5.) Because the illuminated half of the moon faces entirely away from the earth the moon would appear entirely dark to the observer on the earth, except for a faint glow of light reflected to it by the earth. There is another reason, however, why we cannot see the moon at this time. As is evident from the diagram, both the sun and moon are approximately in the same position in the sky so that the sun's blinding rays effectively conceal the moon. In this phase the moon and sun both rise at about the same time and move together across the sky. This statement is, of course,

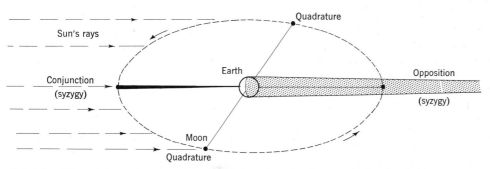

Figure 6.4 These relationships among sun, moon, and earth influence the height of tides.

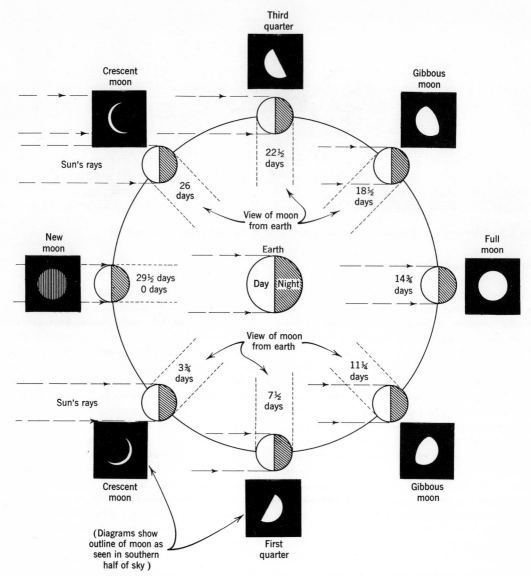

Figure 6.5 Phases of the moon.

generalized, because the moon travels more slowly across the sky and is falling behind at the rate of about 13° every 24 hours.

About 3¾ days after conjunction the moon has traveled one-eighth of the distance around its orbit (Figure 6.5). It is now visible in the sky as a thin crescent whose points are directed away from the sun. This is called the *crescent new moon*. During the preceding 3¾ days the moon has dropped behind the sun in the sky about 45°. Hence the crescent new moon rises in the eastern horizon when the sun has already reached a point in the sky about midway between the horizon and its noon position. The crescent moon follows the same general path as the sun, but is still shining low in the western sky long after the sun has set.

After about 7½ days have elapsed in the synodic month, quadrature is reached (Figure 6.5). The moon is in the phase of *first quarter*, in which it appears as a half circle of light. Roughly speaking, the moon in this phase rises about the time the sun is in its noon position, and reaches its highest point in the sky when the sun is setting. We are here assuming that the sun is rising and setting about 6:00 A.M. and 6:00 P.M., as it would do near the time of equinoxes or near the equator.

By the time the moon has traveled three-eighths of its orbit, and is about 11¼ days old, we see it in the sky as about three-quarters illuminated. This is described as a *gibbous moon*.

When the moon is 14¾ days old in the synodic month, it is in opposition to the sun and is in the phase of *full moon* with the entire illuminated half visible from the earth. Because moon and sun are on opposite sides of the earth, the full moon will be highest in the sky at about midnight. If day and night are about equal in length, the moon will rise when the sun is setting and will set when the sun rises.

Now refer back to Figure 6.3, which shows conditions near the winter solstice in late December. When the moon is full, its north declination is at the maximum and its rays strike the earth surface vertically at about the Tropic of Cancer. The moon's path in the sky is then relatively high for observers in the northern hemisphere, which explains the popular observation that the winter full moon "rides high." At the time of summer solstice, however, the path of full moon is low in the sky and the brilliance of moonlight small as compared with the winter full moon.

The remaining phases of the moon are similar to those already described, except that they occur in the reverse order. One important difference is that the moon appears as if it were the mirror image of its corresponding phases of the first half of the synodic month. For example, the horns of the old crescent moon, though pointing away from the sun, will be directed the opposite way in the sky from those of the new crescent moon.

By the time the phase of old crescent moon is reached, 26 days have elapsed in the synodic month, and the moon will have lagged so far behind the sun in the sky that it seems, instead, to be traveling about $45°$ ahead of the sun. By the 29th day the moon has fallen back to a place almost coincident with the sun and the synodic month draws to a close.

Rotation of the moon

Should we photograph the moon at many different times and carefully compare the photographs, it would be found that 41 per cent of the moon's surface is never seen and that a map of the moon, compiled from the photographs, could show only 59 per cent of the moon's total surface. It is therefore evident that the moon at all times keeps the same side toward the earth. This means that the moon rotates on its axis exactly once in each sidereal month of 27.32166 days. It is believed that tidal friction has been responsible for slowing the moon's rotation to the point where it no longer turns with respect to the earth.

Gravitation and tides[1]

Although it was known from the first century A.D. that the *tide*, or periodic rise and fall of ocean level, is controlled in some manner by the sun and moon, it was not until Sir Isaac Newton published

the law of gravitation in 1686 that the true explanation became known.

Because the tides depend upon gravitation, which is the mutual attraction between any two masses, it is desirable to restate the law of gravitation: two bodies attract each other with a force proportional to the product of their masses and inversely proportional to the square of the distance between them.

According to the first part of this law, if one body is twice as massive as another, the more massive one will exert twice as strong an attractive force as the smaller. According to the second part of the law, if the distance between two masses is doubled, the gravitational force is reduced to one-fourth of what it was.

Lunar tides

Now consider Figure 6.6, in which the earth is represented as having a uniform depth of ocean water covering it. That part of the globe at A is most strongly attracted by the moon because it is closest. Near B, the earth's center, the moon's gravitational attraction is less than at A, and at C it is least of all. Because the gravitational attraction diminishes from A to C, there is a tendency for the earth to be pulled apart. We might imagine that the ocean water at A tries to pull away from the main mass of the earth, centered at B, while the main body of the earth tends to pull away from the ocean water at C. The effect is much like the stretching of a chain of skaters when they crack the whip. It is to tend to stretch the earth along the line to the moon and to deform the earth into a spheroid, represented by the dashed line in Figure 6.6. So far as the subject of ocean tides is concerned, the solid earth can be considered to remain unaffected by the stretching force, or tide-producing force, although slight responses are detectable in the form of *earth tides*. The oceans, however, are composed of fluids that respond readily to small forces, and will move toward centers at A and C. The nature of the forces involved deserves further analysis.

The fundamental tide-producing force can best be analyzed as the difference between gravitational forces at different distances from an arbitrary reference line of zero force running from one polar region to the other, as shown in Figure 6.7A. From this reference line the force difference increases in the direction of the moon (to right) and is greatest at the point T, directly under the moon. An almost equal, but opposite, force difference increases from

[1] Material on tides in this chapter is based largely on H. A. Marmer, *The Tide*, Appleton & Co., New York, 1926, 282 pp.

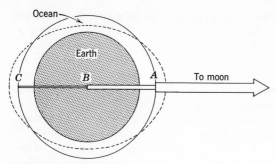

Figure 6.6 Gravitation is the basic tide-producing force.

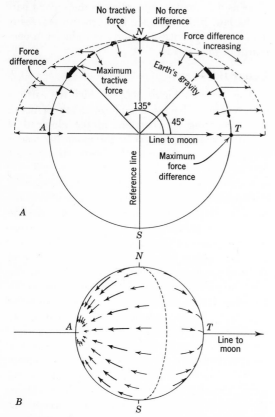

Figure 6.7 Tides are caused by tractive forces directed toward two centers.

zero on the reference line to a maximum at the point *A*, opposite the moon. These force differences act in a set of nearly parallel lines drawn directly from the earth's surface toward and away from the moon's center.

A second force is that of the earth's gravity, pulling all surface objects directly toward the earth's center, as shown by the centripetal arrows of equal length in Figure 6.7*A*. This gravity force is approximately constant at all surface points. A third force acts in a direction parallel with the earth's surface and is directly responsible for causing the ocean waters to move. Called the *tractive force*, because it tends to pull, or drag, the water along the

earth's surface, this force is the horizontal component of the *resultant* of the first and second forces. As shown on Figure 6.7*A*, the tractive force is zero along the line *N–S*, but increases to a maximum at points lying 45° and 135° of arc from point *T*. From this maximum, the tractive force again diminishes to zero at the points *T* and *A*, where the force difference and gravity are exactly opposed.

Seen in three dimensions, as in the perspective sketch of a globe in Figure 6.7*B*, the line of zero tractive force forms a great circle whose plane passes through the center of the earth and is perpendicular to a line joining the center of the earth with the center of the moon. The maximum tractive force is along two small circles lying midway between the great circle and the points *T* and *A*.

The earth is thus marked off into two hemispheres of tidal influence. The ocean water tends to flow toward the centers *T* and *A*, where the water level will rise, but to flow away from the great circle of zero tractive force, where the water level will sink.

Period of lunar tides

Because the earth rotates eastward upon its axis, the two tidal centers move westward with respect to the surface of the earth. At any particular point on the globe near the equator, the passing of either of these centers causes a rise of water level to a maximum called *high water*, whereas halfway between, the ocean level falls to a minimum called *low water*. Between these extremes is *mean tide level*, which is the average of high and low waters taken over a long period.

Because it takes 24 hours and 50 minutes for the earth to turn once with reference to the moon, two high waters and two low waters will occur during that period. Successive high waters therefore occur about 12½ hours apart, and the interval between high water and the next low water is about 6¼ hours. Because our 24-hour calendar day is determined by the mean sun, whereas the tide is governed by the moon, the high or low waters will be found to occur about 50 minutes later on each successive day.

Should we actually compare the time of high water with the time of the moon's meridian passage for a given coastal point, it would be found that the high water may occur several hours after the moon's meridian passage. This lag of the tide behind the moon is known as the *lunitidal interval* or *establishment of the port*. It varies considerably according to the location of a coast and varies at different times of year for the same port. At Fort Hamilton, in New York Harbor, for example, the lunitidal interval is about 7¾ hours.

Typical semi-daily tide curve

Should we make half-hourly observations of the position of water level against a measuring stick, or *tide staff*, attached to a pier or sea wall, we could plot the changes in water level and thus draw a graph of the tide. Figure 6.8 is such a graph constructed for Boston Harbor during a 24-hour period. In agreement with what has been stated so far it can be seen that 12½ hours elapsed between successive high waters and between successive low waters. The time between successive high and low waters was about 6¼ hours. This interval, if averaged out over a long period of observations, would be 6 hours and 12 minutes.

The *range of tide* on the graph is about nine feet. Although the high waters reached the same mark, the low waters differed by half a foot. Observations taken over a long period would show that the range in Boston Harbor averages about ten feet, but may be as great as fourteen feet and may differ greatly from one day to the next.

It is worth nothing further that the half-hourly changes of water level are not by any means uniform. Midway between high and low waters the level rises or drops about one foot per half hour, whereas close to the high- or low-water points, the change amounts to only two to four inches per half hour. To the mathematician, a curve of the type shown here is known as a *sine curve*. To an observer at the seashore the characteristics of this curve are apparent from the fact that high water, once attained, seems to persist for a long time, then is followed by a fairly rapid drop of sea level to low water, which, again, seems to persist for a long period.

Diurnal inequality of the tide

It has already been explained that the moon experiences a declination north and south of the equator, approximately equal in amount to the sun's yearly declination but accomplished during a tropical month of 27.2 days. When the moon's declination is farthest north, the tidal center which lies at the point where the moon's rays strike the earth vertically sweeps westward around the earth about on the Tropic of Cancer (23½ N lat.), whereas the opposite tidal center sweeps around following the Tropic of Capricorn (23½ S lat.) (Figure 6.9). The importance of this fact is that for specific places lying north or south of the equator, successive high or low waters are of unequal size, but alternate ones are equal. This phenomenon is known as the *diurnal inequality* of the tide. It is most marked twice a month when the moon's declination reaches a maximum, at which time the tides are designated *tropic tides*, but disappears at the two times during the month when moon rays fall vertically on the equator, when the tides are termed *equatorial tides*. Figure 6.10 shows two tide curves for Portland, Maine. In *A* is shown the equatorial form in which high and low waters repeat the same levels. In *B* is shown the tropic form

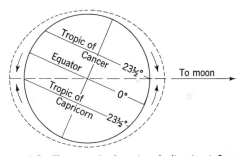

Figure 6.9 The moon's changing declination influences the tide.

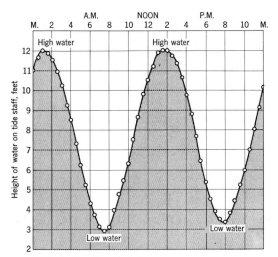

Figure 6.8 This graph shows the height of water at Boston Harbor measured every half hour for a 24-hour period, April 1, 1922. (After H. A. Marmer.)

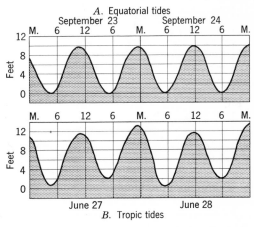

Figure 6.10 Changes in the moon's declination are reflected in these tide curves. (After Rude.)

with about two feet difference in successive high waters, and the same in successive low waters.

Daily, semi-daily, and mixed tides

From the foregoing discussion it can be seen that where diurnal inequality of tides exists, the tidal curve results from the combining of two important component forces, or *constituents:* (1) a *semi-daily* constituent and (2) a *daily* constituent. The semi-daily constituent results from the presence of the two tidal centers and in the pure state gives a tide curve in which successive high and low waters repeat previous levels. This is illustrated by Figure 6.11*A*. The daily constituent is a result of the moon's declination and gives a tide curve having one high and one low water each lunar day. This

is illustrated in Figure 6.11*D*. Most tide curves are combinations of the two constituents and are known as *mixed types*. Where the combination is such that the semi-daily constituent is dominant, the curve will show two high waters and two low waters, but either the high waters or low waters will have strong diurnal inequality. One mixed type is represented in Figure 6.11*B*.

When combined in the ratio such that the daily constituent is twice that of the semi-daily constituent, illustrated in Figure 6.11*C*, a curious curve results. There is one high and one low water, separated by a *stand* of sea level for several hours. The period of stillstand is known as the *vanishing tide*.

Figure 6.11*D* is a daily type of tide curve at

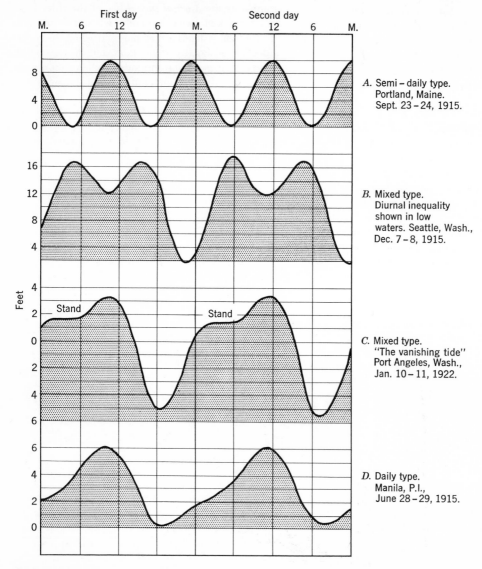

Figure 6.11 Tide curves range from simple semi-daily types, through mixed types, to daily types. (After Rude and Marmer.)

Manila, Philippine Islands, in which the semi-daily constituent is so small as to cause only a slight irregularity in curve form.

Tide curves of the United States coast

Certain general statements may be made about tide curves for the three coasts of the United States. Along the Atlantic coast the typical curve is of the semi-daily type, with little diurnal inequality, as illustrated by the curve for Portland, Maine (Figure 6.11*A*). Tide curves of the North Pacific coast are characteristically of the mixed type, exhibiting strong diurnal inequality as shown by a Seattle, Washington, tide curve (Figure 6.11*B*). On the Gulf of Mexico the daily constituent is very strong, so that tide curves alternate between an equatorial form (*A*), which has two high and two low waters (Figure 6.12), and a tropic form (*C*), having only one high and one low water daily. Of the three curves shown for Galveston, Texas, the upper one (*A*) occurs about 25 per cent of the time, the middle curve (*B*) about 50 per cent, and the lowest one (*C*) about 25 per cent, all being directly dependent upon the moon's declination.

Neap and spring tides

Thus far the tide-producing force of the sun has not been taken into account, although this is an important force, operating in the same way as the moon's tide-producing force. Although enormously larger than the moon, the sun is so very much farther from the earth that its tide-producing power is only five-elevenths that of the moon. The moon always controls the time at which low and high waters occur, whereas the sun's effect is to modify the tidal range greatly at different times in the synodic month.

From the relative position of the sun and moon (Figure 6.4), it becomes evident that in syzygies the tide-producing forces of the sun and moon are exerted in such a way as to complement each other. This produces tides of unusually great range, known as *spring tides*, which occur about twice a month (every 14¾ days), at new moon and full moon, when the moon and sun are in conjunction and opposition respectively (Figure 6.13). When moon and sun are in quadrature, in the phases of first and third quarters, the sun's tide-producing force tends to balance out that of the moon, causing tides of unusually small range, known as *neap tides*. Spring tides are about 20 per cent greater than the average tide; neap tides about 20 per cent less.

Perigean and apogean tides

Still another important variation occurs in the range of tides. When the moon is at perigee in its

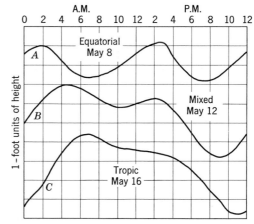

Figure 6.12 At Galveston, Texas, the tide curve varies considerably throughout the lunar month. (After H. A. Marmer.)

orbit, nearest the earth, its tide-producing power is markedly greater than average and results in *perigean tides* which are 15 to 20 per cent greater than average. The time interval from perigee to perigee is 27.5 days. When the moon is at apogee, farthest from the earth, tides are about 20 per cent less than average and are known as *apogean tides*.

On occasions, when spring tides coincide with perigean tides, the tidal range is, of course, abnormally great, but when neap tides and apogean tides occur together the range is abnormally small.

River tides

Many of the world's great rivers experience tides in their lower parts and are known as *tidal rivers*. This condition often results when the coastal area has recently subsided, or the ocean level risen, causing the lower part of the river to be drowned. In a strict sense, such water bodies are not rivers, but are arms of the sea or *estuaries*.

As the tide rises to high water at the seaward mouth of tidal rivers, a wave is generated which runs toward the inner end. Rate of travel of this tidal wave depends upon depth of the water, being faster for deeper water. It is expressed mathematically by the formula

$$v = 3.36 \sqrt{d}$$

where v = speed of wave in knots, d = depth of water in feet.

For example, in a tidal river 50 feet deep the wave would travel about 25 nautical miles per hour. The time of high water for points located 25 nautical miles (29 statute miles) apart would be about one hour different.

One characteristic of river tides, whereby they may be distinguished from tides of the open ocean, is that the interval between one low water and the next high water is distinctly shorter than the interval between high water and the next low water. This is illustrated by a tide curve at Albany, New York (Figure 6.14), which lies near the upper end of the tidal portion of the Hudson River. The inequality may be explained by application of the formula stated above. The crest of an incoming tidal wave travels faster than the trough of low water that precedes and follows it, because the water is deeper. Hence, there is a tendency for high water to catch up with low water, and the effect increases the farther the distance upriver.

In general, the range of river tides decreases toward the head of the tidal river as a result of loss of energy through friction with the channel bottom and sides and because the seaward flow of river water opposes the tidal wave. Thus, the Hudson River, whose width and depth are fairly constant throughout its tidal portion, has an average tidal range of 4.4 feet at its mouth; but 131 miles up-

stream, at Troy, the head of tide water, this range is reduced to 3.0 feet. Exceptions occur where the tidal river or estuary narrows appreciably landward. The tidal range may then increase inland because the energy of the tidal wave is concentrated into a smaller amount of water.

Tidal bores

Where outgoing river currents are fairly strong, and the tidal river or estuary rather shallow, the rapidly rising high water may advance upstream as a nearly vertical wall several feet high, known as a *tidal bore* (Figure 6.15). Bores are characteristic of certain river mouths, such as those of the Amazon, Colorado, Yangtze, Tsientang, Hooghly, Severn, Elbe, and Weser rivers. Where bores are unusually well developed, as in the Tsientang River mouth at Hangchow, China, the moving wall of water may be ten to fifteen or more feet high and

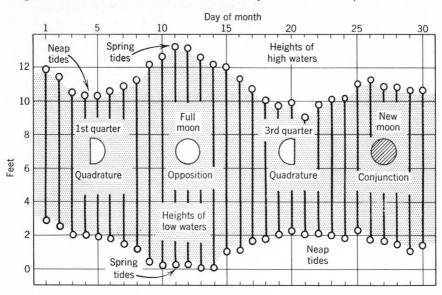

Figure 6.13 Neap and spring tides. (After H. A. Marmer.)

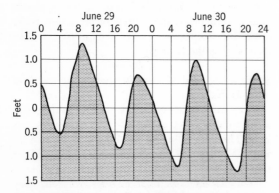

Figure 6.14 A river tide is well shown by this tide curve from the Hudson estuary at Albany, New York, more than 100 miles inland. (After H. A. Marmer.)

is reported to be a terrifying and destructive phenomenon.

Theories of tidal behavior in the open oceans

The reader may have gained the impression from the foregoing discussion of tide-producing forces that there are two regions of high water always present on the globe and that these may be likened to two great water waves, each traveling westward around the earth once every 24 hours and 50 minutes. These *tidal waves* would be of such great breadth and small height as to be imperceptible to observers on shipboard in mid-ocean. Because the globe consists of ocean basins separated by vast continents, this simple concept cannot apply, but it gave rise long ago to the *progressive-wave theory* of tides. In the southern hemisphere, between latitudes 40° and 65° S, a broad expanse of almost unbroken ocean encircles the globe. Just as the prevailing westerly winds in this region have free rein to blow over the sea in great gales, so the tide-producing forces were assumed to have freedom to produce two tidal waves sweeping westward around and around the earth. It was further supposed that the progressive waves generated other tidal waves which swept northward up the Atlantic and Pacific oceans. The speed of these secondary waves would be determined by depth of water, rather than by the lunar period, and would reach points progressively farther north along the coasts at later times. Although the progressive-wave theory thus explained certain characteristics of the tide, it proved to be inadequate to explain many tidal peculiarities brought to light by newer and more abundant data. The progressive-wave theory enjoyed widespread popularity because of its simplicity, but it should be regarded as both outmoded and incorrect.

The *oscillation theory*, now followed in explaining tidal behavior in open ocean basins, is based on the principle that a body of water can be set in rhythmic motion, or oscillation, by the tide-producing forces, but that it will experience periodic rises and falls of level in a manner determined by its size and shape. This is roughly illustrated by the back-and-forth movement of water in a shallow tray caused by a slight uptilting of one end of the tray. Where an ocean body is of such a size and shape that its natural period of oscillation is approximately the same as that of the tide-producing forces, it will respond readily; otherwise it will not have marked tides. The oscillation theory, refined by taking into account the deflective force of the earth's rotation upon flowing water, explains many otherwise anomalous tidal features. For example, the occurrence of a daily tidal curve, with only one high and one low water per day, may result because that particular portion of the ocean has a natural period of oscillation which responds to the daily constituent in the tide-producing force but not to the semidaily constituent. Modern tidal theory is still actively developing and is a highly specialized and mathematical subject of scientific research.

Tidal currents

Our discussion so far has treated only the rising and falling of water level. A related subject is the production of *tidal currents*, or streamlike movements of water in and out of bays and tidal rivers, resulting from the tidal changes in ocean level.

In a tidal river the rise of water is accompanied

Figure 6.15 A small tidal bore coming up the estuary of the Colorado River. (Godfrey Sykes: Colorado Delta, American Geographical Society.)

by an upstream current known as the *flood,* and the falling of ocean level is accompanied by a downstream, or seaward, current known as the *ebb* (Figure 6.16). Velocity of the flood current increases steadily as the tide rises to high water and continues to flow, but with diminishing velocity for one to three hours after high water. A similar condition holds for the ebb current. The moment at which the current ceases before reversing direction, is called *slack water*.

Because most tidal rivers must drain off the river water collected from a considerable land area, the ebb current will be augmented by the river's own outflow, and the flood current will be correspondingly reduced. Thus, in the lower Hudson River the ebb velocity at one point may be 2.4 knots;

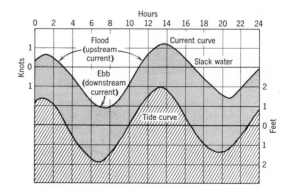

Figure 6.16 Ebb and flood currents at the entrance to New York Harbor follow closely the tide curve. (After H. A. Marmer.)

the flood velocity, 1.6 knots, or about two-thirds as great. Such currents are important in harbor navigation. Considerable skill is required in maneuvering large vessels into their berths and guiding ferryboats into their slips were tidal currents are running past the ends of the piers.

Unusually strong tidal currents result where bays connect with the open ocean by narrow inlets. Because water level in the bay cannot rise sufficiently rapidly to maintain the same level as the rising ocean, a marked difference in the two water levels may develop. A strong *hydraulic* current then pours through the narrow inlet. When, on the other hand, the level of the open ocean falls to low water, the surface of the bay will be higher and a strong hydraulic current will flow seaward through the inlet. Tidal currents of this type may develop velocities of five to ten knots, or even as much as twelve knots if range of tide is great and configuration of the bay especially favorable. Currents of such magnitude may interfere with navigation to the extent that the passage of vessels in and out of harbors may have to wait upon the occurrence of favorable conditions.

Review Questions

1. How does the moon compare with the earth in diameter and mass? Approximately how far is the moon from the earth? In what direction does the moon revolve about the earth?

2. What shape has the moon's orbit about the earth? What are perigee and apogee? Compare these conditions with aphelion and perihelion. What can be said about the moon's speed of revolution at perigee and apogee?

3. How does the moon's position in the sky change from one day to the next, if it is observed at the same hour each day?

4. What is the sidereal month? How is it determined? What is the synodic month? How is it determined? Which of these two periods forms the basis for the phases of the moon and the tide periods?

5. How does the plane of the moon's orbit about the earth lie in relation to the plane of the earth's orbit about the sun? What are the nodes? How does inclination of the plane of the moon's orbit influence the likelihood of the occurrence of solar eclipses?

6. Describe the moon's declination. How great a range of declination is possible? How often does the moon pass through "solstice" and "equinox" positions (using an analogy with the sun's declination)?

7. In winter is full moon associated with high or low path of the moon in the sky? How does this compare with the path of the moon during summer? Explain your answer.

8. Define conjunction, opposition, quadrature, and syzygy. Explain what conditions are required for a solar eclipse; for a lunar eclipse. Which is more commonly seen?

9. Describe the phases of the moon, starting with new moon and continuing through the synodic month. Tell when each phase occurs, and explain the appearance (shape) of the moon. How would you be able to distinguish a new crescent moon from an old crescent moon?

10. How much of the moon's surface is visible from the earth, irrespective of length of time it is observed? Explain your answer.

11. When was the cause of tides first fully understood? State the law of gravitation.

12. Explain how the attraction between moon and earth tends to create a heaping up of ocean waters at two opposite centers. Why is the water not drawn only toward the side nearest the moon?

13. What is meant by high water, low water, and mean sea level? What is the natural period of tides? How does this tide period fit in with our solar time system?

14. What is the lunitidal interval? Is it constant at all times and at all places?

15. Describe the semi-daily tide curve in its simplest form. How might this curve be measured? What is meant by range of tide? What kind of mathematical curve is the simple semi-daily tide curve? Does the hourly amount of rise or fall of water level remain constant?

16. What is diurnal inequality of the tide? Why does it exist? What is the difference between tropic and equatorial tides?

17. Explain the concept of tide constituents. What kind of tide curve results from the semi-daily constituent? from the daily constituent? from various mixtures of both constituents? What is a vanishing tide?

18. Describe the typical tide curves of the Atlantic, Gulf, and Pacific coasts of the United States.

19. What are neap and spring tides? Describe the effect of quadrature and syzygy on tide ranges.

20. What are perigean and apogean tides? When do they occur? What changes in tide range can be expected at apogee and perigee?

21. Explain the movement of tidal waves in tidal rivers. What determines the velocity of wave travel? How does the curve of a river tide differ from the normal tide curve on an open coastline? What is a tidal bore?

22. Explain how the progressive-wave theory of tides differs from the oscillation theory. What features of tides are explained by the oscillation theory that are not explained in the progressive-wave theory?

23. How are tidal currents produced in bays? What is meant by flood and ebb? What is slack water? How can hydraulic tidal currents be produced in bays?

Exercises

1. The figures below give the height of water at San Francisco, California, every hour for October 18, 1922. Plot these on a graph similar to Figure 6.8, and draw a smooth tide curve through the points. (Data from H. A. Marmer.)

Hour	Height, feet	Hour	Height, feet
12 midnight	0.0	1 P.M.	−0.3
1 A.M.	−1.5	2 P.M.	−1.5
2 A.M.	−2.3	3 P.M.	−2.4
3 A.M.	−2.6	4 P.M.	−2.5
4 A.M.	−2.3	5 P.M.	−1.9
5 A.M.	−1.5	6 P.M.	−1.0
6 A.M.	−0.3	7 P.M.	0.1
7 A.M.	0.8	8 P.M.	1.2
8 A.M.	2.0	9 P.M.	2.0
9 A.M.	2.6	10 P.M.	2.3
10 A.M.	2.8	11 P.M.	2.2
11 A.M.	2.3	12 midnight	1.2
12 noon	1.2		

2. (*a*) What type of tide curve is illustrated by the graph that you have just drawn for Exercise 1? (*b*) Give as closely as you can the heights of the two high waters and the two low waters. (*c*) What were the ranges between successive high and low waters? (*d*) Were both low waters at the same mark? (*e*) Were both high waters at the same mark? If not, explain. (*f*) Approximately what was the moon's declination on this date? (*g*) How much time elapsed between the first low water and the next high water? (*h*) How much time elapsed between successive low waters? (*i*) between successive high waters?

3. The figures below give the hourly heights of tide at San Francisco for the date October 24, 1922. Make a graph to show this tide curve, following the same procedure as in Exercise 1. (Data from H. A. Marmer.)

Hour	Height, feet	Hour	Height, feet
12 midnight	0.0	1 P.M.	−2.6
1 A.M.	−0.5	2 P.M.	−3.3
2 A.M.	−0.5	3 P.M.	−3.3
3 A.M.	−0.3	4 P.M.	−2.9
4 A.M.	0.5	5 P.M.	−1.8
5 A.M.	1.4	6 P.M.	−0.9
6 A.M.	2.2	7 P.M.	0.1
7 A.M.	2.7	8 P.M.	1.1
8 A.M.	2.8	9 P.M.	1.6
9 A.M.	2.3	10 P.M.	1.8
10 A.M.	1.3	11 P.M.	1.5
11 A.M.	−0.2	12 midnight	0.9
12 noon	−1.5		

4. (*a*) What type of tide curve is represented by the graph drawn for Exercise 3? (*b*) List the heights of low and high waters as they occurred. (*c*) Explain why the first high water is higher than the second; the second low water much lower than the first. (*d*) What is the maximum range of tide between successive high and low waters on this graph? (*e*) Determine the intervals of time between successive high and low waters. Compare these with data of Exercise 1.

5. Using the same method as for Exercises 1 and 3, plot the tide curve for St. Michael, Alaska, July 29–30, 1898, for which the data are given below. (Data from H. A. Marmer.) Note that heights are given for every second hour and that a two-day period is covered.

	First day		Second day
Hour	Height, feet	Hour	Height, feet
0	1.0	0	1.1
2	2.0	2	2.3
4	2.3	4	3.0
6	1.7	6	2.9
8	0.4	8	1.9
10	−0.5	10	0.4
12 noon	−1.2	12 noon	−0.5
14	−1.6	14	−1.3
16	−1.8	16	−1.8
18	−1.8	18	−2.2
20	−1.6	20	−2.2
22	−0.5	22	−1.8
24	1.1	24	−0.5

6. (*a*) What type of tide curve is represented by the graph drawn for Exercise 5? (*b*) What interval of time elapsed between successive high waters? (*c*) between successive low waters? (*d*) How does this compare with tide periods shown in the graphs of Exercises 1 and 3? (*e*) Explain the differences in the three tide curves in terms of daily and semi-daily constituents.

Part Two
The Weather Elements

CHAPTER SEVEN

Weather elements and air temperature

CLIMATE is one of the most vital of controls by means of which nature limits man's activities. The influences are seen in what man eats and wears, the buildings in which he lives and works, and the forms of transportation and communication. To be sure, this applies less to modern industrial populations than to primitive peoples, but weather and climate still effectively govern agricultural and forest production. Despite man's technological achievements, huge arctic and tropical deserts and equatorial forests remain thinly populated. Even today the success of many forms of commercial and military operations depends upon favorable weather, just as in centuries past.

There is a distinction between weather and climate. *Weather* is the condition of the atmosphere at a given moment or for a short period of time, whereas *climate* is the characteristic weather considered for longer periods of time such as months or seasons of the year. Climate refers not only to average conditions, but to the extremes as well. A statement of climate is thus a statement of the probabilities of occurrence of various ranges of conditions. Climate is based upon statistical analysis of a large number of individual weather determinations, whether they are general impressions gained by an individual who lives in one

locality for many years or mathematical statements derived from carefully recorded data accumulated at an observing station over a long term of years.

Meteorology, a study of the physics of the atmosphere, has advanced far into the realms of theoretical physics and higher mathematics, but the fundamental descriptive principles treated in this book are fairly simple to understand and are adequate for the needs of the geography student whose interest is primarily in climates.

The atmosphere

The *atmosphere*, or air, is a mixture of gases surrounding the earth to a height of many miles. Held to the earth by gravitational attraction, this envelope of air is densest at sea level and thins rapidly upward. Virtually all of it (97 per cent) lies within eighteen miles of the earth.

Pure, dry air is a colorless, odorless substance consisting largely of *nitrogen* (78 per cent) and *oxygen* (21 per cent) by volume. Small quantities of several other gases make up the remaining 1 per cent. Of these *carbon dioxide*, though constituting only 0.03 per cent of the volume of the atmosphere, is extremely important because of its ability to

above: Navy aerographers release a weather balloon.
Official U.S. Navy photograph.

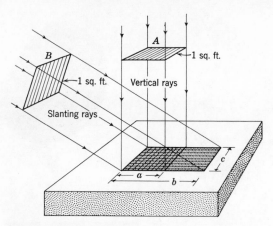

Figure 7.1 The angle of the sun's rays determines the intensity of insolation upon the ground. Whereas the energy of vertical rays A is concentrated in the square a, the same energy in the slanting rays B is spread over a rectangle, b.

absorb heat and thus to promote warming of the air by heat waves coming from the earth and sun. In the lower 30 miles of atmosphere, all of these gases are perfectly diffused among one another so as to give the air definite physical qualities, just as if it were a single gas.

The atmosphere normally contains some *water vapor*, a colorless, odorless gaseous form of water which mixes perfectly with the other gases of the air. The degree to which water vapor is present is designated as the *humidity* and is of tremendous importance in weather phenomena. Water vapor can condense into clouds and fog. If condensation is excessive, rain, snow, hail, or sleet, collectively termed *precipitation*, may result. Where water vapor is present only in small percentages, extreme dryness of air typical of the hot deserts results. There is, in addition, a most important function performed by water vapor. Like carbon dioxide, it is capable of absorbing heat, which penetrates the atmosphere in the form of waves from the sun and earth. Water vapor gives to the lower atmosphere the qualities of an insulating blanket, which prevents the rapid escape of heat from the earth's surface.

The atmosphere contains myriads of tiny dust particles, so small and light that the slightest movements of the air keep them aloft. They have been swept into the air from dry desert plains, lake beds and beaches, or explosive volcanoes. Strong winds blowing over the ocean lift droplets of spray into the air. These may dry out, leaving as residues extremely minute crystals of salt which are carried high into the air. Countless meteors, vaporizing from the heat of friction as they enter the upper layers of air, have contributed dust particles.

Dust in the atmosphere contributes to the occurrence of twilight and the red colors of sunrise and sunset, but the most important function of dust particles is not observable and is rarely appreciated. Certain types of dust particles serve as *nuclei*, or centers, around which water vapor condenses to produce cloud particles. This is illustrated in the air over industrial cities which discharge much chemical dust into the air. So effective are these chemical dusts in causing moisture to collect around them that almost perpetual dense haze, or *smog*, hangs over the city.

Most of the discussion of weather and climate in this and following chapters pertains to the lowermost layer of the atmosphere, some 3½ to 12 miles thick, named the *troposphere*. Virtually all atmospheric moisture and dust, and hence also almost all clouds and all precipitation, are within the troposphere.

The elements of weather and climate

Specific physical conditions prevailing in the atmosphere at a given time and place are termed the *weather elements*. The four basic groups of weather elements are (1) *air temperature;* (2) *air pressure,* the measure of weight of the atmosphere; (3) *winds,* their direction and strength; and (4) *atmospheric moisture,* including (a) *humidity,* (b) *clouds* and *fog,* condensed vapor in minute suspended particles, and (c) *precipitation.* To describe the weather in an orderly and complete fashion, many weather elements are simultaneously measured and described.

Climate consists of the same groups of elements as does weather, but takes the form of averages and generalizations based on long term observations. It also describes the extremes which occur and the frequency with which they may be expected.

Insolation

Heat of the atmosphere and the earth's surface is derived entirely from the sun through a form of transfer of energy termed *solar radiation.* The receipt of this energy by the earth is termed *insolation.* Solar radiation may be described as a form of wave motion encompassing a great range, or *spectrum,* of wave lengths, but traveling at the uniform velocity of 186,000 miles per second. The spectrum of solar radiation, where it first reaches the earth's outer atmosphere consists of the components listed in Table 1. Wavelength is stated in units of the *micron,* which is one ten-thousandth of a centimeter.

The quantity of energy received from the sun at the outer limit of the atmosphere on a surface at right angles to the sun's rays is almost unvarying and has a value of about two calories per square centimeter per minute, a value known as the *solar constant*. Upon entering the upper atmosphere, the X-rays, gamma rays, and shorter ultraviolet rays are quickly absorbed. On reaching a level between 12 and 30 miles above the earth's surface, most of the ultraviolet rays are absorbed by molecules of *ozone*, a form of oxygen molecule present in unusually large concentrations at that level. That part of the solar spectrum reaching the troposphere consists largely of the relatively long infrared rays, of which little is lost, along with much of the original visible light energy. Roughly half of the original quantity of solar energy actually reaches the earth's surface, on the average.

At any particular place on the earth the quantity of insolation received at the outer limits of the atmosphere in one day depends upon two factors: (1) the angle at which the sun's rays strike the earth, and (2) the length of time of exposure to the sun. These factors are controlled by latitude and by the path of the sun in the sky at various seasons. (See Chapter 4.) Figure 7.1 shows that intensity of insolation is greatest where the sun's rays strike vertically, as they do between the tropics of Cancer and Capricorn. With diminishing angles, the same amount of solar energy spreads over a greater area of ground surface. Hence, on the average, the polar regions receive the least heat per unit area. This fact helps to explain the general distribution of air temperatures over the globe, from a maximum at low latitudes to a minimum near either pole.

Because of the inclination of the earth's axis the angle of the sun's rays shifts through 47° from one solstice to the next in regions poleward of the tropics. Although this does not make the yearly total of insolation for the entire globe different from an ideal situation in which the earth's axis would not be inclined, it does cause a great difference in both latitudinal and seasonal distribution of radiant heat energy.

Consider first that if the earth's axis were perpendicular to the ecliptic plane the poles would not receive any insolation, regardless of time of year, whereas the equator would receive an unvarying maximum. The earth's inclination, by exposing the poles alternately to the sun, redistributes the yearly total insolation toward higher latitudes, but deducts somewhat from the equatorial zone.

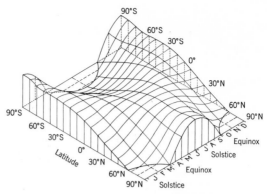

Figure 7.2 The effect of both latitude and season of year on the intensity of insolation is shown here for the whole globe. At any given latitude and date the relative amount of energy received is proportional to the height of the surface point above the flat base of the block. (After W. M. Davis.)

Second, the earth's inclination produces seasonal differences in insolation at any given latitude, and these differences increase toward the poles, where the ultimate in opposites (six months of day; six of night) is reached. Along with the variation in angle of sun's rays operates another factor, the duration of daylight. At the season when the sun's path is highest in the sky, the length of time it is above the horizon is correspondingly greater. The two factors thus work hand in hand to intensify the contrast between amounts of insolation at opposite solstices.

A three-dimensional diagram, Figure 7.2 shows how insolation varies with latitude and with season of year. This diagram shows relative insolation at the outer limits of the atmosphere and thus would apply at the ground surface only for an earth with no atmosphere to absorb or reflect radiation. Notice that the equator receives two maximum periods (corresponding with the equinoxes, when the sun is overhead at the equator) and two minimum periods (corresponding to the solstices, when the sun's declination is farthest north and south of the equator). At the arctic circle, 66½° N, insolation is reduced to nothing on the day of the winter solstice, and with increasing latitude poleward this period of no insolation becomes longer. All latitudes between the Tropics of Cancer and Capricorn have two maxima and two minima, but one maxi-

TABLE 1

		Wavelength	Per cent of total energy
(Shortest)	X-rays and gamma rays	½000 to ⅟100 micron	
	Ultraviolet rays	0.2 to 0.4 micron	9%
	Visible light rays	0.4 to 0.7 micron	41%
	Infrared rays	0.7 to 3 microns	
(Longest)	Heat rays	3 to 3000 microns	50%

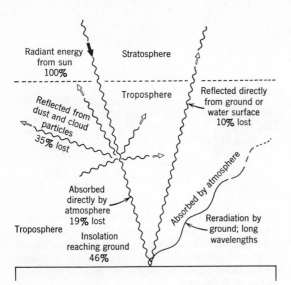

Radiant energy
from sun
100%

Stratosphere

Troposphere

Reflected directly
from ground or
water surface
10% lost

Reflected from
dust and cloud
particles
35% lost

Absorbed
directly by
atmosphere
19% lost

Absorbed by atmosphere

Reradiation by
ground; long
wavelengths

Troposphere

Insolation
reaching ground
46%

Figure 7.3 Solar energy passing through the earth's atmosphere is partly reflected and absorbed.

mum becomes dominant as the tropic is approached. From 23½° to 66½° there is a single continuous insolation cycle with maximum at one solstice, minimum at the other.

How the atmosphere is heated

Heating of the atmosphere by solar radiation is a somewhat more indirect and complex process than might at first be imagined. The visible and infrared rays, which reach the troposphere with little loss, may fail to reach the ground because of two effects. First, the rays are bent and widely scattered by contact with molecules, dust particles, and droplets of cloud and fog. About 35 per cent of the entering radiation is reflected back into space and lost (Figure 7.3). Second, the atmosphere absorbs directly about 19 per cent of the entering radiation, particularly the longer infrared rays, because of the presence of carbon dioxide and water vapor.

Thus about half (46 per cent) of the radiant energy reaches the ground, but this is only an average figure. Day-to-day variations are great, depending on latitude, season, and state of water vapor and clouds. On humid and cloudy days the losses through reflection and direct absorption are great, whereas on dry, clear days they may be quite small.

Of the radiant energy striking the earth's surface, part is reflected directly back into the atmosphere. Though this varies greatly with differing types of surfaces, it has been estimated that on the average about 10 per cent of the total solar energy entering the troposphere is thus turned back. The remainder heats the ground or sea within a limited depth below the surface.

The percentage of radiant energy reflected back by a surface is termed the *albedo*. This is an important property of the earth's surface because it determines the relative rate of heating of the surface when exposed to insolation. Albedo of a water surface is very low (2 per cent) for nearly vertical rays, but high for low angle rays. It is also extremely high for snow or ice (45 to 85 per cent). For fields, forests, and bare ground the albedos are of intermediate value, ranging from as low as 3 per cent to as high as 25 per cent.

Heating by reradiation

It is only after the earth's surface has been heated that the most important part of atmospheric heating can take place. To understand how this comes about it is necessary to review a fundamental principle of physics. Any substance that possesses heat radiates heat waves from its surface. The amount of heat thus sent out is directly proportional to the fourth power of the absolute temperature of the substance. Also, the lower the temperature of the radiating material, the longer are the wave lengths of the rays emitted. The ground or ocean surface, having been heated by absorption of the sun's rays, radiates the energy back into the atmosphere, a process known as *reradiation*. The atmosphere, in turn, loses heat by reradiation of long waves into space. The phenomenon is quite different from reflection, in which the rays are turned back directly without being absorbed. Reradiation from both ground and atmosphere continues during the night, when no solar radiation is being received.

Heat rays reradiated from the ground are easily absorbed by the atmosphere because they consist largely of very long wavelengths (4 to 30 microns), in contrast to the shorter infrared rays (less than 3 microns) which make up most of the entering solar radiation. The longer heat waves cannot pass freely through moist air, glass, or other transparent substances, but are readily absorbed, transferring the heat energy to the absorbing substance. Thus the atmosphere receives heat by an indirect process in which the radiant energy in one form is permitted to pass through, but that in another form is not permitted to escape. For this reason the lower atmosphere with its water vapor and carbon dioxide acts as an insulating blanket to keep earth temperatures from dropping excessively during the night or in winter at middle and high latitudes. The same principle is employed in greenhouses and in homes using the solar-heating method (Figure 7.4). Here the glass permits entry of short wave heat energy but hinders the escape of long wave reradiation. The expression *greenhouse effect* is used to describe this atmospheric heating principle.

Land and water differences

Land and water surfaces have quite different properties in absorption and reradiation of heat. The general law may be stated as follows: Land surfaces are rapidly and intensely heated under the sun's rays, whereas water surfaces are only slowly and moderately heated. On the other hand, land surfaces cool off more rapidly and reach much lower temperatures than water surfaces when solar radiation is cut off. Temperature contrasts are therefore great over land areas, but only moderate over water areas. It is further true that the larger the mass of land, the greater are seasonal temperature contrasts. Because the heating of ground and water surfaces controls heating of the atmosphere above, the same observations apply to air temperature as to surface temperature.

An explanation of the law of land and water contrasts may be found in the application of certain simple principles of physics (Figure 7.5). Water is transparent and permits heat rays to penetrate many feet, thus distributing the heat through a thickness of several feet of water. Ground surfaces, being opaque, absorb heat only at the surface, which thus attains a higher temperature than the water surface. Ocean waters are mixed by currents, allowing heat to be distributed through a great mass of water, but no such movement can occur in the ground. Water surfaces permit continual evaporation, which is a cooling process and serves to alleviate the surface heat. Ground surfaces, however, except where moist or covered by vegetation, do not permit cooling by evaporation. As a further cause of contrast, water must absorb almost five times as much heat energy in order to rise in temperature the same amount as dry ground. If heat is being applied equally to both substances, the ground will attain a high temperature long before the water will; *specific heat* of the water is said to be great, that of rock or soil to be small.

Measurement of air temperature

At every recording weather station, the temperature of the air is read at regular intervals from thermometers mounted inside a boxlike shelter built several feet off the ground (Figure 7.6). The instruments are protected from direct sunlight, but air is allowed to circulate freely through the shelter. Standard equipment consists of a pair of *maximum-minimum* thermometers, one of which shows the maximum temperature, the other the minimum, that have occurred in the period since last reset. In addition, an automatic recording thermometer, called a *thermograph*, may be used to draw a continuous temperature record on a piece of graph paper (Figure 7.7).

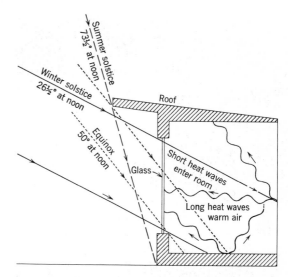

Figure 7.4 The method of solar heating makes use of the principle that short-length heat waves can enter a glass wall, but the reradiated longer-length heat waves are trapped in the room. By careful design of the roof overhang, sun is admitted in winter and excluded in summer.

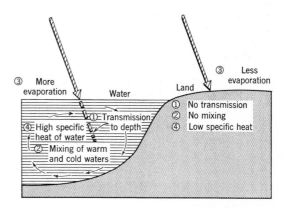

Figure 7.5 Ground surfaces are more rapidly and intensely heated than water surfaces because of four physical differences between the two kinds of substances.

Throughout this book, only the *Fahrenheit* temperature scale is used—the common everyday scale among the general public in the United States. Freezing temperature is 32°; the boiling point is 212° on this scale (Figure 7.8). The U.S. Weather Bureau uses this scale, as do most descriptive elementary textbooks of weather and climate published in this country. One advantage of this scale is that the general reader can relate Fahrenheit temperatures to degrees of bodily comfort or discomfort. The *Centigrade*, or *Celsius*, temperature scale, in which 0° is freezing point and 100° the boiling point, is favored on the European continent and is normally used in physics, chemistry, and advanced meteorology. Fahrenheit and Centigrade

Figure 7.6 This standard U.S. Weather Bureau shelter for maximum and minimum thermometers is used by cooperative observers. The thermometers are sheltered from direct sun, but the air may move freely past them through the louvres. Trees and shrubbery surround the shelter. Note the rain gage at the left. (Courtesy U.S. Weather Bureau.)

(Celsius) measurements are distinguished by the letter "F" or "C" following the figure.

Still another temperature scale, the *Kelvin* scale, is used in meteorology and is designated by the letter "K." The Kelvin degree has the same value as the Centigrade (Celsius) degree, but the Kelvin scale begins at *absolute zero*, which is equivalent to $-273°$ C. Zero on the Centigrade (Celsius)

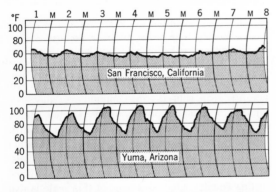

Figure 7.7 Continuous records of temperatures for one week are shown on this thermograph trace sheet. The pen of an automatic recording thermometer has drawn the daily rise and fall of air temperatures. At San Francisco, close to the ocean, temperature variations are small, but at Yuma, Arizona, in a desert interior region, daily variations are great. (After Kincer, U.S. Dept. of Agriculture.)

scale is therefore equivalent to $273°$ K. Where the words "absolute temperature" appear in this text, the Kelvin scale is meant.

Daily cycle of air temperature

If a thermometer is read every hour or half hour throughout 24 hours and the readings are plotted on a graph, the curve usually shows one low point and one high point, with a fairly smooth curve throughout.

Figure 7.9*A* compares incoming heat energy by insolation with outgoing heat energy from ground radiation for a day at equinox. The insolation curve is symmetrical, beginning at sunrise, about 6 A.M. and ending at sunset, about 6 P.M. The ground reradiates heat energy in proportion to the fourth power of its absolute temperature, hence the ground radiation curve trends upward throughout the morning hours and continues to rise for some time after the insolation curve has reversed. Because the lower air is heated largely by long wave ground radiation, air temperature follows a daily cycle of change similar to the curve of ground radiation (Figure 7.10). The time of highest rate of ground radiation, which is also the time of highest air temperature, is thus delayed until a point between 2 and 4 P.M. After this, the ground is losing heat more rapidly than it is gaining heat by insolation, causing a drop in air temperature (Figure 7.9*A*). Ground radiation continues throughout the night, but at a steadily decreasing rate, and does not begin to rise again until shortly after sunrise, when the insolation equals the outgoing ground radiation. The time of lowest air temperature is therefore shortly after sunrise, as shown in Figure 7.10.

In middle and high latitudes, the daily temperature curve is modified by conditions at each solstice. Figure 7.9*B* shows a graph which includes the same insolation curve as Figure 7.9*A* but has, in addition, the insolation curves for the winter and summer solstices in middle latitudes. At summer solstice the sun rises earlier, sets later, and describes a higher path in the sky. Hence, insolation is greater in quantity and occurs for more hours than at the equinox. This has the effect of setting the minimum temperature back to between 4:00 and 5:00 A.M. At winter solstice this effect is just the opposite, with the daily minimum occurring about 7:00 to 8:00 A.M.

Figure 7.10 shows the average daily march of temperature at two places, one of interior continental location in a dry climate, the other very close to the ocean water on a windward coast. Note that the hour of minimum temperature changes with solstice and equinox, but that the hour of maximum temperature remains fairly constant.

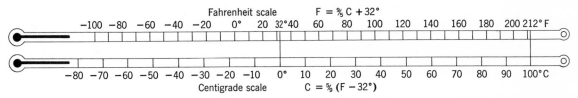

Fahrenheit scale   F = ⅚ C + 32°

Centigrade scale   C = ⅝ (F − 32°)

Figure 7.8 Fahrenheit degrees can be converted to Centigrade by direct reading on this scale or by using the conversion formulas.

These two graphs show the contrasting effects of water and land in controlling the daily and annual temperature ranges.

Annual cycle of air temperature

In order to build statistical information about temperatures for longer periods of time than a single day, a unit known as the *mean daily temperature* is used. The U.S. Weather Bureau follows a very simple method of obtaining the mean daily temperature, using readings made once a day from the maximum-minimum thermometers. The maximum and minimum temperatures for one day are added together and divided by 2. If the mean daily temperatures are collected for many years and averaged for each calendar day or month, then plotted on a graph, a smooth curve somewhat similar to the daily temperature curve is obtained. Figure 7.11 shows such curves for two places at about 40° latitude. Concordia, Kansas, has a midcontinent location; Atlantic City, New Jersey, is near a great ocean body. Although insolation reaches a maximum at summer solstice, the hottest part of the year on land is about a month later, owing to the lag between insolation and air temperature. Similarly, the coldest time of year for land areas is in January, about a month after winter solstice, because the earth continues to lose heat even after insolation begins to increase. Over the oceans there are two differences. (1) Maximum and minimum temperatures are reached about a month later than on land—in August and February respectively—because water bodies heat or cool much more slowly than land areas. (2) The yearly range is less than over land, following the law of temperature differences between land and water surfaces. Coastal regions are usually influenced by the oceans to the extent that maximum and minimum temperatures occur later than in the interior, as is shown nicely on the Atlantic City curve in Figure 7.11.

Several other monthly temperature figures are required for a complete statement of temperature characteristics of a place. These are named and illustrated in Figure 7.12.

Air temperature maps

The distribution of air temperatures over large areas can best be shown by a map composed of

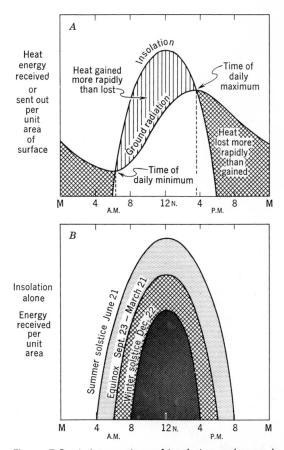

Figure 7.9 A. Intersections of insolation and ground radiation curves at equinox determine the points of minimum and maximum daily air temperatures at a middle-latitude location. B. Insolation curves for the solstices. (After Trewartha, *Introduction to Weather and Climate.*)

isotherms. Similar to topographic contours, whose meaning and construction are discussed at length in Chapter 18, isotherms are drawn to connect all points having the same temperature. Figure 7.13 shows a weather map upon which the observed air temperatures have been recorded in the correct places. These may represent single readings taken at the same time everywhere, or they may represent the averages of many years of records for a particular day or month of a year, depending upon the purposes of the map. Usually, isotherms representing 5° or 10° differences are chosen, but

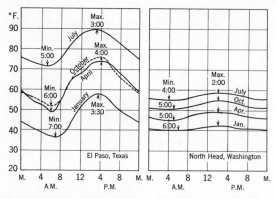

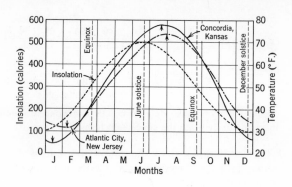

Figure 7.10 The average daily march of air temperatures for two stations. (After J. B. Kincer, U.S. Dept. Agriculture.)

Figure 7.11 The annual march of temperature at two stations in middle latitudes. (Data from Trewartha and U.S. Dept. of Agriculture.)

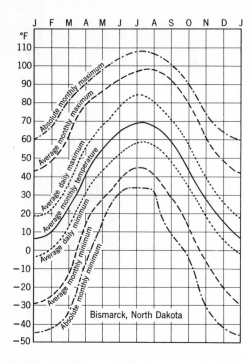

Figure 7.12 A complete statement of the annual temperature characteristics of a place requires seven curves. They give a much better statement of the variability of temperatures than would a single monthly mean temperature curve. (After J. B. Kincer, U.S. Dept. Agriculture.)

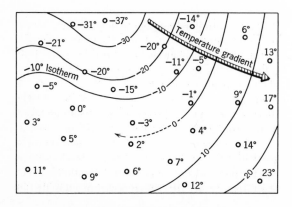

Figure 7.13 Isotherms can be drawn after the temperature readings of many observing stations have been plotted on a map.

they can be drawn for any selected temperatures. The isotherms pass through the observing stations only when the station readings coincide with the value selected for an isotherm. Otherwise it is necessary to draw the isotherms by estimating their proper position between stations. The value of isothermal maps is that they make clearly visible the important characteristics of the prevailing temperatures. Centers of high or low temperature are clearly outlined. Zones of gradation are readily seen. From a mere mass of figures on a map these features are not easily grasped.

World temperature distribution

Isothermal maps of the world for January and July are shown in Figures 7.14 and 7.15. Study of these maps brings out several significant relationships. Isotherms have a general east-west trend around the earth because of the general decrease of insolation from equator to polar regions. The east-west trend and parallelism of isotherms are best developed in the southern hemisphere, south of the 25th parallel, where land areas are small. In the northern hemisphere, isotherms show wide northward and southward deflections where they pass from a land area to an ocean area, particularly in January, when land and ocean surface temperatures are brought most strongly into contrast.

This effect is represented diagrammatically in Figure 7.16, where a land area in the northern hemisphere is shown. The January isotherm is deflected southward over the land, northward over the water. Temperatures along a single parallel are low on land but high on water. In July the reverse is true, and the average position of the isotherm is shifted northward.

Throughout the year isotherms shift through several degrees of latitude, following the declination of the sun but lagging behind a month or so in time. Over large water areas, such as the south Pacific, the annual shift amounts to only about 10°, whereas over land masses, such as Africa, this shift is as much as 20°. (Examine the change in position of the 70° isotherms over Africa.) This, too, is explained by the rapidity and intensity with which lands are heated and cooled as compared with ocean areas.

Certain definite centers of high and low temperature occur and are shown by isotherms which are completely closed to form oval or irregular-shaped enclosures. Note that all of them are over land masses. In January, high-temperature centers occur over south Africa and Australia; in July, over the southwestern United States, North Africa, and southwestern Asia. In January, a continental center of low temperature occurs over Siberia and is strongly developed, with the average January temperatures more than 50° below zero. A similar center of low temperature, but not marked off by circular isotherms, occurs in northernmost North America. That it is not so well developed may be due to the presence of considerable area of Arctic Ocean among the islands of the northern fringe of the landmass and to the smaller size of the North American landmass.

Permanent centers of low temperature exist over Greenland and Antarctica, the two regions of massive icecaps. Temperatures over Greenland do not, however, reach the extreme low of northern Siberia in January, although the annual average temperature of the icecaps is much lower. A comparison of winter temperatures at the two poles is instructive, since one lies in a region of deep ocean, the other in the heart of a continent at high elevation. Because of heat conduction through the floating sea ice (not more than fifteen feet thick), north polar January mean temperature is probably about −30° F. By contrast, the July average at the south pole is about −75° F, because heat radiates rapidly from the elevated plateau. Moreover, much of the insolation is reflected directly back into the atmosphere from the snow surface.

The annual range of monthly mean temperatures at any desired location may be roughly computed from the January and July maps. In northern Siberia the range is about 110° F, greatest of any place on earth. Next is north central Canada, just west of Hudson Bay, and Greenland with ranges of 70° F. The north Polar Sea and surrounding continental fringes have a similar range. Then follow Africa, South America and Australia, with maximum ranges of about 30°. An equatorial belt, about 35° of latitude in width over the oceans and about 10° wide across Africa and South America, has an annual range of 5° or less.

Ocean currents locally exert a noticeable modification upon the isotherms. The North Atlantic current, which runs northeastward close to the British Isles and the Norwegian coast, causes a sharp northward bend of isotherms in winter, when temperature contrasts are generally most marked. A similar situation occurs along the western coasts of South America and Africa, where north-moving, upwelling cold currents cause the isotherms to be bulged equatorward.

Vertical distribution of air temperature

Thus far no mention has been made of the temperature of the atmosphere at increasingly higher elevations above sea level. That air is cooler higher up is evidenced by the pleasant temperatures of mountain resorts in summer and by the existence of permanent accumulations of snow and ice in high mountains. Repeated measurements have

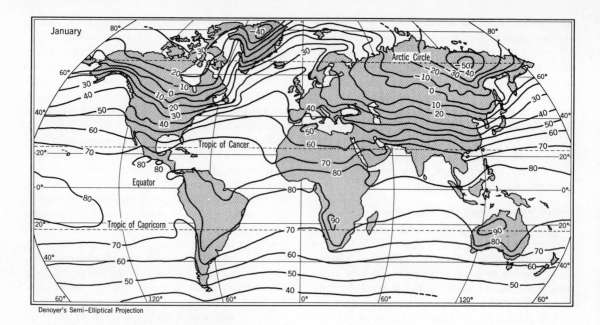

Denoyer's Semi–Elliptical Projection

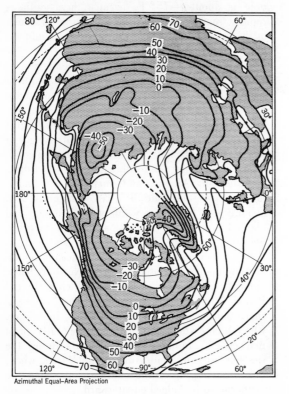

Azimuthal Equal–Area Projection

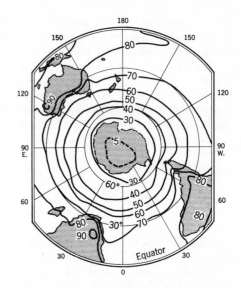

Figure 7.14 Generalized maps of January temperatures in degrees Fahrenheit reduced to sea level. Data come from different sources, and the three maps do not agree closely. (Data from U.S. Navy Hydrographic Office charts, Napier-Shaw, Haurwitz and Austin, Brooks, et al.)

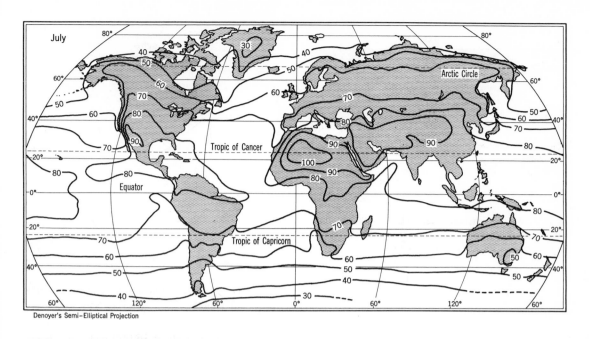

Denoyer's Semi-Elliptical Projection

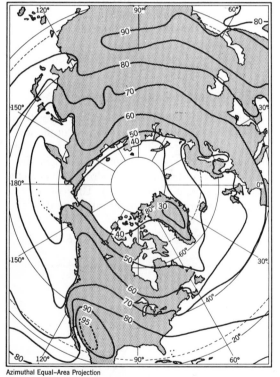

Azimuthal Equal-Area Projection

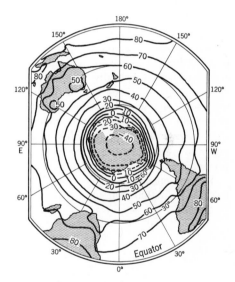

Figure 7.15 Generalized maps of July temperatures in degrees Fahrenheit reduced to sea level. Data sources same as Figure 7.14.

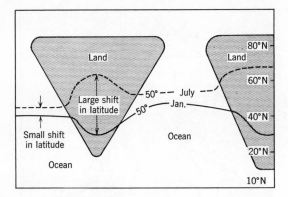

Figure 7.16 This schematic map of part of the northern hemisphere shows how a typical isotherm is shifted over the oceans and lands from January to July.

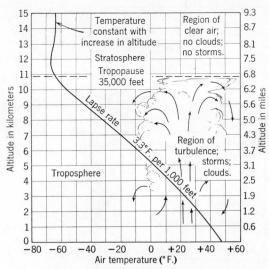

Figure 7.17 Air temperature usually decreases steadily with altitude until the tropopause is reached.

shown that as an average condition, air temperature drops at the rate of about 3½° for every 1000 feet above sea level. This rate is known as the *normal lapse rate.*

Figure 7.17 is a graph showing how air temperature behaves in relation to altitude. In middle latitudes, up to an altitude of about 35,000 feet (6½ miles), the lapse rate holds steady, making a fairly straight line on the graph. Temperature then ceases to fall, despite increasing altitude, causing the curve to bend up vertically. The level at which this change occurs has been named the *tropopause.* It separates two major layers of the earth's atmosphere: the lower, denser *troposphere;* from the *stratosphere,* where the air holds very little water vapor or dust, hence is free of clouds and precipitation.

The tropopause is highest over the equatorial belt, about 55,000 feet, and lowest over the poles,

with a minimum of about 15,000 feet. The change of altitude occurs quite abruptly in the vicinity of 35° to 45° N and S lat. (Figure 7.18). This has the effect of making stratosphere flying much easier to achieve in the polar regions than in middle and low latitudes.

Temperature inversion and frost

Although air temperature usually falls with increasing elevation, weather conditions in the lower air are sometimes such that, instead of falling, the temperature first rises with increasing height above ground before beginning to drop off into the normal lapse rate (Figure 7.19). This condition is termed *temperature inversion* and signifies that warmer air overlies colder air.

Low-level temperature inversion, or *ground inver-*

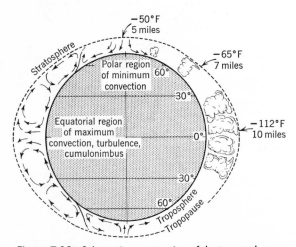

Figure 7.18 Schematic cross-section of the troposphere.

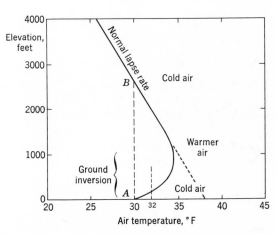

Figure 7.19 A low-level temperature inversion produced by nocturnal reradiation.

sion, commonly results at night from rapid heat loss by reradiation from the ground surface and basal air layer upward into space. Rapid radiation loss is favored by calm air and clear skies. Over snow-covered surfaces on clear winter nights inversion is particularly marked. If the heat loss is great during a night in spring or early fall the air temperature close to the ground may drop below freezing, resulting in a killing frost which damages sensitive crops. There are other causes and varieties of both temperature inversions and killing frosts, but these involve movements of masses of air and are not phenomena of heat radiation. Killing frost may be prevented in orchards and citrus groves by causing a circulation of air that mixes the warmer air above with the cold air layer near the ground. This may be accomplished by the use of heaters, which set up air currents, or by powerful motor-driven propellors that circulate air much as does a fan in a room.

Review Questions

1. Define weather and climate. What is the difference between the two?

2. What are the principal component gases of the atmosphere? In approximately what percentages do they occur?

3. Explain the importance of water vapor and of dust in the atmosphere.

4. What are the weather elements? What constitutes a complete statement of weather conditions?

5. From what source does the earth's atmosphere receive its heat energy? What is insolation? Describe the solar radiation spectrum. What parts are lost by absorption?

6. What factors determine the amount of insolation received each day at a given place on the earth? On the average, throughout the year, how is insolation related to latitude?

7. How does the occurrence of the seasons (changing declination of the sun) affect insolation in equatorial latitudes? in middle latitudes (40° to 50°)? in near-polar regions?

8. Describe the losses in solar radiation in the troposphere. Why should insolation received at the ground surface vary from day to day.

9. How is the earth's atmosphere heated? What has reradiation to do with atmospheric heating? Is direct reflection from the earth's land or water surfaces important in atmospheric heating?

10. What is the principle of solar heating in a home? What is the greenhouse effect?

11. Explain the basic differences of land and water surfaces as regards their properties for absorbing and transmitting insolation. How may these differences be expected to influence air temperatures over continental areas as contrasted with ocean areas?

12. Under what conditions is air temperature measured at standard U.S. Weather Bureau stations? What instrument makes a continuous automatic temperature record?

13. How do Fahrenheit and Centigrade temperature scales compare? Explain how temperature can be converted from one scale to the other. Describe the Kelvin scale.

14. Describe the normal daily temperature curve. When are maximum and minimum air temperatures normally reached? How is the air temperature cycle related to the cycle of insolation? Describe the effect of changing seasons in middle latitudes upon the time of minimum daily temperature.

15. What is the mean daily temperature? How is it computed by the U.S. Weather Bureau?

16. How does the annual temperature curve for a middle-latitude place with an inland location differ from that of a place located on a seacoast? Is there a difference in the times at which maximum and minimum temperatures normally occur in these two locations? Why?

17. What are isotherms? How are they drawn? In what way are isothermal maps more useful in the study of weather and climate than maps showing only the temperature figures?

18. What is the general trend of isotherms on the globe? What influence has the changing sun's declination upon the isotherms of monthly mean temperatures? Is the latitudinal shift of isotherms greater over land or water areas? Explain your answer.

19. What effect have the land masses of North America and Asia upon the isotherms for January and July? Where is the earth's greatest annual temperature range experienced? Where would you expect to find a minimum annual range of temperature?

20. How does air temperature change with increasing elevation? What is the normal lapse rate?

21. Describe the troposphere and the stratosphere. What name is given to the boundary surface between these zones? At what height is the stratosphere encountered in equatorial latitudes? in polar regions?

22. What is a temperature inversion? Explain how a ground inversion occurs. How are killing frosts produced by reradiation of heat?

Exercises

1. (a) Taking into account only latitude, and considering insolation on a unit area of horizontal ground surface at the equator to represent 100 per cent, what percentage of this insolation will be received by a similar unit area of ground surface at 30° N lat. (b) at 45° S? (c) at 60° S? (d) at 90° N? These answers will hold true only for equinox conditions.

2. Using Angot's insolation in table below, prepare graphs to show the changes in insolation throughout the year at the equator, 20° N, 40° N, 60° N, and the north pole.

3. Prepare a temperature graph similar to Figure 7.10 showing temperatures during the 24-hour period for which hourly data are listed in the table. Scale the graph in Fahrenheit units on the left; in Centigrade units on the right. After plotting the points, draw a smooth temperature curve. Label maximum and minimum points.

BISMARCK, North Dakota, July Hourly Averages
(Data from U.S. Dept. of Agriculture)

12 midnight	66.5° F	1 P.M.	76.5° F
1 A.M.	64.5° F	2 P.M.	77.5° F
2 A.M.	63.0° F	3 P.M.	78.5° F
3 A.M.	61.5° F	4 P.M.	80.0° F
4 A.M.	60.0° F	5 P.M.	80.0° F
5 A.M.	59.0° F	6 P.M.	79.0° F
6 A.M.	58.0° F	7 P.M.	78.0° F
7 A.M.	58.5° F	8 P.M.	77.0° F
8 A.M.	61.0° F	9 P.M.	74.0° F
9 A.M.	64.0° F	10 P.M.	70.5° F
10 A.M.	67.0° F	11 P.M.	68.0° F
11 A.M.	72.0° F	12 midnight	66.5° F
12 noon	74.0° F		

4. Convert the following Fahrenheit temperatures to Centigrade: 32°, 0°, 212°, 71°, −22°, 44°.

5. Convert the following Centigrade temperatures to Fahrenheit: 0°, 100°, 32°, 11°, 37°, −40°.

6. The figures given below are mean monthly temperatures (° F) for Buenos Aires, Argentina, located at 35° S lat. (Data from Trewartha.) (a) Prepare a graph similar to Figure 7.12 to illustrate the annual temperature march at this place. Scale the graph both in fahrenheit and centigrade scales. (b) What is the highest monthly average? (c) In what month does it fall? (d) What is the lowest monthly average? (e) In what month does it fall? (f) What is the annual range?

January 74° F	May 55° F	September 55° F
February 73° F	June 50° F	October 60° F
March 69° F	July 49° F	November 66° F
April 61°F	August 51° F	December 71°F

7. On a sheet of tracing paper complete the drawing of isotherms on Figure 7.13. Then draw in red pencil 5° isotherms on the Centigrade temperature scale. This may be done by first converting the desired Centigrade temperature (i.e., 5° C) to Fahrenheit and interpolating this isotherm between the lines already drawn.

8. Some time after being released from an airport whose elevation is 1500 feet, a radio meteorgraph (radiosonde) attached to a free balloon reports an air temperature of 21° F (a) Assuming that temperature close to the ground is 64° F, and that a lapse rate of 3.3° F per 1000 feet holds true, what is the elevation of the balloon? (b) If reduced to sea level, what is the temperature of the airport station?

ANGOT'S INSOLATION TABLE
(To accompany Exercise 2)

Insolation received during each month of the year at various latitudes, assuming a completely transparent atmosphere. The value of one unit used in this table is 889 gram calories per square centimeter, which is the quantity of radiation received at the equator in one day at equinox. (Data from Brunt, *Physical and Dynamical Meteorology*, Cambridge University Press, 1939.)

Latitude		Jan.	Feb.	Mar.	Apr.	May	Jun.	Jul.	Aug.	Sep.	Oct.	Nov.	Dec.	Total for year
	90	...	...	1.9	17.5	31.5	36.4	32.9	21.1	4.6	...	...	...	145.9
	80	...	0.1	5.0	17.5	30.5	35.8	32.4	20.9	7.4	0.6	...	...	150.2
°N	60	3.0	7.4	14.8	23.2	30.2	33.2	31.1	24.9	16.7	9.0	3.8	1.9	199.2
	40	12.5	17.0	23.1	28.6	32.4	33.8	32.8	29.4	24.3	18.4	13.4	11.1	276.8
	20	22.0	25.1	28.6	30.9	31.8	32.0	31.8	30.9	28.9	25.8	22.5	20.9	331.2
Equator		29.4	30.4	30.6	29.6	28.0	27.1	27.6	28.6	30.1	30.2	29.5	28.9	350.0
	20	33.8	32.2	29.0	24.9	21.2	19.6	20.5	23.7	27.7	31.1	33.3	34.1	331.1
	40	34.8	30.4	23.9	17.4	12.5	10.4	11.6	15.8	21.9	28.5	33.6	36.0	276.8
°S	60	33.0	25.3	16.0	8.1	3.3	1.7	2.7	6.5	13.6	22.6	31.1	35.3	199.2
	80	34.2	20.5	6.3	0.3	...	...	...	...	3.8	16.0	31.0	38.1	150.2
	90	34.7	20.7	3.2	...	...	...	...	...	1.0	15.6	31.5	38.7	145.4

CHAPTER EIGHT

Air pressure and winds; global circulation

ALTHOUGH we are not constantly aware of it, air is a tangible, material substance. At sea level, the atmosphere exerts a pressure of about fifteen pounds per square inch on every solid or liquid surface exposed to it. Because this pressure is exactly counterbalanced by the pressure of air within liquids, hollow objects, or porous substances, its ever-present weight creates no special concern. The pressure on one square inch of surface represents the actual weight of a column of air one inch in cross section extending upward to the outer limits of the atmosphere. Because air is readily compressible, that which lies lowest is in a state of being considerably compressed and is, therefore, denser than air above it. In an upward direction, both density and pressure of the air fall off rapidly.

The meteorologist uses another method of stating the pressure of the atmosphere, based on a classic experiment of physics first performed by Torricelli in the year 1643. A glass tube about three feet long, sealed at one end, is completely filled with mercury. The open end is temporarily held closed. Then the tube is inverted and the end is immersed into a dish of mercury. When the opening is uncovered, the mercury in the tube falls a few inches, but then remains fixed at a level about 30 inches above the surface of the mercury

in the dish (Figure 8.1). Atmospheric pressure now balances the weight of the mercury column. Should the air pressure increase or decrease, the mercury level will rise or fall correspondingly. Here, then, is an instrument for measuring air pressure and its variations.

Any instrument which measures atmospheric pressure is a *barometer*. The type devised by Torricelli is known as the *mercurial barometer*. With various refinements over the original simple device it has become the standard instrument. Pressure may be read in *inches of mercury*, the true measure of the height of the mercury column. Standard sea-level pressure is 29.92 inches on this scale. In metric units this is 760 millimeters (mm).

Another unit has been introduced by meteorologists. This is the *millibar* (mb), a unit of pressure equivalent to a force of 100 dynes per square centimeter. One inch of mercury is equivalent to about 33.9 mb. Standard sea-level pressure is 1013.2 mb, and each 1/10 inch of mercury is equal to about 3 mb (0.1 inch = 3.39 mb). In this book both systems of stating air pressure will be used.

above: A fresh breeze on Long Island Sound.
Photograph, Ewing Galloway.

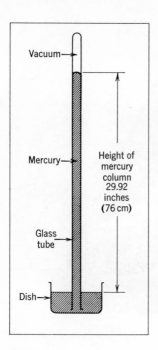

Figure 8.1 A simple mercurial barometer (*left*). Three types of mercurial barometers (*right*). (Photograph by L. E. Johnson. Courtesy of U.S. Weather Bureau.)

Another type of barometer is the *aneroid barometer* (Figure 8.2). It consists of a hollow metal chamber partly emptied of air and sealed. The walls of the chamber are flexible, so that the chamber expands and contracts as the outside air pressure varies. These movements operate a hand which is read against a calibrated circular dial. The aneroid is compact and easily carried in a plane or on the person. Mounted to a revolving drum which turns by clockwork, an aneroid barometer may be made to draw a continuous graph-record of atmospheric pressure. This instrument is a *recording barograph* (Figure 8.3).

Vertical distribution of air pressure

Air, like any gas, is very easily compressed, so that there is a great range in the atmospheric pressure vertically from sea level to the upper layers of the atmosphere. Figure 8.4 is a graph to show how pressure falls with increasing altitude. The rate of fall is approximately one inch of mercury for each 950 feet of rise in elevation, but this figure applies for only the first few thousand feet. A somewhat better way of expressing it is to say that for every 900 feet of rise in elevation the mercury column falls 1/30 of its height. As the graph shows (by a steepening of the curve), the rate of drop of the mercury becomes less and less with increasing altitude until, at a height of fifteen miles, further decrease is extremely slight.

Although the vertical variation of air pressure is

of interest and importance in many phases of weather science and aviation, it is not so important in understanding weather conditions at ground level or world climate types and their distribution. Weather stations that are appreciably above sea level, as most are, have their barometer readings corrected in such a way as to reduce them to sea-level equivalents. Thus, surface weather maps and most climate charts show pressure conditions as if the earth's surface were all at sea level. This adjustment is necessary in order to reveal pressure differences due to factors other than elevation.

Horizontal distribution of air pressure

Comparison of barometric pressures (reduced to sea level) recorded simultaneously at several different observing stations, or a comparison of a sequence of pressure readings taken several hours apart at the same station will show slight differences that are of great importance in analyzing weather conditions. If 29.92 inches (1013 mb) is taken as

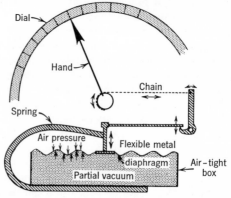

Figure 8.2 Aneroid barometer (*above*) and schematic diagram of workings (*below*). (Photograph by courtesy of U.S. Weather Bureau. Diagram after Wold, College Physics.)

standard sea-level pressure, readings higher than this will frequently be observed, sometimes up to 30.50 inches (1033 mb) or higher. These pressures are designated as *high*. Pressures ranging down from 29.92 to 29.00 inches (982 mb) or below are *low*. As explained later, low-pressure centers normally are commonly associated with unsettled, cloudy, or stormy weather conditions, whereas high-pressure centers generally have fair, dry weather. This explains why mariners have always regarded a falling barometer as a sign of approaching bad weather.

During winter in middle latitudes, a series of observations taken at one locality will reveal that cold spells are commonly accompanied by high pressures, warm or mild spells by low pressures.

The reasons for occurrences of high or low barometric pressures are not, however, found in air temperature differences, but rather in converging and diverging air movements, discussed on later pages.

Isobaric maps

Pressure conditions can be shown on a map by means of *isobars*, which are lines connecting all places having the same barometric pressure. On the daily weather map, which shows conditions for a specific time only, the isobars are essential in showing the location of moving centers of high or low pressure. On climate maps the isobars show average pressures, computed from the accumulated data of many years. It is to the average world conditions that attention is now directed. Figures 8.5 and 8.6 show conditions in January and July, the months in which temperature extremes are reached and contrasts are greatest.

World pressure belts

In the general vicinity of the equator is a broad zone of somewhat lower than normal pressure, between 29.9 and 29.8 inches (1013 and 1009 mb), known as the *equatorial trough*. Lower pressure is made conspicuous by contrast with belts of higher pressure lying to the north and south and centered on about latitudes 30° N and S. These are the *subtropical belts of high pressure*. In the southern hemisphere this belt is clearly defined. In the northern hemisphere it is broken into two oceanic centers or *cells*, one over the eastern Pacific, the other over the eastern North Atlantic. High pressure at this latitude is the result of convergence of air at higher levels and is accompanied by a general subsidence of the air.

Poleward of the subtropical high-pressure belts are broad belts of low pressure, extending roughly from 45° latitude to the ice-covered polar centers. In the southern hemisphere, over the continuous

Figure 8.3 This automatic recording barograph makes a continuous graph of air pressure changes. (Courtesy of U.S. Weather Bureau.)

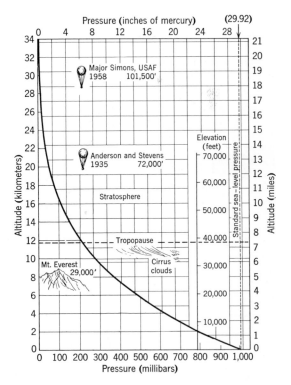

Figure 8.4 Air pressure diminishes rapidly with increasing elevation, as the heavy line shows. No distinctive break in the pressure curve occurs at the tropopause. (Data from Humphreys, *Physics of the Air*.)

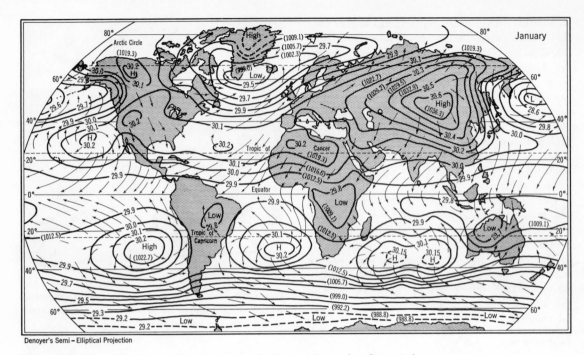

Denoyer's Semi – Elliptical Projection

Figure 8.5 Generalized map of January atmospheric pressures and surface winds. Pressures in inches, reduced to sea level. Equivalents in millibars given in parentheses. (Modified after U.S. Navy Hydrographic Office charts. Trewartha, and McKnight and McKnight.)

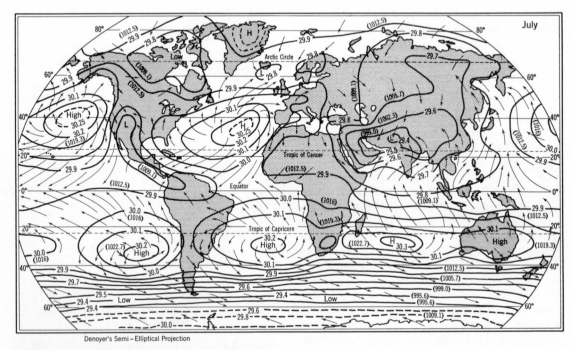

Denoyer's Semi – Elliptical Projection

Figure 8.6 Generalized map of July atmospheric pressures and surface winds. Pressures in inches, reduced to sea level. Equivalents in millibars given in parentheses. (Data sources same as for Figure 8.5.)

expanse of southern ocean there is a well-developed *subpolar low-pressure belt*. Low pressure at these high latitudes is the result of numerous intense storms, each of which is a moving low-pressure center. The pressure belts shift seasonally through several degrees of latitude, just as do the isotherm belts which accompany them. More attention will be given this shift in explaining climates.

Northern hemisphere pressure centers

The vast land masses of North America and Asia, separated by the North Atlantic and North Pacific oceans, exert such a powerful control over pressure conditions in the northern hemisphere that the belted arrangement typical of the southern hemisphere is absent.

Land areas develop high-pressure centers at the same time that winter temperatures fall far below those of adjacent oceans. In summer, land areas develop low-pressure centers, at which season land surface temperatures rise sharply above temperatures over the adjoining oceans. Ocean areas show centers of pressure opposite to those on the lands, as seen in the January and July isobaric maps. In winter, pressure contrasts are greater, just as temperature contrasts are greater. Over north central Asia is developed the *Siberian high*, with pressure average exceeding 30.6 inches (1036 mb). Over central North America is a clearly defined, but much less intense, center of high pressure, called the *Canadian high*. Over the oceans are the *Aleutian low* and the *Icelandic low*, named after the localities over which they are centered. These two low-pressure areas have much cloudy, stormy weather in winter, whereas the continental highs characteristically have a large proportion of clear, dry days.

Figure 8.7 shows diagrammatically the pressure centers as they appear grouped around the north pole. Highs and lows occupy opposite quadrants.

In summer, pressure conditions are exactly the opposite of winter conditions. Asia and North America develop lows, but the low in Asia is more intense. It is centered in southern Asia where it is fused with the equatorial low-pressure belt. Over the Atlantic and Pacific oceans are two well-developed cells of the subtropical belt of high pressure, shifted northward of their winter position and considerably expanded. These are termed the *Bermuda* (or *Azores*) *high* and the *Hawaiian high* respectively.

Local winds

Wind, which is simply defined as air in motion, may be produced on a local scale by processes of heating and cooling of the lower air. In hilly or mountainous regions on clear, calm nights, rapid

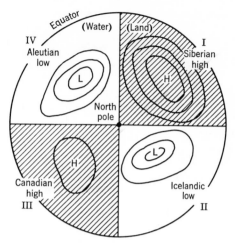

Figure 8.7 A schematic map of the northern hemisphere shows that the semi-permanent centers of high and low pressure occupy opposing quadrants. Under January conditions, shown here, contrasts are strongest.

loss of heat by ground radiation produces a layer of dense, cold air close to the ground. A component of the force of gravity, acting in the downslope direction, causes this cold air to move down the mountain sides, pouring like a liquid into ravines and thence down the grade of the larger valley floors. Mountain breezes of this origin are of a variety termed *katabatic winds*. Particularly strong, persistent katabatic winds are felt on the great ice-caps of Greenland and Antarctica where the lower air layer becomes intensely chilled. Certain occurrences of severe blizzards in these regions are katabatic winds.

In a second category of local winds are *land and sea breezes*, which affect only a coastal belt a few miles in width (Figure 8.8). Heated during the day by ground radiation, air over the land becomes lighter and rises to higher elevations. Somewhat cooler air over the adjoining water then flows landward to replace the rising air, creating a pleasant sea breeze. At night, rapid cooling of the land results in cooler, denser air, which descends and spreads seaward to give a land breeze. These daily alternations of air flow are parts of simple *convection systems* in which the flow of air takes a circular pattern in vertical cross section (Figure 8.8). Land and sea breezes are limited to periods of generally warm, clear weather when regional wind flow is weak, but they form an important element of the summer climate along coasts.

Relation of winds to barometric pressure

Figure 8.9 is an isobaric map of a center of high pressure. Because the center represents the place of maximum pressure, there is progressively lower

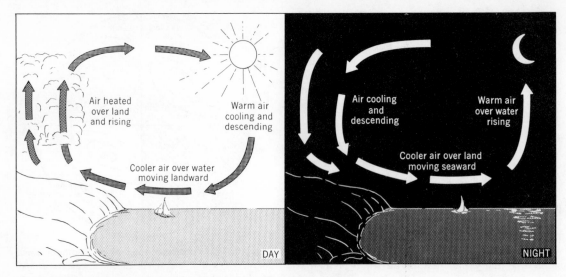

Figure 8.8 Land and sea breezes. (After U.S. Dept. Commerce, C.A.A.)

pressure, or a *barometric slope,* outward in any direction from the center. This slope is also termed the *pressure gradient.* Direction of pressure gradient, indicated by arrows, is always at right angles to the isobars. Whether there are pressure centers or belts, a pressure gradient always exists, running from higher to lower pressure. Closely spaced isobars indicate that the gradient is strong and that pressure changes occur rapidly within a short horizontal distance. Widely spaced isobars indicate a weak gradient.

Most of the widespread and persistent winds of the earth are those movements of air set up in response to pressure differences. The *pressure gradient force,* acting in the direction of the pressure gradient, tends to start the flow of air from higher to lower pressure. Strong pressure gradients, indicated by closely crowded isobars on the map, cause

strong winds, whereas widely spaced isobars can be expected to yield weak winds. Calms exist in the centers of high pressure.

The Coriolis force and geostrophic winds

If the earth did not rotate upon its axis, winds would follow the direction of pressure gradient. Instead, earth rotation produces another force, the *Coriolis force,* which tends to turn the flow of air. The direction of action of the Coriolis force is stated in *Ferrel's law:* Any object or fluid moving horizontally in the northern hemisphere tends to be deflected to the right of its path of motion, regardless of the compass direction of the path. In the southern hemisphere a similar deflection is toward the left of the path of motion. The Coriolis force is absent at the equator but increases progressively poleward. On Figure 8.10 the various arrows show how an initial straight line of motion is modified by the deflective force. Note especially that the compass direction is not of any consequence. If we face down the direction of motion, turning will always be toward the right hand in the northern hemisphere. Because the deflective force is very weak, it is normally apparent only in freely moving fluids such as air or water. Ocean current patterns are to some extent governed by it, and streams occasionally will show a tendency to undercut their right-hand banks in the northern hemisphere. Driftwood floating in rivers at high northerly latitudes concentrates along the right-hand edge of the stream. Rifle bullets are slightly deflected over long ranges.

Applying these principles to the relation of winds to pressure (Figure 8.11), the gradient force (acting in the direction of the pressure gradient) and the Coriolis force (acting to the right of the path of

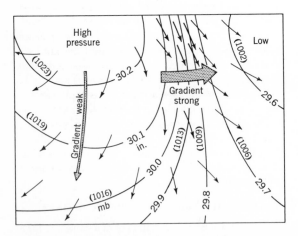

Figure 8.9 The arrangement of isobars determines pressure gradients and surface winds.

flow) reach a balance or equilibrium only when the wind has been turned to the point that it flows in a direction at right angles to the pressure gradient, that is, parallel with the isobars. The ideal wind in this state of balance with respect to the two forces is termed the *geostrophic wind* for cases in which the isobars are straight. In general, air flow at high altitudes parallels the isobars (Figure 8.11). The rule for the relation of wind to pressure in the northern hemisphere is: Stand with your back to the wind and the low pressure will be on your left, the high on your right.

Near the earth's surface, at levels from the ground upward to about 2000 or 3000 feet, still another force modifies the wind direction. This is the force of friction of the air with the ground. It acts in such a way as to counteract in part the Coriolis force and to prevent the wind from being deflected until parallel with the isobars. Instead, the wind blows obliquely across the isobars, the angle being from 20° to 45°. Figure 8.9 illustrates surface winds and is typical of conditions found on the surface weather map.

Measurement of winds

A description of winds requires measurement of two conditions, direction and velocity. Direction is easily determined by a *wind vane*, known to all because it is frequently mounted on rooftops and is one of the commonest of the amateur weather instruments. Wind direction is stated in terms of the direction from which the wind is coming. Thus an east wind comes from the east, but the direction of air movement is toward the west. The direction of movement of low clouds is an excellent indicator of wind direction and can be observed without the aid of instruments.

Strength of wind is measured by an *anemometer*. There are several types. The commonest one seen at weather stations is the *cup anemometer*. It consists of three or four hemispherical cups mounted as if at the ends of spokes of a horizontal wheel (Figure 8.12). The wheel revolves with a speed proportional to the strength of the wind. Other types of anemometers depend on measuring the force exerted by the wind upon an exposed surface. For wind velocities at higher levels a small hydrogen-filled balloon, whose rate of ascent is known, is released into the air and observed through a telescope, of a type known as a *theodolite*. Knowing the balloon's vertical position by measuring the elapsed time, an observer can calculate the horizontal drift of the balloon downwind after reading the vertical angle of sight on the angle scale mounted on the telescope (Figure 8.13). For modern, upper-air measurements of wind velocity and direction the balloon carries a target that reflects radar waves and can thus be

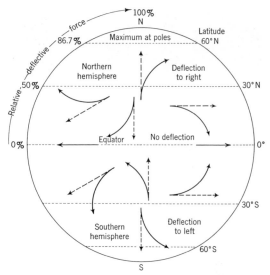

Figure 8.10 Deflective force of the earth's rotation.

followed when the sky is overcast.

Conventional symbols have been established to show wind direction and strength on weather and climate maps. For single observations, such as those on a daily weather map, an arrow of the type shown in Figure 8.14 is used. The circle takes the place of the arrow point and is centered on the observing station. Attached to the shaft of the arrow are short lines, or barbs, and pennants, whose numbers show wind strength according to a predetermined code.

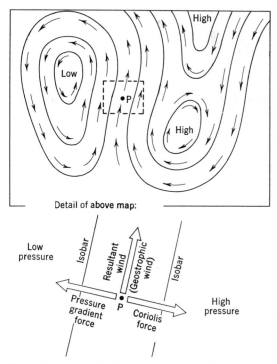

Figure 8.11 Wind follows isobars at high levels.

Figure 8.12 A Robinson four-cup anemometer. (Courtesy of U.S. Weather Bureau.)

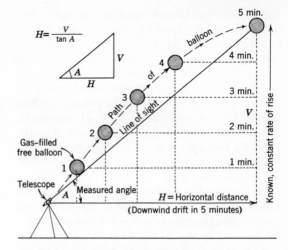

Figure 8.13 The velocity of winds aloft can be calculated by following the path of a free gas-filled balloon with a telescopic instrument.

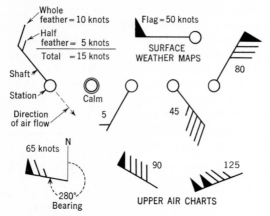

Figure 8.14 Standard symbols on U.S. Weather Bureau maps tell wind direction and strength.

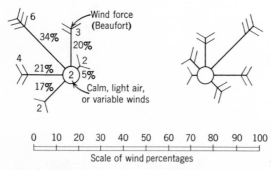

Figure 8.15 On U.S. Navy Hydrographic Office pilot charts of the oceans, a wind rose is used to show the average of wind durations and strengths for each 5° square of latitude and longitude. (After U.S. Navy Hydrographic Office.)

For wind observations collected over a long period of time a device known as a *wind rose* is employed. One is illustrated in Figure 8.15. Wind directions are reduced to eight compass sectors shown by lines radiating from the central point. The percentage of total length of time during which wind blows from these sectors of the compass is indicated by length of the lines. On charts showing wind roses there is printed on the margin a scale from which the percentages may be measured, if desired. Small feather lines attached to the ends of the radial lines are used to show the average wind strength during the period for which the wind rose is constructed.

A scale of numbers was long used to state the strength of wind. This is the *Beaufort scale,* devised by Admiral Sir Francis Beaufort of the British navy in 1806. It consists of numbers ranging from 0 to 12. Table 1 gives a description of this scale, together with the common evidences of the various wind strengths and their equivalent velocities in miles per hour.

The Beaufort force scale of numbers has now been largely replaced by a direct statement of wind velocity in miles per hour or knots.

Earth's surface wind systems

Prevailing surface winds during the months of January and July are suggested by arrows on the pressure maps, Figures 8.5 and 8.6. A highly diagrammatic representation of the wind systems in Figure 8.16 shows the earth as if no land areas existed to modify the belted arrangement of pressure zones.

TABLE 1: THE BEAUFORT SCALE OF WINDS*

Beaufort number	Name of wind	Observable features	Velocity in miles per hour, 20 feet above ground
0	Calm	Smoke rises vertically.	Less than 1
1	Light air	Smoke drifts downwind. Wind does not move wind vane.	1 to 3
2	Light breeze	Wind felt on face; leaves rustle. Vane moved by wind.	4 to 7
3	Gentle breeze	Leaves and twigs in constant motion; wind extends light flag.	8 to 12
4	Moderate breeze	Raises dust and loose paper; small branches are moved.	13 to 18
5	Fresh breeze	Small trees in leaf begin to sway; crested wavelets form on inland waters.	19 to 24
6	Strong breeze	Large branches in motion; whistling heard in telegraph wires; umbrellas used with difficulty.	25 to 31
7	Moderate gale	Whole trees in motion; inconvenience felt in walking against wind.	32 to 38
8	Fresh gale	Twigs break off trees; progress generally impeded.	39 to 46
9	Strong gale	Slight structural damage occurs (chimney pots and slate removed).	47 to 54
10	Whole gale	Seldom experienced inland; trees uprooted; considerable structural damage occurs.	55 to 63
11	Storm	Very rarely experienced; accompanied by widespread destruction.	64 to 75
12	Hurricane		Above 75

* After U.S. Weather Bureau.

In the equatorial trough of low pressure, intense solar heating causes the moist air to break into great convection columns, so that there is a general rise of air. This region, lying roughly between 5° S and 5° N lat. was long called the *equatorial belt of variable winds and calms,* or the *doldrums.* There are no prevailing surface winds here, but a fair distribution of directions around the compass (Figure 8.17). Calms prevail as much as a third of the time. Violent thunderstorms with strong squall winds are common. Centrally located on a belt of low pressure, this zone has no strong pressure gradients to induce a persistent flow of wind.

North and south of the doldrums are the *trade wind* belts, covering roughly the zones lying between 5° and 30° N and S. The trades are a result of a pressure gradient from the subtropical belt of high pressure to the equatorial trough of low pressure. In the northern hemisphere, air moving equatorward is deflected by the earth's rotation to flow southwestward. Thus, the prevailing wind is from the northeast and the winds are termed the *northeast trades.* In the southern hemisphere, deflection of the moving air to the left causes the *southeast trades.*

Trade winds are noted for their steadiness and directional persistence. Figure 8.17 shows wind roses within the trade wind belts. Note that most winds come from one quarter of the compass.

The system of doldrums and trades shifts seasonally north and south, through several degrees of latitude, as do the pressure belts that cause them. Because of the large land areas of the northern hemisphere, there is a tendency for these belts to be shifted farther north in summer (July) than they are shifted south in winter (January). The trades are best developed over the Pacific and Atlantic oceans, but are upset in the Indian Ocean region by the proximity of the great Asiatic land mass.

The trade winds provided a splendid avenue for westward travel in the days of sailing vessels. Steadiness of wind and generally clear weather made this a favorite zone of mariners. Crossing of the doldrums was hazardous because of the possibility of being becalmed for long periods and because of the uncertainty of wind direction. The trade wind belts are not altogether favorable for navigation and flying, however, because over certain oceanic portions, at certain seasons of the year, terrible tropical storms known as hurricanes or typhoons occur (Chapter 11).

Between latitudes 30° and 40° are what have long been called the *subtropical belts of variable*

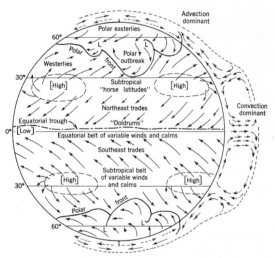

Figure 8.16 The general scheme of atmospheric circulation is shown here on an equatorial orthographic projection.

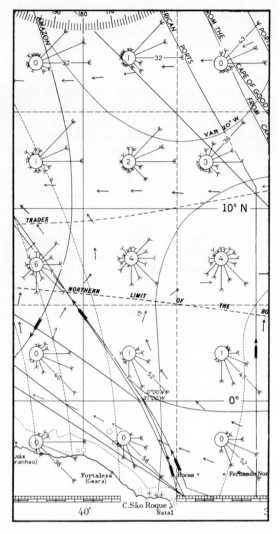

Figure 8.17 This portion of a Hydrographic Office pilot chart of the North Atlantic for July shows parts of both the northeast and southeast trade wind belts, with the narrow doldrum belt lying between. The area shown here extends from 5° S lat. to 20° N lat. Wind roses occupy 5° squares. (U.S. Navy Hydrographic Office, Chart 1400.)

summer (January in the southern hemisphere, July in the northern). There is also a latitudinal shifting following the sun's declination. This amounts to less than 5° in the southern hemisphere, but it is about 8° for the strong Hawaiian high located in the northeastern Pacific.

Wind roses for the horse latitudes are shown in Figure 8.19. Winds are distributed around a considerable range of compass directions. Calms prevail as much as a quarter of the time. The cells of high pressure have generally fair, clear weather, with a strong tendency to dryness. Most of the world's great deserts lie in this zone and in the adjacent trade-wind belt. An explanation of the dry, clear weather lies in the fact that the high-pressure cells are centers of descending air, settling from higher levels of the atmosphere and spreading out near the earth's surface. Descending air, as explained more fully in the next chapter, becomes increasingly dry.

Between latitudes 35° and 60°, both N and S, is the belt of the *westerlies*, or *prevailing westerly winds*. Moving from the subtropical high-pressure centers toward the subpolar lows, these surface winds are shown on Figure 8.16 to blow from a southwesterly quarter in the northern hemisphere, from a northwesterly quarter in the southern hemisphere. This generalization is somewhat misleading, however, because winds from polar directions are frequent and strong. It is more accurate to say that within the westerly wind belt, winds blow from any direction of the compass, but that the westerly components are definitely predominant. Storm winds are common in this belt, as are frequent cloudy days with continued precipitation. Weather

winds and calms, or *horse latitudes,* coinciding with the subtropical high-pressure belt. Instead of being continuous even belts, however, the high-pressure areas are concentrated into distinct centers, or cells, located over the oceans. Figure 8.18 shows high-pressure centers in the northern and southern hemisphere and the resultant surface winds. The apparent outward spiraling movement of air is directed equatorward into the easterly trade wind system; poleward into the westerly wind system. The cells of high pressure are most strongly developed in the

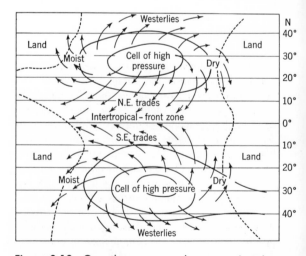

Figure 8.18 Over the oceans semi-permanent centers of high pressure surface winds spiral outward in a clockwise direction in the northern hemisphere, anticlockwise in the southern.

is highly changeable.

In the northern hemisphere, land masses cause considerable disruption of the westerly wind belt, but in the southern hemisphere, between the latitudes 40° and 60° S, there is an almost unbroken belt of ocean. Here the westerlies gain great strength and persistence, giving rise to the mariner's expressions, "the roaring forties," "the furious fifties," and "the screaming sixties." This belt was extensively used for sailing vessels traveling eastward from the South Atlantic Ocean to Australia, Tasmania, New Zealand, and the southern Pacific islands. From these places it was then easier to continue eastward around the world to return to European ports. Rounding Cape Horn was relatively easy on an eastward voyage, but in the opposite direction, in the face of prevailing stormy westerly winds, was fraught with great danger.

Although the westerly wind belts no longer exert a strong influence over the routes of modern ocean vessels, they are important in long-distance flying. Transoceanic and transcontinental flights in the easterly direction require less fuel and a shorter time. On westward flights, strong head winds may eat dangerously into the fuel supply of the plane and in any event necessitate reduced pay loads.

A wind system often termed the *polar easterlies* has been described as characteristic of the arctic and antarctic latitudes (Figure 8.16). The concept is greatly simplified if not actually erroneous. Perhaps in the antarctic, where an icecapped land mass rests squarely upon the pole and is surrounded by a vast oceanic expanse, the outward spiraling flow of polar easterlies is a valid concept. Deflected to the left in the southern hemisphere, the radial winds would spiral counterclockwise, producing a system of southeasterly winds.

Monsoon winds of Asia and North America

Frequent reference has been made to the powerful control which Asia and North America exert upon conditions of temperature and pressure in the northern hemisphere. Because pressure conditions control winds, it is obvious that these areas must develop wind systems relatively independent of the belted system of earth winds so well illustrated in the southern hemisphere.

In summer, southern Asia develops a center of low pressure, into which there is a considerable flow of air. This may be a *heat low*, or *thermal low*, limited to the lower levels of the atmosphere (Figure 8.20). From the Indian Ocean and southwestern Pacific warm, humid air moves northward and northwestward into Asia, passing over India, Indochina, and China. (See Figure 8.6.) This is the *summer monsoon*, which is accompanied by heavy rainfall in southeastern Asia.

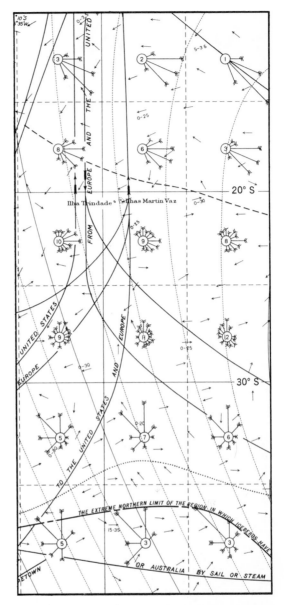

Figure 8.19 The subtropical belt of variable winds and calms (horse latitudes) lies in the center of this portion of a Hydrographic Office pilot chart of the South Atlantic for June–July–August. To the north are the steady southeast trades; to the south, the variable northwesterlies. The area shown here extends from 10° to 40° S lat. Wind roses occupy 5° squares. (U.S. Navy Hydrographic Office, Chart 2600.)

In winter, Asia is dominated by a strong center of high pressure, from which there is an outward flow of air reversing that of the summer monsoon. (See Figure 8.5.) Blowing southward and southeastward toward the equatorial oceans, this *winter monsoon* brings dry, clear weather for a period of several months.

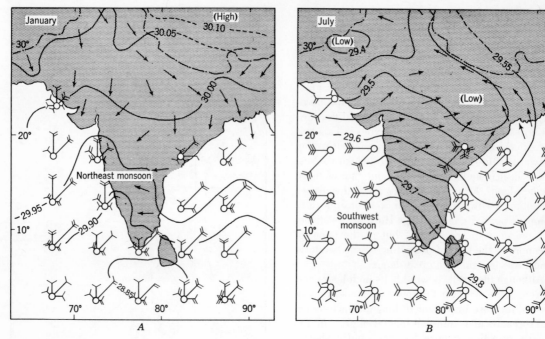

Figure 8.20 Reversal of direction of prevailing winds characterizes the yearly monsoon cycle over India. Wind arrows on land show the average direction, and wind roses over the Arabian Sea and Bay of Bengal show both duration and intensity of the winds. (Data from U.S. Navy Hydrographic Office and Blanford.)

North America, being smaller in extent, does not have the remarkable extremes of monsoon winds experienced by southeastern Asia, but there is nevertheless an alternation of temperature and pressure conditions between winter and summer. Analysis of wind records shows that in summer there is a prevailing tendency for air originating in the Gulf of Mexico to move northward across the central and eastern part of the United States, whereas in winter there is a prevailing tendency for air to move southward from sources in Canada (Figures 8.5 and 8.6). Australia, too, shows a monsoon effect, but being south of the equator it reverses the conditions of Asia.

Global circulation systems

The surface wind systems thus far described represent only a shallow basal air layer a few thousands of feet thick, whereas the troposphere is from five to twelve miles thick. What is the nature of air flow at these higher levels? Since World War II, a vast network of observing stations has been taking upper-air observations extending up to 80,000 feet or higher by means of the *radiosonde*, a compact set of weather instruments that automatically sends back information on pressure, temperature, and humidity by code from a self-contained radio transmitter. Carried aloft by a gas-filled balloon, the radiosonde transmitter can be tracked by means of

a radio direction finder. From observations taken simultaneously at many places, a weather map of upper air conditions can be drawn. It has been found that there are slowly moving high- and low-pressure systems aloft, but that these are generally simple in pattern with smoothly curved isobars. Winds,

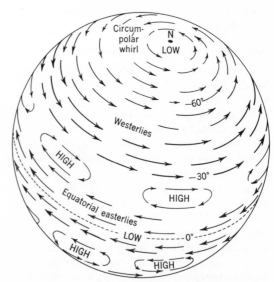

Figure 8.21 Schematic representation of circulation in the upper part of the troposphere (20,000 to 40,000 feet elevation).

which may be extremely strong and follow the isobars closely, move counterclockwise around the lows (northern hemisphere), but clockwise around the highs, as shown in Figure 8.11.

The general or average pattern of upper air flow is sketched in Figure 8.21. Two systems dominate. One is the system of *westerlies* blowing in a complete circuit about the earth from about latitude 20° almost to the poles. At high latitudes these westerlies constitute a *circumpolar whirl*, coinciding with a great polar low pressure center. Toward low latitudes the pressure rises steadily at a given altitude, to form two high-pressure ridges at latitudes 15° to 20° N and S. These are the high-altitude parts of the subtropical highs, but are shifted somewhat equatorward. In the high pressure zones, wind velocities are low, just as in the horse latitudes at sea level. Between the high-pressure ridges is a trough of weak low pressure, in which the winds are easterly, comprising the second major circulation system of the globe, termed the *equatorial easterlies*. At lower elevation their influence spreads into somewhat higher latitudes as the trade winds.

The jet stream

The upper-air westerlies tend to form somewhat serpentine or meandering paths, giving rise to slowly moving *upper air waves*, in which the winds are turned first equatorward, then poleward (Figure 8.22). Associated with the development of such upper air waves at altitudes of 30,000 to 40,000 feet are narrow zones in which wind streams attain velocities up to 200 to 250 miles per hour. This phenomenon, named the *jet stream*, consists of pulselike movements of air following a broadly curving track (Figure 8.22). In cross section the jet may be likened to a stream of water moving through a hose, the center line of highest velocity being surrounded by concentric zones of less rapidly moving fluid, as pictured in Figure 8.23.

It is by means of the upper air waves that warm air of the tropics is carried far north at the same time that cold air of polar regions is brought equatorward. In this way horizontal mixing, or *advection*, develops on a gigantic scale and serves to provide heat exchange between regions of high and low insolation.

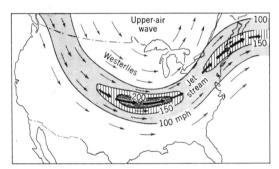

Figure 8.22 The jet stream, shown by lines of equal wind speed, is part of a great upper air wave. (After U.S. Weather Bureau.)

Figure 8.23 The jet stream has a central core of high velocity winds. (From U.S. Weather Bureau, Aviation Series No. 3.)

Review Questions

1. What is atmospheric pressure? How is it measured? Describe Torricelli's experiment, and explain the principle involved.

2. What value is given to standard sea-level pressure in inches of mercury? What is the equivalent value in millibars?

3. Explain the principle of the aneroid barometer. What advantages has this type over the mercurial barometer? Explain how the aneroid barometer can be used as an altimeter for determining elevation in aircraft.

4. At what rate does air pressure diminish with altitude? Is this rate constant? How is elevation taken into account in reducing barometric readings so that they may be compared on a weather map?

5. What range of sea-level air pressures is normally found to occur from day to day and season to season at a given place? What is considered high pressure? What is low pressure?

6. What are isobars? Explain how an isobaric map is prepared.

7. Describe the principal pressure belts of the globe, giving the latitude and approximate pressures for each.

8. Why do the pressure belts shift in latitude throughout the year? Is this shift over as great a latitude as the sun's declination?

9. Why do the land masses of North America and Asia disrupt the belted pressure pattern of the globe? What pressures occur on these land areas in the winter solstice season? in the summer solstice season?

10. What pressure centers dominate the North Atlantic and North Pacific oceans during the summer months? During the winter months? Give the names of the lows and highs.

11. What are katabatic winds? Explain how land and sea breezes are produced.

12. Explain the relation of pressure gradient to isobars and to the production of winds. What is the Coriolis force? State Ferrel's law. What is the geostrophic wind? How is it modified near the earth's surface?

13. Are high-pressure centers places of rising or subsiding air? How can the spacing of isobars on a map indicate whether the winds will be strong or weak?

14. With what instruments are winds measured? What information is needed about winds? How is the direction of a wind designated? How can wind direction and strength in the upper air levels be determined?

15. Explain how a wind rose is constructed. What symbols are used on weather maps to show surface winds? to show winds at high levels?

16. Briefly describe the Beaufort scale.

17. What conditions of winds and calms prevail in the equatorial trough? Why are steady, prevailing winds absent here?

18. Describe the trade winds. Which way do they blow in the northern hemisphere? in the southern hemisphere? Explain the direction of the trade winds. How were the trade winds used by mariners in the days of sailing vessels?

19. What are the subtropical belts of variable winds and calms? Describe the cells of high pressure of which this belt is composed. How do they shift in latitude seasonally?

20. Describe the westerly wind belts. How do the westerlies compare with the trades for constancy of direction and strength? How does the westerly wind belt influence transoceanic sailing and flying?

21. What are the polar easterlies? Why may they be better developed in the southern hemisphere than in the northern?

22. Describe the monsoon wind systems of southeastern Asia. What general type of weather condition is associated with the summer monsoon? with the winter monsoon? Why is a monsoon system not so strongly developed on other continents, such as Africa?

23. How is weather information obtained from the upper levels of the troposphere? How are winds related to isobars at high levels? How does air circulate around a center of low pressure? around a high?

24. Describe the general global circulation in the middle and upper troposphere. What are the westerlies? the equatorial easterlies? What is the circumpolar whirl? With what barometric pressure is it associated?

25. Describe the jet stream and its relation to upper air waves of the westerlies.

Exercises

1. The following air pressures are given in one of three units of measurement: inches, millimeters, millibars. Convert the given figure into the two other units.

Inches	Millimeters	Millibars
30.12	———	———
———	710	———
———	———	1006
5.61	———	———
———	———	984.5

2. Using the graph in Figure 8.4 as a direct source of information, answer the following: (*a*) What is the barometric pressure in inches of mercury on Mt. Everest? (*b*) What is the pressure in millibars at 72,000 feet, the elevation reached by Anderson and Stevens in 1935? at 100,000 feet, reached by man in a balloon in 1958? (*c*) In the region between three and five miles altitude, what is the rate of change of pressure in millibars per kilometer? (*d*) Through how many millibars of pressure does the barometer drop from 30,000 to 60,000 feet?

3. Draw wind arrows of the type used on U.S. Weather Bureau daily maps (Figure 8.14) for each of the following conditions:

	Direction	Velocity knots
(*a*)	SSW	15
(*b*)	N	35
(*c*)	ESE	10
(*d*)	290°	75
(*e*)	260°	110

4. Using the scale of wind percentages given, estimate the percentages of time during which the wind blows from each of the sectors on the wind rose on the right-hand side of Figure 8.15. Total the percentages and subtract from 100 per cent in order to determine the figure that should go in the circle representing light air and calm. (Measure the lengths of shafts from the center of the circle.)

5. Prepare a wind rose for the following data. Use the same method as in Exercise 4. (Data from Hydrographic Office, U.S. Navy.) From what belt of winds was this wind rose taken? Compare with Figures 8.17 and 8.19, and find this wind rose.

Sector	Per cent of time	Average force (Beaufort)
N	21	5
NE	12	5
E	6	5
SE	6	5
S	8	5
SW	10	5
W	12	5
NW	20	5

CHAPTER NINE

Ocean waves, currents, and ice

WINDS blowing over the sea surface generate waves and slow drifts of water. Heating and cooling of water masses affect their motions with respect to one another. Therefore, the preceding chapters on atmospheric temperature, pressure, and winds provide a basis for the study of certain phases of *physical oceanography*—the physical science of the oceans, now considered as belonging within the general field of geophysics.

Composition of sea water

Sea water may be described as a *brine,* or solution of dissolved salts, accumulated over vast periods of geologic time from the inflow of runoff from the continents. There the salts were formed by weathering processes in which weak acids react with rock-forming minerals. Evaporation of sea water, restoring water vapor to the atmosphere, leaves the salts behind to form a brine.

The composition of sea water is a matter of interest to the geographer because of the vast reservoir of mineral matter held by the sea and the possibility that certain constituents may be extracted by man for his use. One way to describe the composition of sea water is to state the principal ingre-

above: Storm waves on the high seas.
Photograph by J. B. Putnam.

dients that would be required to make an artificial brine approximately like sea water. These are listed in Table 1.

TABLE 1

Name of Salt	Chemical formula	Grams of salt per 1000 grams of water
Sodium chloride	NaCl	23
Magnesium chloride	$MgCl_2$	5
Sodium sulphate	Na_2SO_4	4
Calcium chloride	$CaCl_2$	1
Potassium chloride	KCl	0.7
With other minor ingredients, to total		34.5

Of the various elements combined in these salts, chlorine alone makes up 55 per cent by weight of all the dissolved matter, sodium 31 per cent. Important, but less abundant than elements of the five salts listed above, are bromine, carbon, strontium, boron, silicon, and fluorine. At least some trace of half of the known elements can be found in sea water. Sea water also holds in solution small amounts of all of the gases of the atmosphere, principally nitrogen, oxygen, argon, carbon dioxide, and hydrogen.

The proportion of dissolved salts to pure water is the *salinity*, usually stated in units of parts per thousand by weight, and designated by the special symbol ⁰/₀₀. The figure 34.5 ⁰/₀₀, given as the total in Table 1, represents 3.45 per cent. Salinity of sea water varies somewhat from place to place in the oceans. Where diluted by abundant rainfall, as in the equatorial oceans, the salinity may be between 34.5 and 35.0 ⁰/₀₀, whereas in the subtropical high pressure belt, where extreme dryness prevails, evaporation raises the salinity of surface water to more than 35.5 ⁰/₀₀ (Figures 9.1 and 9.2).

Density of sea water

Density of any substance is the weight (mass) of a specified unit volume of the substance. For water, density is commonly stated in *pounds per cubic foot,* the value being 62.4 for water at near-freezing temperature. For purposes of oceanography, density is given in *grams per cubic centimeter.* Water at 39° F (4° C) is at its greatest density, one cubic centimeter of water weighing almost exactly one gram. Using the value of 1.000 as the density of pure fresh water, sea water has a density ranging from 1.027 to 1.028. Two factors determine sea water density: salinity and temperature. Greater salinity gives greater density. Colder temperatures give greater density down to the freezing point, which is about 28½° F (−2° C).

Density is a matter of prime importance in circulation of ocean waters because slight density differences cause water to move. Where denser water is produced by cooling or evaporation at the surface, it will tend to sink, displacing less dense water below. Such vertical currents may be described as convectional and are similar in cause to the convection system of air described in Chapter 8.

Ocean currents

The direction of motion of surface ocean currents is stated in terms of compass direction toward which the water is moving. Much information on the direction and velocity of currents has been gained from *drift bottles,* sealed bottles containing return-addressed cards, set adrift in the hope that the bottle will be found at a distant point and the card returned. To measure currents, anchored vessels may put down *current meters* which tell the direction and speed of water flow. These devices look much like the current meter used in stream gaging (Figure 23.8). Much of our knowledge of currents has been built up from navigational observations. The direction and speed of a current can be computed when a ship's actual position is determined astronomically after a day's run. The true position is compared with the supposed position reckoned from the known rate and direction of course held

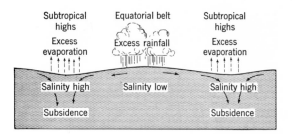

Figure 9.1 Excessive salinity under the subtropical high-pressure centers and excessive accumulation at the equatorial trough tend to produce surface movement of the water.

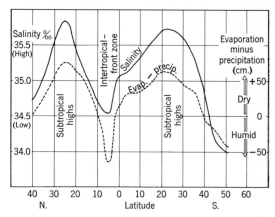

Figure 9.2 Salinity of the ocean water corresponds closely with the ratio of evaporation to rainfall and varies systematically with latitude. (After Sverdrup, *Oceanography for Meteorologists.*)

through the preceding day. The difference in the two positions gives a measure of oblique drifting as a result of traveling at an angle to the current direction (Figure 9.3).

Virtually all of the important surface currents of the oceans are set in motion by prevailing surface winds. Energy is transferred from wind to water by the frictional drag of the air blowing over the water surface. Because of the Coriolis force, the water

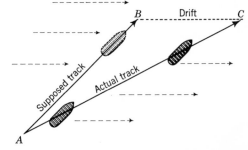

Figure 9.3 The amount and direction of ocean surface drift can be calculated if a ship's speed and compass heading *AB* are known and the ship's position at *A* and *C* is determined by astronomical methods.

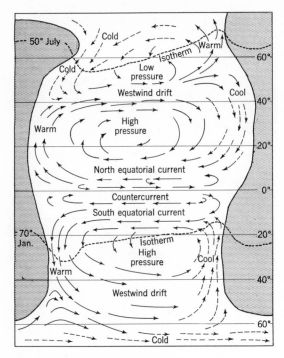

Figure 9.4 This schematic map of an ocean shows the general system of ocean currents and their influence on isotherms.

down-sinking motions besides. In this introductory study, emphasis is on the currents of a shallow surface water zone, insasmuch as these motions directly affect marine navigation and have a strong climatic influence upon the overlying layer of atmosphere.

Generalized scheme of ocean currents

To illustrate surface water circulation an idealized ocean extending across the equator to latitudes of 60° or 70° on either side may be taken for illustration (Figure 9.4). Perhaps the most outstanding features are the circular movements, or *gyrals*, around the subtropical highs, centered about 25° to 30° N and S. An *equatorial current* marks the belt of the trades. Whereas the trades blow to the southwest and northwest, obliquely across the parallels of latitude, the water movement follows the parallels. Thus, ocean currents trend at an angle of about 45° with the prevailing surface winds, because of the deflective force of the earth's rotation.

A slow eastward movement of water over the zone of the westerly winds is named the *west-wind drift*. It covers a broad belt between 35° and 45° in the northern hemisphere, and between 30° or 35° and 70° in the southern where open ocean exists in the higher latitudes.

The equatorial currents are separated by an *equatorial countercurrent*. This is well developed in the Pacific, Atlantic, and Indian oceans (Figure 9.5).

Along the west sides of the oceans in low latitudes the equatorial current turns poleward, forming a warm current paralleling the coast. Examples are the *Gulf Stream* (*Florida* or *Caribbean* stream), the *Japan current* (*Kuroshio*) and the *Brazil current*, which bring higher than average temperatures along these coasts. This is indicated in the idealized diagram (Figure 9.4) by the southward bulge of the 70° January isotherm along the west side of the southern ocean.

The west-wind drift, upon approaching the east side of the ocean, is deflected both south and north along the coast. The equatorward flow is a cool current, produced by upwelling of colder water from greater depths. It is well illustrated by the *Humboldt current* (Peru current) off the coast of Chile and Peru; by the *Benguela current* off the southwest African coast; by the *California current* off the west coast of the United States; and by the *Canaries current*, off the Spanish and North African coast. Note that this cold upwelling causes a marked equatorward deflection of the isotherms, illustrated in Figure 9.4 by the northward bend in the 70° January isotherm along the east side of the southern ocean.

In the northern eastern Atlantic Ocean, the west-

drift is impelled toward the right of its path of motion (northern hemisphere), and therefore the current at the water surface is in a direction about 45° to the right of the wind direction. Under the influence of winds, currents may tend to bank up the water close to the coast of a continent, in which case the force of gravity, tending to equalize the water level, will cause other currents to be set up.

Density differences may also cause flow of ocean water. Such differences arise from greater heating by insolation, or greater cooling by radiation, in one place than another. Thus, surface water chilled in the arctic and polar seas will sink to the ocean floor, spreading equatorward and displacing upward the less dense, warmer water. Density differences can also be set up by salinity differences, as shown in Figure 9.1. A current tends to flow from the area of low salinity to that of high salinity, but is deflected by the Coriolis force through a right angle, so that flow is actually parallel with the slope of the density gradient between the two places.

Still another controlling influence upon water movements is the configuration of the ocean basins and coasts. Currents initially caused by winds impinge upon a coast and are locally deflected to a different path or confined in straits or gulfs.

The combined action of wind and density differences sets up an oceanic circulation system including not only horizontal motions, but upwelling and

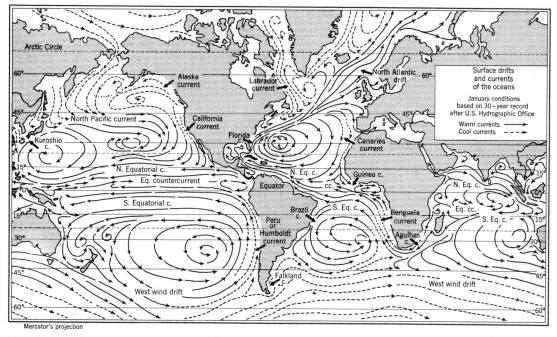

Figure 9.5 Surface drifts and currents of the oceans (January). (After U.S. Navy Hydrographic Office.)

wind drift is deflected poleward as a relatively warm current. This is the *North Atlantic current*, which spreads around the British Isles, into the North Sea, and along the Norwegian coast. The ice-free port of Murmansk, on the Arctic Circle, has year-round navigability by way of this coast. Note that in the idealized diagram the 50° July isotherm is deflected northward where it crosses this current. In winter this effect is much more pronounced.

In the northern hemisphere, where the polar sea is largely landlocked, cold water flows equatorward along the west side of the large straits connecting the Arctic Ocean with the Atlantic basin. Three principal cold currents are the *Kamchatka current,* flowing southward along the Kamchatka Peninsula and Kurile Islands; the *Greenland current,* flowing south along the east Greenland coast through the Denmark Strait; and the *Labrador current,* moving south from the Baffin Bay area, through Davis Strait to reach the coasts of Newfoundland, Nova Scotia, and New England.

In both the north Atlantic and Pacific oceans the Icelandic and Aleutian lows in a very rough way coincide with two centers of counterclockwise circulation involving the cold arctic currents and the west-wind drifts.

The antarctic region has a relatively simple current scheme consisting of a single *antarctic circumpolar current* moving clockwise around the antarctic continent in latitudes 50° to 65° S, where a continuous expanse of open ocean occurs.

Oceanographers today recognize that oceanic circulation involves the complex motions of water masses of different temperature and salinity characteristics. The very simple outline of surface currents given here does not take into account the movements of these water masses at different depths.

Ocean waves

Almost all ocean waves that can be seen and felt are produced by wind, a rare exception being the waves accompanying earthquake shocks. Energy of moving air is transferred to water wave motion, and this in turn is expended upon the coasts of the lands, causing the landforms of erosion and deposition described in Chapter 27. Our concern here is with waves in deep water, their growth and decay.

Wind-generated ocean waves belong to a type known as *progressive oscillatory waves,* inasmuch as the wave form travels through the water and causes an oscillatory water motion. A simple terminology applied to waves is illustrated in Figure 9.6. *Wave height* is the vertical distance between *trough* and *crest,* usually stated in feet or meters. *Wave length* is the horizontal distance from trough to

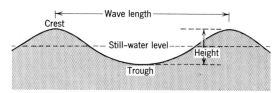

Figure 9.6 Terminology of water waves.

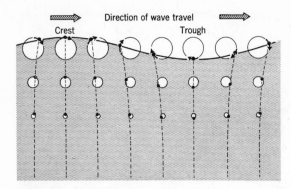

Crest   Trough

Figure 9.7 Orbital motion in deep-water waves of low height.

trough, or crest to crest, also stated in feet or meters. The speed at which the wave advances through the water is the *wave velocity*, given in feet per second or knots (nautical miles per hour). The time elapsed between successive passages of wave crests past a fixed point is the *period*, given in seconds.

In the progressive oscillatory wave a tiny particle, such as a drop of water or a small floating object, completes one vertical circle, or *orbit*, with the passage of each wave length (Figure 9.7). Particles

Figure 9.8 This vertical air view of the sea surface shows the complex pattern produced by intersecting sets of waves. Nevertheless, the generally parallel trend of wave crests is conspicuous. Waves are traveling from top to bottom of the view, but are turned landward by refraction toward the shallow coral reef at the lower right. (Photograph by Luchtvaart-Afdeeling, Bandoeng, Java.)

move forward on the wave crest, backward in the wave trough. At the sea surface the orbit is of the same diameter as the wave height, but dies out rapidly with depth. In long, low waves, the water particles return to the same starting point at the completion of each orbit, hence there is no net motion in the direction of the wind. Only the energy of the wave and its form are transmitted through the water. In steep, high waves, however, the orbits are not perfect circles. The particle moves just a bit faster forward when on the crest than when it returns in the trough, so that at the end of each circuit the particle has made a slight advance. This has the effect of producing a very slow surface drift in the direction in which the waves are traveling, at a rate known as the *mass-transport velocity*. Under favorable conditions, the flow may reach a velocity as high as two knots and will tend to raise the water level along a coast against which the waves are breaking. This motion is not the same as the drift set up by wind friction.

Far from being simple parallel crests and troughs, ocean waves appear highly irregular in height and form because of interference among several wave trains normally present. These are not only of different periods, but travel in slightly different directions, so as to intersect at many points (Figure 9.8). Where two wave crests intersect, the wave height is increased, forming a peak. Where two troughs intersect, the depression is accentuated.

Wind waves

Two forms of waves are distinguished by the oceanographer: *wind waves*, which are being actively formed or maintained by the wind; and *swell*, consisting of wind waves that have left the region where they were formed and are gradually dying out in a region of calm or lesser winds. Wind waves grow through two mechanisms. First, the direct *push* of wind upon the windward slope of the wave drives it forward, just as with any floating object or sail. Second, the *skin drag* of air flowing over the water surface exerts a pull in the direction of wave motion. Over the wave crest, where drag is strongest, the orbital movement is supplemented, adding energy to the wave. In the trough, which is protected, drag is weaker, hence does not counteract the reverse orbital movement as forcefully as it is assisted on the crests. The result is a steady increase in wave height and length to some maximum point possible under a given wind strength. Surprisingly enough, wind waves commonly reach speeds much faster than the winds that produce and sustain them, a condition that would be impossible without the mechanism of skin drag.

Three factors control the maximum height to which wind waves can grow. First, wind velocity is

Figure 9.9 Broken fragments of the ice pack characterize outer fringes of the antarctic sea-ice zone during the southern hemisphere summer. (Official U.S. Coast Guard Photo.)

obviously a major factor, since this determines the amount of energy that can be supplied. Second, duration of the wind determines whether or not the waves have an opportunity to grow to maximum size. Third, the *fetch*, or expanse of open water available, is important because the waves travel as they grow. If waves are developed in a very large body of water over a period of many hours, so that neither duration nor fetch are limiting factors, the maximum wave height varies as the square of the wind velocity. Using the formula *wave height in feet = 0.026 wind velocity in knots squared,* a table can be prepared as follows:

Wind Speed, knots	5.0	10	15	20	25	30	40	50
Wave Height, feet	0.6	2.6	5.9	10.4	16.3	23.4	42	65

This would represent the greatest waves to be expected.

Wind duration is important in the early stages of wave growth. Under strong winds, for example 30 knots, waves will continue to grow for more than 32 hours, although the most rapid growth is in the first 15 hours. Fetch may be an important limiting factor in small bays and straits, but has no appreciable effect for water expanses greater than 1000 miles across.

As waves continue to grow, they not only in-crease their speed of travel, but become longer as well. When they have passed beyond the region of strong winds that formed them, waves are trans-formed into a swell, consisting of very long, low waves of simple form and parallel, even crests. It is said that for each time that the swell has traveled a distance in nautical miles equivalent to its length in feet, the swell loses one-third of its height. The energy is lost by friction from air resistance. Swells increase greatly in both length and period as they travel; those that have traveled 3000 to 4000 miles may have periods of 15 to 20 seconds, whereas the storm waves at the point of origin may have had periods of 6 to 10 seconds.

Seismic sea waves

When sudden displacements of large earth masses occur on the ocean floor, a series of waves is sent out across the ocean. The cause may be slippage along a fault (Chapter 30), a volcanic eruption (Chapter 31), or a large submarine land-slide. The waves thus produced, called *seismic sea waves,* or *tsunami* (Japanese), resemble in many respects the waves sent out from the point where a tossed stone enters a quiet pond. The waves are enormous in length (60 to 120 miles) by compari-son with wind waves. Height of the waves upon

Figure 9.10 The U.S. Coast Guard icebreaker *Northwind* forces a passage through McClure Strait, Banks Island, Canadian Northwest Territory, in mid-August. To the left is an open lead. Cutting across from left to right is a rugged zone of pressure ridges. (Official U.S. Coast Guard photo.)

reaching shore is observed to be as great as 50 feet in many cases; well over 100 feet in rare instances. In the deep ocean, wave height is only a foot or two; and because they are vastly longer than high, such waves would pass unnoticed by observers in a ship at sea. The period of such waves may be 10 to 30 minutes and the wave form travels at speeds of perhaps 300 to 500 miles per hour. Upon reaching the shallow water of a coastline, a seismic sea wave has the effect of causing an unusual rise of water level. Not only are low areas inundated, but the wind waves that are superimposed upon the seismic wave are able to break upon much higher ground than normally. This action may result in drowning of many people and in great property destruction. Although the time and place of occurrence of the earth movement that causes the waves cannot be predicted, it is possible to learn of the event in ample time by

means of the seismograph, which records earthquake waves traveling rapidly through the solid earth. A warning system is maintained by seismologists for the Pacific Ocean, where many seismic waves are generated. The speed of travel of the waves is calculated and warnings sent to the coastal areas of probable influence.

Seismic sea waves should not be confused with two other wave forms of unusual magnitude. One is the tidal wave, which has been explained in Chapter 6. The other is a *storm surge* that may take the form of walls of turbulent water sweeping inland over low-lying coastal areas as a result of the combined action of powerful onshore winds and a high tide. The storm surge has nothing to do with submarine crustal displacements, but is commonly produced by hurricanes (Chapter 11). The seismic sea wave bears no relation to local storms and wind waves.

Figure 9.11 This great iceberg in the east Arctic Ocean dwarfs the U.S. Coast Guard icebreaker *Eastwind*. (Official U.S. Coast Guard photo.)

Figure 9.12 This tabular iceberg was observed near the Bay of Whales, Little America, Antarctica, in January 1947. (Official U.S. Coast Guard photo.)

Sea ice

Greatly increased utilization and study of high latitudes by both military forces and civilian scientist research groups has brought to attention the phenomenon of floating sea ice. Supply of arctic and antarctic outposts by ship, maintenance of observing stations on floating ice masses, and submarine operation in the polar sea are forms of activity influenced by sea ice.

The oceanographer distinguishes *sea ice*, formed by direct freezing of ocean water, from *icebergs*, and *ice islands*, which are bodies of land ice broken free from tide-level glaciers and continental ice shelves. Aside from differences in origin, a major difference between sea ice and floating masses of land ice is in thickness. Sea ice, which begins to form when the surface water is cooled to temperatures of about 28½° F (−2° C) is limited in thickness to about 15 feet, because heat is supplied from the underlying water as rapidly as it is lost upward, once an insulating layer of floating ice has been formed.

Pack ice is the name given to ice that completely covers the sea surface (Figure 9.9). Under the forces of wind and currents, pack ice breaks up into individual patches, termed *ice floes*. The narrow strips of open water between such floes are *leads*. Where ice floes are forcibly brought together by winds, the ice margins buckle and turn upward into pressure ridges resembling walls or irregular hummocks (Figure 9.10). The difficulties of travel on foot across the polar sea ice are made extreme by the presence of such obstacles. The surface zone of sea ice is composed of fresh water, the salt having been excluded in the process of freezing.

The North Polar Sea, which is surrounded by land masses, is normally covered by pack ice throughout the year, although open leads are numerous in the summer. The relatively warm North Atlantic drift maintains an ice-free zone off the northern coast of Norway. The situation is quite different in the antarctic, where a vast open ocean bounds the sea ice zone on the equatorward margin. Because the ice floes can drift freely north into warmer waters, the antarctic ice pack does not spread beyond about 60° S lat. in the cold season. In March, close to the end of the warm season, the ice margin shrinks to a narrow zone bordering the Antarctic continent.

Icebergs and ice islands

Icebergs, formed by the breaking off, or *calving*, of blocks from a valley glacier or tongue of an ice-cap, may be as thick as several hundred feet. Being only slightly less dense than sea water, the iceberg floats very low in the water, about five-sixths of its bulk lying below water level (Figure 9.11). The ice is fresh, of course, since it is formed of compacted and recrystallized snow.

In the northern hemisphere, icebergs are derived largely from glacier tongues of the Greenland icecap (Figure 26.9). They drift slowly south with the Labrador and Greenland currents and may find their way into the North Atlantic in the vicinity of the Grand Banks of Newfoundland. Icebergs of the antarctic are distinctly different. Whereas those of the North Atlantic are irregular in shape and therefore present rather peaked outlines above water, the antarctic icebergs are commonly *tabular* in form, with flat tops and steep clifflike sides (Figure 9.12). This is because tabular bergs are parts of ice shelves, the great, floating platelike extensions of the continental icecap (Chapter 26). In dimensions, a large tabular berg of the antarctic may be tens of miles broad and over 2000 feet thick, with an ice wall rising 200 to 300 feet above sea level.

Somewhat related in origin to the tabular bergs of the antarctic are *ice islands* of the North Polar Sea. These huge plates of floating ice may be 20 miles across and have an area of 300 square miles.

The bordering ice cliff, 20 to 30 feet above the surrounding pack ice, indicates an ice thickness of 200 feet or more. The few ice islands known are probably derived from a shelf of land-fast glacial ice attached to Ellesmere Island, about 83° N lat. The ice islands move slowly with the water drift of the Polar Sea and a charting of their tracks reveals much about circulation in that ocean. As permanent and sturdy platforms, ice islands serve as bases of scientific researches from which observations of oceanography, meteorology, and geophysics can be carried out over long periods.

Review Questions

1. List the major constituent salts of sea water and give approximate proportions of each. List additional elements of importance. What gases are held in solution in sea water?

2. What is salinity? How is it stated? By what amounts does salinity vary over the open oceans? Why?

3. What is density? How dense is fresh water? Compare the densities of sea water and fresh water. What two factors cause variations in the density of sea water?

4. How are the direction and velocity of ocean currents measured?

5. Discuss the causes of surface ocean currents. Show how the Coriolis force modifies the direction of flow.

6. Sketch a hypothetical ocean modeled after the Pacific or Atlantic and indicate the general scheme of surface currents. Label fully.

7. List three warm currents and three cool currents, giving the location and direction of flow of each. What effect have these currents upon isotherms of air temperatures?

8. What current systems conduct very cold water into the northern Atlantic Ocean? What current prevails in the southern ocean?

9. Describe the orbital motion in simple oscillatory waves. How deep does it extend? How may slow net forward movement of the surface water be produced? What effect upon wave form has the combination of wave trains of different periods and directions?

10. Distinguish between wind waves and swell. How are wind waves generated? What factors affect the growth of wind waves? What is the relation of wind velocity to maximum wave height? Explain fetch and its effect. How does a swell change as it travels?

11. What are seismic sea waves? How are they generated? What are their characteristic length, height, and period? How do seismic sea waves imperil coastal habitations? Distinguish between seismic waves, storm surges, and tidal waves.

12. How is sea ice different from icebergs and ice islands? What is the thickness of sea ice? Why is it limited? Describe pack ice, ice floes, leads, and pressure ridges.

13. Explain how the distribution of sea ice differs between the North Polar Sea and the Antarctic Ocean.

14. How are icebergs formed? What proportion is submerged? Compare the form and source of bergs found in the North Atlantic with those of the antarctic region.

15. What is an ice island? What is its origin? How may it serve the purposes of scientific research?

CHAPTER TEN

Moisture, clouds, and precipitation

THE physical nature and importance of water vapor in the atmosphere has already been touched upon in an earlier chapter, in which the capacity of water vapor to absorb radiant heat energy was described. We will consider here the proportions in which water vapor is held in the air and the manner in which vapor may condense to form clouds, fog, rain, and snow.

The amount of water vapor that may be present in the air at a given time varies widely from place to place. It ranges from virtually nothing in the cold, dry air of arctic regions in winter to as much as 4 or 5 per cent of the volume of the atmosphere in humid, hot tropical areas.

Water vapor enters the atmosphere by evaporation from exposed water surfaces such as oceans, lakes, rivers, or moist ground. Some is supplied by plants which transpire water as a physiological function (Chapter 21). With large expanses of ocean and densely forested lands over the globe, there is no lack of evaporation surface.

Water states and heat

Water occurs in three states, (1) frozen as ice, a crystalline *solid*, (2) *liquid* as water, and (3) *gaseous*

above: Photograph, Charles P. Cushing.

as water vapor. From the gaseous vapor state, molecules may pass into the liquid state by *condensation*, or, if temperatures are below the freezing point, can pass by *sublimation* directly into the solid state to form ice crystals. By *evaporation*, molecules can leave a water surface to become gas molecules in water vapor. The analogous change from ice directly into water vapor is also designated sublimation. Then, of course, water may pass from liquid to solid state by *freezing*, and from solid state to liquid state by *melting*. All of this can be represented by a triangle (Figure 10.1) in which the three states of water form the corners. Arrows show the six possible changes of state.

Of great importance in weather science are the exchanges of heat energy accompanying changes of state. For example, when water evaporates, *sensible heat*, which we can feel and measure by thermometer, passes into a hidden form held by the water vapor and known as the *latent heat of vaporization*. This results in a drop in temperature of the remaining liquid. The cooling effect produced by evaporation of perspiration from the skin is perhaps the most obvious example. For every gram of water that is evaporated, about 600 calories change into the latent form. In the reverse process of condensation, an equal amount of energy is released to become sensible heat and the temperature rises correspondingly. Similarly, the freezing process releases heat energy in the amount of about 80 calories per gram of water, whereas melting absorbs an equal quantity of heat. This is referred to as the *latent heat of fusion.* When sublimation occurs, the heat absorbed by vaporization, or released by crystallization, is still greater for each gram of water, for the latent heats of vaporization and fusion are added together.·

Humidity

The term *humidity* simply refers to the degree to which water vapor is present in the air. For any specified temperature there is a definite limit to the quantity of moisture that can be held by the air. This limit is known as the *saturation point.* The proportion of water vapor present relative to the maximum quantity is the *relative humidity,* expressed as a percentage. At the saturation point, relative humidity is 100 per cent; when half of the total possible quantity of vapor is present, relative humidity is 50 per cent, and so on.

A change in relative humidity of the atmosphere can be caused in one of two ways. If an exposed water surface is present, the humidity can be increased by evaporation. This is a slow process, requiring that the water vapor diffuse upward through the air. The other way is through a change of temperature. Even though no water vapor is added, a lowering of temperature results in a rise of relative humidity. This is automatic and is a logical consequence of the fact that the capacity of the air to hold water vapor has been lowered by cooling; thus the existing amount of vapor represents a higher percentage of the total capacity of the air. Similarly, a rise of air temperature results in decreased relative humidity, even though no water vapor has been taken away.

A simple example may be given to illustrate these principles. At a certain place the temperature of the air is 60° F, the relative humidity 50 per cent. Should the air become warmed by the radiant energy from the sun and ground surface to 90° F, the relative humidity automatically drops to 20 per cent, which is very dry air. Should the air become chilled during the night and its temperature fall to 40° F, the relative humidity will automatically rise to 100 per cent, the saturation point. Any further cooling will cause condensation of the excess vapor into liquid form. As the air temperature continues to fall, the humidity remains at 100 per cent, but condensation continues. This may take the form of minute droplets of dew or fog. If the temperature falls below freezing, condensation occurs as frost upon exposed surfaces.

The term *dew point* is applied to the critical

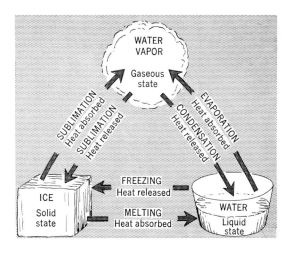

Figure 10.1 Three states of water can exist in the atmosphere. (After *C.A.A. Technical Manual 104,* U.S. Dept. Commerce.)

temperature at which the air is fully saturated, and below which condensation normally occurs. An excellent illustration of condensation due to cooling is seen in summertime when beads of moisture form on the outside surface of a pitcher or glass filled with ice water. Air immediately adjacent to the cold glass or metal surface is sufficiently chilled to fall below the dew point temperature, causing moisture to condense on the surface of the glass.

In understanding the relationships between atmospheric temperature and relative humidity, a very homely analogy may prove helpful. An ordinary sponge, if left to soak up water, will take up moisture to its full capacity. This is analogous to the manner in which air will gradually increase its humidity to the saturation point, if allowed to stand over a water surface and to maintain a constant temperature. If the sponge is now lifted out of the water and held carefully in the hand it will continue to hold the absorbed water. Suppose now the sponge is slowly squeezed. Water is expelled. In a like manner, the lowering of temperature below dew point of the saturated air expels moisture by condensation of the excess water vapor. After most of the water has been squeezed from the sponge it may be released, but not permitted to touch the water. This is analogous to a rise of air temperature back to the previous starting point, but without being permitted to take up water. This condition would prevail over an interior desert region. The air, like the sponge, is now holding only a small fraction of its total possible moisture content. If it is again cooled no condensation will result from the air until a temperature below the previous minimum is reached, just as no water will be released from the sponge until it is squeezed even harder than previously.

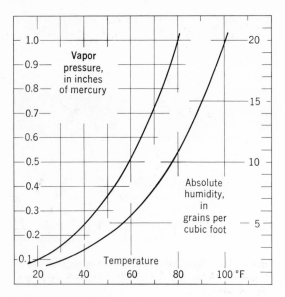

Figure 10.2 This graph shows how vapor pressure and absolute humidity both increase greatly with higher air temperatures.

Although relative humidity is an important indicator of the state of water vapor in the air, it is a statement only of the relative quantity with respect to a saturation quantity. The actual quantity of moisture present is denoted by *absolute humidity*, defined as the weight of water vapor contained in a given volume of air. Weight is stated in *grains*, one grain being about ¹⁄₁₅ of a gram, or ¹⁄₇₀₀₀ of a pound. The unit of volume is a cubic foot. Hence absolute humidity is given in grains per cubic foot, although grams per cubic meter is also used. For any specified air temperature, there is a maximum weight of water vapor that a cubic foot of air can hold (the saturation quantity). Figure 10.2 is a graph showing this maximum moisture content of air for temperatures ranging from 20° to 100° F.

In a sense, the absolute humidity is a geographer's yardstick of a basic natural resource—water—to be applied from equatorial to polar regions. It is a measure of the quantity of water than can be extracted from the atmosphere as precipitation. Cold air can supply only a small quantity of rain or snow; warm air is capable of supplying huge quantities.

Vapor pressure

In Chapter 8, it is explained that the weight of a column of atmosphere counterbalances the mercury column in a barometer and that variations in mercury height measure changes in air pressure. When water vapor is added to otherwise pure, dry air, the water molecules diffuse perfectly among the other gas molecules without displacing them.

Hence, the density of the air is increased by the presence of water vapor. This, in turn, increases the weight of the atmospheric column by a small amount. That part of the total barometric pressure that is due to the water vapor alone is termed the *vapor pressure*. For cold, dry air, the vapor pressure may be as low as 0.05 inch; for very warm, moist air of the equatorial regions, it may be as high as 0.80 inch. This latter figure says that if the mercury column stands at 30.0 inches height, ⁸⁄₁₀ of an inch of that height is counterbalanced by the weight of water vapor in the air.

Figure 10.2, shows the maximum possible vapor pressure for air of a range of temperatures from very cold to very warm. Both vapor pressure and absolute humidity tell the quantity of water vapor present, in the air, but in somewhat different ways.

Specific humidity and the mixing ratio

One disadvantage of using absolute humidity in the study of atmospheric moisture is that when air rises or sinks in elevation, it undergoes corresponding volume changes of expansion or compression. Thus the absolute humidity cannot remain a constant figure for the same body of air. Modern meteorology therefore makes use of another measure of moisture content, *specific humidity*, which is the ratio of weight of water vapor to weight of moist air (including the water vapor). This is stated in units of grams of water vapor per kilogram of moist air. When a given parcel of air is lifted to higher elevations without gain or loss of moisture the specific humidity remains constant, despite volume increase.

Specific humidity is often used to describe the moisture characteristics of a large mass of air. For example, extremely cold, dry air over arctic regions in winter may have a specific humidity of as low as 0.2 grams per kilogram, whereas extremely warm moist air of tropical regions may hold as much as 18 grams per kilogram. The total natural range on a world-wide basis is such that the largest values of specific humidity are from 100 to 200 times as great as the least.

Also of great use to meteorologists is the *mixing ratio*, which is the ratio of weight of water vapor to weight of the dry air (not including the water vapor), stated in units of grams per kilogram. Mixing ratio commonly differs very little in actual numerical value from specific humidity.

How humidity is measured

Humidity of the air can be measured in two ways. An instrument known as a *hygrometer* indicates relative humidity on a calibrated dial. One simple type uses a strand of human hair which lengthens and shortens according to the relative humidity and thereby activates the dial. A continuous record of humidity can be obtained by means of a recording *hygrograph.* Using the same basic mechanism as the hygrometer, a continuous, automatic record is drawn by a pen on a sheet of paper attached to a rotating drum.

A different principle is applied in the *sling psychrometer.* This instrument is simply a pair of thermometers mounted side by side. One is of the ordinary type; the other has a piece of wet cloth around the bulb. If the air is fully saturated (relative humidity 100 per cent), there will be no evaporation from the wet cloth and both thermometers will read the same. If, however, the air is not fully saturated, evaporation will occur, cooling the cloth-covered thermometer below the temperature shown on the ordinary thermometer. Inasmuch as the rate of evaporation depends on dryness of the air, the difference in temperature shown by the two thermometers will increase as relative humidity decreases. Standard tables are available to show the relative humidity for a given combination of wet- and dry-bulb temperatures. In order to be sure that maximum possible evaporation is taking place, the two thermometers are attached by a swivel joint to a handle by which the thermometers can be swung around in a circle by hand. Other types have a fan to blow air past the wet thermometer bulb.

Temperature-humidity index

Human comfort depends not only upon the air temperature, but also upon the relative humidity, which affects the speed of evaporation of perspiration and hence the rate of body cooling. Air at 80° F may feel quite comfortable if the relative humidity is only 20 per cent; but very uncomfortable if the relative humidity is 90 per cent or higher. Additional factors are the rate of heat loss by body radiation into the air and the wind speed. The latter can be largely disregarded for evaluating personal comfort indoors.

The U.S. Weather Bureau, after much study and research, devised the *temperature-humidity index,* or *THI,* as a measure of the degree to which summertime comfort or discomfort is experienced by Americans working indoors without rapid air circulation. The index may be computed by any one of three formulas:

$$THI = 0.4 \ (T_{dry} + T_{wet}) + 15$$
$$THI = 0.55 \ T_{dry} + 0.2 \ T_{dew} + 17.5$$
$$THI = T_{dry} - (0.55 - 0.55 \ RH) \ (T_{dry} - 58)$$

where T_{dry} is the dry-bulb air temperature, ° F

T_{wet} is the wet-bulb air temperature, ° F

T_{dew} is the dew-point temperature, ° F

and   RH is the relative humidity expressed as a decimal (thus 0.35 is used for 35 per cent)

The third formula can be used to advantage with the information contained in the usual local Weather Bureau reports given by telephone or radio. Wet-bulb and dew-point temperatures are not ordinarily stated in weather reports furnished to the public, but can be obtained with the sling psychrometer.

Interpretation of the THI has been obtained from statistical sampling of the opinions of persons working indoors in the summertime. Values of 60 to 65 are accepted by most as comfortable. When the THI reaches 75, at least half the people are uncomfortable. When it reaches 79 few, if any, will feel comfortable. An index of 80 or higher can serve as the basis for closing business offices and dismissing the employees for the day; although a good breeze or strong fans can reduce the discomfort considerably.

How condensation occurs

Actively falling rain, snow, sleet, or hail, referred to collectively as *precipitation,* can result only where large masses of air are experiencing a steady drop in temperature below the dew point. This condition cannot be brought about by the simple process of chilling of the air through loss of heat by radiation during the night. Instead, it is necessary that the large mass of air be rising to higher elevations. This statement requires that a new principle of weather science be explained.

One of the most important laws of meteorology is that rising air (or any gas) experiences a drop in temperature, even though no heat energy is lost to the outside (Figure 10.3). The drop of temperature is a result of the decrease in air pressure at higher elevations. This permits the rising air to expand. Individual molecules of the gas are more widely diffused and do not strike one another so frequently,

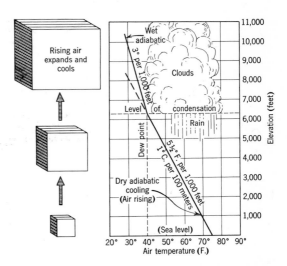

Figure 10.3 Rising air both expands and cools; descending air would contract in volume and become warmer.

hence imparting a lower sensible temperature to the gas. When no condensation is occurring, the rate of drop of temperature, termed the *dry adiabatic rate*, is about 5½° F per 1000 feet of vertical rise of air.

If water vapor in the air is condensing, the adiabatic rate is less, about 3° per 1000 feet, owing to the partial counteraction of temperature loss through the liberation of latent heat during the condensation process. This modified rate is referred to as the *wet adiabatic*, or *saturation adiabatic* rate. Adiabatic cooling rate should not be confused with the lapse rate, explained in Chapter 7. The lapse rate applies only to still air whose temperature is measured at successively higher levels.

The various ways in which large masses of air are induced to rise to higher elevations are treated more fully in a later paragraph. Because the actual fall of rain, snow, or other forms of precipitation is preceded by the formation of clouds, it is desirable first to consider the various types of clouds and their significance.

Clouds

Clouds consist of extremely tiny droplets of water, 20 to 60 microns (0.0008 to 0.0024 inches) in diameter, or minute crystals of ice. These are sustained by the slightest upward movements of air. In order for cloud droplets to form, it is necessary that microscopic dust particles serve as centers, or *nuclei*, of condensation. As noted in an earlier chapter, dusts with a high affinity for water (i.e., *hygroscopic*) are abundant throughout the atmosphere.

Where the air temperature is well below freezing, clouds may form of tiny ice crystals. Water in such minute quantities can remain liquid far below normal freezing temperatures. Thus, water droplets exist at temperatures down to 10° F; a mixture of water droplets and ice crystals from 10° to −20° F or even lower; and predominantly ice crystals below −20° F. Below −40° F all of the cloud is ice. Clouds appear white when thin or when the sun is shining upon the outer surface. When dense and thick, clouds appear gray or black underneath simply because this is the shaded side.

Cloud types may be classified on the basis of two characteristics, general form, and altitude. On the basis of form there are two major groups: *stratiform* or layered types, and *cumuliform* or massive, globular types.

The stratiform clouds are blanketlike, often covering vast areas, but are fairly thin in comparison to horizontal dimensions. Stratiform clouds are subdivided according to the level of elevation at which they lie. The highest type is the *cirrus* cloud and its related forms, *cirrostratus* and *cirrocumulus* (Figures 10.4 and 10.5). These are roughly within the altitude range of 20,000 to 40,000 feet and are composed of ice crystals. Cirrus is a delicate, wispy cloud, often forming streaks or stringers across the sky. It does not interfere with the passage of sunlight or moonlight and appears to the ground observer to be moving very slowly, if at all. Cirrostratus is a more complete layer of cloud, producing a halo about the sun or moon. Where the layer consists of closely packed globular pieces of cloud, ar-

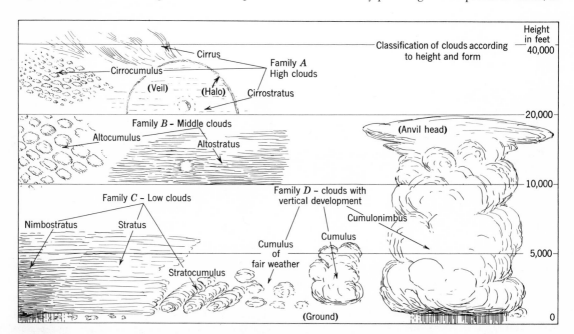

Figure 10.4 Cloud types are grouped into families according to height range and form.

ranged in groups or lines, the name cirrocumulus is given. This is the *mackerel sky* of popular description.

At intermediate height range, from 6500 to 20,000 feet, are the *altostratus* and *altocumulus* clouds. Altostratus is a blanket layer, often smoothly distributed over the entire sky. It is grayish in appearance, usually has a smooth underside, and will often show the sun as a bright spot in the cloud. Altocumulus is a layer of individual cloud masses, fitted closely together in geometric pattern. The masses appear white, or somewhat gray on the shaded sides, and blue sky is seen between individual patches or rows. Altostratus is commonly associated with the development of bad weather, whereas altocumulus is usually characteristic of generally fair conditions.

In the low cloud group, from ground level to 6500 feet, are *stratus, nimbostratus,* and *stratocumulus* clouds. Stratus is a dense, low-lying dark-gray layer (Figure 10.5e). If rain or snow is falling from this cloud, it is termed nimbostratus, the prefix *nimbo* merely meaning that precipitation is coming from the cloud. Stratocumulus is a low-lying cloud layer consisting of distinct grayish masses of cloud between which is open sky. The individual masses often take on the form of long rolls of cloud, oriented at right angles to the direction of wind and cloud motion. Stratocumulus is generally associated with fair or clearing weather, but sometimes rain or snow flurries issue from individual cloud masses.

Fog is simply a form of stratus cloud lying very close to the ground. One type, known as a *radiation fog*, commonly accompanies temperature inversion and is formed at night when temperature of the basal air falls below the dew point. Another type, *advection fog*, results from the movement of warm, moist air over a cold or snow-covered ground surface. Losing heat to the ground, the air layer undergoes a drop of temperature below the dew point, and condensation sets in. A similar type of advection fog is formed over oceans where air from over a warm current blows across the cold surface of an adjacent cold current. Fogs of the Grand Banks off Newfoundland are largely of this origin because here the cold Labrador current comes in contact with warm waters of Gulf Stream origin.

The cumuliform clouds tend to display a height as great as, or greater than, their horizontal dimensions. *Cumulus* is a white, woolpack cloud mass, often showing a flat base and a bumpy upper surface somewhat resembling a head of cauliflower (Figure 10.5g). These clouds look pure white on the side illuminated by the sun, but may be gray or black on the shaded or underneath side. Small cumulus clouds are associated with fair weather. Under different conditions, discussed below, individual masses grow into *cumulonimbus,* the thunderstorm cloud mass of enormous size which brings heavy rainfall, thunder and lightning, and gusty winds (Figure 10.5h). A large cumulonimbus cloud may extend from a height of 1000 to 2000 feet at the base up to 30,000 or 40,000 feet. When seen from a great distance, the top of the cumulonimbus cloud is pure white, but to observers beneath, the sky may be darkened to almost nighttime blackness. More will be said of this cloud in connection with thunderstorms.

Forms of precipitation

Precipitation results when condensation is occurring rapidly within a cloud. *Rain* is formed when cloud droplets in large numbers are caused to coalesce into drops too large to remain suspended in the air. The drops may then grow by colliding with other drops and joining with them to become as large as one-fourth inch (7 mm) in diameter; but above this size they are unstable and break into smaller drops. Falling droplets less than one-fiftieth inch in diameter make a *drizzle*.

Sleet, as the term is used in the United States, consists of pellets of ice produced from freezing of rain. The raindrops form in an upper, warmer layer, but fall into an underlying cold air layer. (In the rest of the English-speaking world sleet means a mixture of rain and snow.)

Snow consists of masses of crystals of ice, grown directly from the water vapor of the air, where air temperature is below freezing. Individual snow crystals, which can be carefully caught upon a black surface and examined with a strong magnifying glass, develop in six-sided, flat crystals, or as prisms. They display infinite variations in their beautiful symmetrical patterns (Figure 10.6).

Hail consists of rounded lumps of ice, having an internal structure of concentric layers, much like an onion. Ordinarily the ice is not clear but has a frosted appearance. Hailstones range from a fraction of an inch up to four or five inches in diameter and may be extremely destructive to crops and light buildings (Figure 10.7). Hail occurs only from the cumulonimbus cloud type, inside of which are extremely strong updrafts of air. Raindrops are carried up to high altitudes, are frozen into ice pellets, then fall again through the cloud. Suspended in powerful updrafts, the hail stone grows by the attachment and freezing of droplets, much as ice accumulates on the leading edge of an airplane wing. Eventually the hailstone escapes from the updrafts and falls to earth.

When rain falls upon a ground surface that is covered by an air layer of below-freezing tempera-

A. Cirrus in parallel trails and small patches. (Photograph by F. Ellerman. Courtesy of U.S. Weather Bureau.)

B. Cirrocumulus (*above*) with tufted cirrus (*below*). (Photograph by F. Ellerman. Courtesy of U.S. Weather Bureau.)

C. Thin altostratus with fractostratus patches below. (Photograph by G. A. Clarke. Courtesy of U.S. Weather Bureau.)

D. Altocumulus; active form. (Photograph by C. F. Brooks. Courtesy of U.S. Weather Bureau.)

Figure 10.5 Cloud types.

E. Stratus, a uniform layer extending below the level of the hilltop, with shreds of fractostratus visible against the hillside. (Photograph by G. A. Clarke. Courtesy of U.S. Weather Bureau.)

F. Stratocumulus in irregular horizontal rolls. (Photograph by W. J. Humphreys. Courtesy of U.S. Weather Bureau.)

G. Cumulus of fair weather. (Photograph by H. T. Floreen. Courtesy of U.S. Weather Bureau.)

H. Cumulonimbus, an isolated thunderstorm showing rain falling from base. (Photograph by Air Service, U.S. Navy. Courtesy of U.S. Weather Bureau.)

Figure 10.5 continued

ture, the water freezes into clear ice after striking the ground or other surfaces such as trees, houses, or wires (Figure 10.8). The coating of ice that results is called a *glaze,* and an *icing storm* is said to have occurred. Actually no ice falls, so that ice glaze is not a form of precipitation. Icing storms cause great damage, especially to telephone, telegraph, and power wires and to tree limbs. Roads and sidewalks are made extremely hazardous.

How precipitation is measured

Precipitation is generally stated in units of inches or millimeters that fall per unit of time. One inch of rainfall, for example, is a quantity sufficient to cover the ground to a depth of one inch, provided that none is lost by runoff, evaporation, or sinking into the ground. A simple form of *rain gage* can be operated merely by setting out a straight-sided, flat-bottomed pan and measuring the depth to which water accumulates during a particular period. Unless this period is short, however, evaporation seriously upsets the results. Furthermore, very small amounts of rainfall, such as 0.1 inch, would make

too thin a layer to be accurately measured. To avoid this difficulty, as well as to reduce evaporation loss, good rain gages are made in the form of a cylinder whose base is a funnel leading into a narrow pipe (Figure 10.9). A small amount of rainfall will fill the narrow pipe to a considerable height, thus making it easy to read accurately, once a simple scale has been provided for the pipe. This gage requires frequent emptying unless it is equipped with automatic devices for this purpose.

Snowfall is measured by melting a sample column of snow and reducing it to an equivalent in water. Thus, rainfall and snowfall records may be combined for purposes of comparison. Ordinarily, a ten-inch layer of snow is equivalent to one inch of rainfall, but this ratio may range from 30 to 1 in very loose snow to 2 to 1 in old, partly melted snow.

Precipitation-producing conditions

Thus far it has been made clear that precipitation results when air rises and is adiabatically cooled below the dew point so rapidly that not only do clouds form, but rain, snow, or hail is produced as well.

Figure 10.6 Snowflakes are made up of aggregates of tiny hexagonal ice crystals such as these. (Photographs by Ewing Galloway.)

Consider, then, how large masses of air are actually induced to rise to higher elevations. The three possible ways are (1) *convectional,* (2) *orographic,* and (3) *cyclonic* or *frontal.*

Convectional precipitation results from a *convection cell,* which is simply an updraft of warmer air, seeking higher altitude because it is lighter than surrounding air (Figure 10.10). The cell is completed by a downdraft of cooler, denser air. Suppose that on a clear, warm summer morning the sun is shining upon a landscape consisting of patches of open fields and woodlands. Certain of these types

Figure 10.7 These hailstones, larger than hen's eggs (arrow), fell at Girard, Illinois, on Aug. 13, 1929. (Courtesy of U.S. Weather Bureau.)

of surfaces, such as the bare ground, heat more rapidly and transmit radiant heat to the overlying air. Air over a warmer patch is thus warmed more than adjacent air and begins to rise in a tall column, much as hot air and smoke rise in a chimney. Vertical currents of this type are often called *thermals* by sailplane pilots who use them to obtain lift.

As the air rises, it is cooled adiabatically so that eventually it will reach the same temperature as the surrounding air and come to rest. Before this happens, however, it may be cooled below the dew point. At once condensation begins, and the rising air column appears as a cumulus cloud whose flat base shows the critical level above which condensation is occurring (Figure 10.10). The bulging "cauliflower" top of the cloud represents the top of the rising warm air column, pushing into higher levels of the atmosphere. Should this convection column continue to develop, the cloud may grow to a cumulonimbus mass, or thunderstorm, from which heavy rain will issue.

The picture outlined above contains a serious defect. Any alert person will wonder why convection continues vigorously after the cloud has grown so large as to shade the ground, or after the cloud has drifted downwind away from the originally heated spot on the ground. Actually, the unequal heating of the ground served only as a trigger effect to release a spontaneous updraft, fed by latent heat energy liberated from the condensing water vapor. Figures 10.11 and 10.12 will help in explaining this principle.

The graph of Figure 10.11 is a plot of altitude against air temperature. The small circles represent a small parcel of air being forced to rise steadily higher, following the same dry adiabatic rate of cooling shown in Figure 10.3. To the right of this line is a solid line showing the temperature of the undisturbed surrounding air; it is the normal lapse rate, such as is shown in Figure 7.17. Suppose that the air parcel is lifted from a point near the ground, where its temperature is 90°. After the air parcel has been carried up 2000 feet, its temperature has fallen about 11° (two times the dry adiabatic lapse rate of 5.5° per 1000 feet) and is now 79°; whereas the surrounding air is cooler by only about 7° (two times the lapse rate of 3½° per 1000 feet), and has a temperature of 83°. The air parcel would thus be cooler than the surrounding air at 2000 feet, and if no longer forcibly carried upward, would tend to sink back to the ground. These conditions represent *stable* air, not likely to produce convection cells, because the air would resist lifting.

When the air layer near the ground is excessively heated by the sun, the lapse rate curve is sharply bent to the right in the altitude-temperature graph (Figure 10.12). The air parcel near the ground begins to rise spontaneously because it is lighter than air over adjacent, less intensely heated ground areas. Although cooled adiabatically while rising, the air parcel at 1000 feet has a temperature of 85°, but this is well above the 80° of the surrounding still air. The air parcel, therefore, is lighter than the surrounding air and continues its rise. At 2000 feet, the dew point is reached and condensation sets in. Now the rising air parcel is cooled at the reduced wet adiabatic rate of 2° to 3° per 1000 feet, because the latent heat liberated in condensation offsets the rate of drop due to expansion. At 3000 feet, the rising air parcel is still several degrees warmer than the surrounding air, and therefore continues its spontaneous rise. The air described here as spontaneously rising during condensation is *unstable* in properties. In such air the updraft tends to increase in intensity as time goes on, much as a bonfire blazes with increasing ferocity as the updraft draws in greater supplies of oxygen. Of course, at very high altitudes, the bulk of the water vapor having condensed and fallen as precipitation, the energy source is gone; the convection cell then weakens and air rise finally ceases.

Figure 10.8 Heavily coated wires and branches caused heavy damage in eastern New York State in January 1943, as a result of this icing storm. (Courtesy of U.S. Weather Bureau, and New York Power and Light Co., Albany, N.Y.)

Figure 10.9 This tipping-bucket rain gage is standard weather-station equipment for measuring rainfall. (Courtesy of U.S. Weather Bureau.)

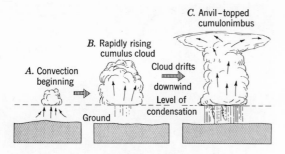

Figure 10.10 Convectional, thunderstorm rainfall may be set off by solar heating and develops rapidly in unstable, moist air masses.

Unstable air, given to spontaneous convection in the form of heavy showers and thunderstorms, is most likely to be found in warm, humid areas such as the equatorial and tropical oceans and their bordering lands throughout the year, and the middle-latitude regions during the summer season.

The second precipitation-producing mechanism is described as *orographic*, which means "related to mountains." Prevailing winds or other moving masses of air may be forced to flow over mountain ranges (Figure 10.13). As the air rises on the windward side of the range, it is cooled at the adiabatic rate. If cooling is sufficient, precipitation will result. After passing over the mountain summit, the air will begin to descend the lee side of the range. Now it will undergo a warming through the same adiabatic process and, having no source from which to

draw up moisture, will become very dry. A belt of dry climate, often called a *rainshadow*, may exist on the lee side of the range. Several of the important dry deserts of the earth are of this type.

Dry, warm *foehn* winds (Europe) and *chinook* winds (northwestern United States), which occur on the lee side of a mountain range, may cause extremely rapid evaporation of snow or soil moisture. These winds result from turbulent mixing of lower and upper air in the lee of the range. The upper air, which has little moisture to begin with, is greatly dried and heated when swept down to low levels.

An excellent illustration of orographic precipitation and rainshadow occurs in the far west of the United States. Prevailing westerly winds bring moist air from the Pacific Ocean over the coast ranges of central and northern California and the great Sierra Nevada Range, whose summits rise 12,000 to 14,000 feet above sea level. (See Figure 15.12.) Heavy rainfall is experienced on the windward slopes of these ranges, nourishing great sequoia groves of the western Sierra Nevada. Passing down the steep eastern face of the Sierras, air must descend nearly to sea level, even below sea level in Death Valley. The adiabatic heating thus caused, and a consequent drop in humidity, produces part of America's great desert zone, covering a strip of eastern California and all of Nevada.

Much orographic rainfall is actually of the convectional type, in that it takes the form of heavy

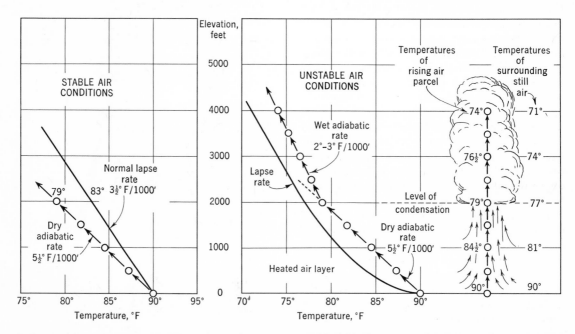

Figure 10.11 (*left*) Under conditions of stability, air forced to rise would cool more rapidly than the surrounding air.

Figure 10.12 (*right*) Unstable air, as it rises, remains warmer than the surrounding air.

convectional showers and storms. The storms are induced, however, by the forced ascent of unstable air as it passes over the mountain barrier.

A third type of precipitation is *cyclonic*. This topic cannot be properly understood until the entire subject of cyclonic storms and fronts has been developed. It will suffice here to note that in middle and high latitudes, much of the precipitation occurs in cyclonic storms, or eastward-moving centers of low pressure into which air is converging and being forced to rise.

Thunderstorms

A *thunderstorm* is an intense local storm associated with a large, dense cumulonimbus cloud in which there are very strong updrafts of air (Figure 10.5*H*). Thunder and lightning normally accompany the storm, and rainfall is heavy, often of cloudburst intensity, for a short period. Violent surface winds may occur at the onset of the storm. A thunderstorm is not a cyclonic type of storm described in Chapter 11 because there is no inspiraling wind system. Instead, it may be described as a convective storm because it is essentially a powerful updraft of air seeking a higher elevation. The cause of precipitation and spontaneous rise of air has been explained in the discussion of unstable air and convectional precipitation.

Thunderstorm development has been studied by coordinated use of aircraft, ground weather stations, radiosonde stations, and long-range radar. Most thunderstorms consist of several cells, each cell being an updraft, usually with an associated downdraft. Individual cells pass through a life cycle as shown in Figure 10.14, and a storm may contain cells in various stages of development. First of three stages is the *cumulus stage*, in which the cell is a simple updraft with a steadily rising cloud top. The

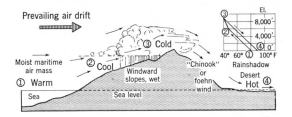

Figure 10.13 Forced ascent of ocean air masses gives heavy rainfall on the windward sides of mountain ranges but rainshadow deserts on the lee sides.

updraft tends to draw in air from the sides as it rises. In the *mature stage*, falling rain has created a downdraft by frictional drag on the air. Reaching the ground and spreading out, this air is cool. Upon first arriving at the ground, the downdraft produces strong gusts which are normally felt before or during the start of the rain.

The *dissipating stage* of the thunderstorm cell is reached after the downdraft has spread across the lower levels of the cell and updraft has ceased. The upper part of the cloud has now taken on a mushroom or anvil form and continues to spread out, forming an altostratus or cirrostratus layer. In a large, complex thunderstorm new cells are forming while others are dissipating, thus maintaining the storm in a condition of constant activity as it drifts along with the regional air movement.

The principal updraft, or chimney, of a thunderstorm cell may have amazingly rapid flow of air. The fact that three-inch hailstones require updrafts of 110 to 120 miles per hour in order to be kept aloft while forming indicates something of the intensity. Updrafts of 6000 feet per minute (68 miles per hour) are not unusual in the mature stage of the storm. In general, warm air is required for

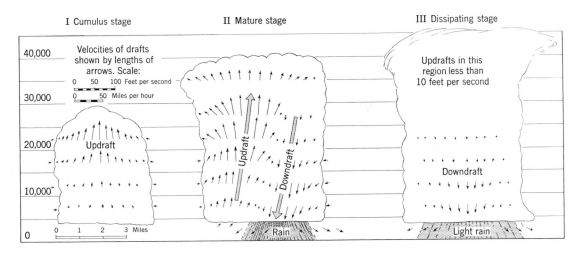

Figure 10.14 Stages in the development of thunderstorm cell. (After Horace R. Byers, 1949.)

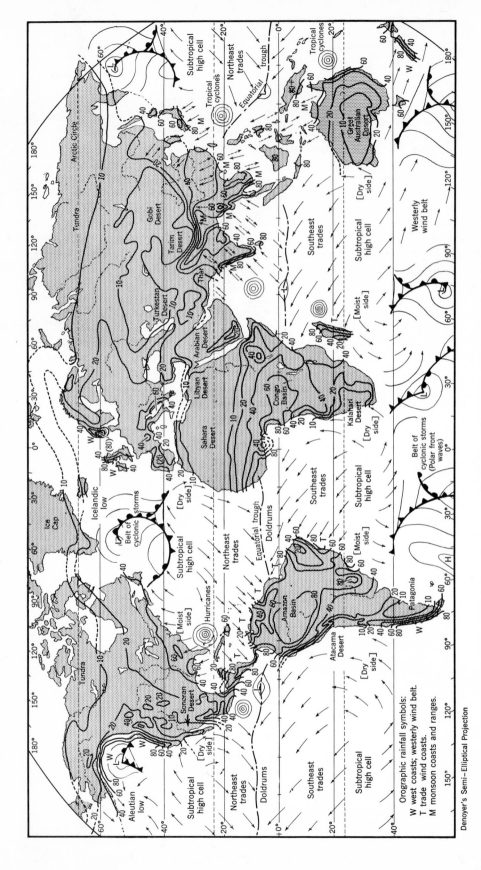

Denoyer's Semi–Elliptical Projection

Figure 10.15 World rainfall map. Rainfall in inches. (Data source: Rainfall from Trewartha, *Introduction to Weather and Climate*.)

thunderstorms because only warm air can hold large quantities of water vapor. Thus thunderstorms are commonest at low latitudes and are virtually absent in polar regions. In middle latitudes thunderstorms are commonest during the summer. (See Figure 14.2.)

Thunderstorms may be classified into several types, based on the mechanism or cause of initial lift of the air column that sets off the spontaneous growth of the storm. One common type is the *thermal*, or *air mass thunderstorm*, which is set off by thermal convection caused by solar heating of the ground and lower air layer. Figure 10.12 illustrates the process. Storms of this type are often widely scattered over a large region covered by warm, moist air. The time of occurrence is typically in the late afternoon because air temperatures near the ground reach their highest levels at this time.

Another type of thunderstorm results from nocturnal cooling of the top layers of clouds by radiation of heat into the upper atmosphere and out into space. The cooled air becomes relatively heavy and sinks rapidly, displacing warmer air at low levels and forcing it to rise. This forced rise sets off thunderstorms in unstable air. Obviously, storms of this origin occur during the hours of darkness.

In the *orographic thunderstorm*, air is forced to rise over a mountain barrier, as shown in Figure 10.13. If the air is warm and moist, with unstable properties, it readily breaks into heavy showers and thunderstorms. The torrential monsoon rains of the Asiatic and East Indian mountain ranges are largely of this type. For example, Cherrapunji, a hill station facing the summer monsoon air drift in northeast India, averages 426 inches of rainfall annually. In the arid southwestern United States, isolated mountain ranges and high plateaus receive abundant summer rain in the form of thunderstorms orographically induced. Here rich forests grow while the surrounding lower areas are barren or sparsely vegetated deserts.

Still other types of thunderstorms are set off by the forced rise of a layer of warm air over a layer of cold air. Such storms, which may be described as *frontal thunderstorms*, are explained in the following chapter.

World distribution of rainfall

Average annual rainfall for the earth is shown in Figure 10.15. Lines termed *isohyets* have been drawn through places having the same annual average rainfall. This map shows how the principles of precipitation are applied to world regions.

Rainfall is very heavy, more than 80 inches, in the equatorial zone, where high temperatures and great oceanic expanses provide large amounts of water vapor and generally unstable atmospheric conditions. Virtually all this rainfall is convectional in origin, although the presence of mountainous belts serves locally to add the orographic effect. Rainfall is very light over the subtropical high-pressure belts, or centers, owing to the general pattern of subsiding air warmed adiabatically and thus made extremely dry. The deserts of North Africa, Arabia, and Iran lie along this zone as well as those of Australia, South Africa, and the west coast of South America. This zone of aridity is extended equatorward into the trade wind belt.

The trade winds should not be thought of as necessarily dry winds. Wherever they blow from the ocean across a coastal belt which is hilly or mountainous, fairly heavy orographic precipitation is caused. One good illustration is Central America; another is Madagascar. In both places the eastern, or windward, coasts receive rainfall of more than 80 inches annually.

On the east side of the oceanic subtropical highs are dry coastal belts, such as the Peruvian coast of South America and the Kalahari Desert of southwest Africa. Here air subsides from above and is adiabatically heated. A more detailed discussion of west coast deserts is given in Chapter 13.

The monsoon winds of Asia largely control rainfall of the southeastern part of that continent. In summer the flow of moist tropical air from the Indian Ocean and western Pacific encounters various mountain chains to give very heavy orographic precipitation. This is vividly illustrated by the narrow strips having precipitation over 80 inches, coinciding with the Himalayas in northern India and their southeastward extensions into Burma and Malaya, and with the high western edge of the Deccan Plateau along the west coast of peninsular India. The rugged mountain chains of the East Indies receive orographic rainfall associated with both sets of monsoon winds which blow between Australia and Asia.

Precipitation in the middle latitudes shows clearly the effect of the prevailing westerly winds. Western continental coasts within the latitude range 35° to 60° appear as narrow strips of heavy precipitation. Most striking are the British Columbia–southeastern Alaska coast in the northern hemisphere, and the Patagonian coast of southernmost South America. Here, copious orographic precipitation is induced by coastal ranges which force a rise of moist air moving in from the Pacific Ocean. The effect is less striking on the Atlantic coast of Europe and the British Isles where relief is less, but it is nevertheless clearly evident. Note, too, that New Zealand, south of 40° S lat., has a marked zoning of precipitation from west to east.

Rainshadow deserts are developed in the westerly wind belt, in the lee of coastal ranges. The best illustration is the Great Basin Desert of Nevada, already cited as an example of the principle of rainshadow development. A similar relation exists in southernmost South America but is not so well developed. Even the Iberian Peninsula shows semi-aridity in its eastern half, as compared with a moist western coast. The vast continent of Eurasia exhibits a generally increasing aridity from west to east. Not only is moist air from the Atlantic dried as it travels eastward, but moist tropical air from the Indian Ocean is blocked by mountain barriers on the south.

Both the eastern United States and the eastern part of Asia, including much of China, Japan, Korea, and Manchuria, is moist, even though located on the eastern, or lee, side of the continents. This is explained by the prevalence of humid masses of air which move northward from the subtropical oceans during the summer months as a part of the monsoon circulation.

In arctic regions, precipitation is very small in terms of total inches annually, as the map clearly shows. The atmosphere here is at prevailingly low temperatures and thus does not hold large quantities of water vapor from which precipitation can be produced. At the same time, low temperatures reduce evaporation to such an extent that there is generally abundant soil moisture and surface water in summer and snow and ice in winter.

Review Questions

1. In what ways is the presence of water vapor in the air important in weather and climate? What is latent heat? What are the sources of atmospheric moisture?

2. Define relative humidity. What effect has a change of air temperature upon the relative humidity of the air? What is the dew point temperature? Explain the phenomenon of condensation of water vapor.

3. How is humidity of the air measured? Explain the principle of the psychrometer.

4. Explain the process whereby condensation and precipitation occur as a result of the lifting of a mass of air. What is the adiabatic rate? How does this differ from the normal lapse rate?

5. Of what are clouds composed? How are clouds classified? Name the common cloud types, give their height ranges, and describe their forms. What are stratiform and cumuliform clouds?

6. Name and describe the various forms of precipitation. Is an icing storm a form of precipitation? How does hail form?

7. In what units is rainfall measured? Describe a rain gage. How is snowfall measured? How does one foot of snow compare with 1 foot of rainfall for relative amounts of water?

8. What are the three ways in which precipitation can occur on a large scale? Describe how a convection column of air operates to produce rainfall. What keeps the updraft in operation during a convectional storm? What is an unstable air mass?

9. Explain how orographic precipitation occurs. Why is there often a dry area, or rainshadow, on the lee side of a mountain chain? Is the air which has reached a rainshadow area normally warmer or cooler than it was at the same elevation over the coastal zone from which it came? Explain.

10. Describe the internal meteorological conditions of a thunderstorm. What size and height do these storms commonly attain? How is hail formed in a thunderstorm? What keeps a thunderstorm active? What is the source of energy?

11. Explain the three common types of thunderstorms. What can be said about time of day and geographical regions of occurrence of each?

12. How can rainfall distribution be represented on a map? Briefly summarize the distribution of annual rainfall over the globe, using the pressure and wind belts as a basis for your discussion. What regions are most favorably located for heavy rainfall? How do the arctic regions compare in total annual precipitation with the equatorial and tropical regions?

Exercises

1. A mass of rising air has a temperature of 65° F at 1000 feet elevation. If the air temperature is falling at the dry adiabatic rate, what will it be at 4000 feet? Assuming that this air has a dew-point temperature of 36° F, at what level will condensation set in? Refer to Figure 10.3 for guidance.

2. The small inset in the upper right-hand corner of Figure 10.13 shows the changes in air temperature accompanying the passage of a mass of air over a mountain range and down the other side. Construct a full-size graph of this type to show what happens during the following sequence of changing conditions:

Air at 84° F at sea level rises up mountain slopes; reaches dew-point temperature of 42° F; condensation sets in. Air continues to rise (at wet-adiabatic rate) until, at the summit, temperature has dropped to 35°. Air descends lee slope of range to floor of an interior basin, 500 feet elevation. (Follows dry adiabatic rate down.)

(*a*) At what elevation was dew-point temperature reached? (*b*) How high was the summit of the range? (*c*) What was the air temperature on arrival at the floor of the interior basin? (*d*) How does the humidity of the air compare at the start and at the finish of this series of changes? (*e*) Suppose the air were next forced to pass over another range of the same elevation farther inland; would the same series of changes happen all over again? Explain.

3. During a torrential summer thunderstorm, an automatic recording rain gage showed that the rainfall in each five-minute interval was as given below. The first period began at 3:40 P.M.

Five-minute period	1	2	3	4	5	6	7	8	9
Rainfall, inches	0.22	0.30	0.42	0.09	0.04	0.02	0.01	0.01	0.00

(*a*) Show this information by a simple bar graph. Let each bar, from left to right, represent one five-minute period. Let the height of each bar be proportional to the amount of rain, using a scale of one inch on the graph equals 0.10 inch of rainfall. (*b*) How much rain, measured in inches, fell during the entire storm? (*c*) Was the heaviest rain near the beginning or end of the rain period? (*d*) How long did the rainfall period last? This exercise illustrates a typical burst of rainfall from a moving thunderstorm.

4. This map of the lower Ohio Valley region shows the total rainfall during a four-day rain storm in October. Lines have been drawn through stations that have received the same amount of rainfall. Lines of this type, termed *isohyetal lines*, are drawn like isobars, isotherms, or topographic contours. Complete the isohyetal lines on this map. Draw these on a sheet of thin tracing paper laid over the map. Label the five- and ten-inch lines. (Data from D. W. Mead, *Hydrology*, McGraw-Hill, 1919.)

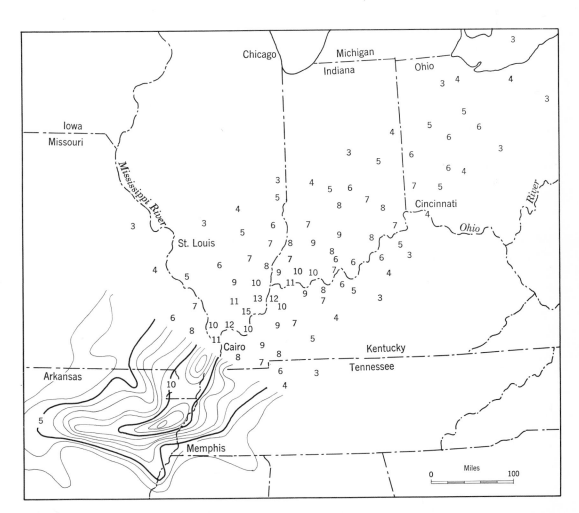

Exercise 4

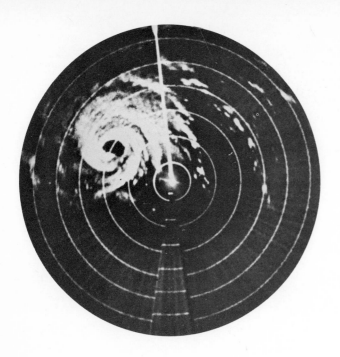

CHAPTER ELEVEN

Cyclonic storms, air masses, weather fronts

MUCH of the unsettled, cloudy weather experienced in middle and high latitudes is associated with traveling *cyclones,* which are moving centers of low barometric pressure. The convergence of masses of air toward these centers is accompanied by lift of air and adiabatic cooling, which, in turn, produces cloudiness and precipitation. In the northern hemisphere, winds spiral in a counterclockwise direction about the cyclone center. By contrast, much fair, sunny weather is associated with traveling *anticyclones,* which are centers of high barometric pressure. Here the air tends to subside and spread outward, causing adiabatic warming, a process that is unfavorable to the development of clouds and precipitation. Winds form a clockwise spiral with respect to the anticyclone center in the northern hemisphere (Figure 8.11).

Cyclones may be very mild in intensity, passing with little more than a period of cloud cover and light rain or snow. On the other hand, if the pressure gradient is strong, winds ranging in strength from moderate to gale force may accompany the cyclone. In such a case, the disturbance may be called a *cyclonic storm.*

above: A hurricane on the radar screen.
Official U.S. Navy photograph.

Moving cyclones fall into three general classes. (1) The *middle-latitude cyclone* (or *extratropical cyclone*) is typical of middle and high latitudes. It ranges in severity from a weak disturbance to a powerful storm. (2) The *tropical cyclone* is found in low latitudes over ocean areas. It ranges from a mild disturbance to the terribly destructive *hurricane,* or *typhoon.* (3) The *tornado,* although a very small storm, is an intense cyclonic vortex of enormously powerful winds. It is on a very much smaller scale of magnitude than other types of cyclones and must be treated separately.

The thunderstorm, described in Chapter 10, is a localized disturbance connected with a large cumulonimbus cloud in which there is a rapid convectional rise of air. It lacks the cyclonic spiral flow of winds. Thunderstorms often occur in large numbers within a single cyclonic storm, and occasionally tornadoes develop within the thunderstorms at the same time.

Moving lows and highs

Before the advent of modern weather theory it was well known that within the middle latitudes, 35° to 65° N and S, weather changes are associated with moving centers of low and high barometric pressure, which can be drawn on the

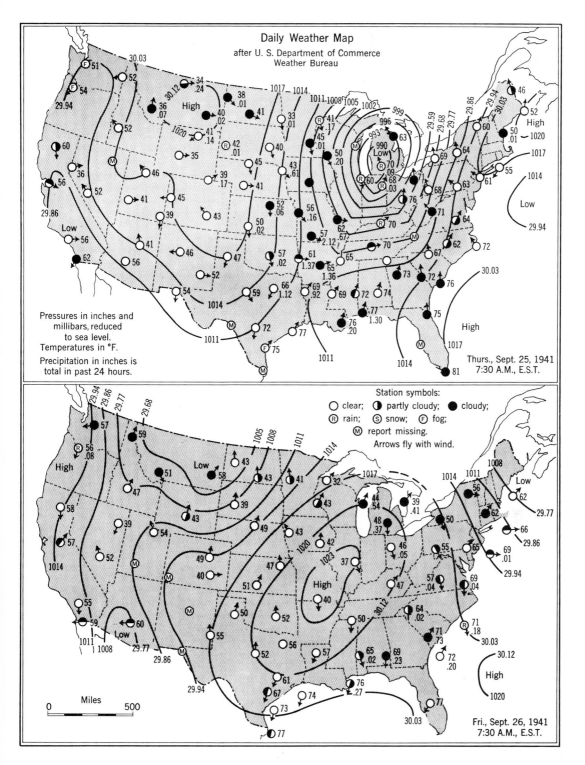

Figure 11.1 These daily weather maps are of the old style and do not include analysis of air masses and fronts. They do, however, show nicely the conditions of pressure, temperature, winds, rainfall, and cloudiness typical of moving lows and highs. In the 24-hour period elapsing between these two maps, the strong low centered over Michigan on the first map has moved northeast to a position off the map, over the Maritime Provinces, while the strong high has moved east and south to dominate the central United States. (Copied with minor changes from *Daily Weather Maps* of Weather Bureau, U.S. Dept. Commerce.)

weather map and followed from day to day in the course of their eastward travel (Figure 11.1). The following description applies particularly to the United States.

Lows, or cyclones, consist of oval-shaped concentric isobars, usually elongate on a northeast to southwest axis. Some show a set of sharp V-shaped bends in the isobars in the southern or southwestern part of the low, the points of the V's falling on a straight or gently curved line and representing a place where the wind invariably shifts from south or southeast to northwest. This line is commonly associated with a line of thunderstorms, following whose passage there occurs a marked drop of air temperature as the wind swings to a northwest quarter. The lows travel 25 to 30 miles per hour, on the average, and have diameters of 500 to 1000 miles. Cloudiness and precipitation generally are located in the eastern or southeastern half, and the northwestern part is usually a zone of clearing weather.

Between successive lows occur anticyclones, which are centers of high pressure, or simply *highs,* bringing cool, fair weather with distinctly drier air than in the lows. In the United States, the highs characteristically move in from the north, whereas the lows more often develop in southerly areas and move northeast, although there are many exceptions.

With the aid of periodic weather maps showing the positions of highs and lows, successful weather forecasting was carried on by experienced men who had come to know the habits of lows as a result of many years of observing their behavior. It was known that lows follow certain common paths, such as moving along the St. Lawrence Valley.

Wave theory of cyclones

The simple analysis of weather outlined above leaves many puzzling things unexplained. During the First World War a Norwegian meteorologist, J. Bjerknes, brought forward a new theory to explain moving extratropical cyclones and anticyclones. In middle latitudes, there exists a line of contact between cold air of arctic or polar origin and warm air of subtropical origin. This fluctuating line of contact was named the *polar front* (Figure 11.2). To any large body of the lower atmosphere having fairly uniform conditions of temperature and moisture, the term *air mass* was applied. We can say that a front separates two air masses of unlike properties.

The term *front,* used by Bjerknes, was particularly apt because of the resemblance of this feature to the fighting fronts in western Europe, then active. Just as vast armies met along a sharply defined front which moved back and forth, so masses of cold polar air meet in conflict with warm, moist air from the subtropical regions. Instead of mixing freely, these unlike air masses remain clearly defined, but interact along the polar front in great whorls whose structure is not unlike the form of an ocean wave seen in cross section.

A series of individual blocks, Figure 11.3 shows the various stages in the life history of an extratropical (middle-latitude) cyclone. Originally, the polar front is simply a smooth boundary along which air of unlike qualities is moving in opposite directions, as shown in Figure 11.2. In Block *A* of Figure 11.3, the polar front shows a bulge, or *wave,* beginning to form. Cold air is turned in a southerly direction, warm air in a northerly direction, as if each would penetrate the domain of the other. The situation is very much as if two individuals enter a revolving door from opposite sides. Pivoting on a center pin, the door permits each to pass into the area vacated by the other. It is now necessary to digress from the series of diagrams of Figure 11.3 to consider what occurs when cold air moves into an area of warm air, or vice versa.

Figure 11.4 shows the structure of a frontal contact zone in which cold air is invading the warm-air zone. A front of this type is termed a *cold front.* The colder air mass, being heavier, remains in contact with the ground and forces the warmer air mass to rise over it. The slope of the cold front surface is greatly exaggerated in the figure, being actually of the order of slope of 1 in 40 to 1 in 80 (meaning that the slope rises 1 foot vertically for each 80 feet of horizontal distance). Cold fronts are associated with strong atmospheric disturbance, the warm air thus lifted often breaking out in violent thunderstorms. Where these violent thunderstorms occur along a line well in advance of the cold front, a *squall line* results (Figure 11.5).

Figure 11.6 illustrates a *warm front* in which warm air is moving into a region of colder air. Here, again, the cold air mass remains in contact with the ground, and the warm air mass is forced to rise as if ascending a long ramp. Warm fronts have lower slopes than cold fronts, being of the order of 1 in 80 to as low as 1 in 200. Moreover, warm fronts are commonly attended by stable atmospheric conditions and lack the turbulent air motions of the cold front. Of course, if the warm air is unstable, it will develop convection cells and there will be heavy showers and thunderstorms. To the list of thunderstorm types described in Chapter 10 can now be added the thunderstorms of both cold front and warm front origin.

Cold fronts normally move along the ground at a faster rate than warm fronts. Hence, when both types are in the same neighborhood, as they are in the cyclonic storm, the cold front may overtake the

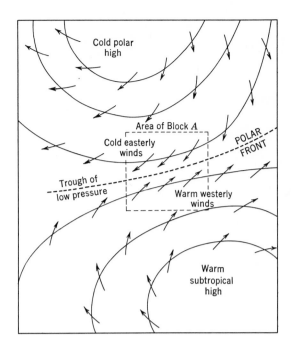

Figure 11.2 The trough between two high-pressure regions is a likely zone for development of a wave cyclone.

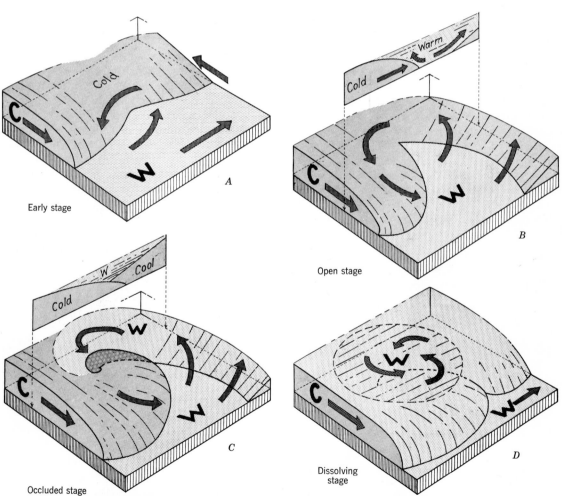

Figure 11.3 The devolopment of a middle-latitude cyclone is shown here in four stages.

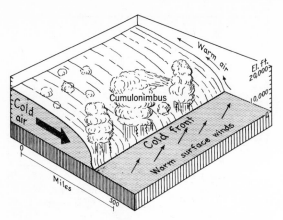

Figure 11.4 A cold front is formed by the underrunning of cold air beneath warm.

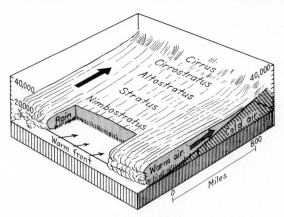

Figure 11.6 A warm front is formed by the sliding up of a warm-air wedge over a colder air mass.

warm front. A curious combination, known as an *occluded front,* then results (Figure 11.7). The colder air of the fast-moving cold front remains next to the ground, forcing both the warm air and the less cold air to rise over it. The warm air mass is lifted completely free of the ground. The relations between warm, cold and occluded fronts will now be introduced into the life history of the cyclone as illustrated in Figure 11.3.

In Block *B,* the wavelike disturbance along the polar front has deepened and intensified. Cold air is now actively pushing southward along a cold front; warm air is actively moving northeastward along a warm front. Each front is convex in the direction of motion. The zone of precipitation is now considerable, but wider along the warm front than along the cold front. In a still later stage the more rapidly moving cold front has reduced the zone of warm air to a narrow sector. In Block *C,* the cold front has overtaken the warm front, pro-

ducing an occluded front and forcing the warm air mass off the ground, isolating it from the parent region of warm air to the south. The source of moisture and energy thus cut off, the cyclonic storm gradually dies out and the polar front is reestablished as originally (Block *D*).

Further details and characteristics of a wave cyclone are illustrated in Figure 11.8, in which two weather maps are shown. These have been redrawn with only slight changes from the U.S. Weather Bureau daily maps for April 4 and 5, 1945. Map A shows a cyclone in a stage approximately equivalent to Block *B* of Figure 11.3. The storm is centered over western Illinois and is moving northeastward. Note the following points: (*a*) Isobars of the low are closed to form an oval-shaped pattern. (*b*) Isobars make a sharp V where crossing the cold front. (*c*) Wind directions, indicated by arrows, are at an angle to the trend of the isobars and form a pattern of counterclockwise

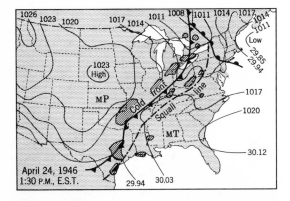

Figure 11.5 A squall line, along which violent thunderstorms break out, sometimes moves ahead of a cold front. Shaded spots are zones in which precipitation has recently occurred. (After U.S. Weather Bureau, *Daily Weather Map.*)

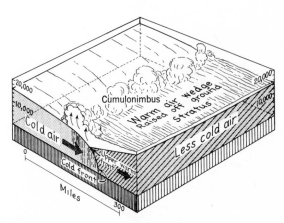

Figure 11.7 In an occluded warm front a warm-air wedge has been raised off the ground.

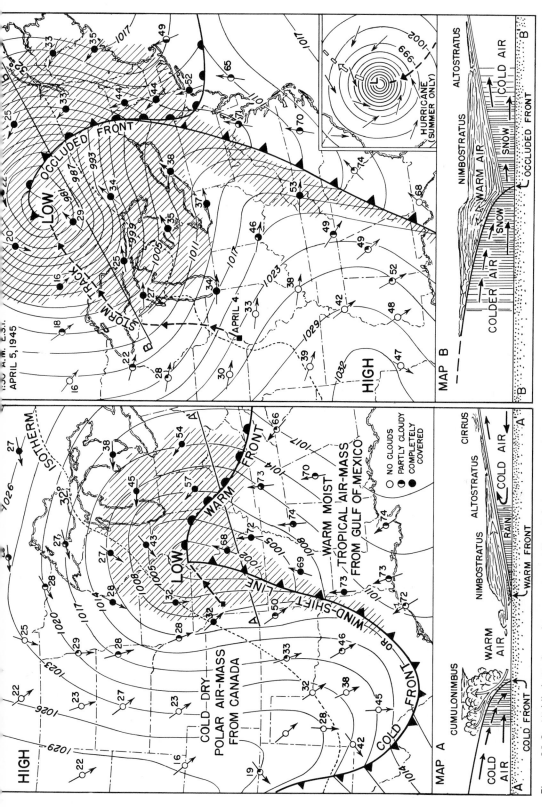

Figure 11.8 Middle-latitude cyclones are wavelike disturbances involving cold and warm fronts along which air masses of unlike qualities are interacting. On these maps, which are simplified from the actual Weather Bureau maps, arrows fly with the wind, isobars are labeled in millibars, and temperature is given in degrees Fahrenheit. Shaded areas have precipitation. The hurricane on Map *B* is shown to correct scale off the Atlantic coast but would not be found in this season of the year. (Modified after *Daily Weather Map, Weather Bureau, U.S. Dept. Commerce. Courtesy of The Geographical Press.)*

spiraling. (d) In the warm-air sector there is north-ward flow of tropical air toward the direction of the warm front. (e) There is a sudden shift of wind direction accompanying the passage of the cold front, as indicated by the widely different wind directions at stations close to the cold front, but on opposite sides. (f) There is a severe drop in temperature accompanying the passage of the cold front, as shown by differences in temperature readings at stations on either side of the cold front. (g) Precipitation, shown by diagonal shading, is over a broad zone near the warm front and in the central area of the cyclone, but extends as a thin band down the length of the cold front. (h) Cloudiness, shown by degree of blackness of station circles, is greatest in the warm sector and northeastern part of the cyclone, but the western part is virtually clear. (i) The low is followed on the west by a high (anti-cyclone) in which low temperatures and clear skies prevail. (j) The 32° isotherm crosses the cyclone diagonally from northeast to southwest, showing that the southeastern part is warmer than the north-western part.

A cross section through Map A along the line AA' shows how the fronts and clouds are related. Along the warm front is a broad area of stratiform clouds. These take the form of a wedge with a thin leading edge of cirrus. Westward this thickens to altostratus, then to stratus, and finally to nimbo-stratus with steady rain. Within the warm air mass sector the sky may partially clear with scattered cumulus. Along the cold front are violent thunder-storms with heavy rains, but this is along a narrow belt that passes quickly.

The second weather map, Map B, shows conditions 24 hours later. The cyclone has moved northeastward into Canada, its path shown by the line labeled storm track. The cyclone has occluded. An occluded front replaces the separate warm and cold fronts in the central part of the disturbance. The high-pressure area, or tongue of cold polar air, has moved in to the west and south of the cyclone, and the cold front is passing over the eastern seaboard states. In another day the entire storm will have passed out to sea, leaving the eastern United States in the grip of cold but clear weather. A cross section below the map shows conditions along the line BB', cutting through the occluded part of the storm. Note that the warm air mass is being lifted higher off the ground and is giving heavy precipitation.

Long observation on the movements of cyclones and anticyclones has revealed that certain tracks are most commonly followed. Figure 11.9 is a map of the United States showing these common paths. Notice that whereas some cyclonic storms travel across the entire United States from places of origin in the North Pacific, such as the Aleutian low, others originate in the Rocky Mountain region, the central states, or the Gulf Coast. Most tracks converge toward the northeastern United States and pass out into the North Atlantic, where they tend to concentrate in the region of the Icelandic low. General world distribution of paths of cyclonic storms is shown in Figure 11.10. Notice the heavy concentration in the neighborhood of the Aleutian and Icelandic lows. In the southern hemisphere, storm tracks are more nearly along a single lane, following the parallels of latitude. This appears to be the result of uniform ocean surface throughout the middle latitudes, only the southern tip of South America breaking the monotonous oceanic expanse. Furthermore, the polar-centered icecap of Antarctica provides a centralized source of polar air.

Air masses and source regions

The wave theory of extratropical cyclones places much emphasis upon the interaction of air masses, which differ in physical properties but which are essentially of uniform nature internally. The general subdivision of air masses of middle latitudes into two major groups, polar and tropical, has already been emphasized in explaining the development of the cyclonic storms. The distinctive properties of an air mass are developed when the air layer lies stagnant over a body of land or ocean, the source region. As the air mass leaves the source region, to travel across other kinds of land or ocean surfaces, the air is cooled or heated, and gains or loses moisture, as the case may be. Thus, an air mass evolves or changes as it follows a characteristic path, or trajectory, which may take it thousands of miles from the source region. The polar air masses are divided into maritime and continental types. The continental polar air masses of North America (symbol, cP) originate over north-central Canada and are characterized by low temperature and low moisture content (Figure 11.11). These air masses form tongues of cold air, which periodically extend south and east from the source region to produce anticyclones accompanied, in winter, by low temperatures and clear skies. Over the North Pacific and Bering Straits originate the maritime polar air masses (symbol, mP). With ample opportunity to absorb moisture both over the source region and throughout their travel south-eastward to the west coast of North America, these air masses are characteristically cool and moist, with a tendency in winter to being unstable, giving heavy precipitation over coastal ranges.

Another maritime polar air mass of the North American region originates over the North Atlantic Ocean (Figure 11.11). It, too, is cool and moist.

Owing to its location, east of the North American continent, it only occasionally reaches the United States when drawn in over New England by a favorably placed cyclone lying south of New England. This situation brings on a *northeaster*, a storm characterized by northeast winds, penetrating cold, and misting rain. The northeaster is restricted to the northeastern states.

Of the tropical air masses, there are also maritime and continental types. The commonest visitor to the central and eastern states is the maritime tropical air mass (symbol, мT) from the Gulf of Mexico (Figure 11.11). It moves northward, bringing warm, moist, unstable air over the eastern part of the country. In the summer, particularly, this air mass brings hot, sultry weather to the east. It gives frequent thunderstorms. Closely related is a maritime tropical air mass from the Atlantic Ocean east of Florida, over the Bahamas. It has characteristics similar to those of the tropical Gulf air mass and brings similar weather conditions.

During the summer there originates over northern Mexico, western Texas, New Mexico, and Arizona a tropical continental air mass (symbol, cT) which is hot and dry. This air mass does not travel widely, but governs weather conditions over the source region.

Over the Pacific Ocean in the cell of high pressure located to the southwest of Lower California is a source region of another maritime tropical

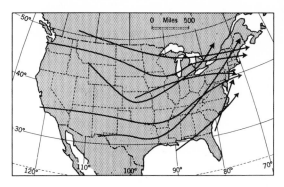

Figure 11.9 Common tracks taken by middle-latitude cyclones passing across the United States. (After Bowie and Weightman.)

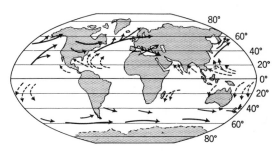

Figure 11.10 Principal tracks of middle-latitude cyclones are shown by solid lines; those of tropical cyclones by dashed lines. (After Petterssen, *Introduction to Meteorology.*)

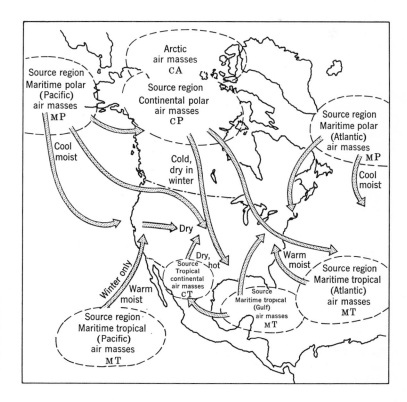

Figure 11.11 The United States and Canada can well be described as a battleground of polar and tropical air masses. This area lies between the two major air mass source regions. (After Haynes, U.S. Dept. Commerce.)

air mass. It visits the United States only in winter and affects only the southern coast of California.

Besides the air masses of middle latitudes already described, there are additional groups typical of polar and equatorial locations. Over the North Polar Sea and its bordering lands there develops the arctic air mass (symbol, A) which is extremely cold and stable. When this air mass invades the United States, it produces a severe cold wave. The Antarctic continent provides a source region for extremely cold air masses, designated as antarctic air masses (symbol, AA).

Over equatorial oceans, in the trough of low pressure toward which the trade winds converge, air becomes very moist, warm, and unstable. It is then classified as an equatorial air mass (symbol, mE). Invasion of southeastern Asia by equatorial air masses occurs during the wet monsoon season and constitutes the source of moisture for torrential rains.

Tropical and equatorial weather

As the study of weather conditions has been extended along modern lines into the low latitudes of the globe, largely as a result of enormously increased aircraft operation during World War II, a much clearer picture has emerged of the relations of air masses and storms in these regions.

Figure 11.12 shows a typical set of weather conditions in the subtropical and equatorial parts of the world, in addition to showing the general scheme of traveling cyclonic waves in middle and high latitudes.

Fundamentally the arrangement consists of two rows of high-pressure cells, one or two cells to each land or ocean body. The northern row lies approximately along the Tropic of Cancer; the southern row, along the Tropic of Capricorn. Between the subtropical highs lies the equatorial trough of low pressure. Toward this trough converge the northeast and southeast trade winds. For this reason the trough is called the *Intertropical convergence zone*. At higher levels in the troposphere, the air flow is almost directly from east to west in the form of persistent *tropical easterlies*, described in Chapter 8.

One of the simplest forms of weather disturbance is an *easterly wave*, a slowly moving trough of low pressure within the belt of tropical easterlies. These waves occur in a zone 5° to 30° latitude over oceans both north and south of the equator, but not over the equator itself. Figure 11.13 is a simplified weather map of an easterly wave, showing isobars, winds, and the zone of rain. The wave is simply a series of indentations in the isobars to form a shallow pressure trough. Note that it travels westward, perhaps 200 to 300 miles per day. Air flow tends to converge on the eastern, or rear, side of the wave axis. This causes the moist air to be lifted and to break out into scattered showers and thunderstorms. The rainy period may last for a day or two.

Another related disturbance is an *equatorial wave*, or *weak equatorial low*, which forms in the center of the equatorial trough (Figure 11.14). Al-

Figure 11.12   A daily weather map of the world for a given day during July or August might look like this map, which is a composite of typical weather conditions. (After M. A. Garbell.)

though the normal air flow is from east to west, there develops an eddy in the tropical easterlies. Here air flow is locally reversed and tends to run opposite to the main stream. The result is a weak low-pressure center, the equatorial wave, into which moist equatorial air masses converge, causing rainfall from many individual convectional storms within the low. Several such weak lows are shown on the world weather map (Figure 11.12), lying along the equatorial trough. Because the map is for a day in July or August, the trough is shifted well north of the equator.

Another distinctive feature of tropical weather is the occasional penetration of powerful tongues of cold polar air from the middle latitudes into very low latitudes. These are known as *polar outbreaks* and bring unusually cool, clear weather with strong, steady winds moving behind a cold front with squalls. The polar outbreak is best developed in the Americas. Outbreaks which move southward from the United States over the Caribbean Sea and Central America are called *northers* or *nortes;* those which move north from Patagonia into tropical South America are called *pamperos* or *friagems.* One such outbreak is shown over South America on the world weather map (Figure 11.12).

Tropical cyclones

One of the most powerful and destructive types of cyclonic storms is the *tropical cyclone,* otherwise known as the *hurricane* or *typhoon.* The storm develops over oceans in latitudes 8° to 15° N and

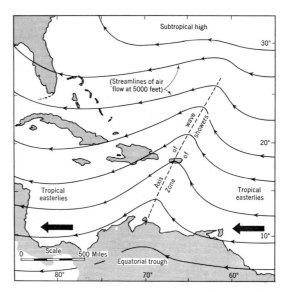

Figure 11.13 An easterly wave passing over the West Indies brings a spell of rain. (After Riehl.)

S, but not close to the equator, where the Coriolis force is extremely weak. In many cases an easterly wave simply deepens and intensifies, growing into a deep, circular low. High sea surface temperatures, which are over 80° F in these latitudes, are of basic importance in the environment of storm origin. Warming of air at low level creates instability and predisposes toward storm formation. Once formed, the storm moves westward and pole-

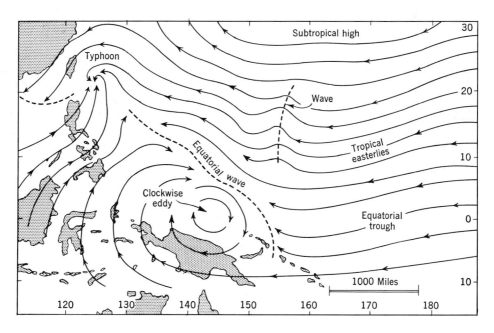

Figure 11.14 An equatorial wave resembles an eddy in the prevailing tropical easterlies. (After Riehl.)

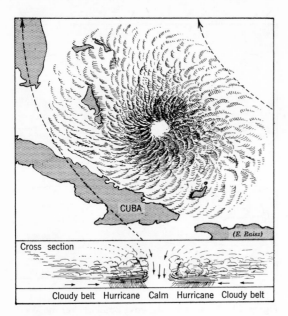

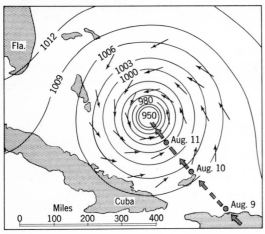

Figure 11.15 A hurricane (tropical cyclone) of the West Indies.

may be veil-like, giving a halo to the sun or moon and producing a red sunset. A long swell is felt on the sea, this being the train of dying storm waves that have outrun the slowly moving storm center. As the storm approaches, the barometer begins to fall. Wind springs up. A great dark wall of cloud approaches. When this envelopes the ship, torrential rainfall begins. The wind rises quickly to gusts more than 75 miles per hour, occasionally up to 125 or 150 miles per hour. Great waves break over the vessel; the spray blows in continuous sheets which reduce visibility to virtually nothing.

This terrible storm continues for several hours and is abruptly followed by total calm and clearing skies, and sometimes by a sharp rise in temperature. The barometer has now reached its lowest point and the vessel is in the calm *central eye* of the storm. This is merely a hollow vortex produced by the rapid spiraling of air in the storm, comparable to the funnel-like air hole in the center of a vortex of water passing down a drain. Although the air is clear and calm, seas are mountainous and rise in great peaklike masses which are of gravest peril to the vessel. The period of calm may last a half hour. Then a great dark wall of cloud strikes the vessel and winds of high velocity again set in, but this time, in reverse direction to those of the first half of the storm. For several hours more the full fury of the storm rages, then gradually the winds abate, the clouds break, and fair weather returns.

World distribution of tropical cyclones is limited to six regions, all of them over tropical and subtropical oceans (Figure 11.10): (1) West Indies, Gulf of Mexico and Caribbean Sea; (2) western North Pacific, including the Philippine Islands, China Sea, and Japanese Islands; (3) Arabian Sea and Bay of Bengal; (4) eastern Pacific coastal region off Mexico and Central America; (5) south Indian Ocean, off Madagascar; and (6) western South Pacific, in the region of Samoa and Fiji Islands and the east coast of Australia. Curiously enough, these storms are unknown in the South Atlantic. Tropical cyclones never originate over land, although they often penetrate the margins of continents.

Paths, or tracks, of tropical cyclones of the North Atlantic (Figure 11.17) show that most of the storms originate at 10° to 20° latitude, travel westward and northwestward through the trades, then turn northeast at about 30° to 35° latitude into the zone of the westerlies. Here the intensity lessens and the storms change into typical middle-latitude cyclones. In the tradewind belt the cyclones travel some 6 to 12 miles per hour; in the westerlies, from 20 to 40 miles per hour.

The occurrence of tropical cyclones is restricted to certain seasons of year, depending on the global location of the storm region. Those of the West

ward through the trade wind belt, often penetrating well into the belt of westerly winds. The tropical cyclone is an almost circular storm center of extremely low pressure into which winds are spiraling with great velocity accompanied by very heavy rainfall (Figure 11.15). The diameter of the storm may be 100 to 300 miles; the wind velocities range from 75 to 125 miles per hour, sometimes much more; and the barometric pressure in the center commonly falls to 28.5 inches (965 mb) or lower (Figure 11.16).

A brief description of the passage of a tropical cyclone at sea might be as follows: During the day preceding the storm the air is generally calm, the pressure somewhat above normal, and the sky shows cirrus clouds in long streamers, seeming to originate from a distant point on the horizon. The cirrus

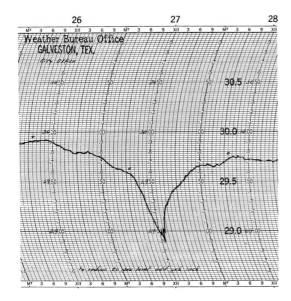

Figure 11.16 This trace sheet from a barograph at Galveston, Texas, shows the fall and rise of air pressure during the hurricane of July 27, 1943. (Courtesy of U.S. Weather Bureau.)

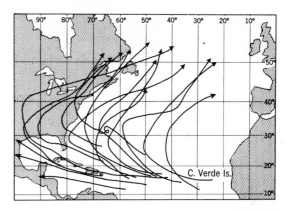

Figure 11.17 Tracks of some typical hurricanes occurring during the month of August over a long period of years show a tendency for the storms to travel northwest in the trade wind belt, then to curve northeast into the zone of the westerlies. (After U.S. Navy Hydrographic Office.)

Figure 11.18 Winds and surf lash at the Florida coast during a severe hurricane. (Courtesy of U.S. Weather Bureau.)

Indies, and off the western coast of Mexico, occur largely from May through November, with maximum frequency in late summer or early autumn. Those of the western North Pacific, Bay of Bengal, and Arabian Sea are spread widely through the year but are dominant from May through November. Those of the South Pacific and south Indian oceans occur from October through April. Thus, they are restricted to the warm season in each hemisphere.

The geographical importance of tropical cyclones lies in their tremendously destructive effect upon island and coastal habitations. Wholesale destruction of cities and their inhabitants has been reported on several occasions (Figure 11.13). A terrible hurricane that struck Barbados in the West Indies in 1780 is reported to have torn stone buildings from their foundations, destroyed forts, and carried

cannon more than a hundred feet from their locations. Trees were torn up and stripped of their bark. More than 6000 persons perished there.[1]

Coastal destruction by storm waves is perhaps the most serious effect of tropical cyclones. Where water level is raised by strong wind pressure, great breaking storm waves sweep far inland over low-lying ground. This is the *storm surge* referred to in Chapter 9. Ships are lifted bodily and carried inland to become stranded. If high tide accompanies the storm the limits reached by inundation are even higher. The terrible hurricane disaster at Galveston, Texas, in 1900 was wrought largely by a sudden storm surge inundating the low coastal city and

[1] I. R. Tannehill, *Hurricanes*, Princeton University Press, 1944, p. 125.

Figure 11.19 The funnel cloud of a tornado in Brookings County, South Dakota, July 9, 1938. (Photograph by King Thoelke. Courtesy of U.S. Weather Bureau.)

Of importance, too, is the large quantity of rainfall produced by tropical cyclones. A considerable part of the summer rainfall of certain coastal regions can often be traced to a few such storms.

Tornadoes

The smallest but most violent of all known storms is the *tornado*. It seems to be a typically American storm, being most frequent and violent in the United States, although occurring in Australia in substantial numbers. Tornadoes are also known throughout tropical and subtropical regions of the globe.

The tornado is a small, intense cyclone in which the air is spiraling at tremendous velocity. It appears as a dark *funnel cloud* (Figure 11.19), hanging from a large cumulonimbus cloud. At its lower end the funnel may be from 300 to 1500 feet in diameter. The funnel appears dark because of the density of condensing moisture, dust, and debris swept up by the wind.

Wind velocities in a tornado exceed anything known in other storms. Estimates of wind velocity run to as high as 500 miles per hour. There is, in addition, a violent updraft in the funnel. As the tornado moves across country the funnel writhes and twists. The end of the funnel cloud may alternately sweep the ground, causing complete destruction of anything in its path, and rise in the air to leave the ground below unharmed. Tornado destruction occurs both from the great wind velocity and from the sudden reduction of air pressure in the vortex of the cyclonic spiral. Closed houses literally explode. It is even reported that the corks will pop out of empty bottles, so great is the difference in air pressure.

Tornadoes occur as parts of powerful cumulo-

drowning about 6000 persons. At the mouth of the Hooghly River on the Bay of Bengal, 300,000 persons died as a result of inundation by a 40-foot storm surge which accompanied a severe cyclone in 1737. Low-lying coral atolls of the western Pacific may be entirely swept over by wind-driven sea water, washing away palm trees and houses and drowning the inhabitants.

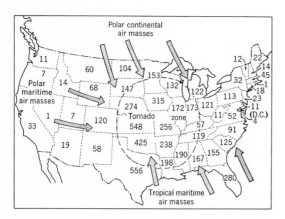

Figure 11.20 Figures tell the total number of days in the 43-year record, 1916–1958, on which one or more tornadoes were reported in some part of each state. (After U.S. Weather Bureau.)

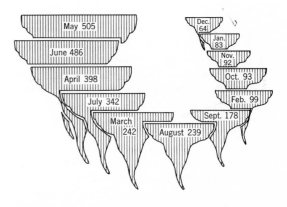

Figure 11.21 Total number of days on which tornadoes were reported in the United States for each month, 1880–1942. (After U.S. Weather Bureau.)

nimbus clouds in the squall line that travels in advance of a cold front. They seem to originate where turbulence is greatest. They are commonest in the spring and summer but may occur in any month. Where polar air lifts warm, moist tropical air on a cold front, conditions may become favorable for tornadoes. They occur in greatest numbers in the Mississippi Valley region and are rare over mountainous and forested regions. They are almost unknown from the Rocky Mountains westward and are relatively few on the eastern seaboard (Figures 11.20 and 11.21).

Devastation from a tornado is complete within the narrow limits of its path (Figure 11.22), but fortunately the storms are uncommon and the total danger small. Even in states having the most tornadoes, deaths from automobile and other accidents are a very much more serious danger. Storm cellars built completely below ground provide satisfactory protection if they can be reached in time. Although a tornado can often be seen or heard approaching, a cold front passing during the hours of darkness, as it often does, may present no warning. The U.S. Weather Bureau maintains a tornado forecasting and warning system. Whenever weather conditions conspire to favor tornado development, the danger area is alerted and systems for observing and reporting a tornado are set in readiness. Communities in the paths of tornadoes may thus be warned in time for inhabitants to take shelter.

Waterspouts are similar in structure to tornadoes but form at sea under cumulonimbus clouds. They are smaller and less powerful than tornadoes. Sea

Figure 11.22 Tornado devastation at Ionia, Iowa, April 23, 1948, included this store, in which two persons were killed. (Courtesy of U.S. Weather Bureau and *Des Moines Register.*)

water may be lifted eight or ten feet above the sea surface, and the spray is carried higher. Waterspouts are commonly found in subtropical waters of the Gulf of Mexico and off the southeastern coast of the United States and seem to result from air turbulence occurring when continental air masses spread out over these oceans.

Review Questions

1. Define a cyclone according to proper usage in meteorology. Is a cyclone the same as a tornado? What is an anticyclone? How do winds flow with respect to cyclones and anticyclones in the northern hemisphere?

2. What kinds of cyclonic storms exist? Is the thunderstorm a cyclonic storm?

3. Describe the weather conditions associated with a middle-latitude cyclone, or low, in the central and eastern United States. Include discussion of the pressure pattern, winds, cloudiness and precipitation areas, temperatures, size, and rate of travel.

4. Describe the weather conditions associated with an anticyclone, or high, such as might normally follow the cyclone mentioned in the previous question.

5. Explain the wave theory of middle-latitude weather which was originated by J. Bjerknes. What is the polar front? What is an air mass?

6. How does a cyclone develop and change along the polar front? Explain a cold front and the air mass relationships involved in it. In a similar manner, describe and explain a warm front and an occluded front.

7. What features of a middle-latitude cyclone are explained in terms of air masses and fronts but were not accounted for in the older type of weather analysis?

8. Describe the changes in wind direction and strength, cloudiness and precipitation, and temperature that an observer experiences when a middle-latitude cyclone passes with its center north of the observer. Do the same for a cyclone in which the center passes south of the observer.

9. What is the prevailing direction of movement of cyclonic storms in the United States? Do storm tracks show any tendency to concentrate at particular places in the northern hemisphere? If so, where? Do you think this may explain the average pressure conditions in these areas as shown on the world pressure maps?

10. How are air masses classified and designated? Discuss the air masses of North America, giving their source regions, paths of movement, and generally associated weather characteristics. What air masses are found over polar regions? over the equatorial belt?

11. What is an easterly wave? What weather does it bring? What is an equatorial wave? What weather does it bring?

12. Describe polar outbreaks of tropical regions. What names do these outbreaks have locally in the Central American area? in South America?

13. Describe the weather elements in a tropical cyclone, or hurricane. Where do these storms originate? What paths do they normally follow? Explain the calm central eye of a tropical cyclone.

14. Name the regions of the world where tropical cyclones occur. Tell the seasons of occurrence of storms in each locality. How is season of storms related to position of the equatorial trough?

15. Describe some of the destructive effects of tropical cyclones along low-lying coasts. How is ocean level affected by these storms?

16. What is a tornado? Where and how does it occur? What wind velocities are thought to exist in a tornado? Why are tornadoes in the United States commonest in the spring? What is a waterspout?

Exercises

1. (*a*) On the weather maps shown in Figure 11.1, draw isotherms for every 5° F (35°, 40°, 45°, 50°, etc.). Draw the lines on a sheet of thin tracing paper laid over the page. Trace off the outline of the United States as well. (*b*) Describe the pattern of isobars on the upper map in relation to the high- and low-pressure centers. Why are surface temperatures low in the high-pressure center over Montana, but high within the isobars belonging to the high off the Florida coast? (*c*) On the same tracing sheet used in (*a*), draw in the cold front in the strong low on the upper map. Show also the probable position of a warm front in this low. (*d*) Draw a pressure profile from coast to coast along a line passing through the high over Montana and the strong low over Michigan in the upper map. The method of drawing this profile is exactly the same as that illustrated in Figure 18.15 for topographic profiles, except that barometric pressure is substituted for altitude. (*e*) Add to the tracing sheet in (*a*) a dashed line on the lower map to show the track of the strong low during the previous 24 hours. Show the track of the high which, on the lower map, is centered on Missouri. How many miles did the high travel in 24 hours? Show also the probable future track of this high. (*Hint:* Pressure centers of unlike type tend to repel each other; those of similar kind tend to be drawn together.)

2. Using the information in Figure 11.15, imagine that this hurricane turns slightly westward so as to head toward Miami, Florida. Describe conditions of winds, pressures, clouds, rainfall, surf, and tides at Miami for each successive day, beginning with August 12. Assume that the center of the storm passes over the city and that the rate of progress of the storm center remains the same as it was between August 10 and 11. (*Hint:* Trace the isobars and wind arrows on transparent paper; then move the tracing to successive positions along the storm track.)

3. (*a*) Using the data shown in Figure 11.21, prepare a bar graph to show the numbers of tornadoes recorded for each consecutive month of the calendar year. From left to right, make vertical bars to show the months, starting with January and ending with December. Scale the height of the bars in proportion to the number of tornadoes. (*b*) Do the maximum and minimum tornado months coincide with the months of maximum and minimum monthly average temperatures? (*c*) Do they coincide with the equinoxes or solstices? (*d*) Why do May and June have the most tornadoes; December and January the fewest?

4. Refer to Figure 11.12 and answer the following questions. (*a*) How many low-pressure centers are shown on this map? (*b*) How many high-pressure centers are shown? (*c*) How many lows fall into each of the following classes? (1) extratropical (middle-latitude) cyclones. (2) tropical cyclones. (3) weak lows of the equatorial trough. (*d*) At what approximate latitude or latitude belt does each of the following lie? (1) equatorial trough. (2) subtropical cells of high pressure, northern hemisphere. (3) subtropical cells of high pressure, southern hemisphere. (4) middle-latitude cyclone centers, northern hemisphere. (5) middle-latitude cyclone centers, southern hemisphere. (*e*) Of the middle-latitude cyclones shown on this map, how many are occluded, how many are not?

Part Three
Climate and Soil

CHAPTER TWELVE

Climates and their classification

THE importance of climate as a geographical control is so marked, and reaches into so many aspects of human life, that it would be difficult to overemphasize.

Climate determines to a large extent the type of soil and native vegetation in a given region and hence influences the utilization of the land, whether for crop cultivation, forest, or grazing. Together with topography, then, climate in part determines the ability of land to support a population. To be sure, the introduction of engineering works has provided irrigation and power where it might not otherwise be available, but the distribution of world population still reflects strongly the advantages of favorable climate and topography.

Climate exerts an important influence on physiology. Cold weather, particularly that involving alternations of cold and mild periods with varying degrees of cloudiness, precipitation, and windiness, is believed to stimulate human mental and physical activity.

A contributing factor to human achievement in middle latitudes is that freezing temperatures reduce the activity of many organisms responsible for disease. In hot, humid tropical areas a great variety of parasitic organisms thrives, together with numerous host insects and animals necessary in their life cycles. Malaria and yellow fever, borne by the mosquito, and sleeping sickness, carried by the tsetse fly, are well-known examples. Fungi in excessively humid tropical areas hasten the corrosion and decay of clothing, furniture, and machines.

Classification of climates

As in dealing with all other natural phenomena, the scientist attempts to devise schemes of classification that will include all variations in climate, yet permit them to be placed in several clearly defined and easily distinguished groups. Success is only partially achieved. Nature resists simple categorical schemes. Thomas A. Blair[1] states:

Climate, which represents a complex and abstract idea and which has no concrete existence at a given instant, is not something which can be evaluated exactly. In forming a picture of the climate at a given location, one cannot take into account the effect of all the weather changes, and it becomes necessary to simplify and generalize. The difficulty increases when we attempt to describe the climate of a considerable area, for the climate changes with the loca-

[1] Reprinted by permission from *Climatology* by Thomas A. Blair. Copyright 1942 by Prentice-Hall.

above: Coney Island on a Sunday in summer.
Photograph, Charles P. Cushing.

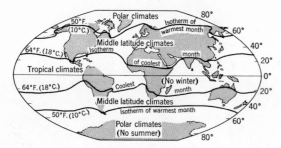

Figure 12.1 On the basis of temperature alone the earth can be divided into three major climate groups.

tion and is not exactly the same in all parts of even a small area.

Maps showing the extent of climate zones are often misleading in that a solid, thin line separates two zones whose shading or color pattern is uniform to the line of contact. Actually, most of these boundaries are transitional, so that intergradation of patterns or colors might be more suitable. Only where the abrupt face of a mountain range creates a sharp climate boundary are the conventional map symbols appropriate. A second misleading quality of most climate maps and classifications is the restriction of the climate zones to land areas. Oceans, though having smaller contrasts in climate, nevertheless can be fitted into the general scheme.

If the weather elements—temperature, pressure, winds, and precipitation—are taken as bases of classification, some useful systems may be devised. The distribution of natural vegetation and soils might suggest still other types of classifications.

Temperature as a basis of climate classification

The general parallelism of isotherms with parallels of latitude has already been pointed out in an earlier chapter and was perhaps the first basis of climate classification. In some older geography books, still occasionally used, the globe is divided by the two tropics (23½° N and S lat.) and the Arctic and Antarctic circles (66½° N and S lat.) into three belts, *torrid zone*, *temperate zone*, and *frigid zone*. Although this generally expresses the temperature relations, the bounding parallels chosen have no special significance in climate. Furthermore, temperatures in the equatorial latitudes do not reach the extremes felt in the southerly part of the temperate zone, and much of the temperate zone has great temperature ranges and storminess not at all suggestive of temperate conditions. Again, the localizing effects of large land and ocean bodies disrupt this simple scheme of climate belts.

With more intelligent application temperature has been made a fundamental factor in most climate classifications. Clearly recognizable are three major climate groups: (I) an *equatorial-tropical group* in which temperatures are uniformly warm and no winter season occurs; (II) a *middle-latitude group*, in which winter and summer alternate; and (III) a *polar-arctic group* in which there is no true summer.

A common boundary between polar climates and middle-latitude climates is the 50° F (10° C) isotherm of the warmest month (July in the northern hemisphere) (Figure 12.1). The area lying north of this boundary has no month with an average temperature higher than 50°.

Between middle-latitude and tropical climates the 64.4° F (18° C) isotherm of the coldest month has been used (Figure 12.1). Thus, the winterless tropical climates have no month in which mean temperature is below 64.4°.

These three climate groups and their temperature boundaries should be noted with particular care because they form part of the climate classification system used in this book.

Temperature alone as a basis of climate classification is unsatisfactory because humid and desert regions receive no distinction. An obvious remedy is a further subdivision according to precipitation.

Precipitation as a basis for climate classification

The profound effect of precipitation on nature of vegetation, drainage systems, soil moisture, and ground water, makes it desirable to consider the amount and seasonal distribution of rainfall and snowfall as a basis of classification.

Blair[2] has outlined a simple scheme of five types.

Climatic type	Rainfall type	Annual rainfall in inches
Arid	Scanty	0–10
Semiarid	Light	10–20
Subhumid	Moderate	20–40
Humid	Heavy	40–80
Very wet	Very heavy	More than 80

A climate map in this scheme would be the same as the mean annual rainfall map (Figure 10.15). An important refinement of this classification would be the subdivision of classes according to distribution of precipitation throughout the year, whether uniform or seasonal.

As a useful climate classification this one fails because it groups cold arctic climates together with the hot deserts of low latitudes. Evaporation, which determines what proportion of the rainfall will remain in the ground, is controlled by air temperature. In general, cold climates are effectively humid with

[2] *Climatology*, 484 pp.; see p. 120.

the same meager precipitation that produces very dry deserts in hot subtropical and tropical latitudes. It would seem, then, that a useful climate system must combine temperature and precipitation classes. Although such combining will increase the number of climate types recognized, each type will be an effective description of a distinctive environment.

The question still remains; what limits of temperature and precipitation shall be set for each climate class? For geographical purposes, the limits are most useful if they define regions favorable and unfavorable to growth of a number of plant groups, for these conditions will closely reflect agricultural and forest productivity.

Vegetation as a basis of climate classification

Plants form an index of climate in that certain types require special conditions of temperature and precipitation. The limits of growth of key types will provide meaningful boundaries for climate zones.

One striking illustration is the northernmost limit of tree growth in the subarctic areas of North America and Asia. The limit coincides approximately with the 50° F (10° C) July isotherm and marks the beginning of the treeless tundra. Another example might be the poleward limit of growth of palms, whose sensitivity to frost limits their extent to about 35° N or S lat.

A map of world distribution of principal vegetative types, Figure 12.2, shows the following major vegetative units.

1. Tropical rainforest. A dense growth of tall, broadleaf evergreen[3] trees and heavy vines. Foliage forms an almost complete shade over ground. Small shrubs and grasses are generally absent. Rainforest (also termed *selva*) indicates abundant rain with no dry season and a fairly uniform high temperature.

2. Lighter tropical forest (tropical semideciduous forest or tropical jungle). A forest growth less dense than rainforest and with smaller trees, but having dense, tangled undergrowth. This type indicates high temperatures throughout the year, but with a short dry season interrupting an otherwise heavy rainfall regime.

3. Scrub and thorn forest. A growth more open and scattered than the tropical jungle. Trees are conditioned to a long dry season alternating with a very wet season. Temperatures are high throughout much of the year.

4. Mediterranean scrub forest. A growth of small deciduous trees such as the scrub oak, and

[3] Not to be confused with coniferous or needle-leaf evergreens (pine, spruce, fir, or hemlock).

various bushy shrubs. This growth indicates a warm, very dry summer alternating with a mild, moist winter.

5. Broadleaf (and mixed broadleaf-coniferous) forest. Deciduous, hardwood trees (oak, maple, ash, or hickory), which shed their leaves each autumn, characterize this unit. This forest type is well distributed over the eastern United States and Europe. Mixed with the broadleaf trees are conifers, whose proportion generally increases toward the northern limit of the zone. Climate of the broadleaf forest zone is controlled by moving cyclonic storms of the middle latitudes and the interplay of tropical and polar air masses. Yearly temperature ranges are great, with cold winters. Rainfall is plentiful and fairly evenly distributed throughout the year.

6. Coniferous forest (*taiga*). A forest of such needle-leaf conifers as spruce, fir, hemlock, and pine, a great belt of which is extensively developed in subarctic regions of North America and Eurasia between 50° and 65° N lat. This zone is one of extreme annual temperature range, long cold winters, and a very short summer. Other areas occur in warmer, moister southerly latitudes and along some mountainous coasts.

7. Savanna. Grasslands with interspersed trees typified by tropical plains areas in Africa, India, and South America. This vegetation zone has a long, very dry season alternating with a wet season, but no winter cold.

8. Prairie. Grasslands on open plains of middle latitudes, widespread in the central United States, eastern Europe, and the Argentina-Uruguay area. These treeless plains are underlain by black or dark brown soils and lie on the boundary zone of dry and humid climates. Great annual ranges of temperature and a slight tendency to aridity are characteristic.

9. Steppe. Short-grass vegetation of plains and plateaus in interior regions of a semi-arid climate. Annual temperature range is usually great, and summers are commonly dry. Although typified by the high plains belt extending from Alberta to Texas, steppe lands are most extensive in central and southwest Asia.

10. Desert shrub and desert waste. Scattered, drought-resistant shrubs of extremely dry, hot deserts of the world. Annual temperature ranges are from moderate to extreme, depending on latitude; rainfall is sporadic.

11. Tundra. Treeless expanses in the summerless arctic regions, covered with sedges, mosses, and lichens. Long, cold winters predominate, and the saturated ground is frozen during much of the year.

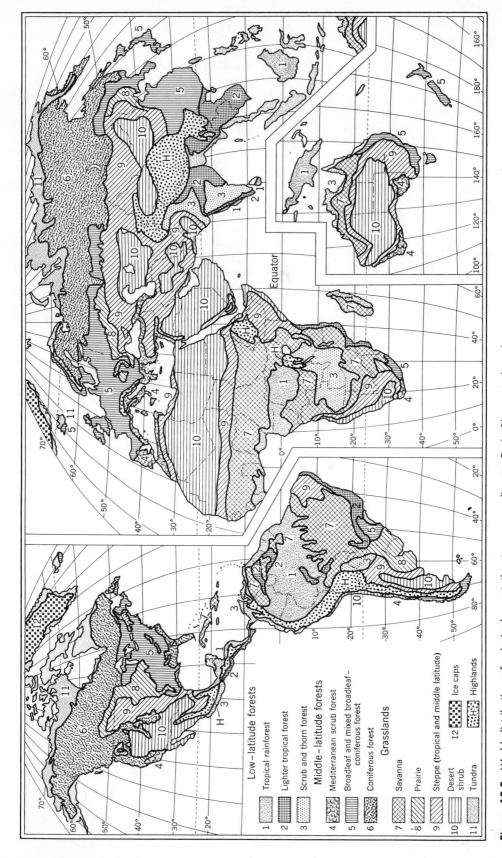

Figure 12.2 World distribution of principal vegetative types according to D. L. Blumenstock and C. W. Thornthwaite. (From *U.S. Dept. Agriculture Yearbook, 1941,* "Climate and Man." Aitoff's equal-area projection adapted by V. C. Finch.)

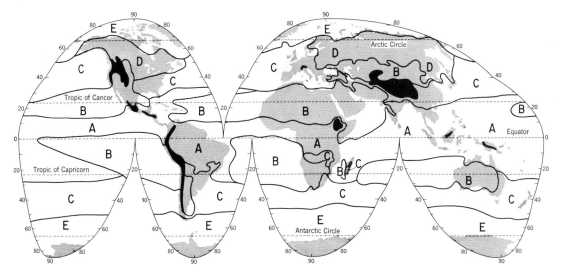

Figure 12.3 Greatly generalized world map of major climatic regions according to the Köppen classification. Highland areas in black. (Based on Goode Base Map. Copyright by the University of Chicago. Used by permission of the University of Chicago Press.)

12. Icecaps. Absolute deserts of ice, comprising most of Greenland and Antarctica.

There is much to recommend a climate classification based on vegetative zones. But vegetation is an effect rather than a cause of climate and cannot, therefore, produce so satisfactory a classification as one based on causes.

The Köppen Climate Classification System

The foregoing proposals to devise climate classes that combine temperature and precipitation characteristics, but to set limits and boundaries fitted into known vegetative distributions, were actually carried out in 1918 by Dr. Wladimir Köppen[4] of the University of Graz in Austria. It was subsequently revised and extended by Köppen and his students to become the most widely used of climatic classifications for geographical purposes.

The Köppen system is strictly empirical. This is to say that each climate is defined according to fixed values of temperature and precipitation, computed according to the averages of the year or of individual months. In such a classification, no concern whatever need be given to the causes of the climate in terms of pressure and wind belts, air masses, fronts, or storms. It is possible to assign a given place to a particular climate subgroup solely

on the basis of the records of temperature and precipitation of that place, provided, of course, that the period of record is long enough to yield meaningful averages. Because air temperature and precipitation are the most easily obtainable surface weather data requiring only simple equipment and the very elementary observer education, a climate system based on these data has a great advantage, in that the areas covered by each subtype of climate can be computed or estimated for large regions of the world.

The Köppen system features a shorthand code of letters designating major climate groups, subgroups within the major groups, and further subdivisions to distinguish particular seasonal characteristics of temperature and precipitation. A thorough and detailed study of the Köppen system is best undertaken in an advanced course in regional climatology, but the main elements of the system are outlined here and will suffice to explain the code system used in following chapters on world climates.

Five major climate groups are designated by capital letters as follows (Figure 12.3). Groups *A*, *C*, and *D* have sufficient heat and precipitation for growth of high-trunk trees (e.g., forests).

A Tropical climates. Average temperature of every month is above 64.4° F (18° C). These climates have no winter season. Annual rainfall is large and exceeds annual evaporation.

B Dry climates. Potential evaporation exceeds precipitation on the average throughout the year. No water surplus; hence no permanent streams originate in *B* climate zones.

[4] American students may pronounce this name as *ker-pen* or *kep-pen*, accenting the first syllable, although the correct pronunciation lies somewhat between these two alternatives.

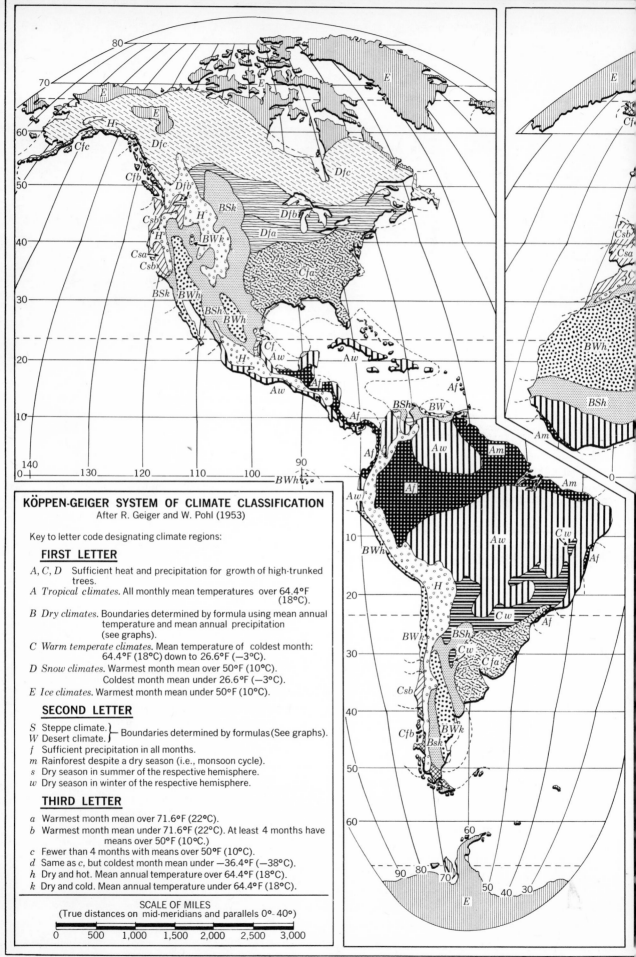

KÖPPEN-GEIGER SYSTEM OF CLIMATE CLASSIFICATION
After R. Geiger and W. Pohl (1953)

Key to letter code designating climate regions:

FIRST LETTER

A, C, D Sufficient heat and precipitation for growth of high-trunked trees.

A *Tropical climates.* All monthly mean temperatures over 64.4°F (18°C).

B *Dry climates.* Boundaries determined by formula using mean annual temperature and mean annual precipitation (see graphs).

C *Warm temperate climates.* Mean temperature of coldest month: 64.4°F (18°C) down to 26.6°F (−3°C).

D *Snow climates.* Warmest month mean over 50°F (10°C). Coldest month mean under 26.6°F (−3°C).

E *Ice climates.* Warmest month mean under 50°F (10°C).

SECOND LETTER

S Steppe climate.
W Desert climate. $\Big\}$ Boundaries determined by formulas (See graphs).

f Sufficient precipitation in all months.
m Rainforest despite a dry season (i.e., monsoon cycle).
s Dry season in summer of the respective hemisphere.
w Dry season in winter of the respective hemisphere.

THIRD LETTER

a Warmest month mean over 71.6°F (22°C).
b Warmest month mean under 71.6°F (22°C). At least 4 months have means over 50°F (10°C.)
c Fewer than 4 months with means over 50°F (10°C).
d Same as c, but coldest month mean under −36.4°F (−38°C).
h Dry and hot. Mean annual temperature over 64.4°F (18°C).
k Dry and cold. Mean annual temperature under 64.4°F (18°C).

SCALE OF MILES
(True distances on mid-meridians and parallels 0°-40°)

0   500   1,000   1,500   2,000   2,500   3,000

Figure 12.4   World map of Köppen-Geiger climate system. Major highland areas designated by letter *H*

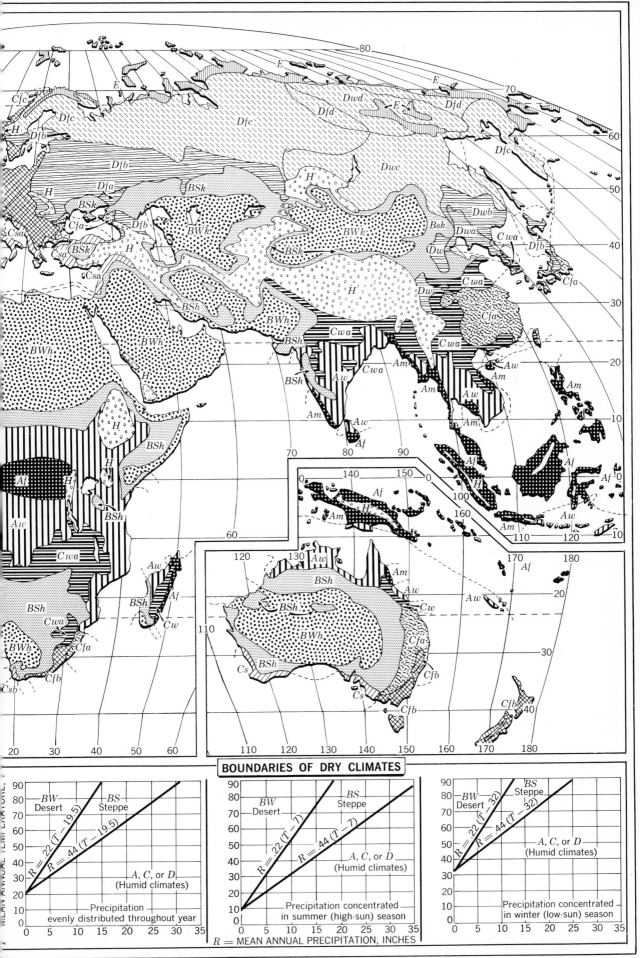

BOUNDARIES OF DRY CLIMATES

Left chart (Precipitation evenly distributed throughout year):
BW Desert — $R = 22 (T - 19.5)$
BS Steppe — $R = 44 (T - 19.5)$
A, C, or D (Humid climates)
Precipitation evenly distributed throughout year

Center chart (Precipitation concentrated in summer (high-sun) season):
BW Desert — $R = 22 (T - 7)$
BS Steppe — $R = 44 (T - 7)$
A, C, or D (Humid climates)
Precipitation concentrated in summer (high-sun) season

Right chart (Precipitation concentrated in winter (low-sun) season):
BW Desert — $R = 22 (T - 32)$
BS Steppe — $R = 44 (T - 32)$
A, C, or D (Humid climates)
Precipitation concentrated in winter (low-sun) season

$R = $ MEAN ANNUAL PRECIPITATION, INCHES

(Based on Goode Base Map. Copyright by the University of Chicago. Used by permission of the University of Chicago Press.)

C *Warm temperate (mesothermal)*[5] *climates.* Coldest month has an average temperature under 64.4° (18° C), but above 26.6° F (−3° C); at least one month has an average temperature above 50° F (10° C). The *C* climates thus have both a summer and a winter season.

D *Snow (microthermal)*[6] *climates.* Coldest month average temperature under 26.6° F (−3° C). Average temperature of warmest month above 50° F (10° C), that isotherm coinciding approximately with poleward limit of forest growth.

E *Ice climates.* Average temperature of warmest month below 50° F (18° C). These climates have no true summer.

Note that four of these five groups (*A, C, D,* and *E*) are defined by temperature averages, whereas one (*B*) is defined by precipitation to evaporation ratios. This may seem to be a fundamental inconsistency.

Subgroups within the five major groups are designated by a second letter according to the following code:

S *Steppe climate:* A semi-arid climate with about 15 to 30 inches of rainfall annually at low latitudes. Exact rainfall boundary determined by formula taking temperature into account.

W *Desert climate:* Arid climate. Most regions included have less than ten inches of rainfall annually. Exact boundary with steppe climate determined by formula.

(The letters *S* and *W* are applied only to the dry *B* climates, yielding two combinations, *BS* and *BW*).

f Moist. Adequate precipitation in all months. No dry season. This modifier is applied to *A, C,* and *D* groups.

w Dry season in winter of the respective hemisphere (low-sun season).

s Dry season in summer of the respective hemisphere (high-sun season).

m Rainforest climate despite short dry season in monsoon type of precipitation cycle. Applies only to *A* climates.

From combinations of the two letter groups, eleven distinct climates emerge as follows:

Af Tropical rainforest (Also *Am,* a variant of *Af*).
Aw Tropical savanna.
BS Steppe climate.
BW Desert climate.
Cw Temperate rainy (humid mesothermal) climate with dry winter.

Cf Temperate rainy (humid mesothermal) climate moist all seasons.
Cs Temperate rainy (humid mesothermal) climate with dry summer.
Df Cold snowy forest (humid microthermal) climate moist in all seasons.
Dw Cold snowy forest (humid microthermal) climate with dry winter.
ET Tundra climate.
EF Climates of perpetual frost (icecaps).

To differentiate still more variations in temperature or other weather elements, Köppen added a third letter to the code group. Meanings are as follows:

a with hot summer; warmest month over 71.6° F (22° C) (*C* and *D* climates).

b with warm summer; warmest month below 71.6° F (22° C) (*C* and *D* climates).

c with cool, short summer; less than four months over 50° F (10° C) (*C* and *D* climates).

d with very cold winter; coldest month below −36.4° F (−38° C) (*D* climates only).

h Dry-hot; mean annual temperature over 64.4° F (18° C) (*B* climates only).

k Dry-cold; mean annual temperature under 64.4° F (18° C) (*B* climates only).

As an example of a complete Köppen climate code, *BWk* would refer to *cool desert climate, Dfc* would refer to *cold snowy forest climate with cool, short summer.* The complete list of climate code designations is included in the summary table of climates to follow. A world map of climates following a later revision of the Köppen system (the Köppen-Geiger system) appears as Figure 12.4.

Need of an explanatory-descriptive climate system

Earlier chapters on weather elements, global circulation, air mass properties and source regions, and cyclonic storms have armed the reader with many principles concerning the causes of weather patterns and their seasonal variations. It would be a pity if this knowledge were left unused with no application in the systematic study of world climates, in favor of a purely empirical system based on temperature and precipitation averages expressed by code letters. The most satisfying systems of natural science classification are those described as *genetic,* meaning that the genesis, or origin, of the phenomena is put first in designing the classification units. Because a genetic system gives an explanation of the things classified, it may be considered as *explanatory.* If the explanation is carried out largely in verbal statements (as distinct from numerical or mathematical statements), it may be described as *descriptive.* This general approach to classification can therefore be designated as *explan-*

---

[5] As already pointed out, the middle latitudes are anything but "temperate" in seasonal and day-to-day weather. *Mesothermal* is widely substituted for *temperate* to imply intermediate temperatures as compared with the extreme heat of dry deserts and the extreme cold of polar and arctic climates.

[6] The term *microthermal,* meaning "small heat," is widely substituted in the United States, along with *mesothermal,* in the titles of Köppen groups *D* and *C* respectively.

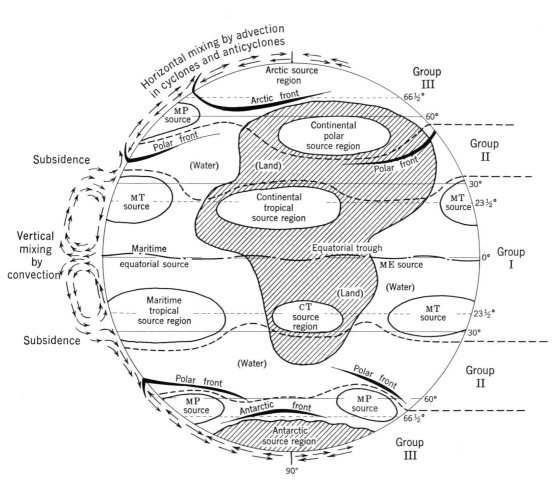

Figure 12.5 Global diagram showing the basis for three major climate groups. (After Petterssen and others.)

atory-descriptive in contrast to the *empirical-quantitative* approach followed in the Köppen system.

In the chapters to follow, world climates are treated by an explanatory-descriptive system based on causes and effects. It will not be difficult to introduce the Köppen code symbols into such a system by way of interrelating the two. In fact, it will soon become apparent that the explanatory-descriptive system is simply providing a reasonable scientific explanation for the existence of Köppen's climate groups and subgroups.

Air mass source regions and frontal zones as a basis of classification

The system of climate analysis used in the succeeding chapters is based on the location of air mass source regions and the nature and movement of air masses, fronts, and cyclonic storms. A schematic global diagram, Figure 12.5, shows the principles of the classification. A world map, Figure 12.6, shows the general locations of each of thirteen fundamental types.

Three major climate groups are shown in Figure 12.5. Group I includes the tropical and equatorial air mass source regions and the equatorial trough or convergence zone between. *Equatorial* is here defined as pertaining to the latitude belt within a few degrees north and south of the equator; *tropical* is defined as referring to the two latitude belts included within a few degrees north and south of the tropics of Cancer and Capricorn.

Climates of Group I are controlled by the dynamic subtropical high-pressure cells, or anticyclones, which are regions of air subsidence and are basically dry, and by the great equatorial trough of convergence that lies between them. Though it is true that air of polar origin occasionally invades the tropical and equatorial latitudes, it may be said of the climates of Group I that they are almost wholly dominated by tropical and equatorial air masses.

Climates of Group II are in a zone of intense interaction between unlike air masses: the *polar front zone*. Tropical air masses moving poleward and polar air masses moving equatorward are in con-

flict in this zone, which contains a procession of east-moving cyclonic storms. Locally and seasonally either tropical or polar air masses may dominate in these regions, but neither has exclusive control.

Climates of Group III are dominated by polar and arctic (including antarctic) air masses.[7] The two polar continental air mass source regions of northern Canada and Siberia fall into this group, but there is no southern hemisphere counterpart to

these continental centers. In the belt of the 60th to 70th parallels, air masses of arctic origin meet polar continental air masses along an *arctic front zone*, creating a series of east-moving cyclones.

Thirteen major climate types are listed below. Where a compound climate type is formed by the alternation of two simple types, it follows them on the list. Simple names are applied to these climate types following common usage among geographers. Numbers correspond with those in Figure 12.6. Köppen symbols are added to the table to show close correspondence of these thirteen types with his eleven climates and their subtypes. Note, however, that the Köppen symbols and climate types can be completely disregarded without affecting the explanatory-descriptive treatment in terms of air masses and frontal zones.

[7] As the reader may have already noticed, the use of *polar* and *arctic* by climatologists is exactly reversed from the logical geographical meanings. Polar source regions should have a polar location; arctic and antarctic source regions should lie near the Arctic and Antarctic circles. To attempt changes in terminology now would result in great confusion in view of the general international adoption of the air mass names.

GROUP I: LOW LATITUDE CLIMATES (CONTROLLED BY EQUATORIAL AND TROPICAL AIR MASSES)

Climate name	Köppen symbol	Air mass source regions and frontal zones, general climate characteristics
1. Equatorial Rainforest Climate 10° N–10° S lat. (Asia 10°–20° N)	Af Tropical rainforest climate, and Am Tropical rainforest climate, monsoon type	Equatorial trough (convergence zone) climates are dominated by warm, moist tropical maritime (MT) and equatorial (ME) air masses yielding heavy rainfall through convectional storms. Remarkably uniform temperatures prevail throughout the year.
2. Trade-Wind Littoral Climate 10°–25° N and S lat.	Included in Af-Am climates	Tropical easterlies (trades) bring maritime tropical (MT) air masses from moist western sides of oceanic subtropical high pressure cells to give narrow east-coast zones of heavy rainfall and uniformly high temperatures. Rainfall shows strong seasonal variation.
3. Tropical Desert and Steppe Climates 15°–35° N and S lat.	BWh Desert climate, hot, and BSh Steppe climate, hot	Source regions of continental-tropical (cT_s) air masses in high-pressure cells at high level over lands astride the Tropics of Cancer and Capricorn give arid to semi-arid climate with very high maximum temperatures and moderate annual range.
4. West Coast Desert Climate 15°–30° N and S lat.	BWk Desert climate, cool, and BWh Desert climate, hot (BWn in earlier versions, n meaning frequent fog)	On west coasts bordering the oceanic subtropical high pressure cells, subsiding maritime tropical (MT_s) air masses are stable and dry. Extremely dry, but relatively cool, foggy desert climates prevail in narrow coastal belts. Annual temperature range is small.
5. Tropical Savanna Climate 5°–25° N and S lat.	Aw Tropical rainy climate, savanna; also Cwa Temperate rainy (Humid mesothermal) climate, dry winter, hot summer	Seasonal alternation of moist MT or ME air masses with dry cT air masses gives climate with wet season at time of high sun, dry season at time of low sun.

GROUP II: MIDDLE LATITUDE CLIMATES (CONTROLLED BY BOTH TROPICAL AND POLAR AIR MASSES)

6. Humid Subtropical Climate 20°–35° N and S lat.	Cfa Temperate rainy (Humid mesothermal) climate, hot summers	Subtropical, eastern continental margins dominated by moist maritime (MT) air masses flowing from the western sides of oceanic high pressure cells. In high-sun season, rainfall is copious and temperatures warm. Winters are cool with frequent continental polar (cP) air mass invasions. Frequent cyclonic storms.

7. Marine West Coast Climate 40°–60° N and S lat.	Cfb	Temperate rainy (Humid mesothermal) climate, warm summers, and
	Cfc	same but cool, short summers

Windward, middle-latitude west coasts receive frequent cyclonic storms with cool, moist maritime polar (MP) air masses. These bring much cloudiness and well-distributed precipitation, but with winter maximum. Annual temperature range is small for middle latitudes.

8. Mediterranean Climate 30°–45° N and S lat.	Csa	Temperate rainy (Humid mesothermal) climate, dry, hot summer, and
	Csb	same, but dry, warm summer

This wet-winter, dry-summer climate results from seasonal alternation of conditions causing climates 4 and 7; MP air masses dominate in winter with cyclonic storms and ample rainfall, MT_s air masses dominate in summer with extreme drought. Moderate annual temperature range.

9. Middle-latitude Desert and Steppe Climates 35°–50° N and S lat.	BWk	Desert climate, cool
	BWk'	same, but cold; and
	BSk	Steppe climate, cool
	BSk'	same, but cold

Interior, middle-latitude deserts and steppes of regions shut off by mountains from invasions of maritime air masses (MT or MP), but dominated by continental tropical (cT) air masses in summer and continental polar (cP) air masses in winter. Great annual temperature range; hot summers, cold winters.

10. Humid Continental Climate 35°–60° N lat.	Dfa	Cold, snowy forest (Humid microthermal) climate, moist all year, hot summers, and
	Dfb	same, but warm summers; also
	Dwa	Cold, snowy forest (Humid microthermal) climate, dry winters, hot summers, and
	Dwb	same, but warm summers

Located in central and eastern parts of continents of middle latitudes, these climates are in the polar front zone, the battle ground of polar and tropical air masses. Seasonal contrasts are strong and weather highly variable. Ample precipitation throughout the year is increased in summer by invading maritime tropical (MT) air masses. Cold winters are dominated by continental polar (cP) air masses invading frequently from northern source regions.

GROUP III: HIGH LATITUDE CLIMATES (CONTROLLED BY POLAR AND ARCTIC AIR MASSES)

11. Subarctic Climate 55°–70° N lat.	Dfc	Cold, snowy forest (Humid microthermal) climate, moist all year, cool summers, and
	Dfd	Same, but very cold winters, also
	Dwc	Cold, snowy forest (Humid microthermal) climate, dry winter, cool summer, and
	Dwd	same, but very cold winter

This climate lies in source region of continental polar (cP) air masses, which in winter are stable and very cold. Summers are short and cool. Annual temperature range is enormous. Cyclonic storms, into which maritime polar (MP) air is drawn, supply light precipitation, but evaporation is small and the climate is therefore effectively moist.

12. Tundra Climate North of 55° N South of 50° S	ET	Polar, tundra climate

The arctic coastal fringes lie along a frontal zone, in which polar (MP, cP) air masses interact with arctic (A) air masses in cyclonic storms. Climate is humid and severely cold with no warm season or summer. Moderating influence of ocean water prevents extreme winter severity as in climate 11.

13. Icecap Climate (Greenland, Antarctica)	EF	Polar climate, perpetual frost

Source regions of arctic (A) and antarctic (AA) air masses situated upon the great continental ice sheets have climate with annual temperature average far below all other climates and no above-freezing monthly average. High altitudes of ice plateaus intensify air mass cold.

Highland Climates

Cool to cold moist climates, occupying high altitude zones of the world's mountain ranges, are localized in extent and not included in classification system.

In the chapters that follow, these climate types are analyzed, the monthly temperature and precipitation averages of representative stations are presented, and the more important influences of the climate upon vegetation and soils are briefly noted.

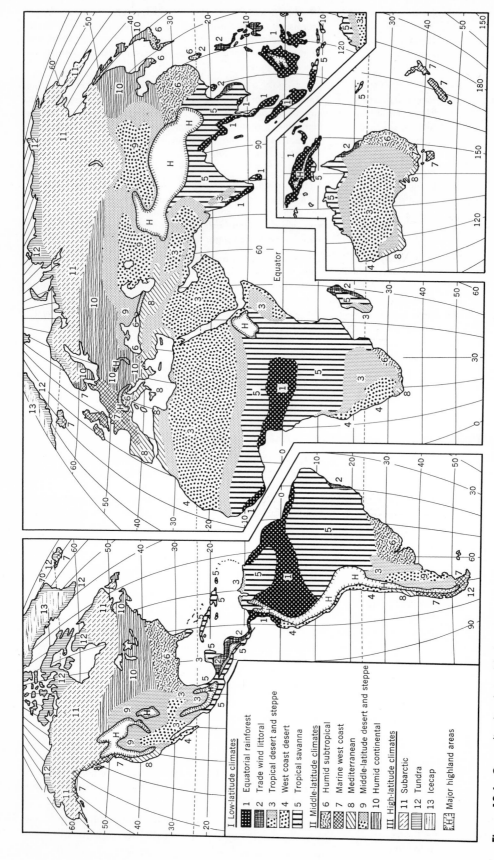

Figure 12.6 Generalized and simplified world map showing distribution of thirteen climates. (Aitoff's equal-area projection adapted by V. C. Finch.)

I Low-latitude climates
1 Equatorial rainforest
2 Trade wind littoral
3 Tropical desert and steppe
4 West coast desert
5 Tropical savanna
II Middle-latitude climates
6 Humid subtropical
7 Marine west coast
8 Mediterranean
9 Middle-latitude desert and steppe
10 Humid continental
III High-latitude climates
11 Subarctic
12 Tundra
13 Icecap
Major highland areas

Review Questions

1. Discuss the importance of climate as a force influencing soils, native vegetation, agriculture, physiology, disease, and other factors that affect human life.

2. What difficulties stand in the way of devising satisfactory climate classifications? In what way can climate maps be misleading?

3. Explain how temperature can be used as a basis for a climate classification. Why is this element alone unsatisfactory as a basis for a climate system?

4. How can annual precipitation be used as a basis for a climate classification? Why does the factor of evaporation make this classification of limited value?

5. Why is it that the distribution of natural vegetation types forms a good basis for distinguishing climate zones? Name and describe the major vegetative types. Explain the general conditions of temperature and precipitation associated with each.

6. Explain the basic principles underlying the Köppen climate system. What are the five major climate groups? What code system is used to designate eleven climates? Name these and give symbols for each.

7. What do each of the following letters mean in the Köppen system: *a, b, c, d, h, k?*

8. Explain how a climate classification system can be based on the air mass source regions, patterns of air mass flow, and frontal zones. What advantage has a natural science classification that is based on origin of the things classified as against one that is based on numerical values?

9. How may the climates of a globe be classified into three major groups on the basis of air mass types.

10. What five climates comprise the group controlled by equatorial and tropical air masses? How are they related to the system of pressure and wind belts? What Köppen climates are equivalent?

11. What five climates are controlled by both tropical and polar air masses? Explain briefly how each type is determined. What Köppen climates are equivalent?

12. What three climates are controlled by polar and arctic air masses? Explain how the large northern hemisphere land masses and icecaps control these climates. What is the arctic front zone? Is there a comparable front zone in the southern hemisphere? What are the equivalent Köppen climates?

CHAPTER THIRTEEN

Equatorial and tropical climates

CLIMATES of Group I are those of low latitudes. They are controlled largely by equatorial and tropical air masses.

1. Equatorial rainforest climate (*Af, Am*)

Bringing together the information on global pattern of weather elements contained in previous chapters and focusing attention on the equatorial belt of the earth, it will be seen that within 5° of latitude north and south of the equator the following conditions prevail:

(*a*) Temperatures average close to 80° for every month (Figures 7.14 and 7.15), so that the annual range is extremely small.

(*b*) Air pressures average between 29.8 and 29.9 inches (1009 and 1012 mb), or slightly less than normal sea-level pressure (Figures 8.5 and 8.6).

(*c*) The general flow of air is from east to west in the tropical easterlies at high altitude, but somewhat more equatorward in the surface trade winds, which originate in the subtropical high-pressure cells. Here, then, is a region of converging warm, unstable air masses meeting along the equatorial trough (Chapter 11).

above: Ploughing for rice in the Padang Highlands, Sumatra. Photograph, Charles P. Cushing.

(*d*) Examination of the world rainfall map (Figure 10.15) shows this to be a belt of heavy rainfall, exceeding 80 inches annually for the most part. This has been explained in Chapter 11 as convectional rainfall from great cumulonimbus masses in weak, slowly moving easterly waves and equatorial lows.

From the above information we can compile a description of the equatorial rainforest climate. Average annual temperatures are close to the 80° F mark; seasonal range of temperature is so slight as to be imperceptible because the sun is high throughout the year. Rainfall is heavy during the entire year, but with considerable differences in monthly averages because of the seasonal shifting of the equatorial convergence zone and a consequent variation in air mass characteristics.

Figure 13.1 is a monthly average temperature-rainfall graph for Iquitos, Peru, a typical equatorial rainforest station located at about 3° S lat. in the broad basin of the Amazon River. Note that the annual range in temperature is only 4° and that the annual rainfall total is more than 100 inches. In all but one month the monthly rainfall averages more than 6 inches. According to Köppen's definition of this *Af* climate, no month averages less than 2.4 in. (6 cm) of rainfall.

Some idea of the extreme monotony of the daily temperature cycle in these climates can be had from Figure 13.2, which shows minimum and maximum daily temperatures for two months at Panama, 9° N lat. An especially noteworthy feature is that the daily range is normally from 15° to 20°, a vastly greater range than the annual range of monthly mean temperatures. In other words, daily variations far exceed seasonal variations in the equatorial rainforest climate.

An illustration of month-to-month differences in average monthly rainfall in the equatorial rainforest climate is given in Figure 13.3. All the stations shown here lie within a few degrees of the equator and are basically similar in climate. The fact that some stations show one maximum and one minimum in the rainfall graph, whereas others have two maxima and two minima is not easily explained, but is probably attributable to a rather complex series of seasonal changes in air mass movements and positions of the equatorial trough.

Because of the abundant rainfall and prevailingly warm temperatures, the equatorial region is characterized by growth of *rainforest*, or *selva*, a vegetation type unexcelled for luxuriance of growth (Figure 13.4). Great broadleaf trees rise to heights of 75 or 100 feet or more, forming a dense leaf canopy through which little sunlight can reach the ground. Giant *lianas* (woody vines) hang from the trees.

Although rainforest is widespread throughout the Amazon basin and the Congo basin, much of this climate zone has a vegetation better described as *jungle*, in which large trees are not so closely set and dense thickets of shrubs and vines form an almost impenetrable mass.

Rainforest and dense jungle are the home of the small forest animals, of which the monkeys are perhaps the best representatives, taking advantage of the continuous forest canopy for living and

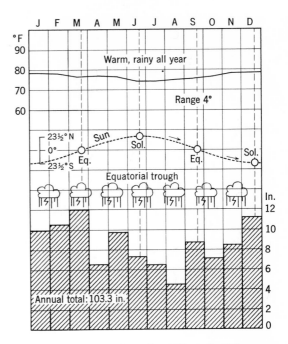

Figure 13.1 Iquitos, Peru, lies 3½° south of the equator in the upper Amazon River basin. Abundant rainfall and uniformly high temperatures make it a representative equatorial rainforest station. (Data from Blair.)

traveling. Birds, too, are numerous in species and spectacularly plumaged.

With copious rainfall and prevailingly high temperatures, chemical processes are continuously active on the rocks and soils in the equatorial rainforest regions. Leaching out of all soluble constituents of the deeply decayed rock results in a distinctive type of soil, termed a *laterite* or *latosol* (Figure 17.8). Reddish or yellowish, and often containing irregular nodules of reddish iron

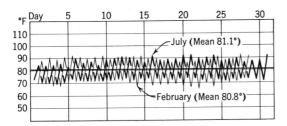

Figure 13.2 July and February are the months of highest and lowest mean temperatures at Panama (9° N lat.), but the difference is hardly detectable. This graph of daily maximum and minimum temperatures emphasizes the monotonous uniformity of the daily temperature cycles in equatorial rainforest climates. (After Mark Jefferson, *Geographical Review*, 1918.)

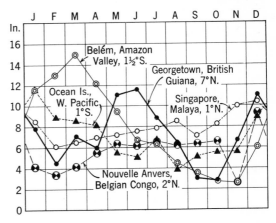

Figure 13.3 Although the equatorial rainforest climates have no dry season, these monthly rainfall averages show marked variation throughout the year, typical of most stations. (Data from Trewartha.)

Figure 13.4 This rainforest near Belém, Brazil, consists of giant trees and lianas. (Photograph by Otto Penner. Courtesy of Instituto Agronómico do Norte.)

hydroxides, this soil is especially rich in hydroxides of iron, manganese, and aluminum. These have been left behind in the soil after the soluble minerals (including silica) have been carried down through the soil and into the streams and rivers. Where large concentrations of the iron, manganese, or aluminum minerals occur as lenses or layers in the soil, they may be extracted as ores of commerical value. *Bauxite* is the foremost ore of aluminum in use today, being extracted, for example, from the Guiana coast of South America. Manganese ores are likewise of great value, but iron ore is as yet not so widely exploited because of its abundance in other forms.

Vegetation and climate work hand in hand to make lateritic soils and ore bodies. At the prevailingly warm temperatures, bacteria in the upper soil layer are unusually vigorous and consume virtually all dead vegetation. Thus *humus*, the black, decomposed vegetable matter present in most soils of middle-latitude and arctic climates, is almost entirely absent. In cooler climates, decomposing plant remains produce organic acids which have the ability to react with the principal oxides of iron, manganese, and aluminum, permitting them to be removed from the soils. In the absence of a surface layer of decomposing organic material and its products, the organic acids, laterites can develop in the equatorial climate. Rotting and decay of bedrock may be very deep in equatorial regions of low topographic relief. It is reported that even to depths as great as 300 feet the rock has been found to be soft and crumbly from chemical action.

Stream flow tends to be fairly constant and extremely copious. River channels are lined along the banks with dense vegetation. Sand bars or sand banks are not so conspicuous as in drier regions. Flood plains have meanders and many swampy sloughs where the river channels have shifted their courses. Although water is abundant, river systems such as the Amazon carry relatively little material in chemical solution. This has been explained as resulting from the thorough leaching of soils, which have little chemical matter left to contribute.

Human transportation is by streams whose sluggish courses can be utilized by dugout canoes or shallow-draft river steamers. The use of light aircraft has, however, greatly simplified long-distance transportation. Villages are built close to the river banks.

Not all equatorial rainforest areas are of low topographic relief. Hilly or mountainous belts have very steep slopes, on which flows, slides, and avalanches of soil and rock frequently occur, stripping away all forest and soil down to the bedrock.

Of economic importance are several forest products. Hardwood lumber, such as mahogany, teak, and rosewood, is a valuable tropical product. Quinine, cocaine, and other drugs come from the bark and leaves of tropical plants; cocoa from the seed kernel of the cacao plant. Rubber, made from the sap of the rubber tree, is now largely an economic product of Malaya, Sumatra and Ceylon, although the tree comes from South America, where it was first exploited.

Although most of the equatorial rainforest climate lies in a belt 10° of latitude on either side of the equator, the Malabar coast of India and the coasts of Burma and Thailand, located between 10° and 25° N lat., have a warm, wet climate with large annual total of rainfall, which also supports

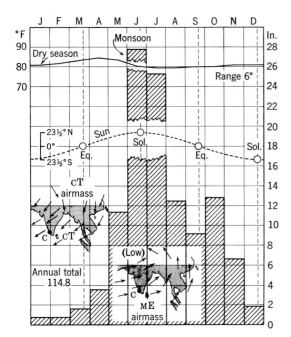

Figure 13.5 Cochin, India, located on the southwest coast at 10° N lat., has a monsoon-controlled variety of equatorial rainforest climate. Enormous precipitation during the rainy monsoon contrasts with a very short dry season, but rainforest vegetation can nevertheless exist. (Data from H. H. Clayton, Smithsonian Institution.)

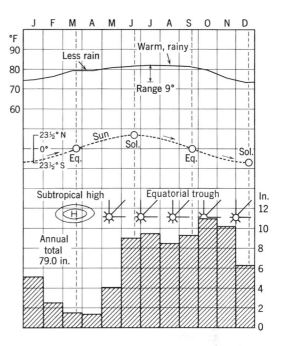

Figure 13.6 Along windward east coasts exposed to trade winds with moist maritime tropical air masses, orographic rainfall is heavy throughout much of the year. This graph for Belize, British Honduras (17° N), is a good example. (Data from Trewartha.)

the rainforest, or selva, vegetation. This Asiatic climate may be considered as a special monsoon type of climate. Under the Köppen system it is designated by the symbol *Am*, with the stipulation that the average rainfall of the driest month shall be less than 2.4 inches (6 cm). Figure 13.5 shows the temperature-precipitation graph of a monsoon type of rainforest climate. A short dry season occurs in the low-sun season, when the winter monsoon is in effect and continental air masses move southward from interior Asia. This dry period is too brief to deplete soil moisture and ground water reserves. Rainforest therefore thrives. Note that the summer (rainy) monsoon brings enormous quantities of rainfall in June and July. This is derived from convectional storms within moist maritime equatorial air masses moving northward from the Indian Ocean.

2. Trade-wind littoral climates (var. of *Af* and *Am*)

A study of the world rainfall map, Figure 10.15, shows that along the east coasts of Central and South America, Madagascar, Indochina, the Philippines, and northeastern Australia, in latitudes 10° to 25°, there are narrow belts of heavy rainfall. These are coasts exposed to moist maritime tropical air masses brought by the tropical easterlies, or trade winds, from the oceanic subtropical highs. These air masses

are abundantly supplied with moisture, as is typical of maritime tropical air on the western sides of the high-pressure cells. When these air masses encounter the hill and mountain slopes of the coasts, a heavy orographic precipitation results. Easterly waves cause periods of rainy weather. In addition, the high-sun solstice period sees the onset of tropical cyclones, to which these coasts are vulnerable.

Because of its coastal position with respect to the easterlies, this climate may be called a *trade-wind littoral climate*. Under the Köppen system it is included with the rainforest climates, *Af* and *Am*. It is treated as a separate climate here because the precipitation characteristics differ from the equatorial rainforest, and the temperatures show a somewhat more pronounced annual range.

The temperature and rainfall graph for a representative station of this climate is shown in Figure 13.6. Belize, British Honduras, is located in Central America at 17° N lat. The total rainfall is great, almost 80 inches annually, and rain is abundant in most months. A tendency toward dryness, typical of the tropical savanna climates which generally elsewhere lie at this same latitude, is seen in the low rainfall of February, March, and April. The temperature cycle has only a small range because of the moderating influence of the nearby ocean.

The warm, wet climates of trade wind coasts support a rainforest vegetation, somewhat similar to that of the equatorial rainforest climates. This represents the farthest poleward limit to which the rainforest extends.

3. Tropical desert and steppe climates (*BWh, BSh*)

In strong contrast to the wet equatorial rainforest climate are the very dry climates controlled by subsiding, outwardly moving air of the continental high-pressure cells which dominate much of the earth's land areas in the latitude belts 15° to 35°, roughly centered on the Tropics of Cancer and Capricorn. Here lie the source regions of the continental tropical (cT_s) air masses. The vast deserts of north Africa, Arabia, Iran, and West Pakistan exemplify this climate type, as do also the Sonoran Desert of the southwestern United States and northern Mexico, and the Australian Desert.

Within this region of general aridity we can recognize the truly arid zones, or *deserts* (*BWh*), in which annual rainfall is less than 10 inches, and the semi-arid zones, or *steppes* (*BSh*), in which rainfall is from 10 to 30 inches annually.

In the continental interiors in these tropical regions, far removed from oceanic sources of moisture, extreme aridity prevails. Average annual rainfall is often less than 5 inches; at some localities a period of several years may pass without measurable rainfall. Because these are regions of subsiding air in the general global scheme of circulation, adiabatic heating reduces the relative humidity of the air to extremely low levels much of the time. Although in the summer low pressure due to ground-surface heating develops over the tropical land masses (as seen in Figures 8.5 and 8.6), this is only a low-level condition, with the permanent highs persisting at higher levels of the atmosphere.

The capacity of tropical desert air for evaporation of exposed water surfaces is enormous (Figure 13.7). In the Sonoran Desert, annual evaporation from a free water surface exceeds 90 or even 100 inches annually, or about 20 times as much as falls in rain. It is obvious that the full amount of evaporation that is possible does not take place in the tropical deserts. Once the stream channels and soil have become dry after a rain, further evaporation is limited to a small amount of moisture slowly brought to the surface locally by capillary movement from moist soil or rock at depth.

Although dryness is the dominant characteristic of the continental tropical air mass source regions, sporadic heavy rainfall does occur from violent convectional storms. Penetration of maritime tropical or equatorial air may be responsible for such storms. During a single cloudburst confined to an area of a few square miles, the major portion of rainfall of one or more years' total may fall, producing debris floods in the stream channels.

The concept of variability in rainfall is an important one in climate study. By variability we mean the degree to which the rainfall of the individual years differs from the average value computed over a long period of years. Figure 13.8 illustrates this principle. The yearly amounts of rainfall are shown by bars for three stations for a period of many years. At the top the record for Padang, Sumatra, gives data for a typical equatorial rainforest climate; the bottom graph gives rainfall for Abbassia, Egypt (near Cairo), a tropical desert station. The middle graph is of a combined climate type (Type 5), discussed later. We say that the rainfall variability of the wet equatorial climate is small because the individual yearly amounts were, in this case, never more than twice the average or less than a third of the average. On the other hand, Abbassia shows great variability because, although several years had no rainfall at all, five of the years had more than twice the average amount and two of the years had four or more times the average.

Rainfall variability has been estimated for the world by Dr. Erwin Biel, a copy of whose map is shown in Figure 13.9. As would be expected, the dry tropical desert areas lying near the tropics of Cancer and Capricorn have the highest variability; the equatorial belt of heavy rainfall, the least variability of the low-latitude part of the globe.

Consider next the temperature conditions of the dry continental tropical air mass source regions. Figure 13.10 shows the yearly march of temperatures at Yuma, Arizona, a representative station of the tropical desert (*BWh*) climate type. Two points are noteworthy: (*a*) temperatures are very high

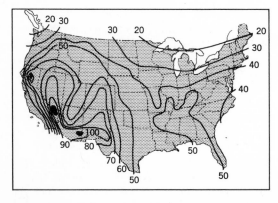

Figure 13.7 Annual evaporation from free water surfaces is very high in the deserts of southwestern United States but relatively low in the cool, humid climates. Figures on this generalized map tell depth of evaporation in inches. (After Mead.)

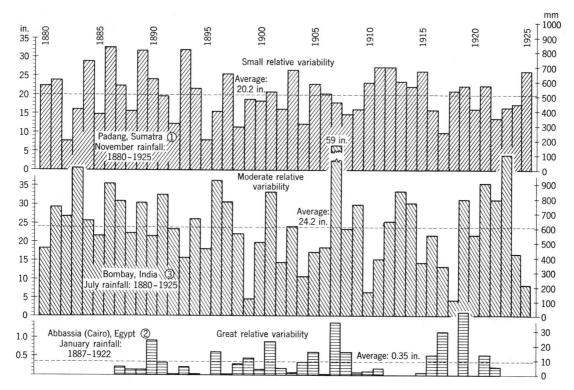

Figure 13.8 These three graphs illustrate the concept of variability of rainfall by showing the actual amount of rain received each year during the month which, on the average, is the rainiest month at that place. (Data from H. H. Clayton, Smithsonian Institution.)

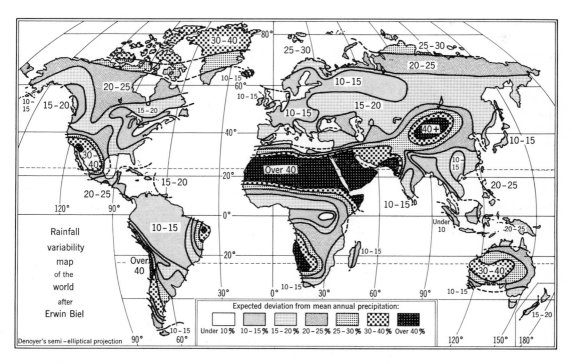

Figure 13.9 Rainfall variability map of the world. (After Erwin Biel. Courtesy of American Geographical Society.)

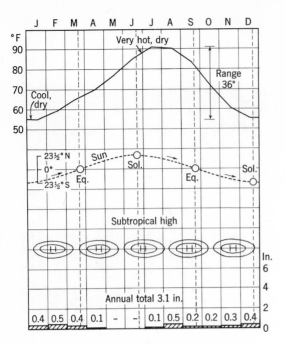

Figure 13.10 Yuma, Arizona, is a station of somewhat more northerly location than the North African–Arabian desert belt. It has a wide annual temperature range and little rainfall in any month. Extreme heat characterizes the summer months. (Data from Trewartha.)

during the period of high sun; (*b*) annual range is moderately strong. Normally the annual range of temperature (hottest-month average minus coolest-month average) in these climates is 20° to 30° and is directly related to the height of the sun in the sky.

More interesting, perhaps, than annual range is the normal daily range of temperatures in the tropical deserts. Figure 13.11 shows maximum and minimum daily readings for the months of January and July at Phoenix, Arizona. Note that the daily range is often as much as 35°, the average daily range about 30°. In no other climate does so great a daily range occur. This is explained by the rapid

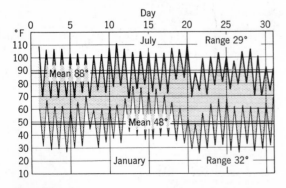

Figure 13.11 Phoenix, Arizona, in the Sonoran Desert affords a good illustration of the large daily and yearly ranges of temperature found in the tropical deserts. (After Mark Jefferson, *Geographical Review*, 1918.)

nightly heat loss from the ground and lower air layers because of the low water-vapor content of the air. On the other hand, insolation during the day is extremely intense and air temperatures soar to great heights. An all-time record range was recorded in Bir Milrha in the Sahara Desert, south of Tripoli, where 31° F and 99° F were recorded on the same day, a range of 68°![1]

The world's highest temperatures are recorded in certain parts of the continental tropical deserts. A world record maximum of 136.4° F was officially observed in the shade under standard shelter at Azizia, 25 miles south of Tripoli. Figure 13.12 shows the highest temperatures ever observed in the western United States. The Sonoran Desert region of the lower Colorado River valley clearly surpasses all other areas for high temperatures.

In the extremely dry deserts (*BWh*), virtually the entire land surface is free of vegetation and consists of bare rock, stream gravels and sands, or drifting dune sands. This does not mean that vegetation is wholly absent, rather, that the many species are thinly spread over the surface and lack foliage to protect or obscure the bare ground. Desert plants are adapted to long drought periods by thick, fleshy leaves and stems, which store water for long periods of time but which do not permit loss of water through the surface. Representative of desert vegetation are the cacti and other shrubs seen in the Sonoran Desert of southwestern United States and northern Mexico (Figure 13.13).

Soils of the deserts are lacking in humus and are of a grayish or reddish color, depending upon the type of iron compound present to produce staining. These soils contain excessive amounts of calcium carbonate and other salts, which are left near the ground surface by evaporating water. In the centers of shallow lakes, the salts concentrate to form white saltflats, entirely sterile and almost perfectly smooth.

For a discussion of landforms and geographic aspects of the mountainous desert topography, the student is referred to Chapter 25 on the fluvial cycle of land mass denudation.

Tropical steppe climate (*BSh*) borders the tropical deserts on both north and south, and in places on the east as well. Locally because of altitude, plateaus and high plains within what would otherwise be desert have the semi-arid steppe climate. Steppe zones lying equatorward of the deserts are transitional into the tropical savanna climate (*Aw*) and resemble it in many ways (Figure 13.14). Steppes on the poleward fringes of the tropical deserts grade into the Mediterranean climate (*Cs*)

[1] G. T. Trewartha, *An Introduction to Weather and Climate*, McGraw-Hill, New York, 1943, p. 367.

in many places. Steppes typically include vast grassy plains and plateaus, able to support limited numbers of grazing animals but not generally moist enough for crop cultivation without irrigation. Soils are commonly of the *brown soil* and *chestnut soil* groups, containing some humus.

4. West coast desert climate (*BWk, BWh*)

Again referring to the world rainfall map, Figure 10.15, it will be seen that all west coasts in latitudes 15° to 30° are extremely dry, generally with less than ten inches of rainfall annually. The arid belt extends continuously eastward to inland continental tropical deserts. Does it not seem strange that extreme dryness exists immediately along the shores of the oceans, close to possible sources of moist maritime air masses? The interior tropical deserts, already discussed, are logically explained by land-centered high-pressure cells into which moist air masses cannot easily drift, but the dry west coast strips are located between the oceanic and continental high-pressure cells where we might expect to find some development of fronts and convergence of air masses. The key to this problem seems to lie in the fact that the oceanic subtropical high-pressure cells are inherently dry on their east sides. This can be attributed to two factors: (1) the air flow from these cells (see Figure 8.18) on their eastern sides is equatorward, and the warming of the air as it moves into lower latitudes would tend to reduce the relative humid-

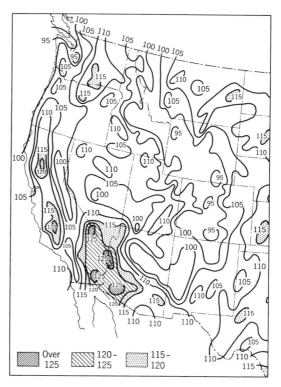

Figure 13.12 The highest temperatures (Fahrenheit) ever observed during the period 1899–1938 are shown on this map. The Sonoran Desert of the lower Colorado River region is clearly the region of record high temperatures. (After J. B. Kincer, U.S. Dept. Agriculture, Yearbook of American Agriculture, 1941.)

Figure 13.13 This Sonoran Desert landscape in western Arizona has a sparse cover of cactus and other drought-resistant plants, but a coarse, bouldery alluvial soil is everywhere exposed on the sloping plains bordering the mountain ranges.

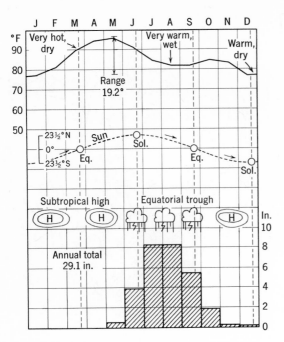

Figure 13.14 The record of Kayes, Sudanese Republic (14½° N lat.), illustrates a steppe climate close to the tropical savanna climate zone. A short wet season occurring a month or two after summer solstice and a long dry season during winter solstice show dominance of the dry continental tropical air masses. (Data from Trewartha.)

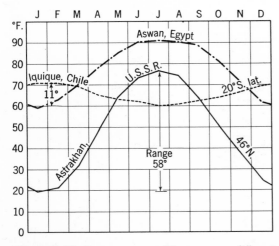

Figure 13.15 Temperature conditions are very different at coastal and interior tropical desert locations. Whereas Iquique on the Chilean coast has a small annual range, Aswan, Egypt, in a vast continental desert has a great annual range. That of a middle-latitude desert, Astrakhan, USSR (46° N), is greater still. (Data from H. H. Clayton, Smithsonian Institution, and Trewartha.)

ity; (2) the circulation in these cells is thought to be such that the air on the east sides is subsiding as it moves outward, hence, is adiabatically heated and its humidity reduced. The result is dry, stable air masses that bring an arid zone not only to the coast but extending far seaward as well. Strangely enough, there are dry deserts over the oceans in these tropical latitudes.

In what respects do the dry west coasts differ in climate from the interior continental deserts which they adjoin? The principal difference is in temperature. The coastal deserts are relatively cool, with annual average temperatures around 65°, whereas the interior continental deserts average some 10° higher. The presence of cool upwelling and equatorward-flowing currents, such as the Humboldt and Benguela currents, explains the lowered temperatures. (See Chapter 9.) More important still is the very low annual range of temperature in the coastal deserts. This is illustrated in Figure 13.15 by the temperature graph of Iquique, Chile (20° S), on the dry Atacama Desert coast of South America. The annual range is only 11°. In contrast, the temperature cycle of Aswan, Egypt (24° N), shows both a higher average and a greater range.

Although treated here as a separate climate from the tropical desert climate, not all climate classifications make the distinction. In the original Köppen classification, the cooler desert west coasts are designated by the symbol *BWn*, in which *n* means *frequent fog* (from the German, *nebel*, meaning fog). Persistent coastal fog banks form in the cool lower air layer overlying the cool ocean water. In the latest versions of the Köppen climate system, the symbols *BWh* and *BWk* are applied to the west coast deserts. The *BWk* climate is limited to the South American and Southwest African coasts in latitudes 20° to 32° S, where the cool ocean currents are most influential.

Vegetation and soils of the cool west coast deserts are essentially similar to those of the interior deserts. An unusually high incidence of fog on these coasts leads to growth of some specialized plants which can exist on condensed moisture close to the shore.

5. Tropical savanna climate (*Aw*, also *Cwa*)

We have thus far considered two extreme climate types. One, a wet climate lying in the equatorial zone, the other a desert climate arranged in two belts along the Tropics of Cancer and Capricorn. What of the intermediate zones where these two climate types come together? Knowing from previous study that the pressure and wind belts of the globe migrate northward at June solstice season, southward at December solstice season, we can infer that the intermediate zones in question will have climates that combine the characteristics of the first two types in a seasonal alternation. This results in the tropical savanna (*Aw*) climate, which has a wet season controlled by moist, warm equatorial and maritime tropical air masses at time of high sun and a dry season controlled by the continental tropical air masses at time of low sun.

The latitude belts in which tropical savanna climate is found lie roughly between 5° and 25° latitude, throughout Central and South America, Africa, and Australia. In southeast Asia this zone is pushed northward to latitudes 10° to 30° because the continental tropical air mass source region in summer is necessarily situated farther north to conform to the Asiatic land mass.

Climate characteristics of the tropical savanna climate can be learned from Figure 13.16, which gives temperature and rainfall data for a representative west African station. This can be studied in conjunction with Figure 13.17, which shows seasonal air mass and flow patterns. Timbo lies closer to the equator than Kayes, representing the tropical steppe (*BSh*) climate (Figure 13.14), hence has a longer wet season and a more even temperature cycle. Note especially the fact that maximum temperatures occur in March, April, or May, rather than in July, because the onset of the rains brings a cloud cover and cooler air temperatures.

The Asiatic savanna climate is somewhat different in that the monsoon controls are strong and bring an extreme contrast of wet and dry conditions. If we now look at the record of Allahabad, India, 25° N lat. (Figure 13.18), the basic similarity to Kayes and Timbo in western Africa (Figures 13.14 and 13.16), is very marked. The higher latitude of Allahabad results in much cooler January temperatures, and a greater annual range, but otherwise the temperature curves show the same dip during the rainy season. Köppen places Allahabad and a large belt of southeastern Asia in latitudes 20° to 25° in the *Cwa* climate (temperate, rainy climate, dry winter, hot summer). The *Cw* climate is a poleward extension of the *Aw* climate both here and in Africa and South and Central America. The two are here treated under the tropical savanna climate inasmuch as tropical air masses dominate.

The contrast in wet and dry season rainfall in the tropical savanna climate is further illustrated in Figure 13.19. Here the rainfall of the one rainiest month is compared with the total for the three consecutive driest months for a number of typical stations. Rainfall is not so reliable in the tropical savanna climates as in the equatorial rainforest

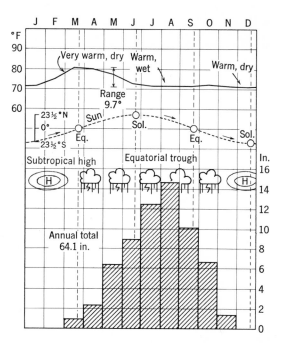

Figure 13.16 Timbo, Republic of Guinea (10° 40′ N lat.), provides a good illustration of alternate rainy and dry seasons found in the savanna climate zone lying between the tropical deserts and the equatorial rainforest. (Data from Trewartha.)

climate but is more reliable than in the very dry tropical deserts. This can be seen from the record of Bombay, India, in Figure 13.8, and is also apparent from the world variability map, Figure 13.9.

Alternation of wet and dry seasons results in the growth of a distinctive native vegetation known generally as the *tropical savanna*. This is characterized by open expanses of tall grasses, interspersed with hardy, drought-resistant shrubs and trees (Figure 13.20). Other areas have a light scrub and thorn forest; some highland areas have a dense jungle of a semi-deciduous type. (See Figure 12.2.)

Savanna and jungle vegetation types of the tropical savanna climates have in common the ability to persist through a yearly drought of two to four months. The long grasses dry up but quickly revive at the onset of the rainy season. Trees are adapted to low moisture losses by having thick, leathery leaves (as on the mango or banyan), or by very tiny leaves (as on the thorny types).

Soils of the tropical savanna climates are mostly yellowish or reddish latosols, similar to those described in connection with the equatorial rainforest climates. Excessive leaching is again the result of the heavy rainfall and high temperatures. In gen-

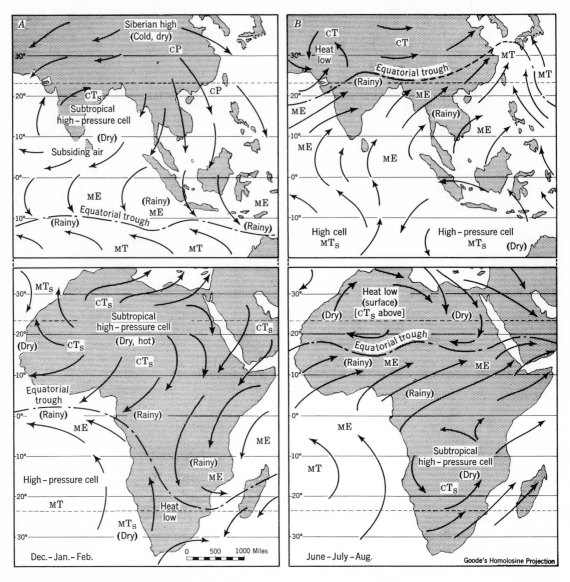

Figure 13.17 These maps of Africa and southern Asia illustrate one interpretation of the air mass source regions and circulation patterns that govern the equatorial and tropical climates. (Modified after M. A. Garbell, *Tropical and Equatorial Meteorology*, New York, 1947. Based on Goode Base Map. Copyright by the University of Chicago. Used by permission of the University of Chicago Press.)

eral, these residual soils are not fertile and are little cultivated in South America and Africa, but flood plain alluvium is highly productive. Stream flow in these regions contrasts greatly with that of the equatorial rainforest climates, in that the former has a very strong seasonal fluctuation. From flood conditions with large low-lying areas under water in the rainy season, the streams and rivers pass to a regime of little or no flow in the dry season, when channel bottoms of sand and gravel are ex-

posed and mud flats dry out.

Closely related to vegetation and climate is the natural animal life of the savanna grasslands and light forest or jungle. These are the regions of the carnivorous game animals and a vast multitude of grazing animals on which they feed. The grasslands of Africa are the natural home of such herbivores as wildebeest, gazelle, deer, antelope, buffalo, rhinoceros, zebra, giraffe, and elephant. On them feed the lion, leopard, hyena, and jackal. Some of the

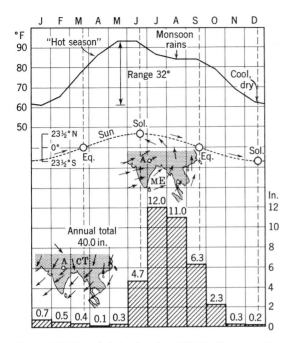

Figure 13.18 Allahabad, India (25° N), illustrates the monsoon-controlled variety of the tropical savanna climate. It is basically similar to the African savanna climate, but has somewhat lower temperatures during the winter-solstice season. (Data from H. H. Clayton, Smithsonian Institution.)

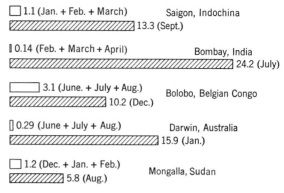

Figure 13.19 Rainfall of the one wettest month is shown contrasted with the total rainfall of the three consecutive driest months for five tropical savanna climate stations. (Data from Clayton and Trewartha.)

Figure 13.20 This African tall-grass savanna in Kenya Colony has a scattering of flat-topped acacia trees. (Richard U. Light, American Geographical Society.)

herbivores depend upon fleetness of foot to escape the predators. Others, such as the rhinoceros, buffalo, and elephant, defend themselves by their size, strength, or armor-thick hide. The giraffe is a peculiar adaptation to savannas; his long neck permits browsing upon the higher foliage of scattered trees.

The dry season brings a severe struggle for existence to animals of the African savannas. As streams and hollows dry up, the few muddy waterholes must supply all drinking water. Danger of attack by carnivores is greatly increased.

The Indian savanna and light jungle has a somewhat similar animal assemblage. Deer and antelope are especially abundant, with some water buffalo and a few rhinoceroses. The tiger replaces the lion as the principal carnivore. The Indian elephant, however, is largely restricted in natural habitat to the rainforest coastal strips of Burma, the Malabar coast, and Ceylon.

Review Questions

1. What conditions of temperature, pressure, and rainfall prevail in the equatorial belt? What air masses are present? Under what conditions does heavy precipitation occur? How does the equatorial trough change position throughout the year?

2. Describe the annual temperature curve for a typical station in the equatorial rainforest (*Af*) climate zone. What range is usually found? How does the daily temperature range compare with the annual range?

3. Approximately how great is the average annual rainfall of the equatorial rainforest climate? How is rainfall distributed throughout the year? Is variability of rainfall great or small?

4. What is rainforest? Of what types of trees and vines is it composed? What is selva?

5. What is a lateritic soil (latosol)? What processes are responsible for development of lateritic soils. Of what economic importance are laterites?

6. Is there much humus in lateritic soils (latosols)? Explain how temperature and bacterial activity affect the accumulation of decomposed vegetation in the hot equatorial regions as contrasted with cold regions.

7. Is the chemical decay of rock relatively small or great in wet equatorial climates?

8. What can be said about stream flow in the equatorial rainforest climate? In what way are rivers of importance to native inhabitants of these regions?

9. In what way does the wet, monsoon-dominated climate of the southern Asiatic coasts (*Am*) differ from that close to the equator (*Af*)?

10. Why is there heavy precipitation on east coast belts in latitudes 10° to 25°? What climate occurs here? What type of climate occurs at inland locations in this same latitude belt?

11. What causes the tropical deserts in latitudes 15° to 35°? Explain these deserts in terms of the global pattern of air circulation. What kind of air mass has its source over these areas?

12. Distinguish between desert and steppe climates. What Köppen symbols denote these climates?

13. Discuss the evaporation of moisture in the tropical deserts. How great is evaporation from a free water surface? What influence has this upon streams and the ground water table?

14. What type of rainfall occurs in the tropical deserts? Is it widespread or localized? Is rainfall variability in these deserts great or small?

15. What is the nature of the annual temperature cycle in the tropical deserts? Explain these characteristics. What is the nature of the daily cycle of temperature? How does it compare with that of the equatorial rainforest climate?

16. What kind of vegetation is native to the tropical deserts? To what extent does it afford cover to the ground? What kinds of soils are typical of these deserts?

17. Explain the west coast deserts in latitudes 15° to 30°. How are these related to the subtropical high pressure cells? Why is the air dry in these locations?

18. What is the outstanding feature of the annual temperature cycle of the west coast deserts? Why is the range small? Why are the temperatures abnormally low for this latitude? Why is fog abundant along these coasts?

19. Explain the characteristic seasonal features of the tropical savanna climate in terms of air masses and seasonal shifting of the pressure and wind belts of the globe.

20. How do annual precipitation and its distribution throughout the year change if we start with the equatorial rainforest climate zone and examine the rainfall records for stations progressively farther north until the Sahara Desert is reached?

21. Describe the annual temperature cycle of the tropical savanna climate. When is the maximum reached? Why does this not coincide with the time of highest sun?

22. In what way does the Asiatic savanna climate differ from that of Africa or South America? Explain. How does Köppen distinguish the climate of north India from the savanna climate of peninsular India?

23. What is the natural vegetation of the tropical savanna climate? What are the characteristics of the wild animal life of these regions? What type of soil is generally present? What effect has the seasonal contrast of dry and wet periods upon stream flow?

Exercises

1. Prepare a rainfall-temperature graph (similar to Figure 13.1) for each of the following stations. (Data from Trewartha.)

(a) *Belém, Brazil, 1° S*

	J	F	M	A	M	J	J	A	S	O	N	D	
Temperature	77.7	77.0	77.5	77.7	78.4	78.3	78.1	78.3	78.6	79.0	79.7	79.0	° F
Precipitation	11.6	12.9	14.9	12.1	9.4	6.7	6.2	4.5	3.5	2.8	2.6	6.0	inches

(b) *Cairo, Egypt, 30° N*

	J	F	M	A	M	J	J	A	S	O	N	D	
Temperature	55	57	63	70	76	80	82	82	78	74	65	58	° F
Precipitation	0.4	0.2	0.2	0.2	. . .	. . .	. . .	. . .	. . .	. . .	0.1	0.2	inches

2. For each of the above stations calculate. **(a)** Average annual temperature. (Add monthly mean temperatures and divide by 12.) **(b)** Annual temperature range. (Difference between means of warmest and coolest months.) **(c)** Average annual total rainfall. (Add monthly rainfall figures.)

3. **(a)** To what climate does each of these stations in Exercise 1 belong? **(b)** Study the data of Belém. If maximum rainfall occurs at times when the sun is highest in the sky, what months should show a maximum rainfall? **(c)** Why does this principle not hold true for Belém? **(d)** Explain the marked maximum of rainfall in January–April and a minimum period April–November.

4. **(a)** How does it happen that Cairo, a great city of over two million population, lies in an extremely dry, tropical desert? **(b)** Name other great cities which lie in true desert climates.

5. Prepare a rainfall-temperature graph similar to Figure 13.1 for each of the following stations. (Data from Trewartha.)

(a) *Akyab, Burma, 20° N*

	J	F	M	A	M	J	J	A	S	O	N	D	
Temperature	70	73	79	83	84	82	81	81	82	82	78	72	° F
Precipitation	0.1	0.2	0.5	2.0	13.7	49.4	53.7	42.5	24.6	11.6	5.0	0.6	inches

(b) *Cuyaba, Brazil, 15½° S*

	J	F	M	A	M	J	J	A	S	O	N	D	
Temperature	81	81	81	80	78	75	76	78	82	82	82	81	° F
Precipitation	9.8	8.3	8.3	4.0	2.1	0.3	0.2	1.1	2.0	4.5	5.9	8.1	inches

(c) *Benares, India, 25° N*

	J	F	M	A	M	J	J	A	S	O	N	D	
Temperature	60	65	77	87	91	89	84	83	83	78	68	60	° F
Precipitation	0.7	0.6	0.4	0.2	0.6	4.8	12.1	11.6	7.1	2.1	0.2	0.2	inches

6. **(a)** Determine average annual temperature, annual temperature range, and annual precipitation for each of the stations in Exercise 5. **(b)** To what climate does each station belong?

7. **(a)** In what way does the temperature cycle at Akyab, Burma, differ from that of Cuyaba, Brazil? (See data in Exercise 5 above.) **(b)** Explain this difference. **(c)** What is the reason that Akyab receives so much more rainfall than Cochin, India (Figure 13.5), although the two are both west coast Asiatic stations subject to similar monsoon conditions?

8. **(a)** Comparing the two tropical savanna climates for which data are given, why does the rainfall of Cuyaba, Brazil (Exercise 5), show a minimum in the period June–August, whereas the minimum for Timbo (Figure 13.16), occurs in the period December–March? (*b*) Of these two stations, which has the drier dry season? Which has the wetter wet season? (*c*) Of these two stations, does the one with greater seasonal rainfall contrast also have the greater annual temperature range? Explain.

9. Prepare a rainfall-temperature graph similar to Figure 13.1 for the following station. (Data from Trewartha.)

Port Nolloth, S. Africa, 29½° S

	J	F	M	A	M	J	J	A	S	O	N	D	
Temperature	60	60	59	58	57	55	55	54	55	58	59	60	° F
Precipitation	. . .	0.1	0.2	0.2	0.4	0.3	0.2	0.4	0.3	. . .	0.2	0.1	inches

10. (*a*) Compare the data of the desert stations in Exercises 1 and 9. (*b*) What two varieties of tropical desert do they represent? (*c*) Why has Port Nolloth such a small annual temperature range? (*d*) Is rainfall greater or less during the warmer months than in the cooler months for these two stations? Explain.

CHAPTER FOURTEEN

Middle-latitude climates

CLIMATES of Group II are those of middle latitudes occupying the polar front zone in which both tropical and polar air masses play an important part. The latitude belt in which these climates lie is subject to cyclonic storms; most of the precipitation in these climates occurs along fronts within these cyclones.

6. Humid subtropical climate (*Cfa*)

The moist nature of the west sides of the oceanic subtropical high-pressure cells has already been discussed in Chapter 11. Not only does maritime tropical (mT) air move toward cooler, higher latitudes, where its relative humidity is increased, but the air in this part of the cell is thought to be rising as it moves outward. Thus, by adiabatic cooling it is brought closer to the dew point. As these moist, unstable maritime tropical air masses move over the eastern continental coasts in latitudes 25° to 35° and drift inland, they bring the necessary moisture and heat energy for heavy precipitation. Lifting occurs along warm and cold fronts where the tropical air encounters polar air. This general pattern of climate, here called the *humid subtropical climate*, is exemplified by the southern Atlantic and Gulf Coast states of the United States; corresponding regions are found in the Argentina-Uruguay-southern Brazil area of South America, in eastern China and southern Japan, along a small part of the southeastern coast of Africa, and on the east Australian coast.

In the Köppen system, these areas lie in the *Cfa* climate, described as a temperate rainy climate with hot summers. Temperature specifications of the *C* climates have been stated in Chapter 12. The *Cfa* climate has no dry season, and even the driest summer month receives more than 1.2 inches (3 cm) of rain. The hot summer specified by the letter *a* is one in which the average temperature of the warmest month is over 71.6° F (22° C).

For an analysis of the temperature and precipitation characteristics of this moist, subtropical climate, we may refer to the record for Charleston, South Carolina (Figure 14.1). Rainfall is ample at all times of the year, but is distinctly greater during the summer when the oceanic high strengthens and the flow of maritime tropical air is increased. Thunderstorms are especially frequent in summer (Figure 14.2). They may be of the thermal (heat) type, or of squall-line or cold front origin. An occasional tropical cyclone may strike the coastal

above: Temple of Castor and Pollux, Girgenti, Italy.
Photograph by Sawders, from Cushing.

209

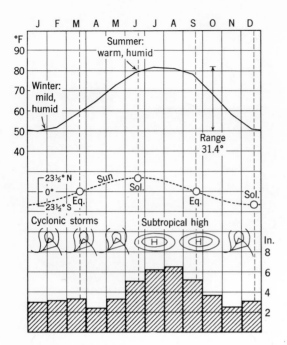

Figure 14.1 Charleston, South Carolina, illustrates the humid subtropical climate of continental margins exposed to frequent invasion by maritime tropical air masses. Temperature and rainfall during the summer months are very much the same as in the equatorial rainforest climates. (Data from Trewartha.)

area, bringing very heavy rains. Winter precipitation, some of it in the form of snow, is of frontal type in the frequent middle-latitude cyclones that sweep over these regions.

Temperatures show a moderately strong range, of very much the same magnitude as in the tropical deserts, but without the extreme heat in summer. Humidity is, of course, very high, in marked contrast to the deserts, and summer climate on the humid east coasts is at times similar to the equatorial rainforest climate in temperature, rainfall, and humidity. Winters show the influence of outbursts of polar air masses, which frequently penetrate into subtropical latitudes and bring below-freezing weather with killing frosts. We might say that this climate type is shared to some extent by both tropical and polar air masses, but that the tropical air masses prevail most of the time and dominate in summer.

In southeast Asia the humid east coast subtropical climate is somewhat modified by intensive monsoon development. Winter air masses from interior Asia are very dry, and a winter scarcity of precipitation develops, whereas maritime air masses in summer, together with occasional typhoons, cause a strongly accentuated maximum in the summer. This shows clearly in the precipitation cycle of Shanghai, China (Exercise 1).

Perhaps the most representative natural vegetation type of the humid subtropical climates is the broadleaf and mixed broadleaf-coniferous forest. This is found over much of the southeastern United States, in China and Japan, in eastern Australia, and in southern Brazil. (See Figure 12.2). Common trees include the oak, chestnut, and pine. The soils of the moister, warmer parts of these regions are strongly leached red-yellow soils related to the latosols of the humid tropical and equatorial climates. Rich in iron and aluminum oxides, these soils are poor in many of the mineral constituents essential for successful agricultural production.

7. Marine west coast climate (*Cfb, Cfc*)

Shifting attention now toward higher latitudes, and using the information about air masses, fronts, and cyclones presented in Chapter 11, we might expect to find that western coasts in the belt of cyclonic storms would receive ample rainfall from maritime polar air masses and would have rather moderate temperature variations because of the proximity to the oceans from which the easterly moving air masses tend to drift landward.

These conditions are fulfilled in west coasts of land masses lying between 40° or 45° and 60° latitude. Situated too far poleward to come under the dry influence of the subtropical oceanic high-pressure cells, these climates lack a dry season. Because the continental polar air masses tend to drift eastward, they rarely move westward to visit the west coasts, hence severe dry-cold conditions are uncommon. Köppen classifies the marine west coast climate as *Cfb*, a temperate rainy climate with warm summers. The average temperature of the warmest month is under 71.6° F (22° C) and at least four months average 50° F (10° C) or more.

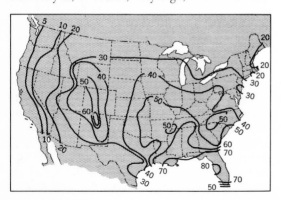

Figure 14.2 Thunderstorms are more common in the humid Gulf Coast states and Florida peninsula than in any other parts of the United States. Figures tell the average annual number of days with thunderstorms, based on records of the period 1899–1938. (After J. B. Kincer, U.S. Dept. Agriculture, *Yearbook of Agriculture, 1941.*)

The cool summer variety *Cfc* has fewer than four months with averages over 50° F (10° C).

Climate of the middle-latitude west coasts is illustrated by the graphs for Brest, France (Figure 14.3), located at 49° N lat. on the Brittany coast. Precipitation is well distributed throughout the year, but shows a distinct reduction during the summer months. This feature is also found on rainfall graphs for coastal stations on the Pacific northwest coast of the United States. Why should this reduction occur? In summer, the oceanic subtropical high is most strongly developed and moves farthest north, bringing its arid influence to bear just enough to make a distinct decrease in summer rainfall. In other words, this is a manifestation of the same mechanism that causes a west coast desert in low latitudes.

Although the total rainfall for Brest and similar marine west coast stations is not great, judged by tropical or equatorial standards, the cooler air temperatures reduce evaporation and produce a very damp, humid climate with much cloud cover. Nearness to the ocean makes for a small annual temperature range, just as it does in lower latitudes on the west coast deserts. Mild winters and relatively cool summers are characteristic. Winters which are severely cold at the same latitudes in midcontinent and east-continent positions are by contrast surprisingly mild on the west coasts.

The influence of coastal ranges upon rainfall is extremely marked in middle latitudes. Whereas low-lying coasts, such as in northern France or southern England, receive only 30 to 40 inches of rainfall annually, mountainous coasts of British Columbia, Alaska, Norway, and Chile get more than 80 inches. This has been a major factor in the development of fiords along the seacoasts. (See Chapter 26.) Heavy snows in the glacial period nourished vigorous valley glaciers which descended to the sea, scouring deep troughs below sea level at their lower ends.

Natural vegetation of the marine west coast climate of Europe is a deciduous forest dominated by oak, beech, and hornbeam, whereas that of North America is of the coniferous forest type on windward mountain slopes. On coast ranges of the Pacific northwest, Douglas fir, red cedar, and spruce grow in magnificent forests (Figure 14.4). Soils of these mountainous slopes are of a strongly leached type, the *podsols*, and are acid in nature. Under cool temperatures, bacterial activity is slow, in contrast to the warm tropics, so that vegetative matter is not consumed and forms a heavy surface humus deposit. Organic acids from the decomposing vegetation react with the soil compounds, resulting in removal of such bases as calcium, sodium, and potassium, and the product is a soil

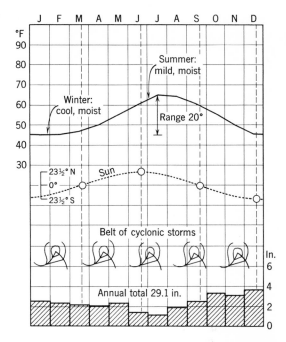

Figure 14.3 Brest, France, on the coast of Brittany (49° N), serves as a representative station for the marine west coast climate in middle latitudes. (Data from Blair.)

adapted well to coniferous trees but generally unsuited to deciduous trees and grasses. Soils of western Europe are of the *gray-brown podzolic* type, well suited to agriculture and to the growth of deciduous forests.

8. Mediterranean climate (*Csa, Csb*)

Lying on west coasts between latitudes 30° and 45° is a zone subject to alternate wet and dry seasons because it is located in the transitional zone between the dry west coast tropical desert on the equatorward side and the wet west coast climate on the poleward side. Because these two climate types have been analyzed and described in previous pages, we need only substitute the information into a compound climate type.

Consider the climate of Monterey, California, as an example (Figure 14.5). In summer, when the oceanic subtropical high is most powerfully developed and farthest north, the desert conditions that prevail permanently farther south along the coast take over control of the climate and bring a severe drought. However, the proximity of the ocean with its cool current keeps summer temperatures to a mild 60° average. In winter, the humid regime of middle-latitude cyclones and moist maritime polar (mP) air masses is felt in the ample precipitation.

The wet-winter dry-summer west coast climate is particularly extensive in the Mediterranean lands. Hence, the name *Mediterranean climate* is com-

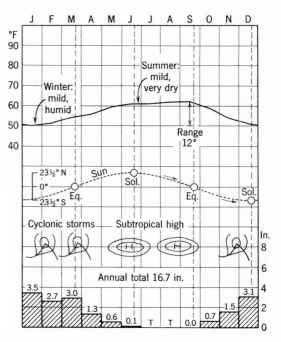

Figure 14.5 Monterey, California, is a good example of a Mediterranean climate station close to the ocean. A summer drought alternating with a moist winter is characteristic of this climate. (Data from Blair.)

Figure 14.4 This mixed stand of white pine, Douglas fir, and Englemann spruce on the western slopes of the Cascade Range in Washington is typical of the rich coniferous forests of the Pacific northwest. (Courtesy of U.S. Forest Service.)

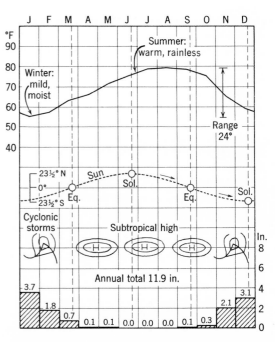

Figure 14.6 Bengasi, Tripoli, lying on the North African coast at latitude 32°, is transitional in climate between the wet-winter dry-summer Mediterranean climate and the tropical steppe climate to the south. Note that rain occurs in time of low sun. (Data from Trewartha.)

monly used for this climate. Köppen classifies the climate of the Mediterranean lands as *Csa*, a temperate rainy climate with dry, hot summers. Those narrow coastal belts directly bordering the cool currents of the open Atlantic, Pacific, and Indian oceans, Köppen designates as *Csb*, distinguished by a markedly cooler summer then the *Csa* climate. Thus Monterey, California, represents a *Csb* climate.

It is apparent that if one travels from the Mediterranean shore into North Africa, he will pass from the Mediterranean climate into the tropical steppe climate of the Sahara. A transition climate type intermediate between the two is nicely shown by the record for Bengasi, Tripoli, at lat. 32° N (Figure 14.6). Note that the temperature record resembles that of the tropical dry climates, although not so hot, but the rainfall distribution is distinctly of the same type as the Mediterranean rainfall, though not so copious.

The occurrence of a wet winter and a dry summer is rather unique among climate types and results in a distinctive native vegetation. Two varieties are found. A dense growth of shrubs and stunted trees, such as the *chaparral* of California or the *maquis* of Mediterranean lands, is one type (Figure 14.7). Another is *Mediterranean woodland*, consisting of scattered trees (oak, olive, or cork oak) and a ground cover of grasses (Figure 14.8). Trees and grasses must withstand the severe summer drought of two to four rainless months and intense evaporation. Soils of the Mediterranean climate are not readily subject to simple classification. Chestnut and brown soils typical of semi-arid climates occur in some parts; red and yellow soils in others. Owing to a combination of geologic causes, much of the land surface is hilly or mountainous, or consists of coarse alluvial material of intermontane basins.

9. Middle-latitude desert and steppe climates (*BWk, BSk*)

The interiors of North America and Asia, in latitudes 35° to 50°, and, to a limited extent, that of southernmost South America have desert and steppe climates of somewhat complex origin. Three basic air mass controls operate. (1) In summer, when pressure and wind belts are shifted poleward, these regions temporarily become the source regions for continental tropical air masses, developed because of intense heating of the large continental interiors. (2) In winter, the intense development of the Siberian and Canadian highs, which are the source areas for continental polar air masses, causes frequent invasions of relatively dry continental air. (3) Mountain ranges separate these deserts from moist maritime polar and maritime tropical air masses which supply abundant rainfall

Figure 14.7 A common scene on the lower Coast Ranges of southern California in the Mediterranean climate is a dense chaparral growth of shrubs and small trees blanketing the steep mountain slopes. Verdugo Hills near Burbank, California.

to the west and southeast coasts. Through forced ascent over these ranges, followed by adiabatic heating upon descending the lee slopes (see Chapter 10), the maritime air masses are deprived of their moisture and raised in temperature as well. Thus the regions in question are poorly situated for obtaining precipitation. Because of the prevailing eastward drift in these latitudes, maritime tropical air masses cannot easily reach these areas from the east. In southern Asia, the northward flow of moist tropical air from the Indian Ocean is blocked by the great Himalayan chain.

Under the Köppen system, two climate varieties are recognized, the semi-arid steppes, *BSk*, and the true desert, *BWk*. The letter *k* signifies a cool climate, with average annual temperature below 64.4° F (18° C). Where the letter *k'* is used, a cold

Figure 14.8 This Mediterranean woodland landscape in Monterey County, California, has scattered oak (*Quercus dumosa*) on the grass-covered slopes near by. On the distant hills the oak woodland becomes dense. (Courtesy of U.S. Forest Service.)

climate is indicated, with the warmest month average below 64.4° F (18° C).

Only a small proportion of the area covered by dry middle-latitude climates is extremely dry: the Turkestan and Gobi deserts of central Asia and parts of the Great Basin in Nevada and Utah. The principal respect in which these deserts differ from the tropical deserts of lower latitudes is that their annual temperature range is much greater and the winter temperatures much lower. Astrakhan, USSR, at 46° N lat., illustrates this feature nicely (Figure 13.15). The enormous annual range of 58° is almost double that of Aswan, Egypt; the January mean temperature is a severe 20°, as compared with 60° for Aswan; and the July maximum is only 15° less than for Aswan.

Of considerably greater importance geographically are the vast semi-arid steppe lands of the middle-latitude dry climates. Partly because of higher elevation, which increases the precipitation, or because of location nearer to maritime air mass invasions, these regions receive from 10 to 20 or 25 inches of rainfall annually and can support a short-grass vegetation cover suited to grazing of cattle and sheep, but inadequate for farming without irrigation or special dry-farming methods.

If the semi-arid steppes are followed from subtropical highlands in Mexico to middle latitudes, the annual temperature cycles show not only progressively lower temperatures but also greatly increased annual ranges (Figure 14.9). A typical steppe climate of intermediate position is that of

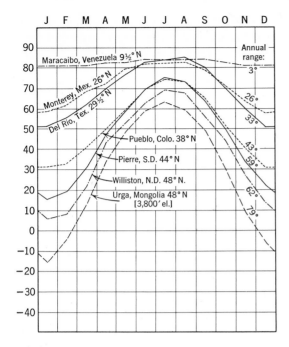

Figure 14.9 With increasing latitude the semi-arid highland steppes show increasing annual temperature ranges. (Data from Trewartha.)

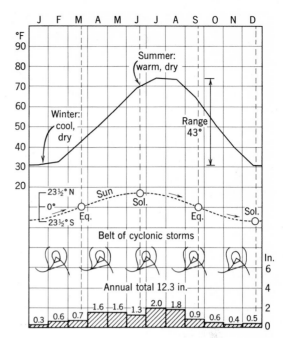

Figure 14.10 Pueblo, Colorado, lat. 38° N, is a representative station of the semi-arid middle-latitude steppes. A strong annual temperature range and a summer maximum of precipitation are typical of mid-continent middle-latitude locations. (Data from Blair.)

Pueblo, Colorado (Figure 14.10). Compared with the Mediterranean climate of Monterey, California (Figure 14.5), which lies at about the same latitude, the annual temperature range of Pueblo is very much greater, the precipitation cycle is just reversed, with the summer maximum clearly marked. Large highs drifting over the central United States produce a northerly return flow of air on their western sides, spreading moist tropical air from the Gulf of Mexico far northward and westward into the continental interior. This air is unstable and readily produces thunderstorms when lifted over a mountain range or along a cold front.

Special attention is given by geographers and climatologists to the boundary between dry and humid climates, particularly because the limits of agriculture without irrigation are drawn by nature as a fluctuating line over a hazardous frontier zone. Here, productivity may in some years be high; in others, drought brings disastrous failures. Figure 14.11 is a map showing rainfall and temperature data for the boundary between dry and humid climates in the Great Plains region of the United States. If a humid climate is defined as one in which the precipitation on the average exceeds evaporation so as to give permanently flowing streams and a generally moist soil, and a dry climate is defined as one in which evaporation on the

average exceeds precipitation so as to give ephemeral streams and a generally dry soil, the humid-dry boundary can be taken as the line along which evaporation balances precipitation. This line cannot be permanently located, but its average position runs somewhere along the dashed north-south line. Note that in North Dakota, the boundary cuts the 15-inch annual rainfall line but in southern Texas runs close to the 25-inch rainfall line. This is explained by the temperatures, which are higher in the south and result in greater evaporation losses.

Middle-latitude steppes are characterized by short grasses and by some types of scattered forest (Figure 14.12). These regions now constitute the great sheep and cattle ranges of the world. On the vast expanses of the High Plains, the American bison lived in great numbers until almost exterminated by hunters. Likewise, the short-grass veldt of South Africa supported much game at one time. Steppe grasses do not form a complete sod cover, and loose, bare soil is exposed between grass clumps. For this reason, overgrazing or a series of dry years often reduces the hold of grasses enough to permit destructive soil erosion and gullying from heavy local downpours. Soils of the steppe lands are deficient in humus, but they may be light brown in the less dry parts. Elsewhere they are reddish or gray. Calcium carbonate is present in

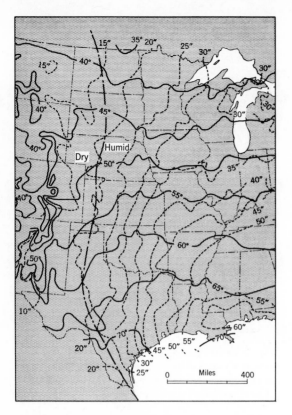

Figure 14.11 On this map the boundary zone between dry and humid climates runs north-south. Superimposed are isotherms of average annual temperature (*solid lines*) and lines of equal average annual precipitation (*broken lines*). (After J. B. Kincer, U.S. Dept. Agriculture.)

on the north and northwest and maritime or continental tropical air masses on the south and southeast. In this polar front zone, maximum interaction between polar and tropical air masses can be expected along warm and cold fronts associated with east-moving cyclones. In winter, the continental polar air masses dominate and much cold weather prevails; in summer, tropical air masses dominate and high temperatures prevail. Thus, strong seasonal temperature contrasts must be expected in this region. Precipitation is ample throughout the year, because the region lies between air mass source areas of anticyclonic nature. Strong contrasts in air masses result in much violent frontal activity and highly changeable weather. This climate may be described as both humid and continental in properties.

The climatic picture drawn above applies well to the north-central and northeastern United States and southeastern Canada as well as to northern China, southern Manchuria, Korea, and northern Japan. Very similar climatic conditions also hold for much of central and eastern Europe, the Balkan countries, and Russia, but this third region differs from the first two in that it is influenced by a great source region of continental-tropical air masses lying to the south and southeast, instead of the oceanic source regions of maritime tropical air masses.

Four varieties of climate, according to Köppen, are found in the regions that we are grouping together as having the humid continental climate. *Dfa* and *Dfb* are cold, snowy, forest climates, the first with a hot summer, the second with a warm summer. The precise definitions of *a* and *b* are as previously given. *Dwa* and *Dwb* climates, found in eastern Siberia, Manchuria, and northern Korea, are cold snowy forest climates with a dry winter. Letters *a* and *b* refer to hot and warm summers, respectively. The winter dryness, typical of all climates of eastern Asia, is explained below.

Some characteristic features of the humid continental climate can be seen from the temperature-precipitation graphs of four stations: Omaha and New York City[1] (Figure 14.13), Moscow, USSR (Figure 14.14), and Peiping, China (Figure 14.15). All four stations have similar temperature curves with a yearly range in the lower 50's for all but New York City, which is moderated by its near-ocean

excess quantities and may form nodules in the soils. Encrustations of calcium carbonate make a hard, whitish crust termed *caliche* in the southwestern United States. These calcium-rich soils are highly fertile in terms of mineral constituents favorable to grain crops, such as wheat, but unless irrigation is employed the advantage is lost. Traced toward humid-climate zones which adjoin the steppes, the soils become darker brown in color, denoting the increasing amounts of humus from heavier growth of grasses. Thus the gray or red desert and steppe soils grade into the rich, dark brown and black soils of the prairies.

10. Humid continental climate (*Dfa, Dfb, Dwa, Dwb*)

Consider a vast region located in a middle latitude, say between 40° and 55°, extending from the continental interior to the east coast. North America and Asia are, of course, the areas that we have in mind. The location is intermediate between the source region of polar continental air masses

---

[1] Köppen places the boundary between *Df* and *Cf* climates north of New York City. Some readers may wish to find fault with a climate system that places New York City and Columbus, Ohio, in the same climate class (*Cfa*) with central Florida and New Orleans, Louisiana! It is intended in this book that the humid-continental climate extend southward to a line running about from the panhandle of Oklahoma to the head of Chesapeake Bay, passing through the southern tip of Illinois.

Figure 14.12 These grasslands of the middle-latitude steppes are on dissected plains near the Missouri River, east of Chamberlin, South Dakota.

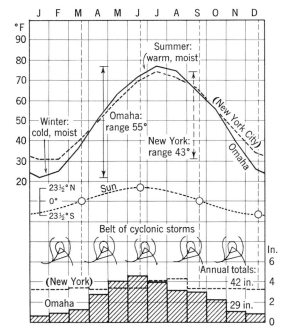

Figure 14.13 A comparison of climates at New York and Omaha, both in the humid continental climate zone, shows that the maritime location of New York results in a lower temperature range and a much more even precipitation distribution. (Data from H. H. Clayton, Smithsonian Institution.)

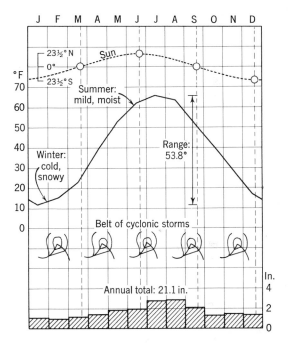

Figure 14.14 Moscow, USSR (56° N), is representative of the humid continental climates of northerly location close to the polar continental air mass source. (Data from Blair.)

location. Omaha and Peiping, located at the same latitude (40° N), have almost identical temperatures; Moscow, being more than 1000 miles farther north (56° N), has a temperature cycle which runs 10° lower than that of Omaha or Peiping.

Precipitation records of the four stations illustrated show certain marked dissimilarities which require explanation. A summer maximum is apparent in all four but is very weakly defined in New York City because maritime air masses, both polar and tropical, have ready access at all times of the year. Omaha and Moscow have well-defined summer maxima and winter minima, reflecting the predominance of tropical air masses in summer and continental-polar air masses in the winter. Moscow, being farther north, near to the source region of polar continental air masses, has less precipitation than the other stations. Peiping shows a very strong summer maximum and a winter drought. This is characteristic of the east Asiatic

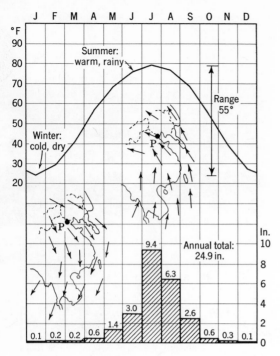

Figure 14.15 Peiping, China (40° N), illustrates the dry-winter, monsoon-controlled variety of the humid continental climate. The winter drought contrasts strongly with heavy summer-monsoon rains. (Data from Trewartha.)

middle-latitude stations and reflects the powerful monsoon control, whereby dry continental air masses dominate exclusively in winter and moisture-laden maritime air masses dominate in summer.

The general temperature pattern of middle-latitude climates is well illustrated by daily temperature graphs of three stations at about the same latitude across North America (Figure 14.16). Victoria, British Columbia, on the west coast, occupies a windward position with respect to maritime polar air masses from the Pacific. Consequently, the contrasts between July and February (the two extreme months of the year) are small. Moreover, the daily ranges are small, especially in winter. The graph of Winnipeg, Manitoba, shows maximum continental influence with strong annual and daily contrasts. Note especially the wide fluctuations in winter, with outbursts of polar and arctic air bringing very low temperatures. St. Johns, Newfoundland, occupies a leeward position with respect to the continent and is accessible to maritime air masses from the Atlantic. It therefore has only a moderate annual temperature range, but the continental influence is nevertheless clearly marked in the sharply fluctuating daily temperature record.

Three major types of vegetation and their associated soils may be recognized in the humid continental climate. The distribution is well illustrated in North America. (See Figures 17.4 and 17.5.)

In the more humid eastern sections, including the warmer parts of the humid continental climate zone (*Dfa*), natural vegetation is of the broadleaf and

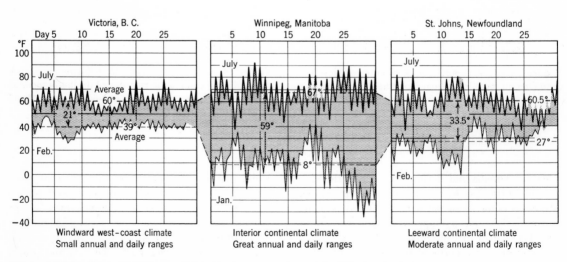

Figure 14.16 Along the 50th parallel in North America lie widely differing climate types. These temperature graphs show the differences between marine and continental locations in this latitude zone. Averages are for months actually shown on graphs. (After Mark Jefferson, *Geographical Review*.)

mixed broadleaf-coniferous forest type (Figure 14.17). Soils are of the *brown forest* and *gray-brown podzolic* types, rich in humus and moderately leached so as to have a distinct light-colored leached zone under the upper dark layer. In this region, diversified farming and dairying are the most successful uses of the land where topography is favorable.

A northern belt of predominantly coniferous forest extends along the entire length of the colder northern parts of the humid continental climate zone (*Dfb*). To this may be added the mountain regions of the Adirondacks and northern New England. Here soils are of the *podsol* type, strongly leached, but with an upper layer of humus. Cool temperatures inhibit bacterial activity which would destroy this organic matter in tropical regions. Podsols are deficient in calcium, potassium, and magnesium, and are, in general, acid in chemical nature. Thus they are not highly productive for crop farming, even though adequate rainfall is generally assured. The podsols are, however, well suited to the growth of coniferous forests.

The drier plains areas of the humid continental climate support a natural tall-grass vegetation termed *prairie*, which grades into the drier steppe regions of short grasses to the west. The *prairie soils* and *chernozem soils*, two major soil groups of these grasslands, are typically dark in color and consist of a single, thick upper layer grading into the parent soil material below. These soils contain abundant calcium, magnesium, and potassium because rainfall is here distinctly less than farther eastward and leaching is less active as a soil-forming process.

Figure 14.17 This stand of beech and hemlock in the Allegheny National Forest, Pennsylvania, is illustrative of the hardwood forests covering a large area of the humid continental climate zone in the northeastern United States. (U.S. Forest Service Photograph.)

Review Questions

1. Explain the occurrence of a moist climate in subtropical latitudes (25° to 35°) along the eastern continental margins. What air masses prevail over this region? What is the nature of these air masses?

2. Describe the annual cycle of temperature and precipitation at a typical humid subtropical climate (*Cfa*) station on the southeastern Atlantic Coast or eastern Gulf Coast of the United States. When is precipitation at a maximum? Why? Are thunderstorms common or rare?

3. What are the characteristics of climate on the southeastern Asiatic coast in the subtropical latitudes? How does the precipitation cycle differ from that in comparable localities in the southeastern United States? Why is there a difference?

4. What is the natural vegetation of the humid subtropical climate of east coasts in latitudes 25° to 35°? What is a characteristic feature of the soils in this climate zone? To what other groups of soils are they most closely related?

5. What are the important characteristics of the climates of west coasts in middle latitudes (40° to 60°)? What air masses are dominant? From what direction do most air masses and cyclonic storms approach these coasts? How is this reflected in the annual temperature cycle?

6. Why does the marine west coast climate (*Cfb*) show a marked reduction in rainfall during the summer, especially between 40° and 50° latitude?

7. What type of forest vegetation is developed on windward mountain slopes in the marine west coast belts. In what way is orographic rainfall related to the development of these forests and their associated soils?

8. Describe and explain the Mediterranean climate (*Csb*) which prevails on west coasts between 30° and 40° latitude. What is unique about the annual precipitation graph of this climate? How does it compare with graphs of the tropical savanna climate (*Aw*)?

9. What is the natural vegetation of the Mediterranean climate (*Csa, Csb*)?

10. Why are dry climates developed in middle latitudes in interior continental locations? Are they related to the presence of mountain barriers? Give examples. Explain the principle of the rainshadow desert.

11. What distinction is made between extremely arid regions and semi-arid regions or steppes? What is the natural vegetation of steppes? of the very dry middle-latitude deserts (*BWk*)?

12. How does altitude influence the degree of aridity in the dry middle-latitude regions?

13. What is noteworthy about the annual temperature cycle of the middle-latitude steppes (*BSk*) and deserts (*BWk*)? How does this cycle differ from that of the tropical deserts?

14. How may the boundary between dry and humid climates be determined? Is it a fixed line, or does it fluctuate? Of what economic importance is this boundary?

15. Of what economic value are the middle-latitude steppe lands of the world? What types of soils underlie these regions? Is the soil suitable for grain crops? What is caliche? How does it form?

16. Describe the climate located in middle latitudes in the central and eastern parts of the continents. What air masses are involved in this climate? How does season of year determine which air masses are dominant?

17. Describe the annual temperature cycle of a typical station in the humid continental climate zone (*Dfa, Dfb*). Is the range great or small? Explain. Is the average temperature of the coldest month below freezing?

18. What can be said about the day-to-day temperature fluctuations in the humid continental climate? How do these variations reflect the conflict in air masses?

19. Discuss the natural vegetation and soils of the humid continental climate (*Dfa, Dfb*) in middle latitudes. How do southerly and northerly locations differ in this respect? How do easterly and westerly locations differ?

Exercises

1. Prepare temperature-precipitation graphs similar to Figure 14.1 for each of the following stations. (Data from Trewartha.)

(a) *Shanghai, China, 31° N*

	J	F	M	A	M	J	J	A	S	O	N	D
Temperature	38	39	46	56	66	73	80	80	73	63	52	42 °F
Precipitation	2.8	2.0	3.9	4.4	3.3	6.6	7.4	4.7	3.9	3.7	1.7	1.3 inches

(b) *Seattle, Washington, 47½° N*

	J	F	M	A	M	J	J	A	S	O	N	D
Temperature	40	42	45	50	55	60	64	64	59	52	46	42 °F
Precipitation	4.9	3.8	3.1	2.4	1.8	1.3	0.6	0.7	1.7	2.8	4.8	5.5 inches

2. For each of the above stations calculate the average annual temperature, annual temperature range, and annual rainfall total.

3. **(a)** Compare the record of Charleston, South Carolina (Figure 14.1), with that of Shanghai, China (Exercise 1). Both are located on east coasts at approximately the same latitude. **(b)** In what climate do they belong? **(c)** Why has Shanghai a colder winter than Charleston? **(d)** Why has Shanghai a rainier summer but a drier winter than Charleston?

4. **(a)** Seattle, Washington, and Brest, France (Figure 14.3), both belong in the humid, marine west coast climate and are located at about the same latitude. Compare the temperature and precipitation figures of the two stations. **(b)** Why does Seattle show greater precipitation in winter but less in summer? **(c)** In what way does Seattle climate resemble the Mediterranean climate of California?

5. Prepare temperature-precipitation graphs similar to Figure 14.1 for each of the following stations. (Data from Trewartha.)

(a) *Valparaiso, Chile, 33° S*

	J	F	M	A	M	J	J	A	S	O	N	D
Temperature	67	66	65	61	59	56	55	56	58	59	62	64 °F
Precipitation	...	...	0.6	0.2	3.5	5.8	4.8	3.2	0.8	0.4	0.1	0.3 inches

(b) *Rome, Italy, 42° N*

	J	F	M	A	M	J	J	A	S	O	N	D
Temperature	45	47	51	57	64	71	76	76	70	62	53	46 °F
Precipitation	3.2	2.7	2.9	2.6	2.2	1.6	0.7	1.0	2.5	5.0	4.4	3.9 inches

6. **(a)** For each of the stations in Exercise 5 compute the annual temperature range and annual precipitation. **(b)** To what type of climate do these stations belong? **(c)** What are the principal differences between the climate of Valparaiso, Chile, and that of Rome, Italy? Explain these differences.

7. Prepare temperature-precipitation graphs similar to Figure 14.1 for each of the following stations. (Data from Trewartha.)

(a) *Lovelock, Nevada, 40° N*

	J	F	M	A	M	J	J	A	S	O	N	D
Temperature	30	36	43	50	58	66	74	72	62	51	40	31 °F
Precipitation	0.7	0.5	0.4	0.4	0.4	0.3	0.2	0.2	0.3	0.4	0.3	0.4 inches

(b) *Williston, North Dakota, 48° N*

	J	F	M	A	M	J	J	A	S	O	N	D
Temperature	6	8	22	43	53	63	69	67	56	44	27	14 °F
Precipitation	0.5	0.4	0.9	1.1	2.1	3.2	1.7	1.7	1.0	0.7	0.6	0.5 inches

8. (*a*) Compute the annual temperature range and total annual precipitation for the stations in Exercise 7. (*b*) To what climates do these stations belong? (*c*) How do the climates of Lovelock, Nevada, and Williston, North Dakota, differ as to temperature cycle and precipitation cycle? Explain these differences.

9. Prepare temperature and precipitation graphs similar to Figure 14.1 for each of the following stations. (Data from Trewartha.)

(*a*) *Bucharest, Rumania, 43½° N*

	J	F	M	A	M	J	J	A	S	O	N	D
Temperature	26	29	40	52	61	68	73	71	64	54	41	30 °F
Precipitation	1.2	1.1	1.7	2.0	2.5	3.3	2.8	1.9	1.5	1.5	1.9	1.7 inches

(*b*) *Marquette, Michigan, 46½° N*

	J	F	M	A	M	J	J	A	S	O	N	D
Temperature	16	16	25	38	49	59	65	63	57	46	33	23 °F
Precipitation	2.2	1.8	2.1	2.3	3.1	3.5	3.1	2.8	3.2	3.0	3.0	2.5 inches

10. For each of the stations in Exercise 9 compute annual temperature range and annual precipitation total.

11. (*a*) Compare the climate of Bucharest, Rumania (Exercise 9), with that of New York City (Figure 14.13), both of which belong to the humid continental climate. Note that summer temperatures are similar but that Bucharest has a colder winter. Why is this so? (*b*) Precipitation is very much less in Bucharest than in New York, especially in the winter months. Why? Explain in terms of air masses.

12. (*a*) Compare the climates of Marquette, Michigan (Exercise 9), and Moscow, USSR (Figure 14.14). (*b*) Moscow lies almost 10° latitude (700 miles) farther north than Marquette. Does this show up in the temperature figures? Explain. (*c*) Compare the precipitation of these stations. Which has more? Why?

CHAPTER FIFTEEN

Polar, arctic, and highland climates

CLIMATES of Group III, located at high latitudes, are controlled largely by polar and arctic air masses. They have low temperatures, low precipitation, and low evaporation.

11. Subarctic climate (*Dfc, Dfd, Dwc, Dwd*)

In the two great land masses of North America and Eurasia, a vast expanse of interior continental area lies between lat. 50° and 70° N. Here are the source regions for the continental polar air masses. In winter, when excessive heat loss by radiation has resulted in the formation of the powerful Siberian and Canadian highs, severely cold air temperatures develop over snow-covered surfaces, forming a cold, heavy air mass. Low in moisture content, this air mass is stable and normally clear. In summer, the source region is shifted farther north; air mass temperatures rise to moderately high levels, but the moisture content, although much greater in summer, is still small by comparison with that of maritime tropical air masses.

We might expect, therefore, a climate type showing very great seasonal temperature range, with extremely severe winters and a small annual total precipitation concentrated in the warm months. This climate, called here the *subarctic climate*, includes four of Köppen's climate types. The largest

area, including belts from Alaska to Labrador and from Scandinavia to Siberia, is classified as *Dfc*, a cold, snowy forest climate, moist all year, with cool short summers. Less than four months of the year have averages over 50° F (10° C). A still colder climate, *Dfd*, found in northern Siberia only, has very cold winters in which the average of the coldest month is below −36.4° F (−38° C). Climates *Dwc* and *Dwd* are also cold, snowy forest climates, but with a dry winter. They are found only in northeastern Asia. The letters *c* and *d* denote a cool summer and a very cold winter respectively.

The subarctic climate, type *Dfc*, is well illustrated by the graph of Ft. Vermilion, Alberta, at 58° N lat. (Figure 15.1). The annual range of 74° is remarkable enough, but it is greatly exceeded by that of Yakutsk, USSR, lying in the *Dwd* climate type. Perhaps the coldest place in the northern hemisphere is Verkhoyansk, USSR, which lies in this climate zone and has a January mean of −59° F and an absolute minimum recorded temperature −93° F.

Summer in the subarctic climate regions is very

above: The White Range, Andes of Peru.
Photograph, Fairchild Aerial Surveys, Inc.

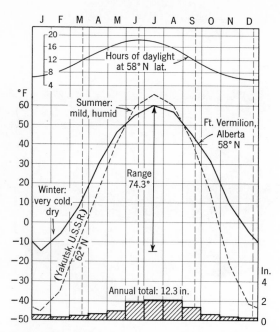

Figure 15.1 The enormous temperature range and the extreme winter cold of the continental polar air mass source regions are well shown in this graph for Ft. Vermilion, Alberta. A still greater temperature extreme is found at Yakutsk, USSR (*dashed line*), in the Lena River basin of Siberia. (Data from Trewartha.)

short. The warmest month average may not greatly exceed 50°, and frosts can occur at any time during the summer. Daily maximum temperatures, however, commonly reach 70°. At these high latitudes the sun is above the horizon for sixteen to eighteen hours from May through August. (See graph on Figure 15.1.) The long hours of sunshine so accelerate the growth of plants that agriculture may be possible despite a very short growing season.

Winter is the dominant season of the subarctic climate. Because subfreezing monthly average temperatures occur for six or seven consecutive months, all moisture in the soil and subsoil is solidly frozen to depths of many feet. (See Figure 15.7.) Summer warmth is insufficient to thaw more than the upper few feet so that a condition of perennially frozen ground, or *permafrost*, prevails over large parts of this and the tundra regions to the north. Seasonal thaw penetrates from two to fourteen feet, depending on location and nature of the ground. This shallow zone of alternate freeze and thaw is termed the *active zone*.

The distribution of permafrost in the northern hemisphere is shown in Figure 15.2. Three zones are recognized. Continuous permafrost, which extends without gaps or interruptions under all topographic features, coincides largely with the tundra climate *(ET)*, but also includes a large part of the subarctic climate *(Dfc, Dfd, Dwd)* in Siberia. Dis-

continuous permafrost, which occurs in patches separated by frost-free zones under lakes and rivers, occupies much of the subarctic climate *(Dfc)* zone of North America and Eurasia. Sporadic occurrence of permafrost in small patches extends into the southern limits of the subarctic climate.

Depth of permafrost reaches 1000 to 1500 feet in the continuous zone near latitude 70° (Figure 15.2). Much of this permanent frost is an inheritance from more severe conditions of the last ice age, but some permafrost bodies may be growing under existing climate conditions.

Permafrost presents problems of great concern in engineering and building construction in these cold regions. Buildings must be insulated underneath to protect the ground moisture beneath from melting; otherwise, the building might literally be engulfed in mud. Another serious problem is in the behavior of streams in winter. As the surface of streams or springs freezes over, the water beneath bursts out from place to place, freezing into huge accumulations of ice. Highways are thus made impassable. Scraping of insulating peat, forest litter, and vegetative cover from the frozen ground to make roads and air fields may result in dire consequences. The summer sun thaws the bare ground, which turns into a liquid mud, often growing into sizable lake basins by melting and sapping around the edges of the exposed areas.

Most of the source areas of the continental polar air masses are in regions of less than 20 inches of precipitation annually, whereas the northerly portions have less than 10 inches. Although this amount would result in dry deserts at low latitudes, evaporation is greatly reduced by prevailingly low temperatures. Thus, essentially humid moisture conditions of air and soil prevail.

Precipitation is largely cyclonic in type and shows a very definite maximum in the summer months. Snowfall, although conspicuous in winter because it remains upon the ground, accounts for only a fraction of an inch of precipitation per month in the coldest months. Cyclonic storms crossing these areas bring little precipitation at this season. In summer, cyclonic rains are frequent, although thunderstorms are few.

The subarctic climate zone coincides with a great belt of coniferous forest known as the *boreal forest*, and a thinner, more open lichen woodland, the *taiga* (Figure 15.3). Spruce and fir are the dominant types. Trees tend to be small, so that they are economically of less value for lumber than for pulpwood. Soils of the *podsol* group are associated with the boreal forest. As explained before, these soils are strongly leached and of acid type. They are light gray and have a very distinct leached layer beneath the uppermost layer of humus and

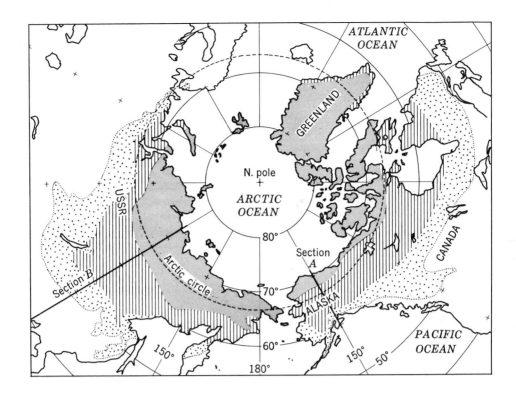

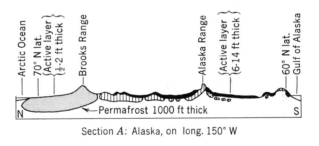

Section A: Alaska, on long. 150° W

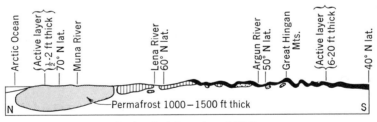

Section B: Asia, on long. 120° E
(Modified from I. V. Poiré)

Diagrammatic cross sections of permafrost

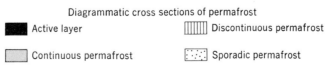

Figure 15.2 Distribution of permafrost in the northern hemisphere, and representative cross sections in Alaska and Asia. (From Robert F. Black, "Permafrost," Chapter 14 of Trask's *Applied Sedimentation,* John Wiley and Sons, 1950.)

Figure 15.3 The arctic coniferous forest is illustrated by this stand of white spruce, lodgepole pine, and aspen near Watson Lake, Yukon, about lat. 60° N. (Courtesy of the *Geographical Review*.)

forest litter. These soils are extremely poor from the standpoint of agriculture. Added to the natural inadequacy of soils of this region is a great prevalence of swamps, bogs, and lakes left by the departed ice sheets. Some rock surfaces were scoured by ice which stripped off the soil entirely. Elsewhere rock basins were formed, or previous stream courses dammed, making countless lakes. Insufficient geologic time has elapsed for good drainage even to begin to be reestablished over large areas.

12. Tundra climate (*ET*)

The northern continental fringes of North America and Eurasia from the Arctic Circle to about the 75th parallel lie within the outer zone of control of arctic-type air masses, whose source region covers the central Arctic Ocean and Greenland. To the south are the continental polar and maritime polar air mass source regions. The land fringes are thus in a frontal zone, which has been known as the *arctic front*, but which may be more simply identified as belonging to a widely shifting polar front, well developed over the northern Pacific and Atlantic oceans. Here many intense east-moving cyclonic storms are formed, and much bad weather may be expected.

These conditions produce a *tundra climate*, described by Köppen with the symbol *ET*. This is a polar climate in which the average temperature of the warmest month is below 50° F (10° C), but above 32° F (0° C).

The tundra climate is illustrated by the temperature-precipitation graph of Upernivik at 73° N lat. on the west Greenland coast (Figure 15.4). Note that (*a*) temperature range is large, but not nearly as great as in the subarctic climate; (*b*) the warmest month averages are in the low 40's and the coldest month average is well below zero; and (*c*) precipitation total is less than ten inches, with an increased amount falling during and after the warm season. Nearness to the Arctic Ocean explains the somewhat more moderate temperature range and minimum, compared to the continental centers. Coolness of the summer is explained by the nearness to the large ocean body, keeping air temperatures down despite large receipts of solar energy at this latitude near summer solstice. Possibly a more persistent cloud cover is also a factor.

A treeless landscape of grasses, sedges, and lichens, along with shrubs of willow and birch, is the natural vegetation of the arctic tundra (Figure 15.5). Traced southward the vegetation passes through a transitional tundra with dwarf birches, then into the dense boreal coniferous forest. In some places a distinct tree line separates the forest and tundra. Coinciding approximately with the 50° isotherm of the warmest month, this line has been used by Köppen as a boundary between *Df* and *ET* climates.

Tundra soils are noteworthy in that the soil particles are produced almost entirely by mechanical breakup of the parent rock and have suffered little or no chemical alteration. Grayish loam and blue-gray clay layers are present with much peat. Continual freezing and thawing of soil moisture has been responsible for disintegration of the soil particles. Like the soils of the northern continental interiors, soils of the tundra are affected by the permanently frozen, or permafrost, condition (Figure 15.2). The permafrost layer is more than 1000 feet thick over most of this region; seasonal thaw reaches only four inches to two feet below the surface.

Geomorphic processes have a somewhat different pattern in the tundra regions, and a variety of curious landforms results. Under a protective sod of small plants, the soil water melts in summer, producing a thick mud which may flow downslope to create bulges and terraces without breaking through the surface. This process is known as *solifluction*, or *sludging*, and forms *solifluction terraces* and *lobes* on slopes (Figures 15.5 and 22.22). In the desert tundra, solifluction occurs without the confining cover and may be described as a layer of thick mud creeping down the slopes. Observers who have studied this flowage find that it is most rapid at midday, the mud flowing at a rate of several feet per hour and carrying along large blocks of rock (Figure 22.25).

The freeze and thaw of water in the soil gives rise to a curious system of polygonal cracks in flat ground (Figure 15.6). They may result from the shrinkage of the clay as water is withdrawn to form ice crystals in lenses or layers within the soil (Figure 15.7). The resulting pattern is termed *polygonal ground*. On hill and mountain summits the cracks are filled with stones, which seem to be gradually sorted and pushed to the sides of each polygon during alternate freeze and thaw of soil water. These forms are called *stone rings*, or *stone polygons*. On slopes, the stone rings are drawn downslope to produce *stone stripes*, appearing from the air like giant hachures on the ground.

13. Icecap climate (*EF*)

Three vast regions of ice exist on the earth. These are the Greenland and Antarctic continental icecaps and the large area of floating sea ice in the North Polar Sea (Figures 15.8 and 26.9). The continental icecaps differ in various ways, both physically and climatically, from the polar sea ice and can be separately treated. Glacial and topographic features of Greenland and Antarctica are treated in Chapter 26. It would be helpful to read pages 394–395 in connection with the climate discussion given here.

Icecap climate has by far the lowest average annual temperature of all global climates. Designated by Köppen *EF*, or polar climate of perpetual frost, this climate has no monthly average above freezing (32 °F, 0° C). Available records indicate mean annual temperatures of −20° to −30° for the Greenland icecap, but about −9° for the North Polar Sea. Compare this with the 10° to 25° mean annual temperature of the tundra climate. The higher Polar Sea temperature is due to its sea-level altitude and the moderating influence of the ocean water, which can supply a continuous amount of heat conducted through the floating ice to the air.

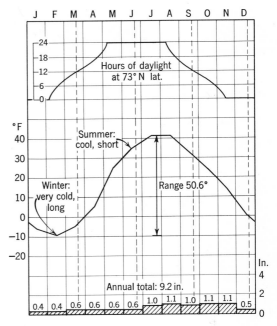

Figure 15.4 Upernivik, an island on the west coast of Greenland at lat. 73° N, is a representative tundra station. (Data from Blair.)

Figure 15.5 Solifluction, a slow soil flowage, has produced this lobate form on a tundra slope on Mt. Pelly, Victoria Island (lat. 69° N, long. 104° W). Surface of lobe stands about six feet above surrounding slope. (Photograph by A. L. Washburn, Arctic Institute of North America.)

Figure 15.6 Tundra polygons on Wollaston Peninsula, Victoria Island (lat. 70° N, long. 112° W), viewed from the air. (Photograph by A. L. Washburn, Arctic Institute of North America.)

Figure 15.7 This vertical river bank exposure near Livengood, Alaska, in the subarctic climate region reveals a V-shaped ice wedge surrounded by layered silt of alluvial origin. (Photograph by T. L. Péwé, U.S. Geological Survey.)

The annual temperature graph for an icecap station, "Eismitte," in Greenland is shown in Figure 15.9. This information was gathered by a German expedition under the direction of Alfred Wegener in the years 1929 through 1931. Note that only in three months of the year did the mean monthly temperatures rise above zero, and then only to a July maximum of 12°. The coldest month was February, with −53°, making an annual range of 65°.

A shallow layer of air over the ice sheet is chilled severely and at times flows downslope under the influence of gravity toward the margins as a severe blizzard wind. It is reported that so great is the chill of the ice upon the air that tiny ice crystals sometimes form within a few feet of the ground. These may make a "snowstorm," above which the head and shoulders of a man rise clear. Driving blizzard winds pack the sandlike snow into a hard, smooth pavement.

Cyclonic storms frequently penetrate Greenland, bringing precipitation to the icecap. Probably the principal nourishment of the ice sheet is from this source.

Climate of the Antarctic icecap was little understood until a number of weather stations were maintained in the International Geophysical Year of 1957–1958. Temperatures in the interior proved to be far lower than any place on earth. The Sovietskaya Base, about 700 miles from the South Pole, may be the world's coldest spot. Here a record low of −124° F (−86.7° C) was observed. At the pole itself (Amundsen-Scott Station), July, August, and September of 1957 had averages about −76° F (−60° C) (Figure 15.9). Temperatures run roughly 40° F higher, month for month, at Little America Station because it is located close to the Ross Sea and is at low elevation.

A remarkable feature of the high, antarctic interior is the intense chilling of air close to the snow surface. A strong temperature inversion develops in winter, so that the air near the surface may be 50° to 60° F colder than air a few hundred feet higher. Downslope flow of this heavy, cold air layer causes blizzard winds to develop in favorable valley locations.

Highland climates

As explained in earlier chapters, increasing elevation brings a great reduction in both pressure and temperature. Thus, climates change greatly within a vertical range of a few thousand feet. In a general way, a rise of altitude is equivalent to an increase in latitude, so that the tundra and icecap climate equivalents can be found among the glaciers of a mountain mass above timber line. In one major respect, however, the analogy is inadequate.

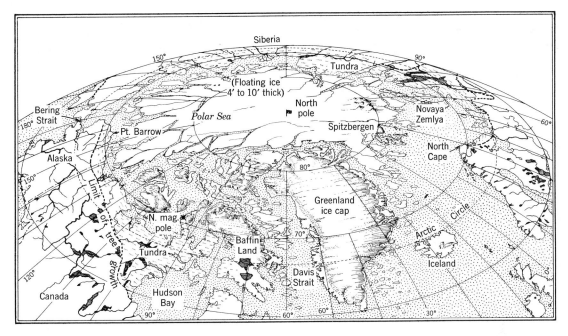

Figure 15.8 The arctic region. (After E. Raisz.)

Whereas intensity of insolation is progressively less toward the poles, it is increased at higher altitudes. Thus, daily temperature ranges are excessive at high altitudes in middle and low latitudes, but are much less pronounced in equivalent arctic climates.

Pressure and temperature

The vertical distribution of atmospheric pressure has been treated in an earlier chapter (Figure 8.4). There it was noted that for every 900 feet of increased elevation the barometric pressure falls about 1 inch, but that this rate holds for only the first few thousand feet, after which the rate of pressure drop becomes less.

The physiological effects of a pressure decrease are well known from the experiences of flying and mountain climbing. The principal influence is that due to insufficient amount of oxygen to supply the blood through the lungs. At altitudes of 10,000 to 15,000 feet mountain sickness, or altitude sickness, occurs, characterized by weakness, headache, nosebleed, or nausea. Persons who remain at these altitudes for a day or two normally adjust to the conditions, but physical exertion is always accompanied by shortness of breath.

At reduced pressures the boiling point of water or other liquids is reduced so that cooking time of various foods is greatly lengthened.

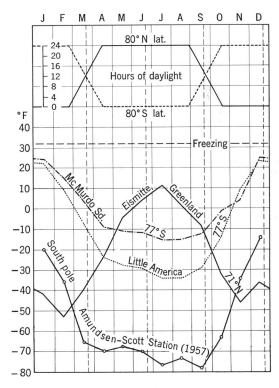

Figure 15.9 Temperature graphs at these four icecap stations are based on short-term records, but illustrate well the prevailingly cold climate throughout the year. (Data from Trewartha and *I.G.Y. Bulletin* 15, 1958.)

Elevation	Pressure	Boiling temperature, ° F
Sea level	29.9	212°
1,000	28.8	210°
3,000	26.8	206°
5,000	24.9	203°
10,000	20.7	194°

The table gives some data on pressure and boiling point relationships. From these figures it is evident that the use of pressure cookers will be of great value above 5000 feet wherever the cooking involves boiling of water.

From the standpoint of weather and climate, reduced atmospheric pressure is principally effective in that the thinner atmosphere contains relatively less carbon dioxide, water vapor, and dust, and hence permits a high intensity of insolation.

Increasing intensity of insolation at higher elevations has a profound influence upon temperature relations. Surfaces exposed to sunlight heat rapidly and intensely, shaded surfaces are quickly and severely cooled. This results in rapid air heating during the day and rapid cooling at night at high-mountain locations (Figure 15.10). Thus at mountain vacation resorts not only is the air pure and the landscape features therefore sharply outlined as if washed clean, but the cool nights and warm days are stimulating physically.

The contrast between exposed and shaded surfaces is particularly noteworthy at high altitudes. It is said that temperatures of objects in the sun and in the shade differ by as much as 40° to 50°.[1]

Increased intensity of insolation is accompanied by an increase in intensity of violet and ultraviolet rays. Sunburn is very much more rapid above 5000 feet than at sea level, as many a person has learned by unfortunate experience. The red and infrared rays of the spectrum, on the other hand, are relatively less intensified by increased elevation because they are better able to pass through a dense atmosphere.

A general decrease in air temperature with elevation has been discussed in Chapter 7, where it was stated that the lapse rate commonly amounts to about 3½° per 1000 feet. Thus, we might expect a station 10,000 feet in elevation to have a temperature about 35° below that of a nearby sea-level station. Actually it is somewhat less than this.

In high altitudes of the equatorial regions, annual range of temperature is very small, much as in the wet equatorial rainforest climates which surround these tropical mountains at low elevations (Figure 15.11). The range at Quito, Ecuador, is thus only 0.7° for the year. Compare this with Figure 13.1.

[1] Thomas A. Blair, *Climatology*, Prentice-Hall, 1942, p. 77.

In middle and high latitudes, on the other hand, a wide annual variation is to be expected, following the marked variations of insolation from summer to winter, as the Longs Peak graph shows (Figure 15.11).

Precipitation

The general influence of increased elevation is to bring an increase in precipitation, at least for the first few thousand feet of elevation. This is due to the production of orographic type of rainfall, generated by the forced ascent of air masses and the resultant cooling of the air. (See Chapter 10.) Above elevations of 6000 to 7000 feet, however, precipitation increase begins to slacken with elevation, owing to the inability of air at the lower temperatures to hold, and therefore to give up, as much moisture.

Generally speaking, mountains and plateaus are humid climate zones. This is particularly striking in an arid or semi-arid region, where the mountains form islands of humid climate surrounded by desert or steppe. Reduction in temperatures results in reduced evaporation, so that a humid condition prevails.

The influence of mountains upon precipitation is strikingly illustrated by the state of California (Figure 15.12), whose topography is greatly diversified. Note that in the Great Valley and Death Valley precipitation is less than 10 inches, but on the west slopes of the Sierra Nevada and Klamath Mountains it is over 70 inches.

From the standpoint of river flow and floods, mountain climates are of greatest importance in middle latitudes. The higher ranges serve as snow storage areas, keeping back the precipitation until early or midsummer, releasing it slowly through melting, and thus aiding in the maintenance of continuous river flow. As melting proceeds to successively higher levels, the melt water is supplied to the drainage basin. Among the snow-fed rivers of the United States are the Columbia, Snake, Missouri, Platte, Arkansas, and Colorado. In the eastern United States, the Appalachians serve in a similar but less pronounced fashion for the Ohio and other rivers. Here, however, the snow is melted in late spring and has no influence in the middle and late summer.

Vegetation and life zones

It has been observed that increased elevation brings climatic conditions approximately equivalent to those encountered by increase in latitude. Consequently there exist distinct zones of vegetation which, in a general way, recapitulate the vegetation types of increasingly high latitudes.

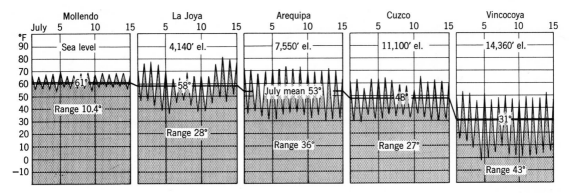

Figure 15.10 In Peru, on the west side of South America in the region of lat. 15° S., one can find stations of great differences in elevation. Increasing altitude brings not only a lower mean temperature but also greatly increased daily temperature range. (After Mark Jefferson, *Geographical Review.*)

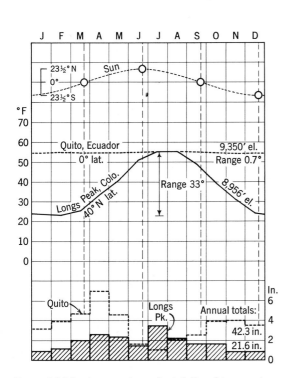

Figure 15.11 A comparison of rainfall and temperature characteristics of two mountain stations shows the control of latitude to be essentially the same as for low-level stations. (Data from Trewartha.)

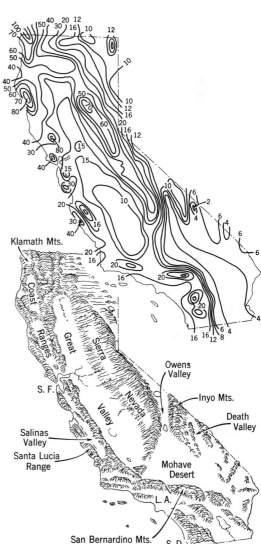

Figure 15.12 The effect of mountain topography on rainfall is well shown by the state of California. (Rainfall map after *U.S. Dept. Agriculture Yearbook, 1941.*)

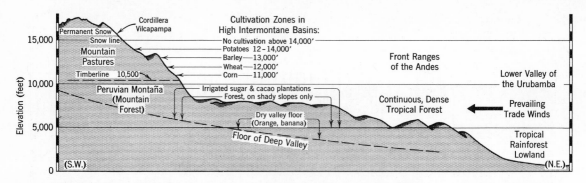

Figure 15.13A Altitude zoning of climates in the equatorial Andes of southern Peru (lat. 10°–15° S) has a profound effect on native vegetation and cultivated crops. This schematic profile shows the generally prevailing conditions from the Andean mountain crests, eastward to the equatorial rainforest lowland of the upper Amazon drainage basin. (After Isaiah Bowman, *The Andes of Southern Peru*, 1916.)

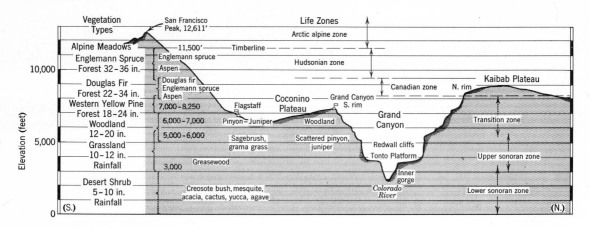

Figure 15.13B Altitude zoning of mountain and plateau climates in the arid southwestern United States gives a remarkable succession of native vegetation types, ranging from desert shrub to coniferous forest. These zones are seen by thousands of American tourists each year in the Grand Canyon–San Francisco Mountain district of northern Arizona. (After G. A. Pearson, C. H. Merriam, and A. N. Strahler.)

For equatorial and tropical regions the vegetation zoning is of considerable importance in that it makes possible the cultivation of certain crops and forest products not otherwise possible in hot, humid conditions. Figure 15.13 shows these relationships for both equatorial and middle-latitude highlands. Note that the coniferous forest equivalent to the taiga is present above a broadleaf forest, such as might be found in the humid middle-latitude continental climates. Above the coniferous zone is a zone of Alpine meadows analogous to the tundra (Figure 15.14). Above this is a zone of permanent snow, corresponding to the icecaps and their associated rocky, barren mountain slopes. As we would expect, the equivalent upper zones are highest in the neighborhood of the equator. Here the snow line is at 14,500 feet, diminishing to 9000 or 10,000 feet in middle latitudes, and finally reaching sea level in the vicinity of 60° to 65° N lat.

Figure 15.14 At timberline in the Arapaho National Forest, Colorado, the coniferous forest gives way to alpine tundra. (Photograph by U.S. Forest Service.)

Review Questions

1. Summarize and explain the characteristics of the subarctic climate. How do the Köppen symbols *Dfc*, *Dfd*, *Dwc*, and *Dwd* distinguish varieties of this climate? What is particularly noteworthy about the annual temperature cycle? Explain the excessively low winter temperatures. Where is the coldest place in the northern hemisphere?

2. What is perennially frozen ground, or permafrost? What is the origin of permafrost? How great a depth of ground is thawed during the summers in the subarctic climate? What are some of the engineering problems associated with permafrost?

3. How does the annual total of precipitation in the northern continental centers compare with that in the tropical deserts? How does evaporation compare in these two regions?

4. What is the taiga? What type of soils are found in the subarctic climate regions? How has glaciation affected the surfaces of these regions?

5. Describe the tundra climate along continental fringes between 65° and 75° N lat. What air masses interact in this zone? In what two regions is cyclonic activity strongly concentrated?

6. Compare the annual temperature cycle of the tundra climate with that of the subarctic climate? Compare ranges, warmest month averages, and coldest month averages.

7. What is the tundra? What types of plants are found on the tundra? What kinds of soils are developed here? Describe permafrost conditions in the tundra regions. To what depth is the soil moisture frozen over most of this area? To what depth does the annual summer thaw extend?

8. What is the tree line of the arctic regions? With what monthly isotherm is it approximately identified?

9. What are some of the unusual geomorphic processes active in the tundra regions? Explain the following terms: solifluction, solifluction terraces, polygonal ground, stone rings, stone stripes.

10. What are the essential characteristics of icecap climate? Describe temperature conditions throughout the year. With what air mass source regions is this climate associated?

11. Describe briefly the Greenland and Antarctic icecaps. How is the Greenland icecap nourished, that is, where does the moisture for the snow fields come from?

12. Discuss the influence of increasing altitude upon air pressure. Describe the effects of high altitudes upon physiological processes and upon the boiling point of liquids.

13. What is the effect of increasing altitude upon air temperature? How are maximum and minimum daily temperatures affected? How is the mean annual temperature affected? Is the annual range significantly changed by increased elevation?

14. What influence has increased elevation upon precipitation? Explain this effect. Cite examples of variation of precipitation with elevation.

15. Explain how snow storage in high mountains affects the flow of rivers. Name some snow-fed rivers of the United States.

16. Describe the influence of increased altitude upon natural vegetation and crop cultivation in equatorial regions, using the Andes of Peru as an illustration.

17. Describe the influence of increased altitude upon vegetation in the southwestern United States, using the Grand Canyon-San Francisco Mountains region as an illustration. How does the elevation of the Alpine meadow zone here compare with that of the upper limit of pastures in the Andes?

Exercises

1. Prepare temperature-precipitation graphs similar to Figure 15.1 for each of the following stations. (Data from Trewartha.)

(a) *Verkhoyansk, USSR,* 67½° N

	J	F	M	A	M	J	J	A	S	O	N	D
Temperature	−58	−48	−24	9	36	56	60	52	36	6	−34	−51 °F
Precipitation	0.2	0.1	0.1	0.2	0.3	0.9	1.0	1.0	0.5	0.4	0.3	0.1 inches

(b) *Point Barrow, Alaska,* 71° N

	J	F	M	A	M	J	J	A	S	O	N	D
Temperature	−19	−13	−14	−2	21	35	40	39	31	16	0	−15 °F
Precipitation	0.3	0.2	0.2	0.3	0.3	0.3	1.1	0.8	0.5	0.8	0.4	0.4 inches

(c) *South Orkneys,* 61° S

	J	F	M	A	M	J	J	A	S	O	N	D
Temperature	32	33	31	27	19	15	13	15	20	25	28	31 °F
Precipitation	1.5	1.5	1.8	1.7	1.3	1.2	1.2	1.4	1.0	1.0	1.4	0.9 inches

2. **(a)** For each of the above stations compute the annual temperature range and annual precipitation total. **(b)** To what climate type does each station belong?

3. **(a)** Verkhoyansk, Siberia (Exercise 1), represents the region of coldest winter temperature of the northern hemisphere climates. Compare the minimum month temperature of Verkhoyansk with Ft. Vermilion, Alberta, and Yakutsk, Siberia (Figure 15.1). **(b)** Study the rate of change of monthly temperature means for successive months in the spring and fall at these stations. What is the greatest change shown for any two successive months?

4. **(a)** Compare the climate of Point Barrow, Alaska (Exercise 1), with that of Upernivik, Greenland (Figure 15.4). **(b)** Which has the colder winter? **(c)** Is January the coldest month for both stations? **(d)** At what time of year does most precipitation occur? **(e)** Compare the precipitation regime of Point Barrow with that of the tropical desert climates in Chapter 13, Exercises 1 and 9. How do the totals compare? **(f)** The South Orkneys (Exercise 1) are a small island group in the South Atlantic. How does the marine location of the Orkneys influence the temperature regime? **(g)** Do the Orkneys receive more or less precipitation than Point Barrow (Exercise 1) and Upernivik (Figure 15.4)?

5. Prepare a temperature-precipitation graph similar to Figure 15.1 for the following station (data from Trewartha).

Kodaikanal, India, 10° N, elevation 7700 feet

	J	F	M	A	M	J	J	A	S	O	N	D
Temperature	55	56	59	61	62	59	58	58	58	57	55	55 °F
Precipitation	2.9	1.4	2.0	4.3	6.0	4.1	5.0	7.0	7.3	9.7	8.2	4.4 inches

6. (*a*) Kodaikanal, a hill station in southern India popular during the hot season, lies in the Palni Hills, a mountain mass surrounded by lowlands with a tropical savanna climate. Madras, a nearby station on the east coast of India, has a maximum in May of 90°, a minimum of 76° in January. How do these monthly average temperatures compare with the same months at Kodaikanal? (*b*) Using the lapse rate of 3½° F per 1000 feet, what difference in temperatures might we expect for these two stations? Is this figure roughly comparable to actual temperature differences? (*c*) Does the rainfall regime of Kodaikanal follow the usual monsoon pattern (see Cochin, India, Figure 13.5)?

CHAPTER SIXTEEN

The soil

AN understanding of fundamental principles of soil science, or *pedology*, is indispensable to a geographer. Soils constitute a major geographical factor, determining by their fertility and special qualities, not only whether a population can be fed, clothed, and housed but also the particular types of food and fiber or lumber products that can be obtained from a region. Although individual types of soils have been briefly mentioned in previous chapters describing climate zones of the world, a systematic study of soils logically follows a study of climates because climate is a primary factor in soil making.

The soil as a dynamic body

Many persons think of the soil as a lifeless, residual layer, which has somehow accumulated over a long period of time and which merely holds a supply of things necessary for plant growth. As soil science has developed, however, it has become known that the soil is a dynamic layer in which many complex chemical, physical, and biological activities are going on constantly. Far from being a static, lifeless zone, it is a changing and developing body. We

above: Soil cultivation in England.
Photograph by Aerofilms, Ltd., from Fairchild.

know now that soils become adjusted to conditions of climate, topography, and vegetation and will change internally when those controlling conditions change.

The soil scientist restricts the word *soil* to the surface material, which, over a long period of years, has come to have distinctive layers, or *horizons.* It has certain distinctive physical, chemical, and biological qualities, which permit it to support plant growth and which set it off from the infertile *subsoil* or bedrock lying beneath. The true soil is composed both of mineral and organic particles, whereas the underlying material may be, and usually is, wholly mineral matter.

Soil is made up of substances existing in three states, solid, liquid, and gaseous. For plant growth a proper balance of all three states of matter is necessary.

The solid portion of soil is both inorganic and organic. Weathering of rock produces the inorganic particles that give a soil the main part of its weight and volume. These fragments range from gravel and sand down to tiny colloidal particles less than 0.00001 inch in diameter. The organic solids consist of both living and decayed plant and animal materials, most being plant roots, fungi, bacteria, worms, insects, and rodents. Colloidal particles of organic matter share with inorganic colloidal particles an important function in soil chemistry.

The liquid portion of soil, the *soil solution*, is a complex solution of chemical compounds necessary for many important activities that go on in the soil. Soil without water cannot have these chemical reactions, nor can it support life. Gases in the open pore spaces of the soil form the third essential component. They are principally the gases of the atmosphere, together with gases liberated by biological and chemical activity in the soil.

For an understanding of soils, information is needed about (1) the physical-chemical properties and materials of soils, and (2) processes that make and maintain soils.

Physical-chemical make-up of soils

Although a minor factor in itself, *soil color* is perhaps the characteristic that is first noticed about a soil. Color can tell much about how a soil is formed and what it is made of. Soil horizons are usually distinguishable by color differences. One sequence of colors ranges from white, through brown, to black as a result of increasing *humus* (decomposed vegetation particles). Abundance of humus depends in a general way on luxuriance of vegetation and upon intensity of microbial activity, which in turn depend on climate. Thus we find that in middle latitudes, soils range from black or dark brown in the cool, humid areas to light brown or gray in the semi-arid steppe lands and deserts. Desert soils have little humus.

Reds and yellows are common colors in soils and are the result of small quantities of iron oxides and hydroxides. Red color indicates that the soil is well drained, but locally the color may be derived from a red source rock such as a red shale or sandstone.

Grayish and bluish colors in soils of humid climates often mean the presence of reduced iron in the soil and indicate poor drainage or bog conditions. Grayish soils in dry climates mean a meager amount of humus; a white color may be a result of the deposit of salts in the soil. Although some recently formed soils retain the color of the parent mantle material or bedrock, the color of fully developed soils is independent of what lies beneath.

Soil texture, a major characteristic of the soil, refers to particle sizes composing the soil. Particles are classified as various grades of gravel, sand, silt, and clay,[1] in decreasing order of size. The Bureau

[1] Fine gravel: particles 1 to 2 mm in diameter. Sand: particles 1 mm. to 0.05 mm in diameter. Silt: particles 0.05 to 0.005 mm in diameter. Clay: particles less than 0.005 mm in diameter.

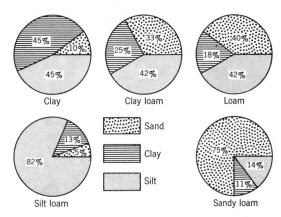

Figure 16.1 Typical compositions of five soil textures illustrate the definitions followed by the Bureau of Soils in classifying soils. (After *U.S. Dept. Agriculture Yearbook, 1938.*)

of Soils of the U.S. Department of Agriculture describes various soil textures as follows (Figure 16.1):

Sand. Contains 80 per cent or more of sand; 20 per cent or less of silt or clay.

Sandy loam. Contains 20 to 50 per cent silt and clay; remainder sand.

Loam. Contains 20 per cent or less of clay; 30 to 50 per cent of silt; 30 to 50 per cent of sand. (Silt loam, if silt predominates; clay loam, if clay predominates.)

Clay. Contains 30 per cent or more of clay; less than 70 per cent of other sizes.

Texture is important because it determines the water condition of the soil. Sand may drain too rapidly; in a clay soil the individual pore spaces are too small for adequate drainage. Generally speaking, the loam textures are best for plant growth.

Soil structure refers to the way in which soil grains are grouped together into larger pieces (Figure 16.2). Irregular pieces with sharp corners and edges give a *blocky* or nutlike structure. More or less spherical pieces make *granular* and *crumb* structure. Some soils have *columnar* and *prismatic* structure, made up of vertical columns or prisms a fraction of an inch up to four inches across. *Platy* soil structure consists of plates, or flat pieces, in a horizontal position. Soil structure influences the rate at which water is absorbed by the soil, the susceptibility of the soil to erosion, and the ease of soil cultivation.

Soil constitution covers such properties as compactness, stickiness, porosity, and consistency. For example, some soils are very porous, with a large proportion of open spaces between the soil particles; others are dense and heavy because of a large clay content.

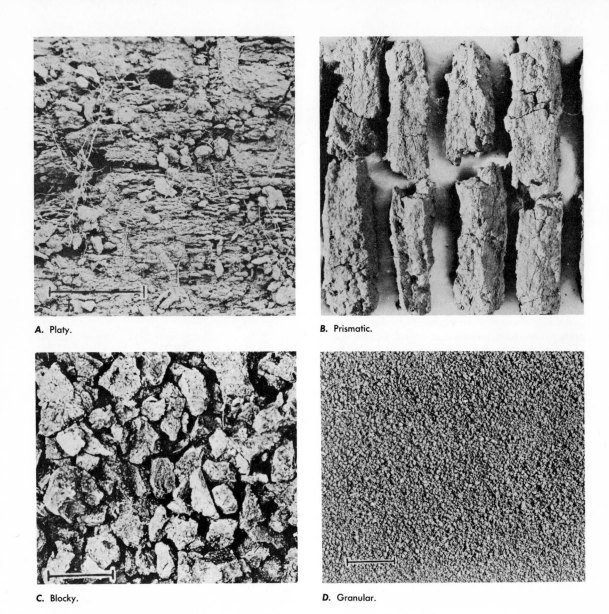

A. Platy.

B. Prismatic.

C. Blocky.

D. Granular.

Figure 16.2 Four basic soil structures are illustrated here. The black bar on each photograph represents one inch. (Photographs A and C by Roy W. Simonson; B and D by C. C. Nikiforoff. Courtesy of Division of Soil Survey, U.S. Dept. Agriculture.)

Soil colloids play a large part in soil development. Colloids are extremely tiny particles of either mineral or organic material. Colloid particles are so small that they cannot be seen by optical microscope and will remain suspended indefinitely in water. They have the property of being electrically charged and can therefore attract and hold *ions*, the unit chemical particles of dissolved substances. Ions of calcium, magnesium, and potassium are known in soil science as *bases*. These bases may be given up by the colloids to plants, which require them for growth, by a process known as *base exchange*. On the other hand, the *hydrogen ion* in the soil solution makes an *acid* condition. The degree to which hydrogen ions are held by soil colloids is known as the pH of the soil, and is a measure of soil acidity or alkalinity. Soil colloids also are useful in holding water in the soil. When present in large quantities they make the soil sticky and tough so that it is difficult to cultivate.

Another constituent of the soil is *soil air*, which occupies the pore spaces of the soil when it is not saturated with water. Soil air has been analyzed and found to contain an excess of carbon dioxide (given off by plants), but a deficiency of oxygen and nitrogen (used by bacteria in the soil).

Soil water, the water temporarily held in the soil, is in reality a complex chemical solution. In it are dilute solutions of such substances as bicarbonates, sulfates, chlorides, nitrates, phosphates, and silicates of calcium, magnesium, potassium, sodium, and iron.

The term *soil profile* denotes the arrangement of the soil into layerlike *horizons* of differing texture, color, and consistency (Figure 16.3). Soils are recognized and classified into broad groups on the basis of the parts of the profile that are present. Basically there are three parts to the soil profile. Horizons A and B represent the true soil, or *solum*; Horizon C is the subsoil, or weathered parent body. Below this is the parent bedrock or other underlying rock, designated as horizon D. The A horizon in humid climates is composed of two very different parts. The upper, or A_1, horizon is rich in organic matter and is dark colored. The lower, or A_2, horizon is a zone of leaching. The B horizon is usually a zone of accumulation of soil colloids and is dark in contrast to the A_2 horizon above it. These processes and the horizons they produce are discussed more fully in later pages.

Soil-forming processes and factors

Many types of processes and influences, known altogether as *soil formers*, act together to develop a soil. Some of these are *passive* condition; others are *active* agents. Five principal soil formers are (1) parent material, (2) topography, or relief, (3) time, (4) climate, and (5) biological activity.

The first of the passive soil formers is *parent material*, the residual or transported mantle of disintegrated rock making up the bulk of the soil. Many of the original rock forming minerals have been thoroughly changed chemically into new compounds and reduced to colloidal size. Although many people think that the type of parent material alone determines the kind of soil that is present, this is an inaccurate concept. For example, the same granite forms the bedrock in the Piedmont region in both Maryland and Georgia, but because of climatic differences the soils of these two states are somewhat different. On the other hand, soils of the same major groups may be found, overlying two different types of parent mantle or bedrock.

An exception to the general rule that soil type is independent of parent material origin is found in young soils that have not had enough time to develop, and in some limestone areas where the influ-

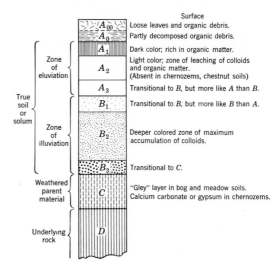

Figure 16.3 The idealized soil profile. (After *U.S. Dept. Agriculture Yearbook, 1938.*)

ence of the rock is especially strong. Parent material may locally exert a strong control over the soil texture. For example, on the sandy cuestas of the New Jersey coastal plain, the soil consists largely of quartz sand and is very porous. On glacial clays of the Hudson Valley the soil is unusually sticky and dense, preventing rainfall from seeping through.

Another passive soil former is *topographic relief* (Figure 16.4). Where slope is steep, surface erosion by runoff is more rapid and water penetration is less than on gentle slopes. This means that the soil will be thinner on steeper slopes, and at the same time the weathering processes will be producing less soil material to replace that removed by erosion. Flat upland areas accumulate a thick soil that has a thick layer of dense clay and is excessively leached. There the products of weathering tend to remain in place. Flat bottom lands likewise have thick soils, but they are poorly drained and dark colored. Here, constant saturation retards decay of vegetation and allows humus to accumulate. Gentle slopes where drainage is good but erosion is slow seem to be ideal for good soil formation. Slow, continuous erosion is a normal, healthy soil process whereby the removal balances the formation of new soil from the parent material. Only when this erosion is greatly accelerated does it become harmful to the soil.

Another aspect of the influence of topographic relief is the direction of exposure of the surface to the slanting rays of the sun. In middle latitudes it is common to find that south-facing slopes, exposed to the warming and drying effects of sunlight, have different conditions of vegetation and soils from north-facing slopes, which retain cold and moisture longer.

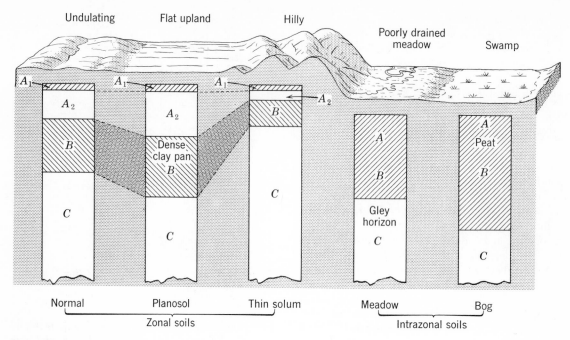

Figure 16.4 Topography is a major factor in soil development. (After *U.S. Dept. Agriculture Yearbook, 1938.*)

A third passive factor in soil formation is *time.* A soil is said to become *mature* when it has been acted upon by all soil-forming processes for a long time and has developed a profile that remains the same with further passage of time. Soils that are evolving from recently deposited river alluvium or glacial till, for example, are considered *young.* In young soils the characteristic horizons are absent or poorly developed. No age in terms of years can be given to all mature soils because the rate at which a mature soil is developed depends on many other factors. Some soils of humid regions in sandy localities may require 100 to 200 years to develop, whereas more commonly, several thousand years may be needed to produce a mature soil. Some soils of tropical regions are thought to be as old as one to six million years, or of Pliocene age. As with development of landforms, age of soils is purely relative. Another way of defining a mature soil might be to say that it is in equilibrium with the many processes and forces acting upon it.

Climate and soil

Of the active soil formers, climate is perhaps the most important. Climatic elements involved in soil development are (1) *moisture conditions,* affecting the soil (precipitation, evaporation, and humidity), (2) *temperature,* and (3) *wind.*

Precipitation provides the soil water, without which chemical and biological activities are not possible. When soluble chemicals are dissolved in water they ionize, or dissociate into positively and negatively charged particles. Without ionization the many complex chemical interchanges of elements necessary to soil development and plant growth cannot take place. An excess of precipitation, however, tends to leach away the colloids and bases. This process of removal by waters percolating through the soil is known as *eluviation.* A distinctive leached horizon of the soil, the A_2 horizon, results from this process. (See Figure 16.3.) The deposition of colloids and bases in the underlying B horizon is a process known as *illuviation.*

Where rainfall is extremely heavy, silica (SiO_2) is largely removed from the soil and carried off in streams. This process is termed *desilication.* Thus tropical soils in the wet equatorial rainforest belts are deficient in silica as well as in such bases as calcium, sodium, magnesium, and potassium, and are generally low in fertility.

In dry climates, evaporation exceeds precipitation and the soil is dry for long periods. Ground water is slowly brought to the surface by capillary attraction and evaporates in the soil, leaving behind the salts that were dissolved in the water. Calcium carbonate, the commonest of these deposits, forms a whitish crust in the soil. In the southwestern United States this is called *caliche,* and in places it makes the soil as hard and resistant to erosion as if it were a limestone. Gypsum (hydrous calcium sulfate) forms similar encrustations. In intermediate precipitation zones, such as the humid eastern border of the middle-latitude steppes, calcium carbonate appears as small nodules in the soil.

Rainfall and evaporation controls result in the formation of two major classes of soils (Figure 16.5). (1) *Pedalfer soils* show pronounced leaching and occur in the eastern United States where the rainfall is more than 25 inches annually. (2) *Pedocal soils* have an excess of calcium carbonate and occur in the western United States where rainfall is less than 25 inches. The names are coined from the chemical content of the soil. The syllables *al* and *fer* in pedalfer refer to aluminum and iron respectively, and were chosen because excessive leaching leaves behind the aluminum and iron hydroxides as residual substances which thus become important in quantity. The syllable *cal* in pedocal refers, of course, to calcium, which is present in the carbonate form in all pedocal soils.

Temperature is another important climatic factor in soil formation. It acts in two ways. (1) Chemical activity is generally increased by higher temperatures but reduced by cold,[2] and it ceases when soil water is frozen. Thus, tropical soils have a parent material which is thoroughly altered chemically, whereas soils of the frozen tundra have a parent material which is composed largely of mechanically broken minerals. (2) Bacterial activity is increased by warmer soil temperatures. Where bacteria thrive, as in the humid tropics, they consume all dead plants that fall to the ground. Thus there is little or no humus in the humid tropics. In cold continental climates, bacterial action is reduced. Hence, humus is preserved in the soil and is an important part of the mature soil profile.

Wind is of minor importance as a climatic factor in soil development. Winds may increase the evaporation from soil surfaces and may remove surface soil in arid regions lacking a plant cover. Wind-blown dust may accumulate and thereby provide the parent material of a soil.

Biological soil formers

Both plants and animals profoundly influence soil development. The plant kingdom consists of the *macroflora* (trees shrubs and grasses) and *microflora* (bacteria and fungi).

Grasses and trees require somewhat different chemical substances for growth. Trees, particularly the conifers, use little calcium and magnesium. Hence they thrive well in the pedalfer soils from which these substances have been leached and which are usually acid. Grasses and small grains

[2] An exception is the process of *carbonation*, or reaction of carbonic acid (H_2CO_3), upon minerals. This process is believed to be quite active at low temperatures because the concentration of carbonic acid is greater in cold water than in warm.

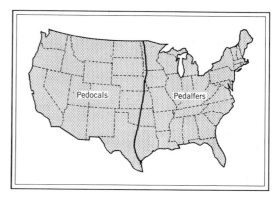

Figure 16.5 Soils of the United States have been divided into two major classes determined by climate. (After C. F. Marbut.)

(wheat, oats, barley) need abundant calcium and magnesium and do well in the pedocal soils of the semi-arid and marginal lands. For grasses to grow well in acid pedalfers, calcium must be added to the soil in the form of lime or crushed limestone. Plants tend to maintain the fertility of soil by bringing the bases (calcium, magnesium, potassium) from lower layers of the soil into the plant stems and leaves, then releasing them to the soil surfaces as the plant decomposes.

Dead plants provide *humus*, the non-living organic matter of the soil. Humus gives a dark brown or black color to the soil, as already noted. Humus particles of colloidal size act in the same way as mineral colloids in holding ions in the soil. The process of humus development, or *humification*, is essentially the slow oxidation, or burning, of the vegetative matter. Acids, known as the *organic acids*, are formed during humification. They aid in decomposing the minerals of the parent soil material. They also tend to combine with the bases, such as potassium, calcium, magnesium, iron, aluminum, and manganese, and are removed in the leaching process. Soils of the cold humid climates are therefore deficient in the bases and are consequently of low fertility for crop farming.

Turning now to the microflora, or bacteria and fungi, we find that bacteria consume humus. In cold climates bacterial growth is slow, hence, humus may accumulate on and in the soil. Soils of the subarctic and tundra climates have much undecomposed organic matter, which locally forms layers of peat, but in humid subtropical and tropical climates, bacterial action is intense and all dead vegetation is oxidized by the bacteria. Here humus is largely or entirely absent. The organic acids formed by humus are therefore also absent, and certain bases such as aluminum, iron, and manganese remain in the soil in excessive quantities. In this way the fundamental differences in soils of cold and warm climates can be traced back to intensity of bacterial activity.

Another function of some bacteria is to take gaseous nitrogen from the air and convert it into a chemical form that can be used by plants. This process is known as *nitrogen fixation.*

The influence of animals in the soil is largely mechanical, but nevertheless important. Earthworms are a particularly important agent in humid regions. They not only continually rework the soil by burrowing, but also change the texture and chemical composition of the soil as it passes through their digestive systems. Ants and termites bring large quantities of soil from lower horizons to the surface. Such burrowing animals as prairie dogs, gophers, ground squirrels, moles, and field mice disturb and rearrange the soil. Digging of burrows brings soil of lower horizons to the surface; collapse of burrows carries surface soil into lower horizons.

Review Questions

1. In what way is the soil a dynamic, rather than a lifeless, static body? To what general influences does the soil respond?

2. How is the term *soil* defined by the soil scientist? Of what three states of matter is soil made up? Are all three necessary for plant growth? Describe the types of substances that make up the soil.

3. What is the significance of soil color? What are some of the common soil colors, and what do they mean? In general, what relationship does soil color bear to climate?

4. What is meant by soil texture? What are the various soil textures recognized by the U.S. Bureau of Soils? What influence has soil texture upon agricultural use of the land?

5. What are some of the common soil structures? Describe four structures. How does soil structure influence the rate at which water is absorbed and transmitted by the soil?

6. What is meant by soil constitution? What properties are included in this term? Of what importance is soil constitution?

7. What are soil colloids? Explain how colloids hold ions. What are the bases commonly present in soils? What is base exchange? What is the influence of the hydrogen ion upon acidity of the soil? What is meant by pH of the soil?

8. What is soil air? In what way is it different from normal air of the free atmosphere? What are some of the substances commonly found in soil water?

9. Describe an idealized soil profile containing *A*, *B*, and *C* horizons. Which of these horizons constitute the true soil?

10. List the five principal soil formers, including both passive conditions and active agents.

11. From what types of parent material can soils be derived? Does the type of parent material strongly control the characteristics of a fully developed soil profile? Give examples to illustrate. How may young soils strongly reflect the nature of the parent materials? Give examples.

12. How does topographic relief influence development of the soil profile? Explain how various degrees of slope influence thickness of the profile. What conditions of slope are best for the development of soils suited to agriculture?

13. What is a mature soil? Does a mature soil profile continue to evolve through a series of changing forms? How long does it take for a mature soil to develop?

14. What influence has precipitation upon the soil profile? What is eluviation? What is illuviation? What horizons of the soil are affected by these processes? What is meant by desilication? Where is this process most intensively developed?

15. How do soils of dry climates differ fundamentally from soils of humid climates? What two major soil classes have been recognized on this basis?

16. How does temperature affect soil formation? Explain the control exerted by temperature over the type of weathering of the parent material and upon the accumulation of organic matter.

17. How are the needs of different plant groups suited to particular groups of soils? Are plants essential in maintaining the profile of a mature soil?

18. Explain the importance of humus in soil development. What is humification? What acids are formed during humification? What is the action of these acids in the soil? How does bacterial activity determine the amount of humus in the soil? How does this factor determine the fundamental difference between soils of equatorial and arctic regions?

19. What is meant by nitrogen fixation? How is it accomplished?

20. What important influence have earthworms, ants, termites, and burrowing animals upon the soil?

CHAPTER SEVENTEEN

The great soil groups

THE soil scientist recognizes that all soils can be subdivided into three orders, known as *zonal, intrazonal,* and *azonal* orders. Zonal soils, formed under conditions of good soil drainage through the prolonged action of climate and vegetation, are by far the most important and widespread of the three orders. Intrazonal soils are simply those formed under conditions of very poor drainage, such as in bogs, flood-plain meadows, or in the playa lake basins of the deserts. Azonal soils have no well-developed characteristics, either because they have had insufficient time to develop or because they are on slopes too steep to allow profile development. Azonal soils include thin, stony mountain soils of the earth's mountain regions (*lithosols*) and freshly laid alluvial materials or sand dunes (*regosols*). These usually have poorly developed profiles and cannot be easily classified, whereas the zonal and intrazonal soils have distinctive characteristics as the result of long development.

The great soil groups

Classification of soils is illustrated in Figure 17.1. There are about a dozen *great soil groups*, including both zonal and intrazonal orders, that have world-wide distributions under similar climatic and topographic conditions. Various zonal soil groups have already been mentioned and briefly discussed in earlier chapters in which the effect of climate on natural vegetation is treated. Combining a knowledge of the soil-forming factors with an understanding of climatic elements, we can proceed to a systematic study of each of the great soil groups. Some of the soil groups bear Russian names, applied by soil scientists of Russia who pioneered in this field.

The podzols

Of the zonal soils of humid climates the most widely distributed are the *podzols*, found closely associated with the subarctic climate, and the more northerly parts of the humid continental climate (Figure 17.2). These soils require a cold winter and adequate precipitation distributed throughout the year.

The podzol profile (Figure 17.3) is the soil profile from which the various soil horizons were originally named. At the very top, lying on the soil surface, is a layer of dead and partly decayed vegetation termed the A_0 horizon. Below this is the first soil layer, designated as the A_1 horizon. It is a thin, acid layer, rich in humus and varying in color from

above: Wheatfields near Bozeman, Montana.
Photograph, Ewing Galloway.

243

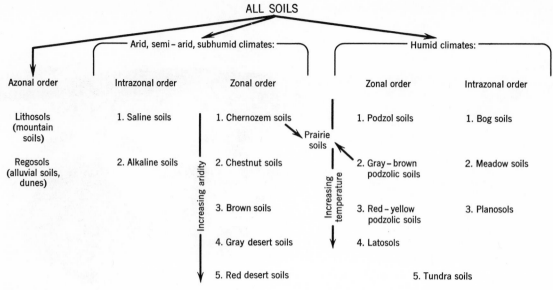

Figure 17.1 Classification of soils into orders and groups.

gray through yellowish brown to a reddish brown. The A_1 horizon is rich in colloids and is a zone of interaction between acids and bases.

Below the A_1 horizon is a distinctive light-colored zone called the A_2 horizon. This is the strongly leached horizon from which colloids and bases have been carried down. It sometimes has a bleached ash-gray or whitish-gray color because coloring agents such as the iron oxides have been removed. The name podzol is of Russian origin and means simply *ash soil*. Leaching such as occurs in the A_2 horizon is given the name *podzolization*.

Below the A_2 horizon of the podzol profile is the B horizon, a brownish zone that is enriched by the colloids and bases brought down from the A_2 horizon. The colloids give a heavy clayey consistency to the B horizon. Excessive deposit of oxides may cause the soil particles in this horizon to become strongly cemented into stony material known as *hardpan*, or, in European soil terminology, *ortstein*. Nodules of soil in the B horizon formed by the same process as hardpan are termed *concretions*. They may be composed of clay cemented by *limonite*, a hydrous iron oxide compound.

In the United States (Figure 17.4), the podzols are found in the northern Great Lakes states, the Adirondacks, and mountainous parts of New England. Here the ample precipitation combined with long, cold winters favors surface accumulation of decomposed vegetation. Organic acids cause a strong leaching of the A_2 horizon. Islands of podzolic soil are found in the Allegheny Mountains, where high altitude gives a cooler climate, and in the sandy New Jersey and Long Island coastal

plain belt, where leaching is intense in the porous sand. Podzols of the United States are but the small southern fringe of a great podzol belt corresponding with the coniferous forest, or taiga, of the subarctic climate zones in Canada and Eurasia (Figure 17.5).

Podzol soils are low in fertility. Leaching of important plant constituents is shown by the association of coniferous forest with this soil. Conifers need little of the calcium, magnesium, potassium, and phosphorus which many other plants require. The Pine Barrens on podzol soils of the New Jersey coastal plain are examples of adaptation of pine and scrub oak forests to podzol soils.

The podzols cannot produce the crops to feed a large population. Addition of lime and fertilizers to the soil will largely correct soil acidity and replenish the leached bases, but the favorable areas for such treatment are limited by the effects of continental glaciation. Bouldery morainal topography interspersed with swamps and lakes still renders much of the area unfit for farming. On the other hand, river terraces and drained lake beds, such as those along the Champlain and St. Lawrence valleys, are well suited topographically to cultivation.

Gray-brown podzolic soils

The second great zonal soil group of humid climates consists of the *gray-brown podzolic soils*. They differ from the podzols in that leaching is less intense and the soil color is brownish (Figure 17.6). The various soil horizons correspond with those of the podzols. The A_1 horizon is a moderately acid humus layer. The A_2 horizon is a gray-

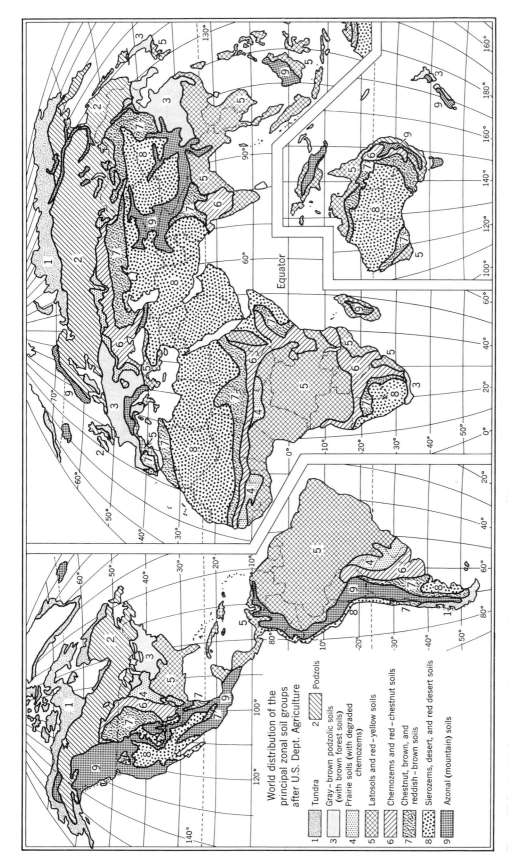

Figure 17.2 World distribution of the principal zonal soil groups. (After Blumenstock and Thornthwaite, "Climate and Man," U.S. Dept. Agriculture Yearbook 1941. Aitoff's equal-area projection, adapted by V. C. Finch.)

World distribution of the principal zonal soil groups after U.S. Dept. Agriculture.

1 Tundra
2 Podzols
3 Gray-brown podzolic soils (with brown forest soils)
4 Prairie soils (with degraded chernozems)
5 Latosols and red-yellow soils
6 Chernozems and red-chestnut soils
7 Chestnut, brown, and reddish-brown soils
8 Sierozems, desert, and red desert soils
9 Azonal (mountain) soils

Figure 17.3 This podzol soil profile was formed from a sandy granitic glacial till in Maine. (Photograph by Charles E. Kellogg. Courtesy of Division of Soil Survey, U.S. Dept. Agriculture.)

brown leached zone. It is less intensely leached than in the podzol and, consequently, is neither so light colored nor so distinctly limited. The B horizon is thick and dark brown. Like the podzols, it has concentrated colloids and bases.

The gray-brown podzolic soils contain more of the important bases than the podzols but are nevertheless somewhat acid. Deciduous forests (maple,

beech, oak) grow luxuriantly on the forest soils. These trees bring the bases up from the B horizon, returning them to the surface as dead leaves and branches. Thus the soil is replenished by these bases in a way not found in the podzols. When cleared for agriculture, the gray-brown podzolic soils make highly productive farms on which diversified crop farming and dairying are well developed. This is seen from the distribution of the gray-brown forest soils in the eastern-central United States where rainfall is 35 to 40 inches yearly in the humid continental climate. Note that southern Wisconsin, southern Michigan, Indiana, Ohio, Kentucky, New York, Pennsylvania, and Maryland, and southern New England are largely underlain by these soils (Figure 17.4). These are states noted for the value of their diversified crop production.

The gray-brown podzolic soils are also found over much of western Europe in both the marine west coast climate and humid continental climate.

Red-yellow podzolic soils

Farther south than the gray-brown podzolic soils, in a zone of increasingly warmer climate but with equally abundant precipitation, lies a great area of red-yellow podzolic soils (Figure 17.4). These soils occupy the southern states from Texas to the Atlantic shore, and coincide fairly well with the extent of the humid subtropical climate.

The red-yellow soils are of the podzolic type and show the same characteristic leaching of the A_2 horizon (Figure 17.7). Warm summers and mild winters favor bacterial action. Humus content is low. The typical red and yellow colors are a staining of iron compounds in the form of hydroxides. The yellow soils are the more strongly leached of the two and are found on sandy coastal plain belts. Aluminum hydroxides are also abundant in these soils, a condition typical of tropical soils in warm, humid regions.

Oak-pine forest was the natural vegetation of the northern part of the red soil belt in the United States. Red-yellow soils of the southern states are cultivated to yield tobacco, cotton, and peanuts, but historical economic influences may be the determining factor in this crop assemblage. Yellow soils, owing to their strong leaching, support natural forests of longleaf, loblolly, and slash pine. The pitch pine of the coastal belt is an important source of turpentine and resin; the slash pine is a good pulpwood tree.

Latosols

Soils of the humid tropics are called *latosols*, or *lateritic soils* (Figure 17.8). They are characterized as follows: (1) Chemical and mechanical decomposition of the parent rock is complete, owing to the

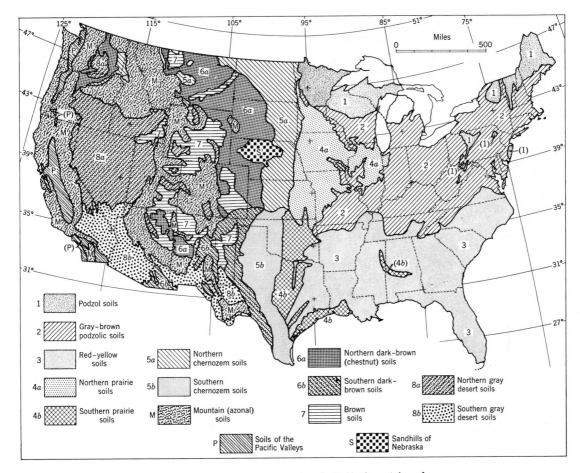

Figure 17.4 Great soil groups of the United States. (After C. F. Marbut, *Atlas of American Agriculture,* U.S. Dept. Agriculture, 1931.)

Legend:

1 — Podzol soils
2 — Gray–brown podzolic soils
3 — Red–yellow soils
4a — Northern prairie soils
4b — Southern prairie soils
5a — Northern chernozem soils
5b — Southern chernozem soils
M — Mountain (azonal) soils
6a — Northern dark–brown (chestnut) soils
6b — Southern dark–brown soils
7 — Brown soils
8a — Northern gray desert soils
8b — Southern gray desert soils
P — Soils of the Pacific Valleys
S — Sandhills of Nebraska

favorable conditions of moisture and heat. (2) Silica (SiO_2) has been almost entirely leached from the soil. (3) Oxides of iron, aluminum, and manganese have accumulated in the soil as permanent residual materials, giving a reddish-brown color to the soil. (4) Humus is almost or entirely lacking because of the rapidity of bacterial action in the prevailingly warm temperatures. (5) The soil is distinctively reddish. The reasons for the development of these conditions have been explained in foregoing pages. The general process of latosol formation is *laterization.*

True latosols are found only in warm, humid regions and, hence, correspond closely with the equatorial rainforest climate and the tropical savanna climate. Though the red-yellow soils of the southeastern United States show the effects of laterization, they are not true latosols.

Latosols quickly lose their fertility under crop cultivation because excessive leaching has removed the plant nutrients in all but a thin surface layer. However, the soil is favorable for the luxuriant growth of hardwoods and lianas in the rainforest and of the scrub and thorn forest or grasslands of the savanna regions.

An interesting feature of latosols is the local development of accumulations of iron and aluminum oxides into layers that can be cut out as building bricks. The material is termed *laterite.* On exposure to the drying effects of the air, these blocks become very hard. In Indochina, particularly, laterite bricks have been much used.

Valuable mineral deposits occur in laterites. These are thick layers of such minerals as *bauxite* (aluminum oxide), *limonite* (iron oxide), and *manganite* (manganese oxide). They are known as *residual ores* because they are not soluble in soil water and have continued to accumulate as the parent rock has weathered away and the silica and other soluble constituents have been removed. Important bauxite deposits of the Guianas of northern South America and of western India are of this type. Valuable resources of manganese are in laterite deposits.

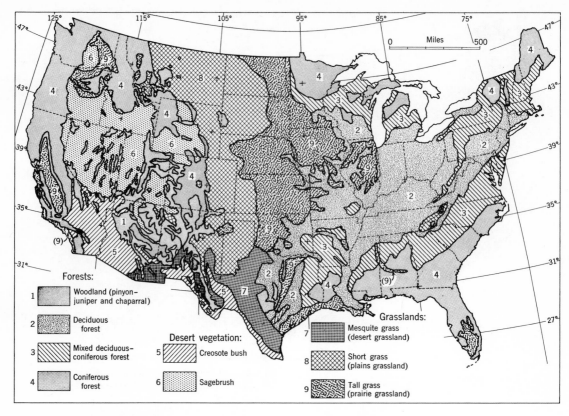

Figure 17.5 Natural vegetation types of the United States. (After H. L. Shantz, *U.S. Dept. Agriculture Yearbook, 1938.*)

Bog and meadow soils (intrazonal)

Bog soils are formed in marshy bottom lands in the humid continental climates and are considered intrazonal in classification. Continental glaciation in North America and Europe left countless basins that have since been largely filled. Here the soil is saturated most of the time and plant decay is greatly retarded. The partly decomposed forest plants of the bog therefore accumulate into an upper peat layer three to four feet thick. Below this is a horizon of sticky, structureless clay, known to soil scientists as the *gley* horizon. It is of gray-blue color and is largely impervious to water seepage.

Meadow soils, another intrazonal type, are formed on the flood plains of streams where drainage is somewhat better than in the bogs, but is nevertheless poor. These areas are extensively used in the humid middle-latitude climates as pastures because the grass grows rapidly and densely. A thick, humus-rich layer is developed, overlying a sticky gley horizon. The name *humic-gley soils* has been proposed for the meadow soils (Figure 17.9).

Planosols (intrazonal)

Soils developed on flat or gently sloping, elevated surfaces are known as *planosols*. The soil horizons are abnormally thick because of slow removal by erosion. Planosols have a thick, dense clay horizon in humid climates. In subhumid climates planosols have a dense, cemented horizon.

Tundra soils

Soils of the arctic tundra are so widespread (Figure 17.2) that they may be considered a zonal type along with the podzols, gray-brown forest soils, red-yellow soils, and latosols, but because they are poorly drained they are sometimes classified as intrazonal.

Climate conditions favorable for tundra soils have been described under tundra climates of the northern continental fringes, Chapter 15. Intensely cold, long winters cause soil moisture to be frozen during many months of the year. Under these cold conditions chemical alteration of the minerals is slow, and much of the parent material of the soil consists of mechanically broken particles. The slow

Figure 17.6 In this profile of a gray-brown podzolic soil, developed under oak-hickory forest, the leached A_2 horizon is not so light as in the podzol, nor is the humus layer so thick. (Photograph by Roy W. Simonson. Courtesy of Division of Soil Survey, U.S. Dept. Agriculture.)

Figure 17.7 A red podzolic soil profile formed from sandy marine sediments in Louisiana. (Photograph by Roy W. Simonson. Courtesy of Division of Soil Survey, U.S. Dept. Agriculture.)

Figure 17.8 This reddish-brown latosol was formed from basalt in the Belgian Congo under conditions of heavy rainfall and high temperatures. (Photograph by Charles E. Kellogg. Courtesy of Division of Soil Survey, U.S. Dept. Agriculture.)

Figure 17.9 A meadow soil, or humic-gley soil, formed from glacial till in Iowa. This belongs to an intrazonal soil group and shows but two horizons, a thick, humus-rich upper dark layer overlying a heavy clay bed. (Photograph by Roy W. Simonson. Courtesy of Division of Soil Survey, U.S. Dept. Agriculture.)

rate of plant decomposition results in the presence of much humus. The tundra soils do not have simple, distinctive soil profiles, but consist of thin layers of sandy clay and humus. The surface may be covered with a sod layer of lichens and mosses two or three inches thick.

In the tundra regions of Siberia and North America, the condition of permanently frozen ground, or *permafrost*, is widespread. (See Chapter 15.) Curious lenses, layers, and vertical wedge-like bodies of ice are present under the soil.

The chernozem

Of the zonal soils in a semi-arid climate one of the most distinctive and widely distributed types is the *chernozem*, or *black earth* (Figure 17.10). A typical chernozem profile appears to consist essentially of two layers. Immediately beneath a grass sod is a black layer, the *A* horizon, two to three feet thick and rich in humus. In this layer the structure is a crumb or nut. The *A* horizon grades downward

into a *B* horizon of brown or yellowish brown color, then, with a sharp line of demarcation, into a light-colored *C* horizon. As in the podzolic soils, in the *B* horizon colloids and bases accumulate by downward percolation through the *A* horizon, but unlike the podzols, the chernozem has no leached A_2 horizon.

The chernozem is rich in calcium, which may appear in excess as precipitated calcium carbonate nodules. It has been noted that the chernozem develops in parent material rich in calcium. The origin and distribution of the chernozem have long attracted the soil scientist. Russian investigators in particular have been intensely interested in the chernozem because it occupies a large area in the Ukraine, surrounding the Black Sea on its west, north, and east sides (Figure 17.2) and continuing in a great belt eastward along the 50th parallel into the heart of Asia. It is important in the United States and Canada, where it forms a north-south belt starting in Alberta and Saskatchewan and running through the Great Plains of the United States to central Texas. A similar north-south belt runs through Argentina. Other extensive areas are mapped in Africa, Australia, and India.

Climate has long been thought to be a determining factor in the development of the chernozem. Comparison of soil and climate maps shows that the middle-latitude chernozems, in the Americas and Europe, lie on the more arid western side of the humid continental climates and with decreasing latitude extend over into the middle-latitude steppe climates. Aridity is therefore a definite contributing cause. The continental location of chernozem areas makes for hot summers and cold winters. Drought periods with strong evaporation dry out the soil, and forests cannot exist. Instead, grasses, which can withstand drought readily and which are tolerant to soils with excesses of mineral salts, flourish on the chernozem. Steppe grasslands and prairies are the natural vegetation of the middle-latitude chernozem.

An important factor in development of the middle-latitude chernozem is its occurrence on *loess*, the wind-transported dust so extensively deposited during the glacial period. (See Chapter 28.) Though the chernozem is not limited to such areas, the texture and lime content of loess, together with the plains topography, have been especially favorable to chernozem development.

Geographically, perhaps the outstanding point of importance regarding the chernozem is its productivity for small grain crops—wheat, oats, barley, and rye. Great grain surpluses are exported from chernozem areas in the United States, Canada, and the Ukraine and Argentine, causing them to be described as breadbaskets of the world.

Prairie soils

Examination of the soil maps (Figure 17.2 and 17.4) will show that between the chernozems and gray-brown podzolic soils in the United States and Eastern Europe lie zones of *prairie soils*. Rainfall is 25 to 40 inches and diminishes greatly across this

Figure 17.10 A chernozem soil profile from glacial till in North Dakota. (Photograph by W. M. Johnson. Courtesy of Division of Soil Survey, U.S. Dept. Agriculture.)

belt (Figure 14.11). This soil group is similar to the chernozems in general profile and appearance, but differs in that it lacks the excess calcium carbonate of the chernozems (Figure 17.11). The prairie soil is, therefore, a transitional type between the major soil divisions: pedocal and pedalfer. In subtropical and tropical regions, prairie soils lie between the chernozems and the lateritic soils.

Of special interest in the United States has been the origin of natural tall-grass prairies of the upper Mississippi Valley and the Great Plains states: Illinois, Iowa, eastern Nebraska, southern Min-

Figure 17.11 This prairie soil profile, developed on loess in Iowa, was formed from the same parent material and lies in the same county as the gray-brown podzolic profile in Figure 17.6. Whereas the podzolic profile was formed under oak-hickory forest, this profile was developed under prairie grass cover. (Photograph by Roy W. Simonson. Courtesy of Division of Soil Survey, U.S. Dept. Agriculture.)

nesota, northern Missouri, and eastern Kansas (Figure 17.5). Here forests were lacking over vast expanses at the time of the coming of white men. Although many explanations have been offered for the existence of the prairies, including the possibility of deforestation by burning, it seems likely that a major contributing factor has been that the prairie soils become almost completely dry between summer rains down to a depth of a foot or so as a result of the dryness and heat of summer air masses. Although the prairie grasses can survive these conditions, deciduous forests, which border the prairies on the east, cannot.

Prairie soils are extremely productive, combining the fertility of the chernozems with somewhat moister climate. Perhaps the outstanding crop associated with the prairie-soil belt is corn. The corn belt is practically identical with the prairie-soil belt, although the corn belt actually extends eastward into the brown forest soil region of Indiana and Ohio. Corn requires not only high temperatures during the growing season but ample moisture as well. This last requirement is met by periods of summer thunderstorms interspersed with hot, dry periods.

Chestnut soils and brown soils

To the arid side of the chernozem belt lies the belt of *chestnut soils* or *dark-brown soils*. They occupy the semi-arid middle-latitude steppe lands, in North America and Asia. The chestnut-soil profile is generally similar to the chernozem, but contains less humus and hence is not so dark in color. The soil structure tends to be prismatic.

The chestnut soils are fertile under conditions of adequate rainfall or irrigation, but lie in a hazardous marginal belt in which years of drought and adequate rainfall are alternated. Bordering on the productive chernozem wheat belt of the Great Plains, the chestnut-soil belt of the United States offers a temptation for expanded wheat cultivation. Under special cultivation practices that conserve soil moisture, a period of moist years brings high grain yields to these marginal belts; but a series of drought years can cause devastation and poverty.

Toward still more arid regions the chestnut soils give way to the *brown soils*, generally similar, but with still less humus and consequently a lighter color (Figure 17.12). In the western United States, the brown soils occupy basins in the central Rockies of Wyoming, the Colorado Piedmont, and parts of the Colorado Plateaus in Colorado, Utah, Arizona, and New Mexico.

The brown soils are typical of the middle-latitude steppes and support a light growth of grasses suitable for livestock grazing. With irrigation they are productive, but farming is not attempted without.

A fine example of the contrast between irrigated and non-irrigated areas is presented by the various small settlements of eastern Utah. Each town with its surrounding farmlands stands as a delightful green oasis in a landscape of bunchgrass and sagebrush or light pinyon-juniper woodland.

Gray desert soils (sierozem) and desert red soils

Soils of the middle-latitude deserts and tropical deserts seem to fall into two great soil groups on the basis of color: (1) *gray desert soils,* or *sierozems,* and (2) *red desert soils.*

The gray soils, or sierozems, are well developed in the western deserts of Nevada, western Utah, and southern portions of Oregon and Idaho. This region is sometimes referred to as the Great Basin because of the prevalence of interior drainage systems ending in evaporating basins. It corresponds approximately with the middle-latitude desert climate and has northward extensions into the middle-latitude steppe climate.

The gray soils contain little humus because of the sparse growth of vegetation, such as sagebrush and bunchgrass. Color ranges from light gray to grayish brown. Horizons are present, but being only slightly differentiated are not conspicuous. Excessive amounts of calcium carbonate are present in the form of *lime crust,* or *caliche,* a deposit of calcium carbonate or hydrous calcium sulfate. In places this deposit has the appearance of a hard rock layer and may even resist erosion in such a way as to produce small mesas or platforms. Gravels deposited by streams are often thus cemented into a conglomerate rock. Lime crust forms during prolonged dry periods when ground waters rise slowly surfaceward by capillary attraction and evaporate near the surface, leaving the salts behind in the soil.

In the more arid, hotter tropical deserts are found the *desert red soils* (also termed the *southern gray desert soils*). These range from a pale reddish gray to a pronounced deep red. Humus is reduced to the minimum, there being only a scattered growth of desert shrubs and cacti. Thus the activity of plants as soil formers reaches its lowest point in the desert red soils, as does also the activity of animals. Color is derived from small amounts of iron compounds. Horizons are poorly developed; texture is often coarse, with many fragments of parent rock throughout the soil. Deposits of lime carbonate are present, as with the gray soils.

The gray and red desert soils are suitable for cultivation only where they are fine textured, as along the flood plains and terraces of exotic streams and on the outer slopes of alluvial fans. Irrigation is essential, whether water is diverted from a river

Figure 17.12 Profile of a brown soil formed from loess in Colorado. The B horizon, which has good prismatic structure, shows the action of salts, commonly present in semi-arid regions. (Photograph by C. C. Nikiforoff. Courtesy of Division of Soil Survey, U.S. Dept. Agriculture.)

or obtained from wells penetrating the ground water reserves in alluvial fans.

Saline soils (intrazonal)

In the steppes and deserts, evaporation on the average exceeds precipitation and there are many topographic depressions that have no outlet to external drainage systems. Here the products of rock weathering are brought by intermittent flowing streams in times of flood and left behind on the basin floor. Along with mud, silt, and sand are the dissolved mineral salts that crystallize out as the water evaporates. Soils containing an excess of salts (particularly the sodium salts) are of the *saline* (or white alkali) group and are classified as intrazonal because they are poorly drained or are of local extent.

Shallow lake basins, or *playas,* of extreme flatness are often covered with only a thin film of water which evaporates rapidly, leaving its salts on the surface. Most persons are familiar with the salt flats of Great Salt Lake in Utah, on which so many automobile speed records have been set. Salts found

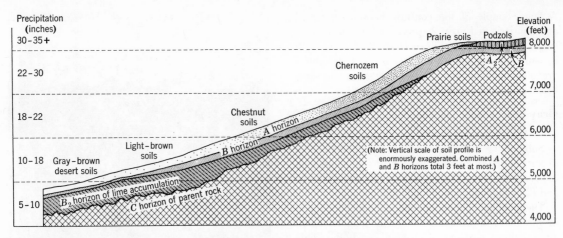

Figure 17.13 This schematic diagram shows the gradation of soils from a dry steppe-climate basin (*left*) to a cool, humid climate (*right*) as one ascends the west slopes of the Bighorn Mountains, Wyoming. (After J. Thorp, 1931.)

in the various playa lakes of the southwestern United States are *soda* (Na_2CO_3), *borax* ($Na_2B_4O_7$), *calcium carbonate* ($CaCO_3$), various sulfates (Na_2SO_4, $MgSO_4$, K_2SO_4), chlorides (NaCl, $CaCl_2$, $MgCl_2$), and many others.

Saline soils are light colored and show poorly developed horizons. Where the salts are thick and pure in the inner parts of the playas there is no soil in the true sense of the word. The term *saline soil* is properly applied to marginal areas where silts and clays make up a large proportion of the body of the soil.

Although there are many species of plants adapted to saline soils the vegetal cover is at best sparse. Agriculture is not possible on saline soils unless they are flushed out with large quantities of irrigation water to remove the salts. This has been done to advantage to reclaim much good agricultural land in the southwestern United States.

Closely related to saline soils are *alkaline soils* (or black alkali soils) of somewhat different chemical properties from the saline soils, but occurring in the same areas. The presence of sodium carbonate (Na_2CO_3) is typical of alkaline soils.

Altitude and soils

As explained in Chapter 15, climate zoning in mountains tends to reproduce world climates in a series of vertical zones, the effect of increasing altitude being much the same as that of increasing latitude. Because climate is a major determining factor in soils, we might also expect increasing altitude to result in a series of great soil groups. Such a series is illustrated by soils of the Big Horn Mountains, Wyoming (Figure 17.13). Starting with gray desert soils at the lowest elevation, the series progresses through the zonal soils of dry climates through prairie soils to podzols at the high elevations.

Review Questions

1. What are the three orders into which all soils can be classified? Under what conditions is each of these orders developed? What kinds of soils are included under the azonal order?

2. Describe the profile of a typical podzol soil. What climatic conditions are required for the development of soils of this group? What is the natural vegetation of this great soil group? How do these soils rate in terms of agricultural productivity? In what way do they require treatment?

3. How do the gray-brown podzolic soils differ from the podzol soils? How do the climatic factors differ? What geographic positions do the gray-brown podzolic soils have with respect to the podzols? How does natural vegetation of the two soil groups differ? Which soil group is better for agricultural purposes? Why?

4. What are the essential characteristics of the red-yellow soils? With what climate are they associated? Explain how temperatures and precipitation determine the features of these soils. What types of natural vegetation are found on the red-yellow soils?

5. What are latosols (lateritic soils)? What are their essential characteristics? What is meant by laterization? How do latosols rate in terms of agricultural productivity?

6. How can laterite be used as a building material? What are some of the residual ores obtained from laterites?

7. Why are the bog and meadow soils classed as intrazonal? What is the appearance of the profiles of these soils? What is the gley horizon? How do meadow soils differ from bog soils?

8. What are planosols? To what order do they belong? Where do planosols develop, and what is different about their profiles as compared with associated zonal soils?

9. Describe a tundra soil. In what respect does it differ from the podzol soils? What effect has excessive cold upon the composition of the parent material of the soil?

10. What is the chernozem? Where was this soil first studied? Where is it best developed? Describe the chernozem profile.

11. What is the essential difference between the chernozems and the podzolic soils? With what climatic characteristics are the chernozem regions associated? What is the natural vegetation of chernozem soils? How is loess associated with the chernozem?

12. In what way are the prairie soils related to both the chernozems and the gray-brown podzolic soils? What is the nature of the geographic and climatic location of the prairie soils?

13. What are the tall-grass prairies? What theories have been advanced for the absence of forests in these areas? With what crops are the prairie regions now associated in the central United States?

14. Where are the chestnut soils (dark-brown soils) located in relation to the chernozems? With what climatic conditions are they associated?

15. How do the brown soils differ from the chestnut soils?

16. Describe the gray desert soils and red desert soils. How do these two groups differ in geographic location and in climatic controls? Are horizons well developed in these soils? What forms do excessive calcium carbonate and hydrous calcium sulfate take in these soils?

17. Where do saline soils form? What are some of the salts found in playa lakes of the dry deserts? How do the alkaline soils (black alkali soils) differ from the saline soils?

18. How does altitude influence the development of soil types? In an arid region in middle latitudes, what succession of soil groups might be encountered in passing from an intermontane basin to a lofty mountain summit?

Part Four
Landforms

CHAPTER EIGHTEEN

Introduction to landform study

TOPOGRAPHIC relief, defined as the configuration or shape of the land surface, is of considerable interest to the geographer because it exerts far-reaching and fundamental influence on the patterns of human activity. The direct influences are obvious to any thoughtful person. A mountain chain is an effective barrier between groups of people who live in adjacent lowlands. A plain, on the other hand, may be densely populated, rich in agricultural resources, and unified culturally and politically by a network of good roads and railroads that permit people with common interests to intercommunicate freely. One coast line, deeply indented with excellent natural harbors but bordered by a rocky rugged coastal belt, may produce a community of seafaring humans, adapted to fishing, ocean commerce, and shipbuilding. Another coast line, whose simple plan and shallow bottom provide not a single good natural harbor, may be bordered by a low, fertile coastal plain. Here human activity turns naturally to agriculture.

Examples of the direct effect of topographic relief on human beings could be cited almost without end, but there are, in addition, indirect geographical influences to be considered. As we have seen in the study of rainfall distribution, a high mountain range profoundly influences climate in adjacent

areas. If it shields a nearby lowland from prevailing moisture-bearing winds, a desert results. On mountain slopes, climates become cooler and moister with increased altitude, bringing a changing succession of agricultural and forest conditions, which, in turn, determine to what extent occupation is possible and what natural products can be obtained. Steepness of slopes is closely associated with fertility of soils. Hill and mountain slopes have thin, relatively poor soils, readily subject to devastating soil erosion when exposed by axe or plow. Plains may have thick, rich soils, not easily eroded even under poor farming practices.

The systematic study of topographic relief forms is known as *geomorphology* (*geo*, earth; *morph*, form; *ology*, science), but for simplicity may well be called "the study of landforms." Landscape features must be sorted out into classes or groups of those essentially similar both in outward form and in origin. The geomorphologist is equally interested in forms and in the processes and stages of development of those forms. This book will treat landforms in terms of how they came about. Landscape features pass through an orderly series

above: Bryce Canyon, Utah.
Photograph by Sawders, from Cushing.

259

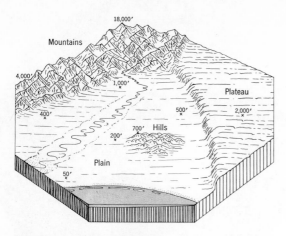

Figure 18.1 Major relief features of the landscape.

of changes, just as do human beings in their life span. Once these life stages are known, any landscape feature can be related to a particular event in the life cycle of landforms, thereby lending order and natural law to our concepts of landform development.

Common topographic terms

Before entering into a study of the origin and development of landforms, it is desirable to review and clarify some terms that apply to various simple topographic relief forms or assemblages of forms. Definitions conform to common language usage and tell nothing about the geological origins of the forms.

Of the larger relief forms there are three major groups, *plains, plateaus,* and *mountains* and *hills* (Figure 18.1). A plain is a land area whose surface is nearly flat or gently rolling and whose elevation is usually low. Most plains lie less than a few hundred feet above sea level, but if they slope upward in an inland direction they may reach elevations of a few thousand feet, in which event they might be termed *high plains.* The word *lowland* is often used in the same sense as plain but does not necessarily imply the low relief that a plain must have.

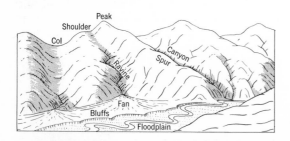

Figure 18.2 Examples of minor topographic forms.

A plateau is a tablelike land surface, fairly flat or moderately rolling, and bounded on at least one side by steeper slopes descending to areas at least several hundred feet lower. Elsewhere a plateau may be bounded by rising mountain or cliff slopes. Plateaus are often cut by deep canyons, numerous enough to divide the plateau surface into many separate parts. Nevertheless, as long as the intercanyon areas are reasonably flat and all lie at about the same elevation, the region is called a plateau.

Mountains are regions of moderate to steep slopes which meet to form narrow divides, ridges, and peaks. Most minor valleys and ravines in a mountainous region are narrow and V-shaped, formed by the meeting of steep mountain slopes. Slopes of 20° to 45° are considered steep, but slopes may be as steep as 60° or 70° in some ranges. Summits are often of various different elevations and have little or no flat ground on top. Hills differ in no distinct way from mountains but are merely smaller forms. Hill slopes are perhaps, on the average, less than most mountain slopes, although this might not be true in an isolated comparison. Some geographers attempt to set definite elevation figures to distinguish hills and mountains. For instance, hills might be defined as all steep-sided landforms whose summits rise no more than 500 feet above the adjacent lowlands. Actually, it is a matter of human judgment and comparison. What are called mountains in one region may be the same size as features elsewhere called hills. The Palni Hills of southern India rise to 5000 and 6000 feet above the surrounding plain, but are only hills in contrast to the gigantic Himalayan Range of northern India and Tibet. Yet in New England no one would think to question the name "White Mountains" although they rise no higher than the Palni Hills of India.

The various kinds of smaller relief features are too numerous to treat here; a handful are illustrated in Figure 18.2. Throughout the following chapters many such words will be used. Some will be defined and explained in the text; others will be used without explanation because they are part of everyday language and can be found in most abridged dictionaries.

Genetic landform description

It is possible, of course, to describe all landscape features by tabulating their size, shape, angles of slope, and orientation without thought to their origin or development. This is an empirical approach to natural science. Volumes of figures and other factual data would be required to convey the proper description of even the simplest assemblages of landforms. If, on the other hand, the development of landforms is carefully examined, it is seen that the same series of forms is repeated with remarkable similarity over and over again in nature. In order to classify and describe the host of forms in terms of orderly sequences of development, a single brief statement giving (*a*) the *process* which sculptured the landform and (*b*) the *stage* of its development is needed to convey an accurate idea of what it looks like. The person who hears or reads such a description, knowing what the ideal forms are like, can relate any particular landform to its proper place in the natural scheme.

The systematic study of landforms according to their origin and stage of development was introduced by Professor William Morris Davis, of Harvard University, about 1890. His influence has been so profound that many English-speaking geomorphologists follow the basic plans that he laid down.

Agents of land sculpture

Most landforms are products of one or more of the land-sculpturing agents, running water, waves, ice, and wind. These erosional agents, aided by processes of rock decay and downslope movements of soil and rock under gravitational force, attack from the outside all continental masses that become elevated by mountain-making upheavals or warping of the earth's solid crust. No part of the land surface is immune from attack. As soon as any mass comes to be exposed to the air or to wave attack it is set upon by these denudational agents and processes. They work to one ultimate goal—wearing away the land until it becomes a low plain, which is then slowly consumed by waves and finally covered by ocean waters. The disintegration products are spread over the sea floors surrounding the continents. The processes act with extreme slowness, to be sure, but geologic time is enormously great. Streams and waves seen in action today have had millions of years to do their work. Geologists believe that all landscape features can be explained as results of processes that can be seen acting at the present time.

In the wearing down of land masses, a great variety of topographic forms results. Where rock is eroded away, valleys or topographic depressions of one sort or another are formed. Between the eroded depressions are ridges, hills, or mountains representing unconsumed parts of land masses. All such landforms shaped by progressive removal of the bedrock mass are designated *erosional landforms*.

Rock and soil fragments that were removed are deposited elsewhere to make an entirely different set of topographic features, the *depositional landforms*. Figure 18.2 illustrates these forms. The ravine, canyon, peak, and spur are erosional land-

forms; the fan, built of rock fragments below the mouth of the ravine, is a depositional landform.

In terms of the grand scale of geological processes there are two fundamental varieties of landforms. First, there are the original crustal masses raised by internal earth forces and by volcanic eruptions. These comprise the *initial landforms* (Figure 18.3*A*). Second, there are the erosional and depositional forms made by agents of denudation. Because these follow the initial forms and occur in orderly sequences, they are called collectively the *sequential landforms* (Figure 18.3*B*).

Any landscape is really nothing more than the existing stage in a great struggle or contest. The internal earth forces spasmodically push up parts of the crust to create initial landforms. The external agents patiently keep wearing these masses down and carving them into vast numbers of smaller sequential landforms. All stages of this struggle can be seen in various parts of the world. Where high, rugged mountains exist, the internal earth forces have recently dominated. Where certain low plains exist today, denudational forces have finally triumphed. All intermediate stages can be found. Because the internal earth forces act repeatedly, new land masses keep coming into existence as old ones are subdued. Judging from conditions in various periods of the geologic past, we are now in a time when continents stand relatively high above sea level. This suggests that internal forces were active relatively recently, geologically speaking.

Topographic maps

The most important tools available for laboratory study of landforms are topographic maps and air photographs. The student of geomorphology must be able to read and interpret topographic

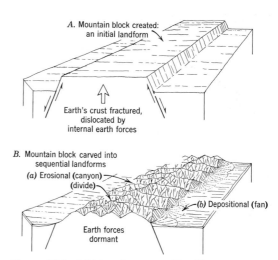

A. Mountain block created: an initial landform

Earth's crust fractured, dislocated by internal earth forces

B. Mountain block carved into sequential landforms
(*a*) Erosional (canyon)
(divide)
(*b*) Depositional (fan)

Earth forces dormant

Figure 18.3 Initial and sequential landforms.

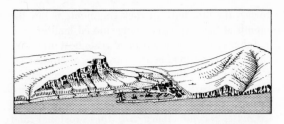

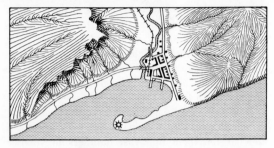

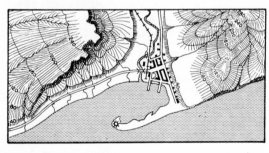

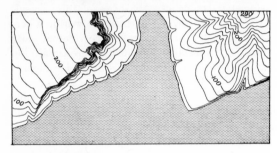

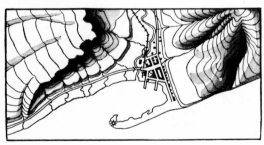

Figure 18.4 Various ways in which relief can be shown are, from top to bottom: (1) perspective diagram or terrain sketch, (2) hachures, (3) contours, (4) hachures and contours combined, and (5) plastic shading and contours combined. (Drawn by E. Raisz.)

maps quickly and accurately, translating the characteristic forms he sees on maps into verbal statements covering classifications, descriptions, and evolutionary aspects of each.

Several methods have been used to show accurately the configuration of the land surface on topographic maps. Methods described in this chapter are *plastic shading, altitude tints, hachures,* and *contours* (Figure 18.4). The first three processes give a strong visual effect of three dimensions so that even untutored persons can grasp the essential character of the landscape features without preliminary explanation. But, as compensation for ease of understanding, such methods of showing relief are inadequate because they do not tell the reader the elevation above sea level of all points on the map, or how steep the slopes are. The method of topographic contours, however, gives this information and makes the most useful type of topographic map.

Plastic shading

Maps using plastic shading to show relief look very much like photographs taken down upon a plaster relief model of the land surface illuminated from directly above or from an oblique angle (Figure 18.4). They may also be likened to air photographs taken when the sun's rays are striking the earth at a fairly low angle (Figure 18.5). The effect of relief is produced by gray or brown tones applied according to one of two principles. In the *oblique illumination* method, light rays are imagined as coming from a point in the northwestern sky somewhere intermediate between the horizon and zenith. Thus all slopes facing southeast receive the heaviest shades and are darkest where the slopes are steepest (Figure 18.6). Northwest-facing slopes are light in tone and lightest where the slope most nearly approaches a right angle to the imaginary rays. Although it is true that in the northern hemisphere the sun's rays illuminate the ground from the southeast, south, and southwest, it has been found that an imaginary light source from the south side of a map gives an inverted or "negative" effect to the relief. To demonstrate this, turn the page upside down and look at Figure 18.6. For many persons the relief will seem to reverse itself, so that the stream valleys look like ridges, and vice versa.

An alternative method of applying plastic shading is that of *vertical illumination*, in which a light source is imagined as located directly above the map. This might seem at first thought to produce no relief effect at all, because no shadows would be cast, but on a sloping surface the illumination must be spread over a larger area than on a horizontal surface. Consequently, sloping surfaces are

Figure 18.5 A vertical air photograph (*above*) is a kind of topographic map, showing all relief details but lacking elevation information. The contour topographic map (*below*) covers the same area and shows a small side canyon of the Grand Canyon. North is toward the bottom of these maps to give the proper effect of relief in the photograph. (U.S. Forest Service and U.S. Geological Survey.)

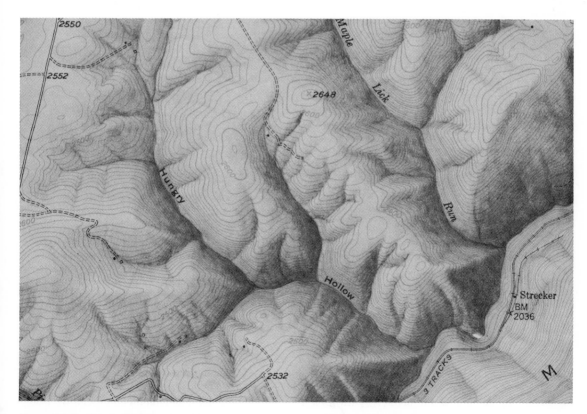

Figure 18.6 Plastic shading combined with contours greatly enhances the visual effect of relief. (Portion of U.S. Geological Survey, Kitzmiller, Md.–W. Va., topographic quadrangle, scale 1:24,000.

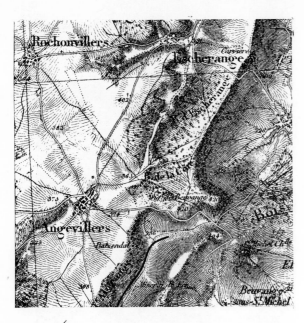

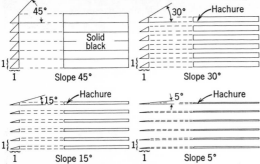

Figure 18.7 A portion of the Metz sheet is shown above to correct scale. This map is one of the French 1:80,000 topographic series using black hachures and spot heights. The Lehmann system of hachuring, shown below, varies the thickness of hachure line according to ground slope.

somewhat darker than horizontal ones and the darkness increases where the slopes steepen. One advantage possessed by vertical illumination is that surfaces of equal slope have the same tone and, by the use of a standard scale of tones, the steepness of slope can be approximately determined. On some maps, shading of both kinds is used simultaneously and seems to enhance the effect of three dimensions.

Altitude tints

In its simplest form, altitude tinting consists of assigning a certain color, or a certain depth of tone of a color, to all areas on the map lying within a specified range of elevation. Schoolroom wall maps commonly show low areas by deep green, intermediate ranges of elevations by successive shades

of buff and light brown, and high mountain elevations in darker shades of brown or red. The method is effective for small-scale maps that are viewed at some distance. A psychological disadvantage is that green suggests a fertile plain with luxuriant vegetation whereas the area may actually be a dry desert. One application of altitude tinting has been in air navigation maps. At high speed a plane passes so rapidly over topographic features that little time is available for detailed map study. Altitude tinting in which livid color shades are applied to high mountain masses brings the dangerous areas forcibly to the attention of pilots or navigators.

Two methods of altitude tinting are used. The change from one solid color tone to the next may be made abruptly along the line where two elevations zones meet. This method is easy to produce, but may appear unreal and give some erroneous ideas about the topography. The second method employs a gradual merging of color tones with rising elevations. Where colors are tastefully selected and lightly applied, a pleasing effect results. Merged altitude tints have been successfully used in combination with other relief methods on recent sheets of the British Ordnance Survey on a scale of one inch to one mile.

Hachures

Hachures are tiny, short lines arranged in such a way as to look as if someone had placed thousands of match sticks side by side into roughly parallel rows. Each hachure line lies along the direction of the steepest slope and represents the direction that would be taken by water flowing down the surface.

A precise system of hachures, adapted to representation of detailed topographic features on accurate, large-scale maps, was invented by a Saxon army officer, Major J. G. Lehmann (1765–1811), and was widely used on military maps of European countries throughout the nineteenth century. In the Lehmann system, steepness of slope is indicated by thickness of the hachure line. For steep slopes, the hachures are heavy, giving the appearance of dark shading on the map. For gentle slopes, hachures are thin, hairlike lines, giving a light shading on the map. A hachure map following the Lehmann system is shown in Figure 18.7, together with a greatly enlarged diagram illustrating the Lehmann principle of determining width of the line. The Lehmann system of hachures attained wide popularity in Europe during the nineteenth century, but died out rapidly when multicolor printing made possible the production of clear contour lines.

Because hachures do not tell the elevation of surface points, it is necessary to print numerous elevation figures on hilltops, road intersections, towns and other strategic locations. These numbers are known as *spot heights*. Without them a hachure map would be of little practical value.

A variation of the Lehmann system carries hachures to a very specialized degree of development. If hachures are made thicker on southeast slopes and thinner on northwest slopes, an effect of plastic shading under oblique illumination can be obtained. The method is most effective in rugged mountain regions and was used in the Dufour maps of Switzerland, famous as remarkable examples of the art of cartography (Figure 18.8).

Although hachure maps have now been superseded by other types, the hachure principle still finds occasional use. Where steep cliffs and rock crags occur they may be missed completely or partially by contour lines. A line of hachures, inserted in addition to contour lines, thus adds important information to the map. Some European cartographers go so far as actually to draw in miniature the form of cliffs and rocky crags. The method is sometimes referred to as *rock drawing* (Figure 18.9).

Contours

A *contour* may be defined as an imaginary line on the ground, every point of which is at the same altitude, or elevation, above sea level. *Contour lines* on a map are simply the graphic representations of ground contours, drawn for each of a series of specified elevations such as 10, 20, 30, 40, or 50 feet above sea level or any other chosen base, known as a *datum plane*. The resulting line pattern not only gives a visual impression of topography to the experienced student of maps but also supplies accurate information about true elevations and slopes.

In order to clarify the contour principle, various commonplace things can be used for illustration. Imagine, for example, a small island, as shown in Figure 18.10. The shoreline is a natural contour line because it is a line connecting all points having zero elevation. Suppose that sea level could be made to rise exactly ten feet (or that the island could be made to sink exactly ten feet); the water would come to rest along the line labeled "10." This would be the 10-foot contour because it connects all points on the island that are exactly ten feet higher than the original shoreline. By successive rises in water level, each exactly ten feet more than the last, the positions of the remaining contours would be fixed.

Although contours are almost never obtained in this way, a very similar procedure was followed in the mapping of some parts of the valley that Lake Mead occupies behind Boulder Dam. As the lake

Figure 18.8 The Dufour map of Switzerland, a portion of which is shown here to correct scale (1:100,000), adds the effect of oblique shading to the Lehmann system of hachuring.

Figure 18.9 Rocky cliffs and crags may be shown by rock drawing superimposed on a contour map. Portion of topographic map of Switzerland, Biasca Sheet, reproduced to correct scale, 1:50,000.

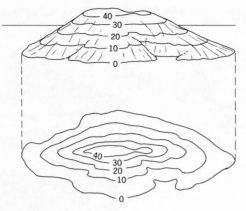

Figure 18.10 Contours on a small island.

level slowly rose, airplane photographs were taken. With each rise of two feet in lake level, the successive shorelines accurately showed positions of the contours.

Contour interval

Contour interval is the vertical distance separating successive contours. The interval remains constant over the entire map, except in special cases where two or more intervals are used on the map sheet. It is essential then that full information be present on the map margin, describing the areas in which each interval is used.

Because the vertical contour interval is fixed, horizontal spacing of contours on a given map varies with changes in land slope. The general rule is: close crowding of contour lines represents a steep slope; wide spacing represents a gentle slope. Figure 18.11 shows a small island, one side of which is a steep, clifflike slope. From the summit point *B* to the cliff base at *A* the contours are crossed within a short horizontal distance and therefore appear closely spaced on the map. From *B* to the shore at *C* the same total vertical descent is

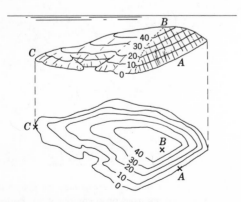

Figure 18.11 On the steep side of this island the contours appear more closely spaced.

made, but because the slope is gentle, the horizontal distance is much greater. Hence, the contours between *B* and *C* are widely spaced on the map.

Selection of contour interval depends both on relief of the land and on scale of the map. Topographic maps showing regions of strong relief require a large interval, such as 50, 100, or 200 feet; regions of moderate relief, intervals such as 10, 20, or 25 feet. In flat country an interval of 5 feet or less may be required. Large intervals are used on small-scale maps both because a greater range of elevation is likely to be included and because there is a limit to how closely contours can be printed without fusing into a dense mass.

Because by far the greatest parts of the earth's land surfaces are sculptured by streams flowing in valleys, special note should be made of how contours behave when crossing a stream valley. Figure 18.12 is a small contour sketch map illustrating some stream valleys. Notice that each contour is bent into a V whose apex lies on the stream and points in an upstream direction. The reason for this deflection is that the contour must maintain the same elevation, hence must follow the valley side upstream to a point where the stream gradient brings the stream to the same elevation as the contour. On most topographic maps only the larger streams are actually shown by any line, but the positions of numerous small channels can be deduced from V indentations of the contours.

Determining elevations by means of contours

Although each contour stands for a certain precise elevation, it is not practical to number all the lines, or to place the numbers so close together as to be always close at hand. A common practice is to make every fifth contour line much heavier than the rest, and to number the heavy lines at frequent intervals. This not only makes it easier to grasp essential features of the topography but also facilitates finding the elevation numbers.

Figure 18.12 can be used to illustrate the determination of elevations. Point *B* is easy to determine because it lies exactly on the 1300-foot contour. Point *C* requires interpolation. Because it lies midway between the 1100- and 1200-foot lines, its elevation is likewise the midvalue of the vertical interval, or 1150 feet. Point *D* lies about one-fifth of the distance from the 1000 to the 1100-foot contours. Inasmuch as one-fifth of the contour interval is 20 feet, point *D* has an approximate elevation of 1020 feet. For the last two points only a guess has been made as to the true elevation, but if the ground is not too irregular the error will probably be small. Determination of the summit elevation, point *A*, involves still more uncertainty. It is certain that the summit point is more than 1700 feet and less than 1800 because the 1700-foot contour is the highest one shown. Because a sizable area is included within the 1700-foot contour, it may be supposed that the summit rises appreciably higher than 1700. A guess would place the true elevation at about 1750 feet.

On many topographic maps the elevation of hilltops, road intersections, bridges, lakes, etc., is printed on the map to the nearest foot or meter. These spot heights do away with the need for estimating elevations at key points.

Federal agencies, such as the U.S. Coast and Geodetic Survey and the U.S. Geological Survey, in mapping an area carefully determine elevation and position of convenient reference points. These are known as *bench marks*. On the map they are designated by the letters B.M., together with the elevation stated to the nearest foot (Figure 18.13). The brass discs are firmly embedded in rock or concrete, or in the masonry of buildings, and are inscribed with the elevation.

Depression contours

A special type of contour is used where the land surface has basinlike hollows, or *closed depressions,* which would make small lakes if they could be filled with water. This is the *hachured contour,* or *depression contour.* Figure 18.14 is a sketch of a depression in a gently sloping plain. Below it is the corresponding contour map. Hachured contours have the same elevations and contour intervals as regular contours on the same map. If, as often happens, the closed depressions are so small that the hachured contours cannot be numbered, the hachured contour allows the reader to distinguish a closed depression from a small hill of similar size. Not all closed depressions are shown this way, however. Very large basins, such as the floor of Death Valley, are shown by regular contours, because such a large number of hachured lines would make a bad appearance on the map.

Topographic profiles

In order to get a better idea of the nature of the relief, *topographic profiles* are sometimes drawn. These are lines that show the rise and fall of the land surface along a selected line crossing the map. Figure 18.15 illustrates the construction of a profile. A line, *XY,* is lightly drawn across the map at the desired location. A piece of paper, ruled with horizontal lines, is placed so that its top edge lies along the line *XY.* Each horizontal line represents a contour level and is so numbered along the left-hand side. Starting at the left, a perpendicular is dropped from the point *a* where the map contour intersects the profile line, *XY,* down to the corres-

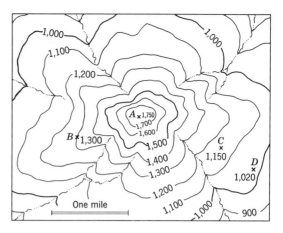

Figure 18.12 Stream valleys produce V-shaped indentations of the contours.

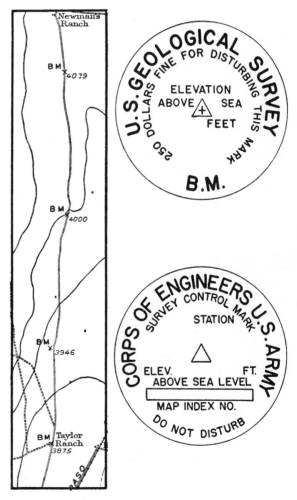

Figure 18.13 A bench mark is a permanently fixed brass plate whose elevation has been carefully surveyed. (U.S. Geological Survey.)

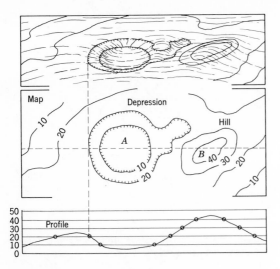

Figure 18.14 Contours which close in a circular manner show either closed depressions or hills.

ponding horizontal level. A point a' is marked on the horizontal line. Next, the procedure is repeated for the 400-foot contour at point b, and so on, until all points have been plotted. A smooth line is then drawn through all the points, completing the profile. Where contours are widely spaced, some judgment is required in drawing of the profile.

Figure 18.15 shows two profiles, both of which are drawn along the same line XY. The difference is one of degree of exaggeration of the vertical scale. In this illustration, horizontal map scale is 1 inch to 10,000 feet, or 1:120,000, whereas the vertical scale of the upper profile is 1 inch to 1000 feet, or 1:12,000. The vertical scale is thus ten

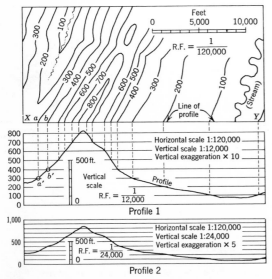

Figure 18.15 A topographic profile can be constructed from a contour map along any desired line.

times as large as the horizontal map scale, and the profile is said to have a *vertical exaggeration* of ten times. In the lower profile the horizontal scale remains the same, of course, but the vertical scale is 1 inch to 2000 feet, or 1:24,000. The vertical exaggeration is therefore five times. Some degree of vertical exaggeration is usually needed to bring out the nature of the topography. A *natural scale* profile, one in which the vertical and horizontal scales are the same, would give a profile with such tiny fluctuations as to be not only difficult to read but also difficult to draw or reproduce. The human eye exaggerates the height of topographic features and the steepness of slopes when they are seen from ground level. For this reason, a moderate degree of profile exaggeration may seem perfectly natural. Excessive exaggeration should be avoided. In Figure 18.15 the upper profile is excessively exaggerated, but the lower one is more suitable for general purposes.

Topographic profiles are used in highway and railroad planning to estimate the degree of cutting or filling needed to establish a smooth grade. In military operations, profiles are required to determine the limits of visibility from key observation points.

How contour maps are made

An understanding of the methods of making contour maps will help the student to judge what can and cannot be safely interpreted from the contours. A topographic surveying party takes into the field a large map board called a *plane table*, which is set up firmly on a tripod at a point commanding a good view of the surrounding ground (Figure 18.16). A telescope, called an *alidade*, mounted on a flat brass plate and containing cross hairs in the eyepiece, is placed on the plane table so that it can be moved around freely (Figure 18.17). Because the straight metal edge of the telescope base is exactly parallel to the telescope tube, lines drawn along the straight edge onto a sheet of heavy paper tacked to the plane table board represent true sight lines.

One of the party takes a *rod,* a flat strip of wood about twelve feet long marked off plainly in 1-foot and 0.1-foot divisions. This he sets up vertically on a distant point. The man at the plane table sights the rod through his telescope and, by means of a *stadia system* of cross hairs, is able to calculate the distance to the rod. The stadia principle is simply that the segment of rod seen between two horizontal hairs in the eyepiece is proportioned to the distance between telescope and rod. Using the straight edge of the brass plate under the telescope as a guide, he draws a line from the point representing his own position toward the point where the rod is located.

Figure 18.16 The instrument man at his plane table is sighting through a telescopic alidade to the stadia rod held by a distant rod man. (U.S. Geological Survey photograph.)

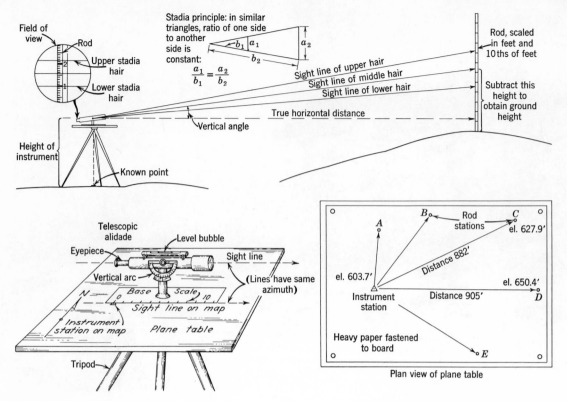

Figure 18.17 Topographic mapping in the field requires telescopic alidade, plane table, and rod. The stadia principle is used to determine distances.

On this line he scales off the distance and thus locates exactly on his map the position of the distant point. At the same time, he computes the difference in elevation between himself and the distant point. This he can do because he has determined the distance and can read the vertical angle of his line of sight.

After many points have thus been located and their elevations determined, the topographer draws in the contours. Since very few of the points actually fall on exact contour elevations, it is necessary to interpolate the position of the contour line; and because the points may be scattered widely, the topographer must use his best judgment in sketching in the contours so as to show various minor details of the topography. Usually a topographer who understands geology and knows the typical form that contours take on certain types of rocks will make a better map than a topographer who is not acquainted with geology.

In view of what has been said above, it is obvious that the accuracy of a map depends on various things not evident from the map itself. The speed with which topographic parties work determines how much detail they can put into a map. The speed is itself influenced by the appropriation of money available for the job. The purpose for which the map was made is a factor. A reconnaissance contour map to accompany a geographic report cannot be expected to be as accurate as a large-scale highway planning map from which estimates of volume of cut and fill are to be derived. The geographer must be alert for any clues as to the reliability of the map and must not place more confidence on data derived from a map than the accuracy of the map itself permits.

Contour mapping from air photographs

Shortly before World War II, the Topographic Division of the U.S. Geological Survey began to use precision optical instruments by means of which a trained operator working in a laboratory can draw contours from series of overlapping aerial photographs taken with cameras mounted in aircraft (Figure 18.18). In general, the science of

Figure 18.18 This *multiplex*, a precision optical device, enables contours to be drawn directly from sets of overlapping air photographs. (U.S. Geological Survey photograph.)

mapping and surveying by means of photographs taken from the air or ground is termed *photogrammetry*, a specialized field of cartography based on mathematical and geometrical principles that accurately relate the forms seen on the photograph to the true forms on the ground surface. The science of photogrammetry developed rapidly during World War II and has since provided the principal means of constructing large-scale contour maps. The rate of contour map production by government agencies has therefore increased enormously. Whereas formerly a small, but steady, stream of topographic quadrangles on the scale of 1:62,500 (15-minute quadrangles) was being distributed by the U.S. Geological Survey, there is now a veritable flood of quadrangles on the larger scale of 1:24,000, each sheet covering 7½ minutes of latitude and longitude. Other United States governmental agencies, notably the Army Map Service of the Department of the Army, have contributed heavily to the mapping program, but all topographic maps are distributed to the public through the Geological Survey, which edits and publishes most of the maps.

The use of air photo plotting instruments has by no means done away with the need for ground surveys. It is still necessary to survey control points on the ground and to check the laboratory map in the field by direct comparison with landforms and cultural features. Furthermore, a heavy forest cover may so obscure the ground from photography that field surveys by plane table and alidade are necessary.

National standards for contour map accuracy were agreed upon in 1942 and include the provision that (1) horizontally, 90 per cent of the well-defined planimetric features shall be plotted in correct position on the published map sheet within a tolerance of one-fiftieth inch; and (2) vertically, 90 per cent of the elevations interpolated from the contours shall be correct within a tolerance of one-half contour interval. (On a map of scale 1:24,000, one-fiftieth inch is approximately equivalent to 40 feet on the ground.) Maps conforming to these specifications bear a statement to that effect printed in the lower map margin.

In several of the chapters which follow, portions of topographic maps have been reproduced for landform study laboratory exercises. Although originally printed in brown, the contour lines have necessarily been reproduced in black. To simplify these maps, most of the cultural features have been deleted. Changes of scale and contour interval have been required in some cases to emphasize the landforms of interest. In all cases the source maps are described; most are available by direct purchase from the U.S. Geological Survey, which will supply information on availability and price. Index maps of each state are available to show the name, scale, location, and year of publication of all quadrangles.

Portions of four topographic quadrangles are reproduced as end papers of this book. Contour lines are in brown; hydrographic features are in blue. Black and red overprints, used for cultural features, have been omitted.

Review Questions

1. What is topographic relief? What is geomorphology? Of what importance is topographic relief to the geographer? Cite several examples.

2. Explain the terms *plain, plateau, mountain,* and *hill.*

3. What advantage is there to describing and classifying landforms according to process and stage? Explain these terms.

4. What are the agents of land sculpture? Toward what goal do they work?

5. Explain what is meant by the terms *erosional landforms* and *depositional landforms.*

6. What is the basis for dividing all landforms into initial and sequential groups? Into what smaller classes are the sequential forms divided?

7. Explain how a landscape reflects the work of both internal and external earth forces and processes.

8. List the methods used to show relief features on maps.

9. What two kinds of plastic shading can be used? What are the advantages of each method?

10. For what kinds of maps are altitude tints most effective?

11. What are hachures? Explain how the Lehmann system of hachures is applied. How are differences in steepness of slope shown? What disadvantages does the hachure system have in the making and using of maps?

12. How do Dufour maps differ from maps using the Lehmann hachure system? What is rock drawing?

13. What is a contour line? What is contour interval? What factors determine the selection of contour interval?

14. How do contours give indication of a stream valley? How is a hilltop shown by contours?

15. How can the elevations of points be determined if they fall in the spaces between contours?

16. What are spot heights? What are bench marks? Of what value are bench marks?

17. How are closed depressions shown by contours? How can the depth of the bottom of the depression below the lowest point in the rim be estimated from the contour?

18. What is a topographic profile? How is it constructed? What is vertical exaggeration? When should it be used?

19. Explain the general principles of topographic field surveying. What instruments are needed? How can distances be determined without measuring with a tape? Where should points be located to provide most effective aid in drawing contours?

20. What is photogrammetry? How have air photo methods influenced the production of topographic quadrangles? Why are field surveys still necessary?

21. State the accuracy standards set for horizontal and vertical features on a modern map.

Exercises

1. Show by contours alone each of the following geometric forms. Construct these carefully with compass and straightedge. (*a*) A straight-sided cone. (*b*) A cone with sides concave-up. (*c*) A hemisphere. (*d*) A cube.

2. Make a contour map of a semi-circular island, the straight side of which has a very steep slope as compared with the rest of the island. The summit of the island is 105 feet above sea level. The contour interval is 10 feet. Two stream valleys extend down the gently sloping sides of the island. The island is about 4 miles wide. Use a map scale of 1 inch to 1 mile.

3. The accompanying map shows contouring only about half completed. (*a*) Using the elevations printed on the left-hand side of the map, complete the drawing of the 100-foot contours. (The contours may be drawn on a sheet of thin tracing paper laid over the page.) (*b*) Make a profile along the line *AB*, using a vertical exaggeration of five times. (*c*) Determine the fractional scale of the map. (*d*) How high is the cliff at the point *C* in the southeastern part of the map? (*e*) What is the amount of the magnetic declination in this area?

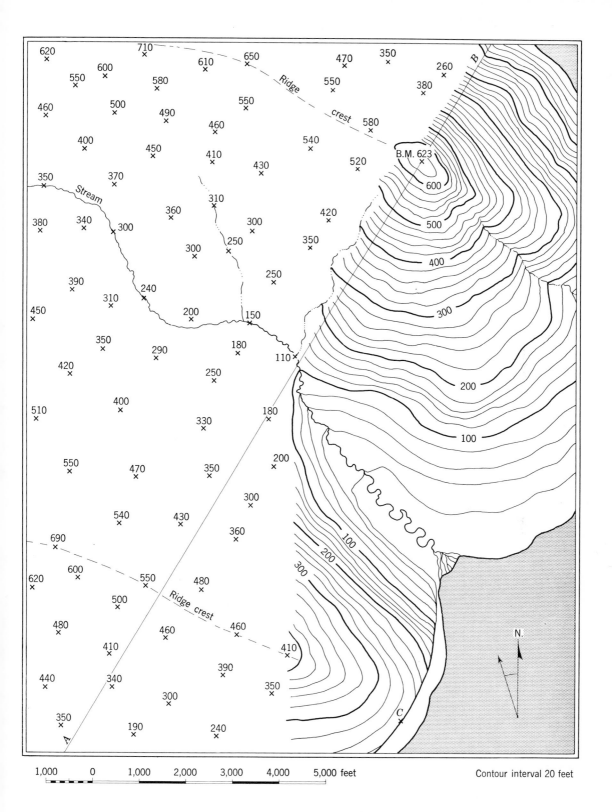

620
×

710
×

650
×

470
×

350
×

B
×

550
×

600
×

610
×

260
×

460
×

580
×

550
×

380
×

580
×

500
×

490
×

550
×

540
×

B.M. 623
×

400
×

450
×

460
×

410
×

430
×

520
×

350
×
Stream

370
×

310
×

420
×

380
×

340
×

300
×

360
×

300
×

300
×

300
×

250
×

350
×

250
×

390
×

240
×

200
×

250
×

450
×

310
×

150
×

350
×

290
×

180
×

110
×

420
×

250
×

510
×

400
×

330
×

180
×

200
×

550
×

470
×

350
×

300
×

540
×

430
×

360
×

690
×

600
×

550
×

480
×

620
×

500
×

460
×

460
×

480
×

410
×

410
×

440
×

340
×

390
×

350
×

350
×

300
×

240
×

190
×

Ridge crest

Ridge crest

A
×

C
×

N.

| 1,000 | 0 | 1,000 | 2,000 | 3,000 | 4,000 | 5,000 feet |

Contour interval 20 feet

CHAPTER NINETEEN

Rocks and their structures

JUST as a sculptor uses various kinds of materials, such as clay, marble or granite, for his work, so nature provides various kinds of rocks and materials with which the denudational agents shape their landforms. The influence of earth materials on landforms is so profound as to require the professional geomorphologist to study all phases of geology. Because this textbook of physical geography assumes no previous acquaintance with geology, it will be necessary to supply a certain minimum amount of geological information as the study of landforms requires.

Bedrock, soil, and residual mantle

Examination of a freshly cut cliff, such as that in a new highway cut or quarry wall, will reveal several kinds of earth materials, shown in Figure 19.1. Solid, hard rock which is still in place and relatively unchanged is called *bedrock*. It grades upward into a zone where the rock has become decayed and has disintegrated into clay, silt, and sand particles. This may be called the *weathered mantle* or *residual mantle*. At the top is a layer of true *soil*, often called *topsoil* by farmers and

above: Rock of Ages granite quarry, Barre, Vermont.
Photograph by Rothstein, from Cushing.

gardeners. It is usually only a few inches to two or three feet thick, and in humid regions may be relatively dark in color in comparison with the mantle material below. Soil properties, soil forming processes, and soil classification were treated in Chapters 16 and 17. Over the soil may be a protective layer of grass, shrubs, or trees.

One or more of these zones may be missing. Sometimes everything is stripped off down to the bedrock, which then appears at the surface as an *outcrop*. Sometimes following cultivation or forest fires the true soil only is eroded away, leaving exposed the mantle, which is infertile and may become scored by deep gullies. The thickness of soil and mantle is quite variable. Although the true soil is rarely more than a few feet thick, the residual mantle of decayed and fragmented rock may extend down tens or even hundreds of feet. Formation of the mantle is greatly aided by the presence of innumerable bedrock cracks termed *joints* (Figure 19.1), along which water can move easily to promote rock decay.

Transported mantle

Another variety of mantle that may be found covering the bedrock is *transported mantle*. It consists of such materials as stream-laid gravels and sands, flood-plain silts, clays of lake bottoms, beach and dune sands, or rubble left by a melting glacier. All types have in common a history of having been transported by streams, ice, waves, or wind.

Whereas residual mantle, formed in place by disintegration of bedrock below it, is of local origin, transported mantle consists of rock and mineral varieties from distant sources and may be quite unlike the underlying minerals and rocks. Figure 19.2 shows stream valley deposits, called *alluvium*, which would be designated as transported mantle in contrast to residual mantle of the adjacent hill slope. Once deposited, transported mantle may remain undisturbed for many thousands of years, in which case a true soil is formed in its uppermost layer.

In a broad sense all of the materials of which the depositional landforms are built up are of transported mantle. In later chapters many kinds of depositional landforms are described and explained in terms of the processes by which the particles are carried.

Influence of rocks on landforms

Bedrock strongly influences shape, size, and development of the erosional landforms. In some places, rock takes the form of thin layers, lying horizontally, tilted, folded, or broken, as the case may be. Elsewhere it consists of thick, irregular masses extending down to great depths. Some varieties of rock are soft and are readily washed away by streams and waves; others are extremely resistant to all agents of weathering and erosion. To a considerable degree the weakness or resistance of

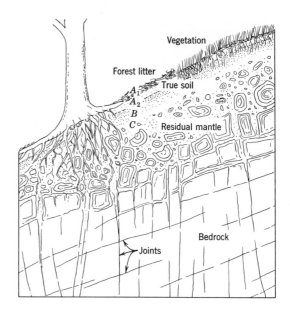

Figure 19.1 The bedrock is commonly overlain by a mantle of decomposed rock, topped by soil.

rocks is determined by their origin and age. When varied rocks lie side by side near the surface of the earth's crust the agents of denudation etch them out according to their degree of resistance, the weak rock tending to form valleys or other types of depressions, the resistant ones standing out in bold relief as hills, mountains, or plateaus. Consequently, landforms reflect closely the shape and arrangement of the original rock masses and will show certain distinctive qualities whereby they may be referred to an orderly classification.

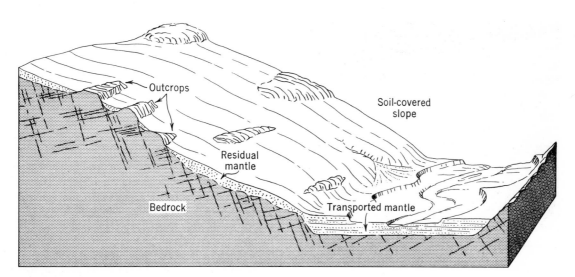

Figure 19.2 Residual mantle on the hillside is derived from bedrock beneath, whereas transported mantle of the valley bottom has been brought from some distance by a stream.

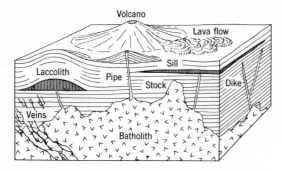

Figure 19.3 Igneous rock may solidify below the surface, forming intrusive bodies, or may be forced out upon the surface to make extrusive forms.

Igneous rocks

Rocks may be divided into three major classes: (1) *igneous*, (2) *sedimentary*, and (3) *metamorphic*, according to their origin. *Igneous rocks* solidify from a molten state. The highly heated fluid rock, termed *magma*, originates at considerable depths beneath the earth's surface and is forced by great internal pressures to erupt through the solid, brittle outer crust of the earth (Figure 19.3). It should not be supposed that the whole interior of the earth is molten. It seems more likely that local pockets of magma, lying some ten or more miles down, are formed in various places and eventually are forced toward the surface. The nature and origin of molten rocks bodies and the forces that control their behavior comprise a highly speculative phase of geology. Unlike the study of landforms, in which both the landform and the erosional

Figure 19.4 Seen close up, this granite, a coarse-grained intrusive rock, proves to be made of tightly interlocking crystals of a few kinds of minerals.

process can be observed in their entirety, the study of deep-seated igneous rock masses cannot be made during their formation, but can only be interpreted in the light of the appearance and composition of the rock after it has cooled and become solidified, then exposed to the surface by long ages of land-mass denudation.

Intrusive and extrusive igneous rocks

Molten masses that do not reach the surface but solidify in cavities or cracks that they have made by pushing the surrounding rock apart or melting or dissolving it are termed *intrusive* igneous rocks (Figure 19.3). They do, in fact, intrude or invade the previously formed rock. Where the intrusion has been violent the surrounding rocks may show breaking, crushing, folding or uparching around the newly formed rock body. Where the intrusion has been gradual and the surrounding rock slowly melted or dissolved, no disturbance of the adjoining rock may result.

A second class of igneous rock, termed *extrusive*, is that which reaches the ground surface, issuing from a pipe or crack and pouring out upon the ground, then quickly solidifying into a hard rock. Volcanoes and lava flows are the principal products of igneous rock extrusion (Figure 19.3).

Intrusive rocks differ from extrusive rocks considerably in both gross outward form and details of internal structure and texture. Intrusive rocks commonly occur in enormous masses, termed *batholiths*, covering areas as great as an entire state and extending many miles down (Figure 19.3). The adjective *plutonic* is commonly used for this and other deep-seated intrusive rock bodies. Such large masses cooled very slowly; consequently, the individual mineral crystals of which the rock is composed are relatively large (Figure 19.4), commonly measuring one-eighth to one-half inch across. Much larger crystals occur—from several inches to several feet long—in a type of vein known as a *pegmatite*. Crystal grains of intrusive igneous rock interlock closely so as to produce a dense, strong rock, free of cavities.

Minerals

A *mineral* is a naturally occurring, inorganic substance that has a definite or fairly definite chemical composition and a characteristic crystal form, together with certain distinctive qualities of color, hardness, luster, and fracture habit. Although a few kinds of rocks consist almost wholly of a single mineral variety, most rock types are aggregates or physical mixtures of two or more minerals. Both the mineral varieties present and the proportions in which they are mixed determine the name and properties of a given rock variety.

Mineralogy, the study of minerals, and *petrology*, the study of rocks, are important branches of geology. Several thousand mineral varieties have been identified and named; the list of rock varieties runs into the hundreds. Fortunately, only a few minerals are so abundant in volume and world-wide distribution as to combine into major rock types. This introductory study goes little further than to describe a few of the commonest igneous rocks and to name the principal constituent minerals.

Common varieties of intrusive rocks

One of the most abundant and best known of the intrusive rocks is *granite*, composed of a mixture of these minerals: *quartz* (silicon dioxide), *potash feldspar* (an aluminum silicate of potassium), *hornblende* (an aluminum silicate of iron and magnesium), and *biotite mica* (a complex aluminum

silicate with manganese and iron) (Figure 19.5). Because quartz and feldspar, which together may comprise three-quarters of the rock, are light colored, whereas hornblende and biotite mica are black, granite has a speckled appearance when closely examined (Figure 19.4).

The potash feldspar grains will be identified by their opacity, blocklike outlines, and shiny luster on cleavage surfaces. In some granites this feldspar is almost white, producing gray granite; in others, the feldspar is salmon pink, producing pink granite. The quartz grains are clear and appear glassy beside the feldspar grains. Quartz grains tend to have irregular outlines and break irregularly, after the manner of glass. Both hornblende and biotite crystals are black, but the biotite mica is soft and can be split into thin flakes with the point of a knife or needle.

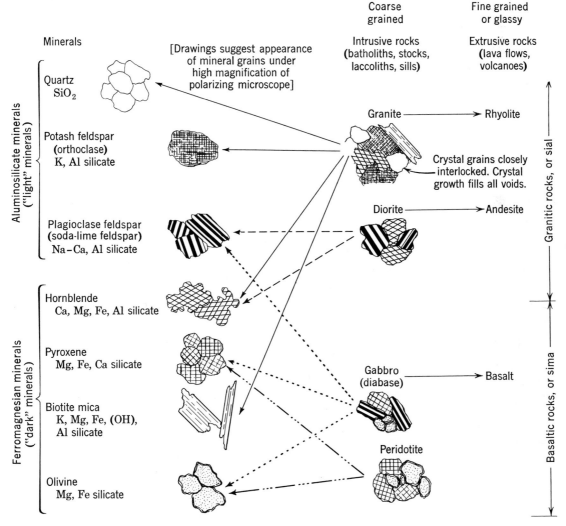

Figure 19.5 Various combinations of light and dark minerals produce the igneous rocks, a few of which are listed here.

A second variety of intrusive igneous rock is *diorite*. Not nearly so widespread in occurrence as granite, it illustrates a rock of more limited mineral composition, in that quartz is entirely lacking and only two minerals dominate: (1) *plagioclase feldspar* (soda-lime feldspar), which is an aluminum silicate mineral with varying proportions of sodium and calcium, and (2) a dark mineral, which may be either *hornblende* or *pyroxene*. The plagioclase feldspar, which is milky white to gray in color, with vitreous luster on its cleavage surfaces, makes up about three-fourths of the rock. Both hornblende and pyroxene are commonly black and are extremely difficult to tell apart without the aid of a microscope. Pyroxene, like hornblende, is a silicate mineral with magnesium, iron, and calcium, but pyroxene is often lacking in aluminum.

A third intrusive igneous rock of importance is *gabbro*, composed primarily of two minerals, plagioclase feldspar and pyroxene. The difference between this rock and diorite is largely in the proportions of the two minerals. Feldspar dominates in diorite, but makes up only about 50 per cent in gabbro. Another mineral, *olivine*, is commonly present in gabbro. Olivine, a silicate of magnesium and iron, is commonly green in color. Gabbro is a coarse-grained, plutonic rock like granite or diorite and also occurs in great masses. Where the crystals of gabbro are tiny, because of more rapid cooling in intrusive layers such as sills or dikes, the name *diabase* is commonly applied instead of gabbro. The difference is one of texture, not composition.

A fourth intrusive rock variety is *peridotite*, a dense, dark rock composed largely of pyroxene and olivine. Little or no feldspar is present. Peridotite is found usually in small masses or dikes, not in vast batholiths such as granite.

Granitic and basaltic rock groups

As Figure 19.5 shows, the four examples of intrusive igneous rocks have been placed in an orderly arrangement, such that the light-colored minerals, quartz and feldspar, decrease in proportion while the dark-colored minerals increase in proportion. In granite and diorite there is a preponderance of quartz and feldspar, which are light-colored minerals of low density. A cube of granite will weigh about 2.6 times as much as a similar volume of water; its relative density, or *specific gravity*, is therefore stated as 2.6. Igneous rocks containing largely light-colored minerals of low density, rich in aluminum silicate combined with potassium, sodium, and calcium (as in the feldspars), are said to belong to the *granitic group*. Geologists often refer to these rocks collectively as *sial*, a word coined from *si*, for silica, and *al*, for alumina.

Gabbro and peridotite, on the other hand, are composed predominately of minerals rich in magnesium and iron, the so-called *ferromagnesian minerals*. These minerals are relatively dense, so that peridotite, for example, may have a specific gravity over 3.2, which is roughly 25 per cent greater than granite. Rocks composed largely of the dark, dense, ferromagnesian minerals belong to the *basaltic group* (or *basic* group). The word *sima*, coined for these rocks collectively in distinction to sial, is taken from *si* for alumina and *ma* for magnesium. The importance of granitic and basaltic (or sialic and simatic) groups of rocks in the great layers of the earth's crust is discussed in Chapter 20.

Extrusive igneous rocks

The extrusive igneous rocks take two forms: (*a*) fluid magma flows in the form of thin tongues or sheets, called *lava flows*, and (*b*) solid or near-solid pieces blown violently from volcanic vents and collectively termed *volcanic ejecta*. (See Figure 31.9). Some lava flows may have a rough, blocky surface; others a smooth billowy surface. Usually flows are dark red or black in surface color. Because of the rapid cooling, mineral crystals have little or no opportunity to develop during the solidification and cannot be detected with the unaided eye. Expanding gases may fill the rock with countless bubblelike cavities, producing a texture of rock called *scoria* (Figure 19.6). Where solidification is extremely rapid, a glass is formed. This glass goes by the name *obsidian*, or simply *volcanic glass* (Figure 19.6).

Lavas may be similar in composition to the various kinds of intrusive igneous rocks, inasmuch as the same magma may reach the surface in one place but not in another. The lava that corresponds to granite is *rhyolite* (Figure 19.5). That which corresponds to diorite is *andesite*. These are both rather light gray or pink on freshly broken surfaces. Even close study will show only a dull rock surface, the crystals being too fine to see with the naked eye. Such a texture is termed *aphanitic*, from the Greek, meaning "not visible." In some lavas, however, there is a sprinkling of large crystals of feldspar easily seen in outline against the fine-grained background. These large crystals are *phenocrysts;* the texture of a rock containing them is *porphyritic* (Figure 19.7).

The extrusive equivalent of diabase is *basalt*, a dense black rock which is perhaps the commonest and most widespread of the lavas. Areas of huge size, such as the Columbia River plateaus in Washington, Oregon, and Idaho or the Deccan region of western India, are underlain by thousands of feet of thickness of basalt lavas, poured out in tremendous upwellings through long cracks known as *fissures*. A horizontal layer of basalt, upon cool-

ing, shrinks somewhat and forms into four-, five-, or six-sided columns which stand vertically. The structure is termed *columnar jointing* and gives a most striking appearance to cliffs of basalt (Figure 19.8).

Volcanic ejecta come in various sizes and shapes. Very fine material is termed *volcanic dust* or *volcanic ash*. Coarser particles, a fraction of an inch to two or three inches across, are termed *cinder* and resemble the clinkers from a coal furnace. Still larger masses are *volcanic bombs* (Figure 31.9). These may be still plastic when blown from a volcanic vent and become shaped into rounded masses resembling a loaf of bread. Volcanic ejecta result from the presence of large amounts of gas under high pressure in the magma. As it approaches the surface the gas is released from confining pressure

Figure 19.6 *Above:* The outer surface of lava has wrinkles produced by flowage. *Below:* A frothy, gaseous lava solidifies into a light, porous *scoria* (left). Rapidly cooled lava may form a dark *volcanic glass* (right).

Figure 19.7 This andesite prophyry has large grains (phenocrysts) scattered through an aphanitic ground mass. Specimen is three inches wide.

Figure 19.8 This cliff of old lava has weathered away, revealing the columnar jointing system formed during cooling. (Photograph by Gifford.)

Figure 19.9 These limestone strata in Oklahoma were steeply tilted long after being laid down. (Photograph by Lofman. Courtesy of Standard Oil Co., New Jersey)

and expands, frothing the magma into a bubbly foam and producing the violent explosions that blow the fragments into the air. One particularly spongy, foamlike variety of lava is *pumice*, so light that it floats on water.

Sedimentary rocks

Those rocks that are composed of particles derived from previously existing rock, then laid down after transportation by streams, ocean or wave currents, wind, or ice are *sedimentary rocks*. Rocks of any origin whatsoever may be the parent material for sediment. In addition, sediment may result from chemical reaction and precipitation. As the solid particles settle out, a layer is formed. Should the size or composition of the particles change repeatedly, the result will be a series of layers of varied type. Thus a series of muds or clays, sands, or gravels might be deposited upon an ocean or lake bottom, or upon land if the material is deposited from streams, winds, or glaciers. In their original state, these sediments are soft, but in time they become hardened into rocks as we are accustomed to seeing them. Hardening occurs both because of pressure compaction driving out water, and because chemical deposits of calcium carbonate or silicon dioxide form between the particles, causing them to be cemented together.

Sedimentary rocks are distinguished from igneous rocks by the usual presence of layers resulting from changing size and composition of sediment.

The layers are termed *strata*, or simply *beds*. The planes of separation between successive layers are *planes of stratification*, or *bedding planes*. The rock is said to be *stratified* or *bedded*. (See Figures 29.14, 29.15, 29.16). Bedding planes in their original condition are nearly horizontal but may be tilted to any angle by subsequent movements of the earth's crust (Figure 19.9).

Groups of contiguous rock strata having some common properties of rock variety or geologic age or both are designated as *formations* and are usually named for the geographic locality at which they are well displayed for study, or were first described by the geologist. For example, the *Mesa Verde Formation* is a sandstone named for its striking cliff exposures at Mesa Verde, in southwestern Colorado, yet it is found in several states and is believed to have been once a vast, continuous layer of sands laid down in the floor of an ancient shallow sea.

Clastic sediments

One great class of sedimentary rocks is described as *clastic*, meaning that the particles are produced by disintegration of previous rocks through the combined weathering processes (Chapter 22). Processes of transportation in water or wind tend to sort the particles into various size grades, from which the clastic sedimentary rocks are named as follows:

Rock name	Particle name	Diameter or fineness of grains
CONGLOMERATE	Boulders	Over 10 inches
	Cobbles	2½ to 10 inches
	Pebbles (gravel)	⅛ to 2½ inches
SANDSTONE	Sand	10 to 1000 per inch
SILTSTONE	Silt	1000 to 10,000 per inch
SHALE	Clay	Finer than 10,000 per inch

Conglomerate, although named for the presence of boulders, cobbles, or pebbles, has a large proportion of sand filling the interstices. The larger particles are usually well rounded from tumbling on stream beds or in the surf zone of beaches (Figure 19.10). In fact, conglomerates may be thought of as fossil gravel bars or beaches of ancient rivers or shorelines. Where the large fragments are angular, instead of rounded, the rock is called a *breccia*, rather than a conglomerate. Breccia might be formed of rock fragments rolled from a cliff, crushed within a landslide, or swept from a steep ravine in a brief torrential flood.

Sandstone and siltstone grade into one another and are distinguished much as coarse sandpaper is distinguished from very fine. The grains of sandstone may be of any durable mineral, such as those described in the foregoing section on igneous rocks. Nevertheless, the long distance of travel of the grains in rivers or along shores eliminates the soft, easily powdered minerals and allows chemical decay to turn others, such as the feldspars and ferromagnesian minerals, into soft clay. Therefore, the commonest mineral of sandstones is quartz, whose resistance to mechanical and chemical attack is phenomenal. A few grains of dark minerals may be present, as well as tiny gleaming mica flakes. Sandstone, siltstone, and conglomerate owe their hardness to cementation following deposition. Gradually, in the vast spans of geologic time that follow deposition and burial, deposits of silica (SiO_2) or calcium carbonate ($CaCO_3$) accumulate in the pore spaces between sand grains, producing a solid, strong rock. The cementing substances are carried in solution by slowly moving underground water. Cementing material rarely fills all of the openings of a sandstone, so that the rock can hold large stores of fluids such as water or oil. We depend on sandstones as reservoirs of our natural gas, petroleum, and in many cases for ground water supplies as well (Chapter 21).

Shale is simply compacted clay or mud, greatly increased in density and hardness by the application of pressure from overlying strata. Clays commonly consist of submicroscopic flakes of mineral matter, an example of which is shown in Figure 19.11. Such particles behave as colloids, which have a strong affinity for water. Under sufficient pressure, the excess water is largely driven off; an extremely dense rock results. Whereas a clay or mud will soften and swell when soaked for a short time in water, shale will not. Shales are gray, earthred, or black. The red color is due to presence of iron oxides; black may indicate the presence of finely divided organic matter in the form of carbon compounds. Shales have a soft, smooth feel in contrast to the gritty surface texture of sandstones. Furthermore, shale is mechanically weak and can easily be shattered into thin flakes and plates. For this reason shale plays the geomorphic role of a weak rock, easily carved away by the agents of land erosion to produce valleys and broad lowlands.

Pyroclastic rocks

A special class of clastic rocks results from the violent eruption of volcanoes, where fine ash is belched from the vent in great clouds. Sediment settling from the air during such explosions is described as *pyroclastic* material. An important variety of pyroclastic rock is *tuff*, a fine-grained, light-gray rock composed of compacted volcanic ash. Scattered small crystals of igneous minerals, blown from the vent, are sometimes visible in the

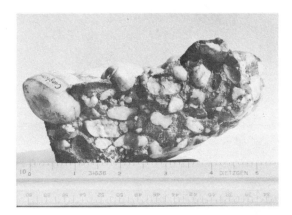

Figure 19.10 Conglomerate is a mixture of gravel and sand cemented into a hard rock.

tuff. If the ash has been picked up by streams and carried into a body of standing water, the tuff may be reformed into a distinctly stratified sedimentary rock. Other volcanic ash outbursts were carried by gases of such high temperature that the ash was fused into a hard rock known as *welded tuff*.

Organic and chemical sedimentary rocks

A second important class of sedimentary rocks, described as *organic*, consists of rock matter produced by the growth activities of plants and animals. A sedimentary rock variety of major importance is

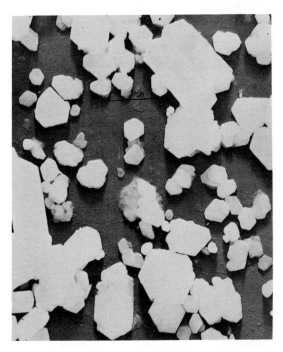

Figure 19.11 Kaolinite crystals, enlarged 20,000 times by the electron microscope, illustrate one variety of clay particles. (Photograph by Paul F. Kerr.)

Figure 19.12 A limestone made up largely of shell fragments.

limestone (Figure 19.9), much of which is formed from the limy parts of such organisms as corals, algae, foraminifera, clams and snails. The organic origin is obvious where large shell fragments have been cemented into a variety of limestone termed *coquina* (Figure 19.12), but less obvious if the organisms are extremely tiny or if the hard parts have been finely pulverized. (In the sense that such rocks are made of mechanically broken particles they are often classified as clastic rather than organic.)

Limestone in its pure state consists of *calcite* (calcium carbonate), a mineral easily scratched with the sharp point of a knife and responding by vigorous effervescence when a drop of dilute hydrochloric acid is placed on its surface. Limestones may be pure white, as in the case of a very soft variety termed *chalk*, or gray to black in the more common dense varieties. Limestone may also form by direct chemical precipitation from waters of lakes or oceans heavily charged with lime in solu-

tion. The soft limestone thus formed is termed *marl*. Because of its susceptibility to weak acids present in the rain water, soil water, and streams, limestone is rapidly eaten away in regions of humid climates, forming valleys and broad lowlands.

Many limestones have considerable amounts of the mineral *dolomite* (calcium-magnesium carbonate) incorporated with the calcite. Where the mineral dolomite predominates, the rock itself is called *dolomite*. The origin of dolomite is not fully understood, but it is thought that perhaps the calcium of pure limestone is gradually replaced by magnesium through the action of underground waters acting over vast periods of geologic time.

Quite different from limestone is another organic type of sedimentary rock, *coal*, formed of vast swamp accumulations of partly decayed plant matter. In the early stages of its formation, coal passes through the stage of *peat*, a soft brown, combustible mass of plant fragments. Through later burial and compaction, water and certain volatile compounds are slowly driven off, yielding dense, black, rocklike layers of coal which contain a high proportion of fixed carbon.

Of great importance economically, though not abundant in comparison with limestone, are a group of chemical sediments termed *evaporites*. These are salts that have been precipitated from waters of shallow desert lakes or constricted bays of the ocean, where evaporation of the water is rapid. One evaporite which is found in rock layers of wide extent is *anhydrite* (calcium sulfate). Closely related is *gypsum* (hydrous calcium sulfate), a soft white mineral. Gypsum is often found interlayered with shales and limestones. Another evaporite familiar to all is rock salt, occurring as the mineral *halite* (sodium chloride), which forms thick sedimentary rock layers along with shales in a few localities.

Sedimentary rocks as landform controls

Figure 19.13 shows five types of sedimentary rock together with a mass of much older igneous rock upon which the sediments were laid. Their usual landform habit, whether to form valleys or mountains, is indicated, together with the conventional symbols used on cross sections by geologists. These rock strata have been strongly tilted and deeply eroded, so that there is maximum opportunity for the development of relief as a consequence of the different degrees of resistance offered to denudational processes.

Metamorphic rocks

Any of the types of igneous or sedimentary rocks may be altered by the tremendous pressures and high temperatures that accompany mountain-

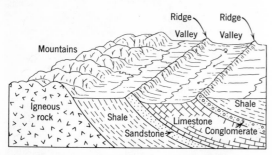

Figure 19.13 Many landscape features originate through the slow erosional removal of weaker rock, leaving the more resistant rock standing as ridges or mountains.

building movements of the earth's crust. The result is a rock so greatly changed in appearance and composition as to be classified as a *metamorphic rock*. Generally speaking, metamorphic rocks are harder and more compact than their original types, except when the latter are igneous rocks. Moreover, the kneading action and baking that metamorphic rocks have undergone produces new structures and even new minerals. Each sedimentary and igneous rock has an equivalent metamorphic rock. The term *metasediment* conveniently covers all metamorphic rocks derived from sedimentary strata.

Shale, on being squeezed and sheared under mountain-making forces, turns into *slate*, a gray or brick-red rock that splits neatly into thin plates so familiar to all as roofing shingles and flagstones of patios and walks. The planes of splitting form a structure called *slaty cleavage*. This is a new structure imposed upon the rock during the process of internal slippage during metamorphism, not merely stratification or bedding. Slate is fine textured and of rather dull surface texture. It can be distinguished from shale by the fact that a thin slab of slate rings when struck sharply. Closely related to slate, because it represents a continuation of the process of metamorphism to a more advanced degree, is *phyllite*. It, too, breaks into thin slabs, but these may be wavy or curved. Moreover, phyllite shows a satiny sheen on the cleavage surfaces, a result of light reflection from innumerable tiny crystals of mica.

With continued application of pressure and internal shearing, phyllite changes into *schist*, the most advanced grade of metamorphic rock. Schist has a structure termed *foliation*, consisting of thin but rough and irregularly curved planes of parting in the rock. Schist is set apart from slate and phyllite by the coarse texture of the mineral grains, the abundance of mica, and the presence of scattered large crystals of new minerals such as *garnet* and *staurolite*, which have grown during the process of internal shearing of the rock (Figure 19.14).

Slates, phyllites, and schists are relatively resistant to the processes of denudation and tend to form hills and uplands. In comparison with granite, however, these rocks are less resistant, so that granites will usually form markedly higher mountain masses.

The metamorphic equivalent of conglomerate, sandstone, and siltstone is *quartzite*, formed by the addition of silica (SiO_2) to fill completely the interstices between grains, most of which are normally quartz (also silica). This process is carried out by the slow movement of underground waters carrying the silica into the sandstone, where it is deposited. Pressure and kneading of the rock is

Figure 19.14 This fragment of schist, six inches long, has a glistening, undulating surface (above) consisting largely of mica flakes. An edgewise view (below) of the same specimen shows the wavy faliation planes.

not essential in producing a quartzite, but may deform the quartz grains. When a quartzite is fractured, as with a hammer blow, the break will cut across sand grains and pebbles in the rock. In this way, quartzite can be distinguished from a sandstone, which usually breaks around the grains, leaving them mostly intact. The extreme hardness of quartzite, combined with its high immunity to chemical decay, makes it the most resistant of all rocks. Many prominent ridge crests and peaks in a region of metamorphic rock will be found to be composed of quartzite.

Limestone, upon metamorphism, becomes *marble*, commonly a white rock of sugary texture when freshly broken. During the process of internal shearing, the calcite mineral of the limestone has reformed into larger, more uniform crystals than before. Bedding planes are obscured and masses of mineral impurities are drawn out into swirling streaks and bands. Like limestone, marble is easily decomposed by weak acids in the soil water and streams, hence, is usually found occupying valleys and lowlands.

Finally, the important metamorphic rock, *gneiss*, may be formed either from intrusive igneous rocks, or as a metasediment from strata that have been in close contact with intrusive magmas.

A single description will not fit all gneisses, which vary considerably in appearance, mineral composition, and structure. One common variety is *granite gneiss*, formed directly by flowage of granite in a somewhat plastic state. Granite gneiss resembles granite in its massiveness, general texture, and mineral components, but possesses a streaked appearance, called *lineation*, produced by parallelism of dark minerals which have been drawn out into long, pencil-like shapes in the direction of flow. Still other gneisses are strongly banded into

Figure 19.15 Gneiss shows a banded surface, as if the rock had been drawn out in a plastic condition.

light and dark layers or lenses (Figure 19.15), which may be contorted into wavy folds. It is possible that in some instances these bands, which have differing mineral compositions, may be the relics of sedimentary strata such as shale and sandstone to which new mineral matter has been added from nearby intrusive rocks. Some bands seem to be true igneous layers of granite composition, forced between the sedimentary layers. Gneiss of this type is designated *injection gneiss*. Gneisses are strong, resistant rocks, which, like granite, generally form bold highlands or mountain chains. Figure 19.16 shows the topographic expressions we would expect in regions where various metamorphic rocks rest side by side and have been acted upon for vast spans of time by the agents of land-mass denudation.

Dip and strike

Because natural planes are characteristic of the structure of each type of rock, the geologist requires a system of geometry to enable him to measure and describe the attitude of these natural planes and to indicate them on maps. Examples of such planes are the bedding layers of sedimentary strata, the sides of a dike, the upper and lower sur-

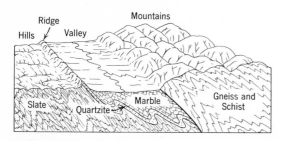

Figure 19.16 Metamorphic rocks tend to form elongate, parallel belts of valleys and mountains.

faces of a sill, slaty cleavage of slates, and the joints in a granite. Rarely are these planes truly horizontal. Even if formed in a nearly horizontal attitude, as in sedimentary strata, the geologic processes of crustal movement will probably have warped or tilted the planes to some degree of slope with respect to the horizontal.

The acute angle formed between a natural rock plane and an imaginary horizontal plane is termed the *dip*, and is stated in degrees ranging from 0° for a horizontal plane to 90° for a vertical plane. Figure 19.17 shows the dip angle for an outcropping layer of sandstone, against which rests a horizontal water surface. In instruments used to measure dip a level bubble conveniently shows horizontality. Direction is also given when stating dip, that is, the direction in which water would run on the sloping plane. In Figure 19.17 the direction of dip is west.

The compass direction, or bearing, of the line of intersection between the inclined rock plane and an imaginary horizontal plane is the *strike*. In Figure 19.17 the strike is north, identical with the compass direction of the water line where the rock plane plunges beneath the water. Strike is conventionally stated by compass quadrants in exactly the same terms as bearing (See Chapter 2); for example, *N 30° E* or *N 45° W*. Any horizontal line has two possible directions, but that with reference to north is conventionally stated.

The geologist also uses "strike" in a very loose sense as a verb synonymous with "to bear" or "to trend" in denoting the orientation of any linear feature, whether of bedrock or terrain. Thus he may speak of "valleys which strike east-west." He also uses "dip" in a loose usage synonymous with the verb "to slope" or "to tilt." For example, he says, "the beds dip radially outward from the center of the dome."

Faults and folds

Repeatedly in writings on geology, reference is made to a *fault*, or surface of breakage in the earth's crust along which a slipping movement has taken place, one mass sliding past the other. Faults are of great importance geologically because they result in unlike rock types being brought into contact at the same level. Various types of faults and the landforms developed on them are discussed in Chapter 30.

Many layered rocks, such as sedimentary strata or lavas, have experienced compressional forces in the earth's crust, which bend the layers into wavelike corrugations, termed *folds*. This happens not only on a vast scale of mountain dimensions, but also on smaller scales down to tiny wrinkles a fraction of an inch from crest to crest. Often, as in marble and slate, many scales of folds are super-imposed in the same rock mass. Large folds have a strong influence in shaping landforms, a subject treated in detail in Chapter 30.

Geologic maps and structure sections

The geographer must train himself to read many sorts of maps, among them the *areal geologic map*, which show by means of colors or patterns the surface distribution of each rock unit with special emphasis upon the lines of contact of rocks unlike in variety or age. Faults are shown as lines. Strikes and dips of strata are added by special symbols. Reference to a geologic map will often provide the explanation for the presence of a landform variety in one locality, but its absence in another. Prominent escarpments, ridges, and valleys commonly reflect geologic contacts and faults. Soil types may prove closely related to rock types in some regions. Occurrence of mineral fuels, ores, and construction materials of economic importance can often be predicted or understood from a knowledge of rock varieties and their surface distribution.

Figure 19.18 is a simple geologic map of the same area shown by a perspective diagram in Figure 19.13. If map reproduction is limited to black and white, patterns are applied to differentiate the rock units. Shorthand letter combinations may be added as a code to set apart formations of different ages. Small T-shaped symbols, seen on the map, tell strike-and-dip. The long bar gives direction of strike; the short bar which abuts it at right angles show direction of dip. Amount of dip in degrees is given by a figure beside the symbol. A small fault, cutting across the northwest corner of the map, is shown by a solid line. The letters *D* and *U* indicate which side slipped downward, which upward.

To show the internal geologic structure of an area the geologist resorts to the *structure section*, an imaginary vertical slice through the rocks. Samples are seen in the front surfaces of the blocks of earth crust shown in figures 19.3, 19.13, and 19.16. Where a deep canyon has exposed a great wall of rock, as at Grand Canyon, Arizona, the geologist needs only to record what he sees to produce an accurate cross section. More often, a cross section is constructed solely from surface outcrops and a few well borings.

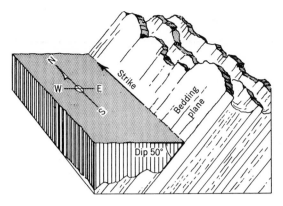

Figure 19.17 Strike and dip define the position of an inclined rock plane.

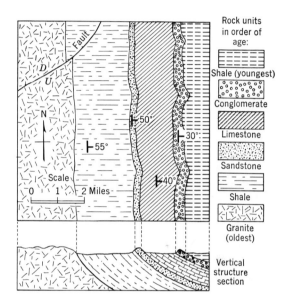

Figure 19.18 A geologic map shows the surface distribution of rocks and structures. The structure section shows rocks at depth.

The brief treatment of rocks and structures given in this chapter cannot take the place of a full course in principles of geology, supplemented with laboratory study and field trips, but it may provide terms and explanations essential to the understanding of evolution of landforms as controlled by structure.

Review Questions

1. Define bedrock, mantle, and soil. What is an outcrop?

2. What is the distinction between transported and residual mantle? What is the relation between transported mantle and the depositional landforms?

3. In what way is an understanding of rocks and their structures necessary in explaining landforms?

4. What are igneous rocks? What is a magma? What is the difference between intrusive and extrusive igneous rocks? How does each type occur? What difference is there in the texture of extrusive and intrusive rocks? Why?

5. What is a mineral? How does a mineral differ from a rock? What name is given to the science of minerals? Of rocks?

6. What is granite? Of what minerals is it composed? Give the names and mineral components of at least two other intrusive igneous rocks.

7. What minerals tend to make an igneous rock light in color and low in specific gravity? What minerals tend to make an igneous rock dark and high in specific gravity? How do the words *sial* and *sima* serve to distinguish two major divisions of igneous rocks?

8. What forms do extrusive igneous rocks take? What is lava? How does the texture of lava differ from that of the intrusive igneous rocks? Why? Through what kind of passages do extrusive rocks reach the earth's surface? What is columnar jointing?

9. How are volcanic ejecta classified according to the sizes of the fragments? How are pyroclastic sedimentary rocks related to volcanic ejecta?

10. What is a sedimentary rock? How are sedimentary materials hardened into rock? What are the sources of sediment? Define strata; stratification planes.

11. On what basis are formations set apart as units in sedimentary rock?

12. Name in order of size the particles that make up clastic sediments and the rock name for each grade. In what way is conglomerate different from breccia? What is the principal mineral of sandstone? What characterizes the shape and properties of particles which make up shale? Name a pyroclastic rock and explain how it is formed.

13. How does limestone differ from the clastic sedimentary rocks? In what ways may limestone be formed? What is chalk? What is marl? What mineral composes pure limestone? How does dolomite differ from limestone in chemical composition and origin?

14. How are peat and coal produced? What class of sedimentary rocks do they illustrate? Explain how an evaporite forms. Name two common evaporites and give their compositions.

15. How do the various kinds of sedimentary rocks influence the development of landforms? Which form valleys? Which form mountains and ridges? How do the sedimentary rocks compare with the igneous rocks in this respect?

16. What are metamorphic rocks? How are they formed? From what other rocks may they be derived? Describe slate, phyllite, schist, quartzite, marble, and gneiss. Which of these rock types generally form valleys? Which form ridges or mountains?

17. Explain how dip and strike tell the orientation in space of an inclined rock plane. Define a fault; a fold.

18. How can geologic maps provide information of interest to the geographer? How are rock units shown on a geologic map? What symbols indicate strike and dip? Faults? What is a structure section and how is the information obtained for its construction?

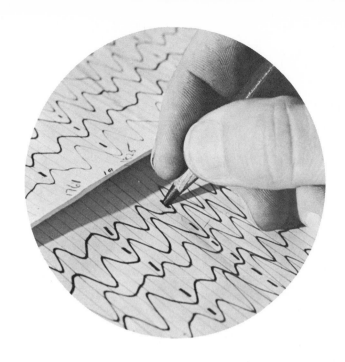

CHAPTER TWENTY

The earth's crust

THE geographer concerned largely with man's occupation of the earth's surface may justifiably feel little need to study those branches of geology dealing with the earth's interior, the subsurface structures of the continents, the relief features of the ocean floor, and the events of ancient geologic history. It is true that the remoteness of these things—whether in place or in time—relegate them to indirect or remote roles in man's economic, social, and cultural processes, inasmuch as few immediate or direct environmental effects can be established. Nevertheless, it is worthwhile for the student of physical geography to place the surficial elements of the lands, atmosphere, and oceans in the broader setting of global geology.

Internal structure of the earth

The earth is an almost spherical body approximately 8000 miles in diameter (Chapter 1), but man's direct observation of the composition and physical properties of the earth's interior is limited by mining and drilling operations to depths of a few miles at best, so that he must turn to indirect means of obtaining information. The science of *geophysics* is concerned largely with obtaining information about the physical properties of the earth by means of instruments that measure earth-quake waves, earth magnetism, and the force of gravity. Interpretation of these data through established laws of physics has yielded surprisingly detailed knowledge of the earth's structure and properties.

Figure 20.1 is a cutaway diagram of the earth to show its major parts. The center is occupied by the *core*, a spherical zone about 2160 miles in radius. Because of the sudden change in behavior of earthquake waves upon reaching this zone, it has been concluded that the core has the properties of a liquid, in abrupt contrast to a solid mass which surrounds it. More recent studies suggest, however, that the innermost part of the core may be solid, or crystalline. Through astronomical calculations it can be shown that the earth has a specific gravity of about 5½, whereas the surface rocks average 3 or less (Chapter 19). This must mean that specific gravity increases greatly toward the interior, where it may be about from 10 to 15. Iron, with a small proportion of nickel, is considered as the probable substance comprising the liquid core. This conclusion is supported by the fact that many meteorites, representing disrupted

above: Seismogram used in geophysical exploration for petroleum.   Photograph, Shell Oil Company.

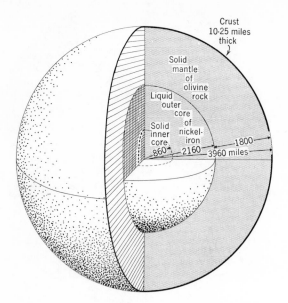

Figure 20.1 Concentric zones make up the earth's interior.

fragments of our solar system are of iron-nickel composition. Temperatures in the earth's core may lie between 3500° and 7500° F; pressures are as high as three to four million times the pressure of the atmosphere at sea level.

Outside of the core lies the *mantle*,[1] a layer about 1800 miles thick, composed of mineral matter in a solid state. Judging from the behavior of earthquake waves, the mantle is probably composed largely of the mineral olivine (magnesium iron silicate), which comprises a basic rock variety called *dunite*. This rock, which may be in a glassy state, exhibits qualities of great rigidity and high density in response to sudden stresses of earthquake waves which pass through it. On the other hand, the mantle rock can adjust by slow flowage to unequal forces which act over great periods of time. In this respect it is somewhat like cold tar, which is hard and shatters easily if struck, but which will slowly flow downhill if left undisturbed for a long time.

The crust

Outermost and thinnest of the earth zones is the *crust*, a layer some 10 to 30 miles thick. Formed of crystalline rocks, largely igneous in classification, the crust exhibits properties of brittleness when subjected to mountain-building forces and therefore may break along great faults. The base of the crust, where it contacts the mantle, is sharply defined, a fact known because earthquake waves

[1] Not to be confused with residual and transported mantle materials close to the earth's surface, described in Chapter 19.

change velocity abruptly at that level (Figure 20.2*A*). The surface of separation between crust and mantle is called the *Moho*, a simplification of Mohorovičić, the name of the seismologist who discovered it.

From a study of earthquake waves it is concluded that the crust consists of two layers: (1) a lower, continuous layer of basaltic rock otherwise termed *sima* (See Chapter 19); (2) an upper layer of granitic rock, otherwise termed *sial*, which constitutes the continents. The granitic layer is therefore discontinuous in areal extent, being absent over the ocean basins. Figure 20.2*B* shows schematically a small part of the crust near the margin of a continent. The sedimentary strata of the continents are on the average merely a thin skin, not shown on this diagram, although locally they are several thousand feet thick.

Those parts of the crust forming the continents are much thicker than the crust under the ocean basins, and may be likened to vast icebergs floating in the sea with only a small part visible above the water, but with a great bulk deeply submerged. The glassy rock of the earth's mantle has yielded by slow flowage, much like a very viscous fluid; this has permitted the lighter, rigid, continental plates of the crust to come to rest in the manner of the floating iceberg.

Distribution of continents and ocean basins

From a globe or atlas we can compute that about 29 per cent of the globe is land; 71 per cent oceans. If, however, the seas were to drain away, it would become apparent that broad areas lying close to the continental shores are actually covered by shallow water, less than 500 or 600 feet deep. From these relatively shallow *continental shelves* the ocean floor drops rapidly to depths of thousands of feet. In a sense, then, the ocean basins are brim-full of water and have even spread over the margins of ground that would more reasonably be assigned to the continents. If the ocean level were to drop by 600 feet (100 fathoms) the surface area of continents would increase to 35 per cent; the ocean basins decrease to 65 per cent; figures which we may regard as representative of the true relative proportions.

Figure 20.3 shows graphically the percentage distribution of the earth's surface area with respect to elevation both above and below sea level. Note that most of the land surface of the continents is less than 3300 feet (1 kilometer) above sea level. There is a rapid drop off from about −3000 to −10,000 feet until the ocean floor is reached. A predominant part of the ocean floor lies between 10,000 and 20,000 feet below sea level. Disregarding the earth's curvature, the continents can be visualized as platformlike masses; the oceans as broad, flat-floored basins.

Scale of the earth's relief features

Before turning to a description of the major topographic features of the continents and ocean basins, it is revealing to consider the true scale of the earth's relief forms in comparison with the earth as a sphere. Most of the relief globes and pictorial relief maps seen commonly in magazines and atlases are greatly exaggerated in vertical scale. For a true-scale profile around the earth we might draw a chalk-line circle 21 feet in diameter, representing the earth's circumference on a scale of 1:2,000,000. A chalk line three-eighths inch wide would include within its limits not only the highest point on the earth, Mt. Everest (+29,000 feet), but also the deepest known ocean trenches (−35,000 feet).

Figure 20.4 shows profiles correctly curved and scaled to fit a globe whose diameter is 21 feet. The topographic profile is drawn to natural scale, without vertical exaggeration. Although the most imposing relief features of Asia and North America are shown, they seem little more than trivial irregularities on the great global circle.

Relief features of the ocean basins

The North Atlantic Ocean illustrates certain typical features of the ocean basins and continents (Figure 20.5). Along the eastern margin of North America lies the *continental shelf*, a fairly smooth, sloping plain 75 to 100 miles wide and reaching a depth of 100 fathoms (600 feet) at the outer edge. This shelf, a part of the true continent, is essentially a zone of deposition of sedimentary rock layers built of material brought from the eastern United States by streams and spread over the sea floor by

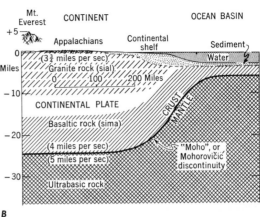

Figure 20.2 The earth's crust is much thicker under continents than beneath the ocean basins.

currents. At its outer edge, the shelf abruptly gives way to a descending *continental slope* leading down to the true ocean basin floor at a depth of about 2000 fathoms (12,000 feet). The slope is scored by strange *submarine canyons* (Figure 20.5), whose origin has been strongly debated. The canyons seem to be the work of eroding streams, very likely flows of muddy water, called *turbidity currents*, which are produced when storms or earthquake shocks disturb soft sediment at the canyon heads. These flows travel swiftly down the continental slope because their density is greater than that of the surrounding sea water. Spreading out upon the deep sea floor, turbidity currents

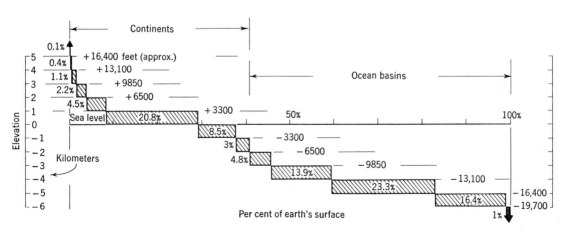

Figure 20.3 Distribution of the earth's solid surface in successively lower altitude zones.

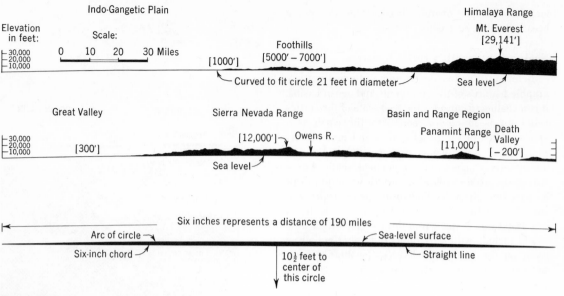

Figure 20.4 These profiles show the earth's great relief features in true scale with sea-level curvature fitted to a globe 21 feet in diameter.

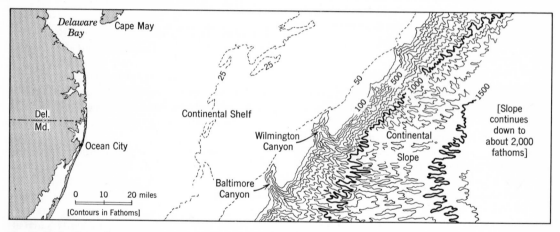

Figure 20.5 Two submarine canyons notch the outer edge of the Atlantic continental shelf off the Delaware-Maryland coast. (After Veatch and Smith.)

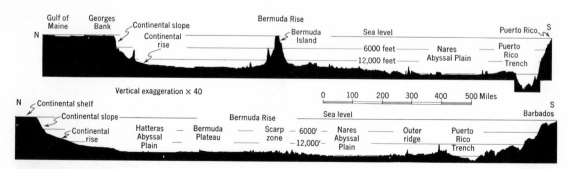

Figure 20.6 Profiles across the Atlantic Ocean basin reveal continental shelf and slope, abyssal plain, trench, and various minor irregularities. (After Bruce C. Heezen, Lamont Geological Observatory of Columbia University.)

come slowly to rest. The sediment is spread in broad layers which have accumulated over millions of years, gradually burying the irregular topographic features of the sea floor and producing vast, flat *abyssal plains* (Figure 20.6). The broad basin of the North Atlantic thus has a remarkably smooth floor over large areas at a depth of about 3000 fathoms (18,000 feet).

Rising abruptly from the floor are isolated submarine mountains, named *seamounts,* some of which may be ancient volcanoes. In the center of the Atlantic lies a great submarine mountain range, the *Mid-Atlantic Ridge,* comparable with the Rocky Mountain chain in size and relief but entirely submerged except for the Azores Islands. This ridge is merely a part of a single, continuous midocean ridge traced through the South Atlantic, Indian, South and East Pacific, and Arctic oceans. It seems to be the expression of a major fracture system of the earth's crust.

Other features of the ocean floor are *trenches,* or *foredeeps*—long, narrow depressions whose bottoms reach depths of 4,000 to 5,000 fathoms (24,000 to 30,000 feet) or more (Figure 20.7). The trenches are thought by geologists to represent downfolded zones associated with recent mountain-building movements. Accumulation of sediment on the trench floors has been so slow that these depressions are not filled in, as they would be if above sea level.

Geologists and geophysicists have long been convinced that the continents and ocean basins have endured throughout all recorded geologic time and have not exchanged places by crustal warping. Evidence for this belief lies in the fact that most sedimentary rocks of past geologic ages seen on the continents are of types deposited in fairly shallow depths, whereas the very fine-grained deep-sea clays, or *oozes,* which settle out upon seamounts and isolated submarine ridges, are absent from geological strata of the continents. Sample submarine cores, penetrating as much as 30 feet into such oozes, show thin clay layers dating back as far as 100 million years and indicating that the rain of sediment from the overlying ocean water has been extremely slow as compared to deposition on continental shelves and in shallow inland seas. The lower, deeper parts of the ocean basins have, however, received the deposition of thousands of feet of layered clay and sand carried by turbidity currents from continental margins.

Present-day mountain building near the margins of the ocean basins is distributed along long, narrow, curving zones, known as *island arcs* (Figure 20.8). Each arc represents a zone of sharp folding or compression and is associated with active volcanoes and earthquakes. The great ocean deeps generally lie along the outer side of the island arcs.

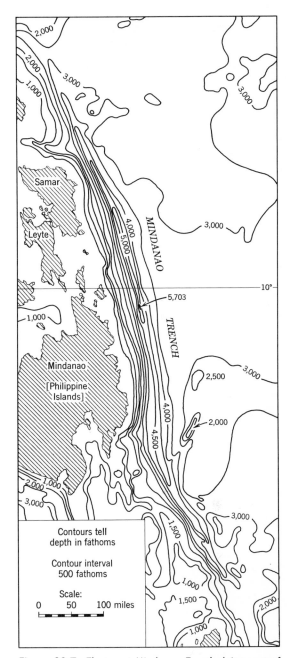

Figure 20.7 The great Mindanao Trench, lying east of the Philippines, reaches a maximum depth of 5703 fathoms (34,218 feet), which is considerably deeper than Mt. Everest (29,000 feet) is high. (After H. H. Hess, Hydrographic Office Chart 5485.)

Relief features of the continents

Perhaps the most conspicuous of the major relief features of the continents are the *mountain arcs,* similar in plan and in origin to the island arcs. Figure 20.9 shows the outlines of Eurasian mountain arcs, both those of ancient geological date which have since been worn down to their

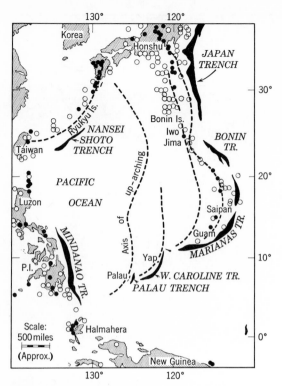

Figure 20.8 This map of the western Pacific shows trenches (solid black), island arcs (dashed lines), active volcanoes (black dots), and deep-focus earthquake centers (circles). (After H. H. Hess.)

ever, undergone repeated broad-scale uplift and sinking movements involving entire continents or subcontinents. Little or no visible disturbance of the rock resulted from these *epeirogenic* warpings of the crust, in contrast with the violent breakage and folding of orogenic movements. When epeirogenic movements were of a negative, or sinking, type, large parts of the shields became submerged as shallow seas and continental shelves. This gave opportunity for sedimentary strata to be deposited on the old metamorphic and igneous rocks. Later positive, or rising, epeirogenic movements brought the sedimentary cover above sea level where it has since been carved up by streams into hills and plateaus.

Shields of the Northern Hemisphere are shown in Figure 20.10. North America's geological heartland is the *Canadian Shield;* that of Europe is the *Russian-Baltic Shield,* also called the *Fenno-Scandian Shield.* Rocks in both of these regions date back to the oldest era of geologic time, from one to three billion years ago. In the southern hemisphere, similar shield areas occupy parts of Australia, South Africa, and the Antarctic.

The geologic time scale

To discuss the development of relief features of the continents requires at least occasional brief reference to events of the geologic past. Even the explanation of landforms produced in the more recent of the geological periods requires some knowledge of the length and sequence of geologic time units. The economic geographer interested in the occurrence and distribution of ores and mineral fuels will find that a knowledge of historical geology will be extremely helpful in gaining understanding of the occurrence of economic mineral deposits in various parts of the world. The table on p. 293 therefore outlines the important events and subdivisions of geologic history. Note that the upper part of the table, representing the younger or more recent events, subdivides geologic time into small intervals, whereas with increasing age the units are larger and more generalized. This is because the geologic record is most fragmentary for the oldest ages but becomes generally more detailed as the recent is approached.

Absolute ages given in the table have been verified by means of chemical analyses of radioactive mineral substances and are generally accepted by geologists, subject to a small percentage of error. In every period of geologic time there were widespread accumulations of sedimentary strata; in fact, the strata comprise the record itself and constitute sole evidence of the climatic and geographic conditions of the time, as well as containing the fossil remains of plant and animal life. Generally

roots, and the great modern alpine chains of which the Alps, Atlas, Caucasus, Hindu Kush, Himalaya, and East Indian ranges are prominent parts. The younger mountain arcs consist of sedimentary strata which have been greatly crumpled and broken. In some places the sediments have been metamorphosed into slates and schists. Deeper in these ranges granite intrusions are often encountered. Chains of volcanoes mark certain of the ranges. Great amounts of crustal shortening have occurred across the mountain arcs, judging from the fact that the same rock layer may be found doubled up on itself repeatedly. Mountain-making processes are described under the general term *orogeny;* the mountain arcs are said to *orogenic belts.*

In marked contrast to the mountain arcs are vast expanses of geologically ancient rocks known as *shields* (Figure 20.10). Although covered in part by younger sedimentary strata, the shields are underlain largely be metamorphic and igneous rocks formed during orogenies of extremely ancient date, but have long been relatively stable and quiet areas. Agents of denudation have had ample time to reduce the shields to low-lying erosion plains, exposing igneous and metamorphic rock that formerly lay many miles deep. The shields have, how-

TABLE OF GEOLOGICAL HISTORY

ERA	PERIOD	EPOCH	Absolute age in years before present	Major geologic events in United States given in order of increasing age	Distinctive features of plant and animal life	
CENOZOIC	QUATERNARY	Recent	10,000	Minor changes in land forms by work of streams, waves, wind	Rise of civilizations	Age of Man
		PLEISTOCENE		Four stages of spread of continental ice sheets and mountain glaciers	Development of man; extinction of large mammals	
	TERTIARY	PLIOCENE	1,000,000 — Cascadian orogeny: Cascade and Sierra Nevada ranges uplifted; volcanoes built		Early evolution of man; dominance of elephants, horses, and large carnivores	Age of Mammals
		MIOCENE	12,000,000	Marine sediments deposited on Atlantic and Gulf coastal plain; stream deposits spread over Great Plains and Rocky Mountain basins; thick marine sediments deposited in Pacific coastal region	Development of whales, bats, monkeys	
		OLIGOCENE	25,000,000		Rise of anthropoids	
		EOCENE	35,000,000		Development of primitive mammals; rise of grasses, cereals, fruits	
		PALEOCENE	60,000,000		Earliest horses	
MESOZOIC	CRETACEOUS		70,000,000 — Laramide orogeny: Rocky Mountains formed	Marine sediment deposition over Atlantic and Gulf coastal plain and in geosyncline of Rocky Mountain region	Extinction of dinosaurs; development of flowering plants	Age of Reptiles
	JURASSIC		130,000,000 — Nevadian orogeny: Intrusion of batholith of Sierra Nevada region	Marine sediment deposition in seas of western United States; desert sands deposited in Colorado Plateau	Culmination of dinosaurs; first birds appear	
	TRIASSIC		165,000,000 — Palisadian disturbance: Block faulting in eastern United States	Deposition of red beds in fault basins of eastern United States and in shallow basins of western United States	First dinosaurs; first primitive mammals; spread of cycads and conifers	
PALEOZOIC	PERMIAN		200,000,000 — Appalachian orogeny: Folding of Paleozoic strata of Appalachian geosyncline	Deposition of red shales and limestones in southwestern United States; much salt and gypsum (glaciation of southern hemisphere continents)	Conifers abundant; reptiles developed; spread of insects and amphibians; trilobites become extinct.	Age of Amphibians
	CARBONIFEROUS — PENNSYLVANIAN		235,000,000	Deposition of coal-bearing strata in eastern and central United States	Widespread forests of coal-forming spore-bearing plants; first reptiles; abundant insects	
	CARBONIFEROUS — MISSISSIPPIAN		260,000,000	Deposition of limy, shaly sediments in widespread, shallow seas of central and eastern United States	Spread of sharks; culmination of crinoids	
	DEVONIAN		285,000,000 — Acadian orogeny: Folding and igneous rock intrusion in New England	Deposition of thick marine strata in geosynclines of eastern and western United States	First amphibians; many corals; earliest forests spread over lands	Age of Fishes
	SILURIAN		325,000,000		First land plants and air-breathing animals; development of fishes	
	ORDOVICIAN		350,000,000 — Taconian orogeny: Folding of rocks in eastern United States, Nevada, and Utah	Deposition of thick marine strata in geosynclines of eastern and western United States	Life only in seas; spread of molluscs; culmination of trilobites	Age of Marine Invertebrates
	CAMBRIAN		410,000,000		Trilobites predominant; many marine invertebrates	
	Pre-Cambrian time; age goes back to nearly three billion years		500,000,000	Many periods of sediment deposition alternating with orogeny	Earliest known forms of life; few fossils known	

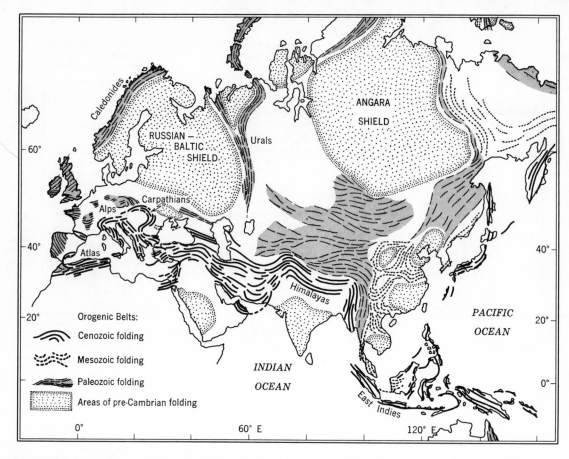

Figure 20.9 Mountain arcs of Eurasia, both ancient and modern, are shown by curving line patterns. (After Umbgrove.)

speaking, each major time unit was brought to a close by orogeny, also called *revolution*, disrupting the sequence of sediment deposition. The largest time unit is the *era* of which the last three are the *Cenozoic, Mesozoic,* and *Paleozoic,* in order of increasing age. All time before this is designated as belonging to the *pre-Cambrian* time. Eras have been recognized within the pre-Cambrian, but the record tends to fragmentary and confused. The second order of time unit is the *period*, of which the Paleozoic era has seven; the Mesozoic era three; the Cenozoic two. *Epochs* are still shorter units of time, listed on the table only for the Cenozoic era.

Scheme of major geologic events

It is beyond the scope of this volume to treat physical and historical geology. But some brief insight into a general scheme of geologic events which has been repeated many times in the past may be had from the diagrams of Figure 20.11. These represent certain inferred events in the development of the Hudson Valley region throughout

the Paleozoic, Mesozoic, and Cenozoic eras encompassing approximately the last 500 million years.

In Block *A* the region is shown as a Paleozoic seaway in which thousands of feet of sedimentary strata had accumulated. An inland seaway of this nature is called a *geosyncline*. The source of sediment was in large part from a chain of volcanic islands lying to the east. The Paleozoic era was brought to a close by a great orogeny, the *Appalachian Revolution*. Sedimentary strata of the geosyncline were severely crumpled, as well as broken into slices which slid over one another (Block *B*). As a result, a great mountain range stood where formerly there had been a seaway. The bending of the strata is generally referred to as *folding*, and the corrugated structures thus produced are simply termed *folds*. The slanting surfaces upon which sliding occurred are termed *overthrust faults*, the process being known as *overthrusting*. Mountain topography thus produced by folding and thrusting is composed of initial landforms, as explained in Chapter 18. The agents of

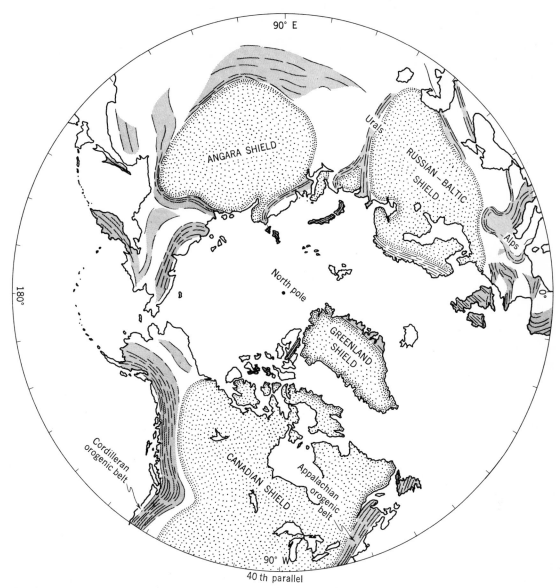

Figure 20.10 Shields are bounded by mountain belts (dashed lines) of Paleozoic age. (After A. J. Eardley, *Structural Geology of North America*.)

denudation are nevertheless shown to be dissecting the initial mountain forms even before the folding and thrusting have ceased.

After the Appalachian Revolution the region shown here remained essentially stable and quiescent for many millions of years. The mountains were reduced by the denudational processes to a land surface of very faint relief termed a *peneplain*. The position of the peneplain is shown in Block *B* by a dashed line. Note that the oldest rock, a gneiss of pre-Cambrian age, is exposed in the core of the mountain belt, whereas the youngest sedimentary layers, of Paleozoic age, remain in the zone of least disturbance, at the left end of the diagram.

In Block *C*, the region is shown to have been again subjected to crustal movement, but of a quite different nature from previous movements. This was the *Palisadian disturbance*, which began in the Triassic period. The region has been broken into a series of blocks, each tilted with respect to its neighbor. The fractures are a type of fault, but are different from overthrust faults by having nearly vertical inclination of the breaks and by the absence of any pronounced crustal compression and shortening. The entire breakage scheme may be termed *block faulting*. The peneplain made before faulting forms the smooth, sloping surfaces of the fault blocks.

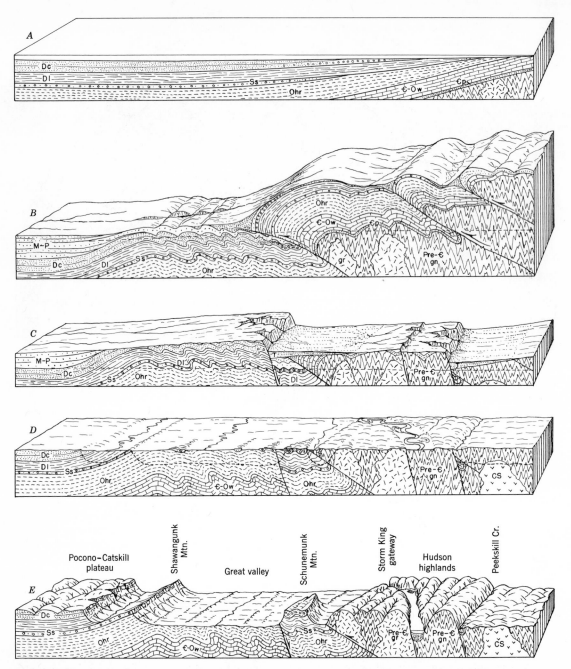

Figure 20.11 A sequence of events which has been generally repeated throughout geologic time over the continents of the globe is well illustrated in the Hudson Valley region. In these diagrams northwest is to the left, southeast to the right. *A.* A shallow inland seaway accumulated thousands of feet of sediments during the Paleozoic era. *B.* Mountain making at the end of the Paleozoic era produced a series of folds and thrust faults. A general uplifting brought a large mass above sea level. *C.* Following a long period of erosion, a peneplain was produced (along the dashed line shown on block *B*). Then faulting in the Triassic period produced these gently tilted blocks. *D.* A second long period of erosion resulted in another peneplain. *E.* The region today owes its relief to different rates of removal of the various kinds of rocks.

In Block *D*, the region has again been reduced to a peneplain, indicating another prolonged period of relative stability of the earth's crust lasting into the Tertiary period. The more resistant gneiss, granite, conglomerate, and sandstone rise as low hills between broad, flat lowlands underlain by shale.

The region next experienced still another crustal movement, of epeirogenic nature. This was a very simple rising, or upwarping. No faulting or folding occurred. Consequently, the peneplain of Diagram *D* was merely uplifted about 2000 feet. Streams and other agents of land denudation again set to work and excavated the weaker rocks to form valleys. The resistant sandstones, conglomerates, granites, and gneisses were left as ridges and mountain masses, as shown in Diagram *E*, representing the present. The topography of today is solely the result of different rates of downwasting of the ground surface upon complex rock structures formed through a long series of geologic events.

Chapters 29, 30, and 31 treat the individual peculiarities of landforms developed on flat-lying strata, folded strata, domed strata, block faults, and the extrusive and intrusive igneous rocks. Before starting such a study, it is well to consider in detail the processes of denudation which shape the forms.

Review Questions

1. Describe the earth's core and mantle, giving dimensions, mineral composition, and physical properties. What type of evidence is used to obtain this information? What temperatures and pressures may be expected at the earth's center?

2. What is the earth's crust? How thick is it? How can it be distinguished in properties from the underlying mantle? Of what two rock layers does the crust consist? What is the general distribution of sima and sial over the earth?

3. Describe the general form of the continents and ocean basins as regards the levels of concentration of surface areas. If sea level were lowered by 100 fathoms what per cent of the earth would be land?

4. On a globe 21 feet in diameter how far would the greatest relief features of the earth depart from a perfect circle drawn to represent sea level?

5. What is a continental shelf? By what type of rock material is it underlain? What is a continental slope? What relation do submarine canyons bear to these features?

6. What are turbidity currents? What work do they perform? What deposits do they build?

7. What kinds of relief features are found on the floors of the ocean basins? Describe seamounts, trenches (foredeeps), and submarine mountain ridges.

8. With what sort of crustal deformation are the island arcs and deep trenches of the ocean basins associated?

9. Why are the continents and ocean basins thought to have remained as permanent features throughout known geologic history? What is the evidence?

10. Describe the form and structure of mountain arcs. Explain what is meant by orogeny. Contrast orogenic crustal movements with epeirogenic movements.

11. What are the continental shields? Of what rock types are they composed? Give the name and location of three shield areas of the northern hemisphere.

12. Name the eras of geologic time and give the total duration of each in years. For each of the eras, name the periods of geologic time. Into what epochs is the Tertiary period subdivided? What great events occurred during the Pleistocene epoch?

13. What type of geologic event has brought to a close each era and many of the periods? What is the known duration of pre-Cambrian time? How much longer is pre-Cambrian time than all of post-Cambrian time?

14. Explain the general scheme of geologic events in which sedimentary rocks are deposited, then deformed, and finally reduced by erosion. What is a geosyncline? What is a revolution?

15. What is meant by folding and overthrusting of strata? Do these deformations require compression or tension of the earth's outer crust?

16. What is a peneplain? At what level do peneplains form? How long a period of time is required to reduce a mountain range to a peneplain?

17. What is meant by faulting? How does block faulting differ from overthrust faulting? Why would you not expect both types to occur simultaneously in the same region?

18. When a peneplain is upwarped what type of landform development follows? What happens to the peneplain?

CHAPTER TWENTY-ONE

Water in the soil and rock

AS the agents of earth sculpture operate upon bedrock and mantle materials, highly complex forces work together to prepare the bedrock for transportation and to move finely divided matter to progressively lower levels and more distant locations. The study of the work of water in shaping erosional landforms is perhaps the most important topic of geomorphology. This is because by far the greatest part of the earth's land surface is shaped by water in the liquid state, flowing over the ground surface, flowing in channels, or percolating downward through the soil and mantle. We shall therefore need to learn something about the role of water in landform development. The source of this water, its paths of travel, and the changes that it affects both upon and below the surface are the subject of this and the following chapters.

A knowledge of the role of water upon and beneath the ground surface is not only essential in understanding landform development; it is of great concern to the geographer because this water is a basic natural resource. Water in the soil is the essential ingredient of all plant life and hence of the source of all crop production. Water deep beneath

above: Artesian well at Oneco, Florida.
Photograph, Ewing Galloway.

the surface, or flowing in streams, or held in lakes, is the source of man's domestic and industrial water supplies. Wise use of all of these forms of water, both to increase their yield and to prevent depletion through over-use is an important concern of the geographer interested in economic development of any region. His grasp of the scientific principles of the role of water should be sufficiently developed that he can communicate with the technical specialists in this field—the hydrologist, geologist, soil scientist, climatologist, and hydraulic engineer —all of whom deal with some phase of water upon or below the ground surface.

Surface and subsurface water

We may classify water according to whether it is *surface water*, flowing exposed or ponded upon the land, or *subsurface water*, occupying openings in the soil, mantle, or bedrock. That which is held in the soil or mantle within a few feet of the surface is termed *soil water*, and is the particular concern of the soil scientist and agricultural engineer. That which is held in the openings of the bedrock or deep within thick layers of transported mantle is usually referred to as *ground water*, studied by the geologist or engineer, who is concerned with the storage and flow of this water in various kinds of rocks and structures.

The hydrologic cycle

Water of oceans, atmosphere, and lands moves in a great series of continuous interchanges of both geographic position and physical state, known as the *hydrologic cycle* (Figure 21.1). A particular molecule of water might, if we could trace it continuously, travel through any one of a number of possible circuits involving alternately the water vapor state and the liquid or solid state. A good place to start the description of the hydrologic cycle would be the oceans, which cover nearly three-quarters of the globe. It has been estimated that some 80,000 cubic miles of water are evaporated each year from the oceans, another 15,000 cubic miles from the lakes and moist land surfaces of the continents. The total yearly evaporation figure (95,000 cubic miles) must exactly balance, on the average, the total quantity of water restored to the earth's surface by condensation from the atmosphere. About 24,000 cubic miles of water falls as precipitation upon the earth's land surfaces each year—enough to cover an area the size of Texas to a depth of 475 feet. We see that considerably more water falls upon the lands than is returned to the atmosphere by evaporation from the lands. Therefore, much of what falls returns to the sea in liquid form.

Those parts of the hydrologic cycle dealing with water vapor, its movement toward the lands in maritime air masses, and eventual precipitation from clouds, has been treated in Chapters 10 and 11 as a phase of meterology. Some of the falling precipitation evaporates directly before reaching the ground. Part of that which reaches the ground may be quickly returned to the atmosphere in water vapor form by evaporation from vegetative and soil surfaces, but if rainfall is heavy and long continued, much will soak into the soil to become a part of the soil water. If close to the ground surface, soil water may be returned to the atmosphere by plants which take up the water through their roots and release it into the air through their leaves. Some soil water will evaporate directly into the soil air, which permeates soil openings. Should rain continue to fall, water will percolate through the soil under gravitational pull and will reach the bedrock, or will penetrate deep deposits of transported mantle materials. This ground water moves very slowly but at length emerges in streams, lakes, or even from the ocean floor in the form of seepages and springs. If the ability of the soil to receive and transmit heavy and long-continued rainfall is exceeded, surface flow occurs, conducting the water directly down slopes into streams and

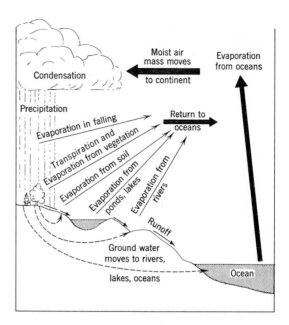

Figure 21.1 The hydrologic cycle traces moisture from its source in the ocean through various paths on land areas to its eventual return to the ocean. (After Holtzman.)

lakes. From these exposed surfaces the water may evaporate directly into the atmosphere or may reach the oceans by stream flow. Now that we have traced water through its full hydrologic cycle, we turn to a closer study of the way that precipitation is absorbed and held by the soil.

Infiltration and runoff

Most soil surfaces in their undisturbed, natural states are capable of absorbing the water from light or moderate rains, a process known as *infiltration*. Such soils have natural passageways between poorly fitting soil particles, as well as larger openings, such as earth cracks resulting from soil drying, borings of worms and animals, cavities left from decay of plant roots, or openings made by heaving and collapse of soil as frost crystals alternately grow and melt. A mat of decaying leaves and stems breaks the force of falling drops and helps to keep these openings clear. If rain falls too rapidly to be passed downward through these soil openings the excess amount flows as a surface water film or sheet down the direction of ground slope, a runoff process termed *overland flow*.

As stated in Chapter 10, rainfall is measured in units of inches per hour. This is the depth to which water will accumulate in each hour if rain is caught in a flat-bottomed, straight-sided container, assuming none to be lost by evaporation or splashing out. Similarly, infiltration is stated in inches per hour and might be thought of as the rate at which the water

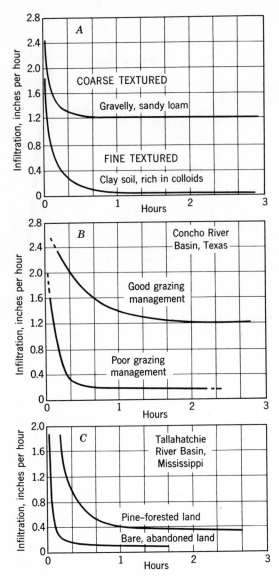

Figure 21.2 Infiltration rates vary greatly according to soil texture and land use. (Data from Sherman and Musgrave; Foster.)

the soil openings rapidly become clogged by particles brought from above, or tend to close up as the soil clays take up water and swell. From this we can easily reason that a sandy soil with little or no clay will not suffer so great a drop in infiltration capacity, but will continue to let the water through indefinitely at a generous rate. In contrast, the clay-rich soil is quickly sealed to the point that it allows only a very slow rate of infiltration. This principle is illustrated by the graph in Figure 21.2A showing the infiltration curves of two soils, one sandy, one rich in clay.

It also follows that a sandy soil may be able to infiltrate even a heavy, long-continued rain without any surface runoff occurring, whereas the clay soil must divert much of the rain into overland flow, a process that may lead to erosion by gullies. Many forms of artificial disturbance of natural soils tend to decrease the infiltration capacity and to increase the amount of surface runoff (Figure 21.2B, C). Cultivation tends to leave the soil exposed so that rain beat quickly seals the soil pores. Fires, by destroying the protective vegetation and surface litter, also expose the soil to rain beat. Trampling by livestock will tamp the porous soil into a dense, hard layer. It is little wonder, then, that man has, through his farming and grazing practices, radically changed the original proportions of infiltration to runoff in such a way as to result in severe erosion damage and at the same time to decrease the reserves of soil moisture which might otherwise sustain plant growth and stream flow in droughts.

Evaporation and transpiration

Between periods of rain, water held in the soil is gradually given up by a twofold drying process. First, direct evaporation into the open air occurs at the soil surface and progresses downward. Air also enters the soil freely and may actually be forced alternately in and out of the soil by atmospheric pressure changes. Even if the soil did not "breathe" in this way, there would be a slow diffusion of water vapor surfaceward through the open soil pores. Ordinarily only the first foot of soil is dried by evaporation in a single dry season, but in the prolonged drought of deserts, drying will extend to depths of many feet. Second, plants draw the soil water into their systems through vast networks of tiny rootlets. This water, after being carried upward through the trunk and branches into the leaves, is discharged in the form of water vapor, through the leaf pores into the atmosphere, a process termed *transpiration*. Few persons are aware of the enormous quantities of water given off by plants in transpiration.

A single corn plant . . . between May 5 and September

level in the same container might drop if the water were leaking through a porous base. Runoff, also stated in inches per hour, may be thought of as the amount of overflow of the container per hour when rain falls too fast to be disposed of by leaking through the base.

Now, it is an important fact about soils that their *infiltration capacity*, or ability to infiltrate rainfall, is usually great at the start of a rain which has been preceded by a dry spell, but drops rapidly as the rain continues to fall and to soak into the soil. After several hours the soil's infiltration capacity becomes almost constant. The reason for the high starting value and its rapid drop is, of course, that

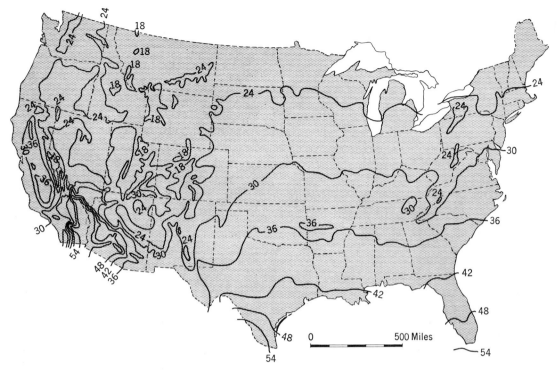

Figure 21.3 Average annual potential evapotranspiration in the United States. (From Thornthwaite, *Geographical Review*, 1948.)

8, transpired 54 gallons of water. An acre of such plants (6000 plants) would transpire during the season 324,000 gallons of water, which is equivalent to a sheet of water 11 inches deep over the entire acre. It has been estimated that an acre of red maple trees, growing in a soil with ample moisture, may lose in a growing season an amount of water sufficient to cover the acre with 28.3 inches of water. A soil clothed with plants is depleted of its moisture at a much more rapid rate than one that is bare. Nearly all the water loss from a soil below the first 6 to 8 inches results from absorption and transpiration by plants.[1]

In studies of climate and hydrology it is convenient to use the term *evapotranspiration* to cover the combined moisture loss from direct evaporation and the transpiration of plants. The rate of evapotranspiration slows down as soil moisture supply becomes depleted during a dry summer period. In general, the less moisture remaining, the slower is the loss through evapotranspiration. Consequently, it is necessary to define two forms of evapotranspiration: (1) *Potential evapotranspiration* is the maximum loss of water possible under the given conditions of plant cover and climatic factors, assuming that we can continue to supply the soil by irrigation with all of the water which the plants can use and the soil pores can hold. (2) *Actual evapotranspira-*

tion is the true or observed quantity of evapotranspiration, decreasing in rate as the soil moisture is depleted. Figure 21.3 is a map of the United States showing the average annual potential evapotranspiration. This map does not, however, take into account humidities, nor the variations in density and type of vegetative cover through which transpiration may be expected to occur.

Figure 21.4 shows diagrammatically the various terms explained up to this point and serves to give a more detailed picture of that part of the hydrologic cycle involving the soil. As the plus signs show, the soil belt gains water through precipitation and infiltration. As the minus signs show, the soil belt loses water through transpiration, evaporation, and overland flow, and by gravity percolation downward through the soil to the ground water zone below.

Moisture in the soil

When infiltration occurs during heavy and prolonged rains (or when a snow cover is melting) the water is drawn downward by gravity through the soil pores, wetting successively lower layers. Soon the soil openings are filled with water moving downward, except for some air entrapped in the form of bubbles. Then the percolation continues downward into the bedrock where it moves into

[1] W. W. Robbins, T. E. Weier, and C. R. Stocking, *Botany, An Introduction to Plant Science*, John Wiley and Sons, New York, 1957, 2nd ed., p. 187.

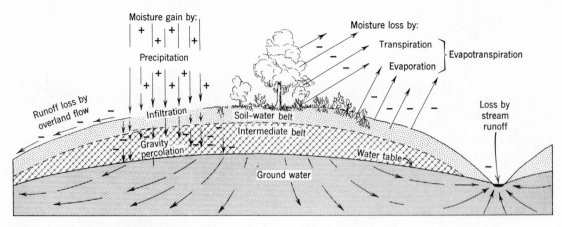

Figure 21.4 The soil water belt occupies an important position in the hydrologic cycle.

rock pores, joint cracks, and along bedding planes. Suppose now that the rain stops and a period of several days of dry weather follows. The excess soil water continues to drain downward, but some water clings to the soil particles and completely resists the pull of gravity through the force of *capillary tension*. We are all familiar with the way in which a water droplet seems to be enclosed in a "skin" of surface molecules, drawing the droplet together into a rounded outline, so that it clings to the side of a glass indefinitely without flowing down. Similarly, tiny films of water adhere to the soil grains, particularly at the points of grain contacts, and will stay until disposed of by evaporation or by absorption into plant rootlets.

When a soil has first been saturated by water, then allowed to drain under gravity until no more water moves downward, the soil is said to be holding its *field capacity* of water. This takes no more than two or three days for most soils. Most is drained out within one day. Field capacity is measured in units of depth, usually inches, just as with precipitation. This means that for a given cube of soil, say twelve inches on a side (one cubic foot), if we were to extract all of the field moisture, it might form a layer of water three inches deep in a pan one foot square. This would be equivalent to complete absorption of a three-inch rainfall by a completely dry twelve-inch layer of soil.

Field capacity of a given soil depends largely on its texture. Sandy soil has a very low field capacity; clay soil has high field capacity. This is shown in Figure 21.5, a graph in which field capacity in terms of inches of water per foot of soil thickness is plotted against soil texture, from coarse to fine. It should also be noted that sandy soils reach their field capacity very quickly, both because of the ease with which the water penetrates and the low

quantity required. Clay soils take long rain periods to reach field capacity because the infiltration is slow and the total quantity required to be absorbed is great.

Agricultural scientists also use a measure of soil moisture termed the *wilting point*. This is the quantity of soil water below which plants will be unable to extract further moisture from the soil and the foliage will wilt. As Figure 21.5 shows, the wilting point also depends upon particle size.

The soil water budget

Equipped with the foregoing explanations of processes and terms relating to water gains and losses in the soil, we can turn next to consider the annual water budget of the soil, involving principles of great concern not only in agriculture, but in the further study of ground water, surface runoff, stream flow, and therefore of the sculpturing of land slopes.

Figure 21.6 shows the annual cycle of soil water for the year 1944 at an agricultural experiment station in Coshocton, Ohio. If we follow the changes in this example, the cycle it shows can be considered generally representative of conditions in humid, middle-latitude climates where there is a strong temperature contrast between winter and summer. Let us start with the early spring (March). At this time the evaporation rate is low, because of low temperatures. The abundance of melting snows and rains has restored the soil moisture to a surplus quantity. For two months the quantity of water percolating through the soil and entering the ground water keeps the soil pores nearly filled with water. This is the time of year when one encounters soft, muddy ground conditions, whether driving on dirt roads or walking across country. This, too, is the season when runoff is heavy and major floods

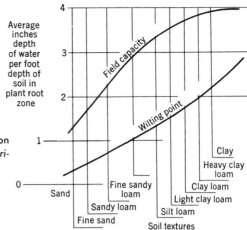

Figure 21.5 Field capacity and wilting point depend on soil texture. (After Smith and Ruhe, *Yearbook of Agriculture*, 1955.)

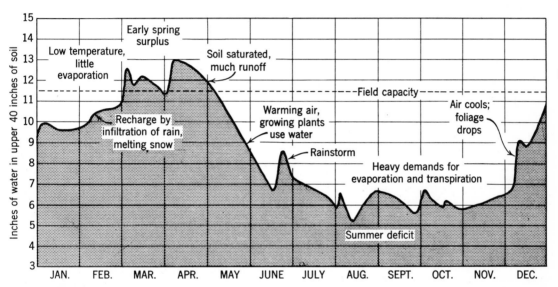

Figure 21.6 Soil moisture follows an annual cycle of surplus and deficit. (After Thornthwaite and Mather, *The Water Balance*, 1955.)

may be expected on larger streams and rivers. In terms of the soil water budget, a surplus exists.

By May, the rising air temperatures, increasing evaporation, and the full growth of plant foliage, bringing on heavy transpiration, have reduced the soil moisture to a quantity below field capacity, although it may be restored temporarily by unusually heavy rains in some years. By midsummer, a state of heavy moisture deficit exists in the water budget. Even the occasional heavy thunderstorm rains of summer cannot restore the water lost by steady and heavy evapotranspiration. Small springs and streams dry up, the soil becomes firm and dry. By November (and sometimes in September), however, the soil moisture again begins to increase. This is because the plants go into a dormant state,

sharply reducing transpiration losses, while, at the same time, falling air temperatures reduce evaporation. By late winter, usually in February at this location, the field capacity of the soil is again restored.

Of course, we have examined the annual cycle for only one climatic region. The annual cycle would be very different for certain other climates. There are moist equatorial climates in which no moisture deficit would be found throughout the year. By contrast, there are dry deserts where a permanent deficit exists.

With this specific example of the yearly cycle of soil water we turn to a more generalized concept of the water budget in terms of three changing quantities, (1) precipitation, (2) potential evapo-

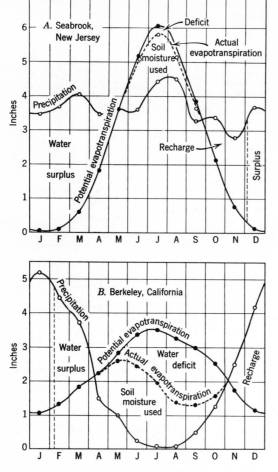

transpiration and, (3) actual evapotranspiration. These are shown in a graph in Figure 21.7 for two quite different climates, represented by Seabrook, New Jersey, and Berkeley, California. Where more rain falls than is lost through evapotranspiration, a water surplus develops. This is the winter season in both places, but is a shorter period at Berkeley than at Seabrook. Where evapotranspiration rises to a maximum in the summer months, a period of moisture shortage develops, but it is much more severe and prolonged at Berkeley because little or no rain falls there in midsummer, whereas rainfall is quite uniform at Seabrook. During the moisture deficit period two evapotranspiration curves are shown. The potential evapotranspiration curve is theoretical, in that it would apply only if the soil could be kept supplied with water up to the limit of field capacity by irrigation. The actual evapotranspiration curve is the real, or observed, state of

affairs, because the rate of moisture loss actually declines as the quantity of soil moisture available declines. The difference between the actual and potential evapotranspiration curves in summer represents the water deficit from the agricultural standpoint because crop growth, to be maintained in a fully vigorous state, requires irrigation in the amount of this difference.

In the autumn, beyond the point where precipitation becomes greater than evapotranspiration, a period of soil water recharge sets in. When field capacity is reached, a period of soil water surplus begins, the surplus water percolating downward to become a part of the ground water. Note that the surplus period begins earlier and lasts much longer at Seabrook than at Berkeley, because the summer deficit at Seabrook has been much less.

These water budget principles with concepts of moisture deficits and surpluses have been developed largely by Dr. C. Warren Thornthwaite, a climatologist who has applied his knowledge to practical problems of agriculture as well as to a world-wide system of climate classification based on the relations between precipitation and evapotranspiration.

Ground water

Water that is drawn downward by gravity through the soil zone to lower levels becomes part of the ground water body, the relations of which are shown in Figure 21.8. Strictly speaking, *ground water* is that part of subsurface water which fully saturates the pore spaces of the rock or mantle and which behaves in response to gravitational force. The ground water occupies the *zone of saturation.* Above it is the *zone of aeration,* in which water does not fully saturate the pores. We have seen that the soil water belt is the uppermost layer of the zone of aeration and that moisture is held in this belt by capillary force in tiny films adhering to the soil particles. A similar condition prevails through the underlying *intermediate belt.* The sole basis for distinguishing these two belts is that the soil belt represents a shallow zone of moisture usable by plants, whereas the intermediate belt is too deep for capillary water to be returned to the atmosphere by either direct evaporation or transpiration. The depth of the zone of aeration may be very shallow or missing (when the ground water is close to the surface in low, flat regions), or up to several hundred feet thick in hilly or mountainous regions with low ground water level.

At the base of the zone of aeration is the *capillary fringe,* a thin layer in which the water has been drawn upward from the ground water body through capillary force. The action is much like the rise of kerosene in a lamp wick, or of water in a blotter whose edge is immersed. Water in the capillary fringe largely fills the soil pores, hence, is continuous with the ground water body. Thickness of the capillary fringe depends on the soil texture, because capillary rise is higher when the openings are smaller. Thus, in a silty material the capillary fringe may be two feet thick, but only a fraction of an inch thick in coarse sand or fine gravel with large pore spaces.

Ground water in the zone of saturation moves under the force of gravity and therefore its upper surface, the *water table*, tends to become a horizontal surface, just as with a free water body such as a lake. But because water moves very slowly through the rock, the water table actually maintains a sloping surface, highest under the hill tops and divides, lowest in valleys.

Pore spaces in the ground water zone

Ground water can saturate a great variety of geological materials ranging from relatively soft mantle, of both residual and transported types, to hard bedrock of any origin. The term *porosity* refers to the total volume of pore space present in a given volume of rock. The amount of water that can be held in storage in a rock is measured by its porosity. A knowledge of rocks enables us to understand something of the variation in porosity that might be expected in rocks. Among the sedimentary rocks, the coarse-grained clastic rocks, such as sandstone or conglomerate, can have large porosity. Similarly, any transported mantle consisting of sands and gravels laid down by streams or shore currents will have large porosity. Shale, because of its dense compaction, will have relatively low porosity, but soft clay or mud, by contrast, has high porosity even though the pores are extremely tiny. Limestones may have large openings, such as caverns, produced by solution of the rock. Scoriaceous lavas commonly have great porosity.

Dense, massive rocks, such as the igneous and metamorphic types, have little or no pore space between the individual mineral crystals, but the presence of numerous fractures, such as joints and faults, offers a large number of interconnected openings in which water can be stored and through which it can move. In sedimentary strata the bedding planes may provide additional openings.

How far down into the earth does the ground water zone extend? No single depth can be stated in answer to this question, but it is certain from experience with deep wells that water becomes very scanty at depths of more than two miles. Furthermore, geologists have evidence that at depths greater than about ten miles, rock is under such great pressure that it yields by slow flowage, tightly closing any natural openings in the rock and preventing any water from entering or remaining in

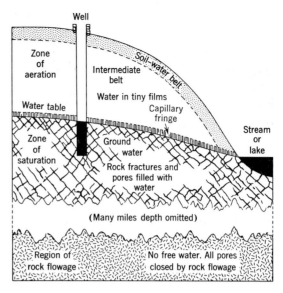

Figure 21.8 Ground water and soil water belts and zones. (After Ackerman, Colman, and Ogrosky.)

the rock. We may call this the *region of rock flowage* and say that it limits the extent of the ground water body in depth (Figure 21.8).

Still another property besides porosity determines whether ground water will move through a rock mass. This is *permeability*, or the ease with which water may be forced through the rock. Obviously, pore spaces in a rock, even though large, may offer no free passage to water if each pore is sealed off from its neighbors by mineral matter. Thus the degree to which openings are interconnected is important in determining permeability. Second, the size of the openings exerts a strong influence upon rate of flow. Coarse sands or gravels permit rapid flow and are therefore rated as highly permeable materials. The microscopic pores of a clay impede flow of water so effectively that clays and rocks containing much clay are commonly *impermeable* (not permeable), at least for practical purposes of obtaining useful flow of water from them. Although intrusive igneous rocks are highly impermeable where massive and not decomposed, they may actually constitute highly permeable bodies if broken by numerous, closely set systems of joints and fractures.

The water table

Ground water is extracted for man's use from wells dug or drilled to reach the ground water zone. In the ordinary shallow well, water rises to the same height as the ground water table, not including the capillary fringe (Figure 21.8). The upper limit of saturation is actually at the upper limit of the capillary fringe. In coarse sands and gravels the capillary fringe is too thin to take into

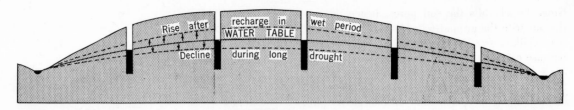

Figure 21.9 The water table conforms to surface topography.

account, but in some fine-textured materials the capillary fringe is from several inches to several feet thick.

If wells are numerous in an area, the position of the water table can be mapped in detail by plotting the water heights and noting the trends in elevation from one well to the other. When this is done it is usually seen that the water table is highest under the highest areas of surface, namely, hilltops and divides, but descends toward the valleys where it may appear at the surface close to streams, lakes, or marshes. The reason for such a configuration of the water table is that water percolating down through the zone of aeration tends to raise the water table, whereas seepage into streams, swamps, and lakes tends to draw off ground water and to lower its level. Because ground water moves extremely slowly, a difference in water table level, or *head*, is built up and maintained between areas of high elevation and those of low elevation. In periods of excessive rainfall this head is increased by rise in water table over divide areas; in drought periods the

water table slowly falls (Figure 21.9). Large fluctuations such as these are usually seen only in periods of excessive rain or drought lasting several years, but in humid, middle-latitude regions of strong seasonal contrasts, a distinct annual cycle of rise and fall of water table is present. This cycle is illustrated in the graphical record of water table and precipitation by months based on the level of an observation well at Washington, D.C., extending from 1929 to 1931 (Figure 21.10). These were unusually dry years. Note that the water table dropped steadily in the latter part of 1929, even though considerable rain fell in September and October. This continued drop is explained by the fact that the soil belt and intermediate belt absorbed and held all of the water which infiltrated the surface, allowing none to get down to the water table. By late winter, however, considerable amounts of water were reaching the ground water zone, because the overlying belts in the zone of aeration had taken up all the water they could hold. Such a rise in water table illustrates the *recharge* of

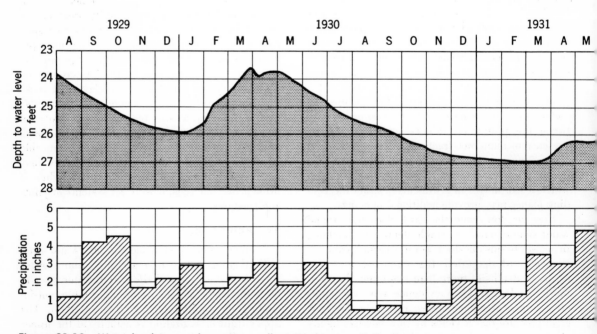

Figure 21.10 Water level in an observation well at Washington, D.C., shows seasonal fluctuations. (After Meinzer, *The Berkey Volume*, 1950.)

ground water supplies by percolation of surface water. By early summer of 1930, the water table again declined because soil moisture losses through evapotranspiration had again depleted the soil water so that all of the rain which fell was absorbed by the soil, leaving none to percolate down to the water table. By the spring of 1931, the water table was again starting its annual rise.

Aquifers, aquicludes, perched water tables, and artesian wells

Where rock layers lie nearly horizontal, or in gently inclined positions, the ground water relations may be quite different from the simple pattern illustrated in Figure 21.9 in which completely uniform geologic materials were assumed to exist. Suppose, for example, that the region is one of sedimentary strata with beds of sandstone alternating with beds of shale (Figure 21.11). Sandstone is commonly both porous and permeable, providing a large ground water storage reservoir through which water may move easily. Such a rock body is termed an *aquifer*. By contrast, a shale bed with low permeability virtually prevents flow of ground water and is called an *aquiclude*. In the particular case shown in Figure 21.11, a thin bed of shale has effectively blocked the downward percolation of water to the main water table below, creating a *perched water table*, separated from the main water table by a zone of aeration. Where the perched water table meets the valley side a *seep* or *spring* (that is, a slow flow of water emerging from the ground) is formed.

Most natural springs are mere trickles of water, unseen and unnoticed under a cover of dense vegetation. A few springs, however, discharge enormous volumes of water where an unusually good aquifer, abundantly fed from a large source area, is exposed in a deep valley or canyon (Figure 21.12).

Where strata are inclined, or dipping, a favorable situation may exist for development of an *artesian* spring or well, one in which the water flows upward to the surface through its own pressure. In Figure 21.13 we see a highly diagrammatic representation of such conditions, the vertical exaggeration being very great merely to show the principle. The eroded edge of a sandstone aquifer is exposed to intake of water at a high position. Water entering here passes deep underground to a position below the valley floor, at which point the water is under a strong pressure, or head, from the weight of the overlying water. This pressure is sufficient to force water up to the surface in a well drilled down through the impervious shale layer into the aquifer. Similar flow as an artesian spring may occur naturally if there are faults in the strata which permit water to seep upward through the

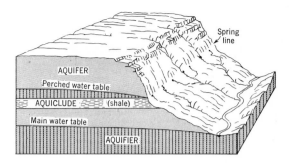

Figure 21.11 A perched water table requires special geological conditions.

Figure 21.12 Thousand Springs, Idaho, emerges from the north side of the Snake River Canyon, opposite the mouth of the Salmon River. The spring extends for half a mile and issues from a scoriaceous basalt layer with a nearly constant discharge of 500 cubic feet per second. (Photograph by I. C. Russell U.S. Geological Survey.)

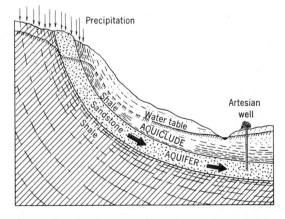

Figure 21.13 Geological conditions that produce artesian flow are illustrated here in a highly diagrammatic way.

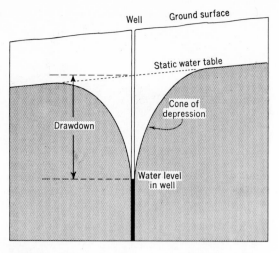

Figure 21.14 Drawdown and cone of depression in a pumped well.

shale layer. In a later discussion of coastal plains, a somewhat more realistic diagram of artesian geological conditions is illustrated (Figure 29.8).

Pumping, drawdown, and recharge of wells

Of increasing importance in economic geography is the effect on the water table of man's withdrawals of ground water. The drilling of vast numbers of wells, from which water is forced out in great volumes by powerful pumps, has profoundly altered nature's balance of ground water recharge and loss, which is a part of the hydrologic cycle. Increased urban populations and industrial developments require larger water supplies, needs that cannot always be met from construction of new surface water reservoirs. In agricultural lands of the semi-arid and desert climates, heavy dependence is placed upon irrigation water from pumped wells, especially since many of the major river systems have already been fully developed for irrigation from surface supplies. Wells can be drilled within the limits of a given agricultural or industrial property, hence provide immediate supplies of water without need to construct expensive canals or aqueducts. A few of the physical principles of water wells are treated here to aid the geography student in understanding the basis of complex economic and legal problems arising from ground water development.

Formerly the small wells needed to supply domestic and livestock needs of a home or farmstead were actually dug by hand as a large cylindrical hole, lined with masonry where required. By contrast, the modern well put down to supply irrigation and industrial water is drilled by powerful machinery which may bore a hole twelve to sixteen inches or more in diameter to depths of 1000 or

more feet, although much smaller-scaled wells and well-boring machines suffice for domestic purposes. Drilled wells are sealed off by metal casings which exclude impure near-surface water and prevent clogging of the tube by caving of the walls. Near the lower end of the hole, where it enters the aquifer, the casing is perforated so as to admit the water through a considerable surface area. Rate of flow of a well or spring is stated in units of gallons per minute or per day. The yields of single wells range from as low as a few gallons per day in a domestic well to many millions of gallons per day for large, deep industrial or irrigation wells.

In most wells, powerful pumps can easily bring water to the surface more rapidly than it can enter the well, so that the delivery of ground water is limited by the properties of the aquifer rather than by the mechanical equipment. Figure 21.14 shows the effects of rapid pumping. The rate at which water can enter the well depends on the permeability of the aquifer, which limits the rate of flow of water through the aquifer from the surrounding area. Flow of ground water is extremely slow, in any case, compared to flow of streams. It is estimated that ground water may move at a speed of 5 feet per day through a formation in which wells of good yield are developed, that in exceptional cases of coarse gravels the velocity may reach 30 to 60 feet per day. In dense clays and shales the rate may be immeasurably slow.

When rate of pumping of the well exceeds the rate at which water can enter, the level of water in the well drops and the surrounding water table is lowered in the shape of a conical surface, termed the *cone of depression*, the height of which is termed the *drawdown* (Figure 21.14). By producing a steeper gradient of the water table, the flow of ground water toward the well is also increased, so that the well will yield more water. This holds only for a limited amount of drawdown, beyond which the yield fails to increase. The cone of depression may extend as far out as eight to ten or more miles from a well where very heavy pumping is continued. Where many wells are in operation, their intersecting cones produce a general lowering of the water table. Depletion often greatly exceeds the rate at which the ground water of the area is recharged by percolation from rain or from the beds of streams. In an arid region, much of the ground water for irrigation is from wells driven into thick sands and gravels which are lowland deposits of transported mantle of a type termed *alluvium*. (These features are described in Chapter 24.) Recharge of such deposits depends on the seasonal flows of water from streams heading high in adjacent mountain ranges. Where such highly permeable materials exist, the extraction of ground water by pumping can greatly exceed the recharge by stream flow. Cones of depression deepen and widen; deeper wells and more powerful pumps are then required. Overdrafts of water accumulate and the result is exhaustion of a natural resource not renewable except by long lapses of time. In humid areas where annual rainfall is copious—from 30 to 50 inches annually—natural recharge is by general percolation over the ground area surrounding the well. Here the prospects of achieving a balance of recharge and withdrawal are highly favorable through the control of pumping and the return of waste waters or stream waters to the ground water table by means of other wells in which water flows down, rather than up.

Natural discharge of ground water

The subsurface phase of the hydrologic cycle, which is the main theme of this chapter, is completed when the ground water emerges along lines or zones where the water table intersects the ground surface. Such places are the channels of streams and the floors of marshes and lakes. By slow seepage and spring flow the water must emerge in sufficient quantity to balance that which enters the ground water table by percolation through the zone of aeration.

Contrary to what the average person might predict, all of the ground water does not move directly from divides to the lines of seepage by flow close to the top of the water table. If such were the case, the lower parts of the ground water body would be stagnant. Certain geological phenomena, such as the cementation of rocks and the transfer of dissolved mineral matter from place to place, would not take place without some ground water flow, even though extremely slow.

Figure 21.15 shows the theoretical paths of flow of ground water as calculated by use of basic principles of the physics of fluids. Water follows paths curved concavely upward. Water entering the slope

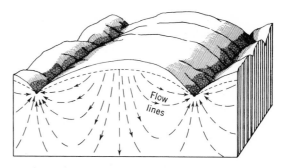

Figure 21.15 Theoretical paths of ground water movement under divides and valleys. (After M. K. Hubbert.)

midway between divide and stream flows rather directly. Close to the divide point on the water table, however, the flow lines go almost straight down to great depths in the earth from which they recurve upward to points under the streams. Progress along these deep paths would be incredibly slow; that near the surface would be faster. The most rapid flow is encountered close to the line of discharge in the stream, where the arrows are shown to converge.

Of considerable interest in economic geography of coastal regions is the problem of the relation of fresh water to salt ground water, because wells put down close to the shore may encounter salt water, or may, through overdraft, cause salt water to be drawn into the well and render it unfit for use. Figure 21.16 shows an idealized diagram through an island or a narrow peninsula. The body of fresh ground water takes the shape of gigantic lens with convex faces, except that the upper surface has only a broad curvature whereas the lower surface, in contact with the salt ground water, bulges deeply downward. Because fresh water is less dense than salt, we can think of this fresh water lens as floating upon the salt water, pushing it down much as the hull of an ocean liner pushes aside the surrounding water. The ratio of densities of fresh water to salt water is as 40 to 41. Hence, if

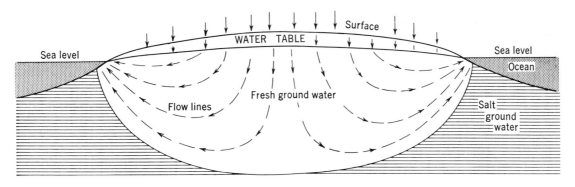

Figure 21.16 Fresh water and salt water relations in an island or peninsula. (After G. Parker.)

the water table is, say, 10 feet above sea level, the bottom of the fresh-water lens will be located 400 feet below sea level, or forty times as deep as the water table is high with respect to sea level.

The fresh ground water extends seaward some distance beyond the shoreline. Although the salt ground water is stagnant, the fresh water travels in the curved paths shown by arrows in Figure 21.16. If water is pumped excessively from wells close to the coast, the contact of salt with fresh ground water shifts landward, where it may intersect the wells and contaminate the fresh water. When such a condition exists, the only cure is to cease pump-ing and allow the fresh water slowly to push the contact back toward its original seaward position, or to create a fresh water recharge barrier between the wells and the coastline. Resumed pumping must then be regulated to a lower rate.

Having reviewed the principles of soil and ground water, we are equipped to investigate the processes of slope wasting which are closely tied in with the hydrologic cycle. Following this, our detailed examination of the hydrologic cycle can be resumed in a study of surface water flow in streams and rivers, whereby the hydrologic cycle is completed as the water reaches the oceans.

Review Questions

1. Explain why an understanding of subsurface water is important to the student of economic geography.

2. Distinguish between surface water and subsurface water; between soil water and ground water.

3. Give a complete general account of the hydrologic cycle. What quantities of water are evaporated annually from the oceans? from the lands? How is this balanced by precipitation and runoff?

4. What is infiltration? What is overland flow? In what units is each stated? How does infiltration capacity change when rain falls? Explain. How do soils differ in this respect? In what ways does man alter infiltration capacity?

5. To what depth does soil moisture evaporate? How do atmospheric pressure changes assist in this process?

6. Explain the process of transpiration by plants. What quantities of soil water are thus lost? To what depth does this loss extend? Define evapotranspiration. Distinguish between potential and actual evapotranspiration.

7. How is soil water held in place? What is the source of soil moisture? What is field capacity? How does it vary with soil texture? What is the wilting point?

8. Describe the annual cycle of soil water in humid, middle-latitude climates. When and why do water surpluses and deficits occur?

9. Sketch a typical annual water budget cycle by months, showing precipitation, potential evapotranspiration, and actual evapotranspiration. When is irrigation needed?

10. Define ground water. How does one distinguish between zones of saturation and aeration? Between soil water and intermediate water belts? What is the capillary fringe? How does its thickness vary with soil texture? What is the water table?

11. Distinguish between porosity and permeability of rocks. Cite varieties of rocks and transported mantle materials to illustrate extremes of porosity and permeability. What is the region of rock flowage? What ground water conditions exist there?

12. Describe the form of the water table under a hilly topography. What fluctuations may be expected in the water table? What is ground water recharge and how does it take place?

13. Explain how layered rocks can cause a perched water table. How can springs be so formed? What geologic conditions are required for artesian wells and springs?

14. How does pumping cause drawdown of water table? What is the cone of depression? How far may it extend from a well? How rapidly is ground water recharged from alluvial deposits of arid regions?

15. Where is ground water discharged from the ground to become runoff? Describe the paths of ground water flow from divide to stream.

16. Describe and explain the relation of a fresh ground water body to the salt ground water beneath an island. What physical principle governs the relation of water table elevation to depth of fresh water? How is salt water contamination of wells caused?

CHAPTER TWENTY-TWO

The wasting of slopes

THE term *slope*, as used throughout the science of geomorphology, designates some small element or area of the land surface which is inclined from the horizontal. Thus, we speak of "mountain slopes," "hill slopes," or "valley-side slopes" with reference to the inclined ground surfaces extending from divides and summits down to valley bottoms.[1] Slopes are required for the flow of surface water under the influence of gravity. Therefore, slopes are fitted together to take the forms of drainage systems in which the overland flow converges into stream channels, these, in turn, conducting the water and rock waste to the oceans to complete the hydrologic cycle. Nature has so completely provided the earth's land surfaces with slopes that perfectly horizontal or vertical surfaces are extremely rare. Consider that the methods of showing relief—hachures, contours, or shading—are unable to depict landscape forms composed wholly of horizontal and vertical planes, such as a set of cubes resting on a table top.

Our concern in this chapter is with the wasting of land slopes under the dominant influence of water acting in conjunction with gravity. Emphasis

is on the slow processes whereby bedrock is transformed into residual mantle. This in turn moves down the slopes to channels where it can be taken by stream flow to still more distant, lower areas. Slopes are also shaped by other processes—glaciers, winds, and waves—which are treated in later chapters.

Weathering and mass wasting

Weathering is the combined action of all processes whereby rock is decomposed and disintegrated because of exposure at or near the earth's surface. Weathering normally changes hard, massive rock into finely fragmented, soft residual mantle. For this reason, weathering is often described as the preparation of rock materials for transportation by the agents of land erosion—flowing water, glacial ice, waves, and wind. Because gravity exerts its force on all matter, both bedrock and the products of weathering tend to slide, roll, flow, or creep down all slopes in a variety of types of earth and rock movements grouped under the term *mass wasting*.

Weathering processes may be subdivided into

---

[1] *Slope* is also used to mean inclination, from the horizontal, measured as in *dip* (Chapter 19); or as a verb *to slope*, meaning *to incline*.

above: Sugar Loaf from Urca Beach, Rio de Janeiro, Brazil.
Photograph, Pan American Airways.

two large groups, *physical* (*mechanical*) *weathering* and *chemical weathering.* Although these processes are extremely complex and act in combinations that are hard to separate into simple concepts, we shall attempt to identify the most important individual changes and to show what landforms or surface features of the rock and soil are caused by each.

Geometry of rock breakup

Before examining weathering processes, it is well to introduce four terms applied to the geometrical manner in which bedrock breaks into smaller pieces. In so doing we are not considering the possible forces involved, merely the shapes of the rock fragments as they appear to the eye. Rocks composed of rather coarse mineral grains (intrusive igneous rocks of granitoid texture and coarse clastic sedimentary rocks) commonly fall apart grain by grain, a form of breakup termed *granular disintegration* (Figure 22.1). The result is a gravel or sand in which each grain consists of a single mineral particle separated from its fellows along the original crystal or grain boundaries. *Exfoliation* is the formation of curved rock shells which separate in succession from the original rock mass,

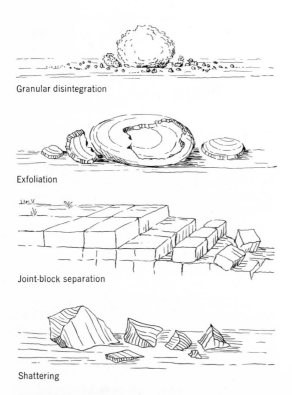

Granular disintegration

Exfoliation

Joint-block separation

Shattering

Figure 22.1 Rock breakup takes various forms.

leaving behind successively smaller spheroidal bodies (Figure 22.14). This type of breakup is also called *spalling.*

Where a rock has numerous joints produced previously by mountain-making pressures or by shrinkage during cooling from a magma, the common form of breakup is by *joint-block separation* (Figure 22.1). Obviously, comparatively weak forces can separate such blocks, whereas great forces are required to make fresh fractures through solid rock. In sedimentary rocks the planes of stratification, or bedding planes, comprise one set of planes of weakness commonly cutting at right angles to the joints. Figures 22.9 and 22.11 show joint blocks being separated by weathering forces. Of course, it is quite possible that a single, solid joint block will later break up either by granular disintegration or by exfoliation.

Shattering is the disintegration of rock along new surfaces of breakage in otherwise massive, strong rock, to produce highly angular pieces with sharp corners and edges (Figure 22.1). The surface of fracture may pass between individual mineral crystals or grains, or may cut through them. Blocks seen in Figure 22.2 are joint blocks, many of which have been shattered into smaller pieces.

A number of other, less common, forms of rock breakup are found in particular rock varieties having characteristic structures. Thus, slate tends to split along the slaty cleavage, schist along the foliation surfaces.

Physical weathering processes and forms

The physical, or mechanical, processes of weathering produce fine particles from massive rock by the exertion of stresses sufficient to fracture the rock, but do not change its chemical composition. One of the most important physical weathering processes in cold climates is the repeated growth and melting of ice crystals in the pore spaces or fractures of soil and rock. As water in joints freezes, it forms needlelike ice crystals extending across the openings. As these ice needles grow, they exert tremendous force against the confining walls and can easily pry apart the joint blocks. Even massive rocks can be shattered by the growth of ice crystals created from water that has previously soaked into the rock. Where soil water freezes, it tends to form ice layers parallel with the ground surface, *heaving* the soil upward in an uneven manner.

Freezing water strongly affects soil and rock in all middle- and high-latitude regions having a cold winter season, but its effects are most striking in high mountains, above the timberline. Here the separation and shattering of joint blocks may produce an extensive ground surface littered with angular blocks (Figure 22.2). Such a surface is termed a *felsenmeer* (rock sea), or *boulder field.* Where cliffs of bare rock exist at high altitudes, fragments fall from the cliff face, building up piles of loose blocks into conical forms, termed *talus cones* (Figure 22.3).

Closely related to the growth of ice crystals is the weathering process of rock disintegration by growth of salt crystals. This process operates extensively in dry climates and is responsible for many of the niches, shallow caves, rock arches, and pits in sandstone formations. During long drought periods, ground water is drawn to the surface of the rock by capillary force. As evaporation of the water takes place in the porous outer zone of the sandstone, tiny crystals of salts are left behind. The growth force of these crystals is capable of producing granular disintegration of the sandstone, which crumbles into a sand and is swept away by wind and rain. Especially susceptible are zones of rock lying close to the base of a cliff, for here the ground water tends to seep outward, perhaps prevented from further downward percolation by impervious layers below (Figure 22.4). In the southwestern United States, many of the deep niches thus formed were occupied by Indians, whose cliff dwellings obtained protection from the elements as well as safety from armed attack (Figure 22.5).

An important but little appreciated process of physical weathering is the continual swelling and shrinking of soils as the particles of fine silt and clay absorb or give up soil water in alternate periods of rain and drought. Shrinkage forms soil cracks in dry periods, making the infiltration of rainfall much more rapid in early stages of an ensuing rain. In clay-rich sedimentary rocks such as shales, the swelling is largely responsible for a spontaneous breakup known as *slaking,* in which the shale crumbles into small chips or pencil-like fragments when exposed to the air.

Most crystalline solids, such as the minerals of rocks, tend to expand when heated and to contract when cooled. Where rock surfaces are exposed daily to the intense heating of the sun alternating with nightly cooling, the resulting expansion and contraction exerts powerful forces upon the rock. Given sufficient time (tens of thousands of such daily alternations), even the strongest rocks may develop fractures. These can take the form of exfoliation shells, or may simply separate the rock into its component grains. As yet, the importance of heating and cooling upon rock disintegration is not fully evaluated, but it is possibly an important form of physical weathering. Forest and brush fires, which raise the rock surface to intense heat in a few minutes time, are known to cause severe

Figurre 22.2 A felsenmeer atop Medicine Bow Peak, Snowy Range, Wyoming, at 12,000 feet elevation. The rock is quartzite.

Figure 22.3 Talus cones have been built out from the base of a steep mountain face, toward a debris-covered glacier seen in the foreground. Bishop Range, British Columbia. (Photograph by H. Palmer.)

Physical weathering processes and forms | 313

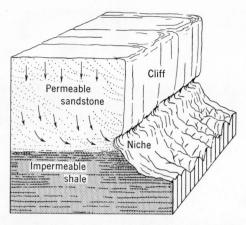

Figure 22.4 Seepage of water from the cliff base localizes development of niches through rock weathering.

Figure 22.5 White House Ruin occupies a deep niche in the sandstone wall of Canyon de Chelly, Arizona. (Photograph by M. A. Melton.)

Figure 22.6 Sheeting of granite, a large scale form of exfoliation, facilitates quarrying operations. (Photograph by Raymond Granite Co., Knowles, California.)

rock exfoliation, but this may be due in part to the formation of steam from water which the rock has previously absorbed.

A curious but widespread process related to physical weathering results from *unloading*, the relief of confining pressure, as rock is brought nearer to the earth's surface through the erosional removal of overlying rock. Geologists think that rock formed at great depth beneath the earth's surface (particularly igneous and metamorphic rock) is in a slightly contracted state because of the tremendous pressures applied during mountain-making crustal deformations. On being brought to the surface, the rock expands slightly in volume and, in so doing, great shells of rock break free from the parent mass below. The new surfaces of fracture are a form of joint termed *sheeting structure* and show best in massive rocks such as granite and marble, because in a closely jointed rock the expansion would be taken up among the blocks. The rock sheets or shells produced by unloading generally parallel the ground surface and therefore tend to dip valleyward. On granite coasts the shells are found to dip seaward at all points along the shore. Sheeting structure is well seen in quarries, where it greatly facilitates the removal of rock (Figure 22.6).

Where sheeting structure has formed over the top of a single large body of massive rock, an *exfoliation dome* is produced (Figure 22.7, 22.8). These are among the largest of the landforms due primarily to weathering. In the Yosemite Valley region, California, where domes are spectacularly displayed, the individual rock shells may be as thick as 20 to 50 feet.

Other large, smooth-sided rock domes lacking in shells are not true exfoliation domes, but are formed by granular disintegration of a single body of hard, coarse-grained intrusive igneous rock lacking in joints. Examples are the Sugar Loaf of Rio de Janeiro, seen in the photograph on p. 311, and Stone Mountain, Georgia (Figure 25.4), which rise prominently above surrounding areas of weaker rock.

Finally, in this list of physical weathering processes, the wedging of plant roots deserves consideration as a possible mechanism whereby joint blocks may be separated. We have all seen at one time or another a tree whose lower trunk and roots are firmly wedged between two great joint blocks of massive rock (Figure 22.9). Whether the tree has actually been able to spread the blocks farther apart is doubtful at best. However, it is certain that the growth of tiny rootlets in joint fractures must be of great importance in loosening countless small rock scales and grains, particularly when a rock has already been softened by decay or fractured by frost action.

Figure 22.7 North Dome and Basket Dome in Yosemite National Park, California, are exfoliation domes developed from huge masses of solid igneous rock. (Photograph by Douglas Johnson.)

Figure 22.8 Exfoliation domes take a variety of shapes. (Drawn by E. Raisz.)

Chemical weathering processes and forms

Chemical weathering denotes changes in chemical properties of rock-forming minerals to produce new minerals better suited to existing at the relatively low temperatures and pressures found at the earth's surface. One group of these changes involves addition of oxygen and water, both of which are abundantly available in the soil and bedrock. A second group of changes is the reaction of natural acids of the soil solution with rock-forming minerals to yield salts which are readily carried away by ground water movement. Third, certain salts of the type known as *evaporites* (See Chapter 19), found in layers in sedimentary strata, are readily dissolved without change in chemical composition and are

Figure 22.10 Weathering converts rectangular blocks into rounded forms. (Drawn by E. Raisz.)

Figure 22.9 Jointing in sandstone resembles pavement blocks at Artists View, Catskill Mountains, New York.

Figure 22.11 Egg-shaped granite boulders are produced from joint blocks by granular disintegration in a semi-arid climate near Prescott, Arizona.

carried away in ground water flow. The first two groups of chemical processes are considered in somewhat more detail.

Water enters into a permanent chemical union with many common rock-forming minerals in a chemical change termed *hydrolysis*. The igneous rocks are particularly susceptible. Feldspar commonly turns to a clay mineral known as *kaolin*. When this happens in a granite, in which potash feldspar is an important constituent, the granite will undergo granular disintegration. Not only is the kaolin a soft mineral, but it tends to swell and thus to burst the grains apart. Similarly, the iron magnesian minerals such as hornblende and biotite decompose and soften, causing disintegration of basic rocks such as gabbro or basalt. The iron thus released unites with oxygen and water to form *limonite*, a soft, yellowish mineral that is responsible for much of the staining of rock surfaces with earth-red colors.

The hydrolysis of granite, with accompanying granular disintegration and some exfoliation of thin scales, produces many interesting boulder and pinnacle forms by rounding of angular joint blocks (Figures 22.10, 22.11, 22.12, 22.13). These forms are particularly conspicuous in arid regions because of the absence of any thick cover of soil and vegetation. There is ample moisture in most deserts for hydrolysis to act, given sufficient time. Hydrolysis in fine-grained basic igneous rocks, such as basalt, commonly gives small-scale exfoliation of a type called *spheroidal weathering* (Figure 22.14).

In warm, humid climates, hydrolysis of suscepti-ble rocks goes on below the soil and may result in the deep decay or rotting of igneous and meta-morphic rocks to depths as much as 100 to 300 feet. Geologists who first studied this deep rock decay in the Southern Appalachian region termed the rotted layer *saprolite*. To the engineer, such oc-currences of deep weathering are of major importance in construction of highways, dams, or other heavy structures. Advantageous as is the property of soft-ness of the saprolite, so as to be removable by power shovels with little blasting, there is serious danger in the weakness of the material in bearing heavy loads, as well as undesirable plastic proper-ties because of a high content of clay minerals.

Of the acid reactions that affect rock-forming minerals, perhaps the most important is that caused by *carbonic acid*, a weak acid formed when carbon dioxide gas of the atmosphere is dissolved in soil and ground water. Particularly susceptible is lime-

Figure 22.12 These granitic boulders on the desert near the Rand Mountains, California, resulted from granular disintegration. (After W. M. Davis.)

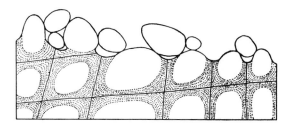

Figure 22.13 Stages in the development of egg-shaped boulders from rectangular joint blocks. (After W. M. Davis.)

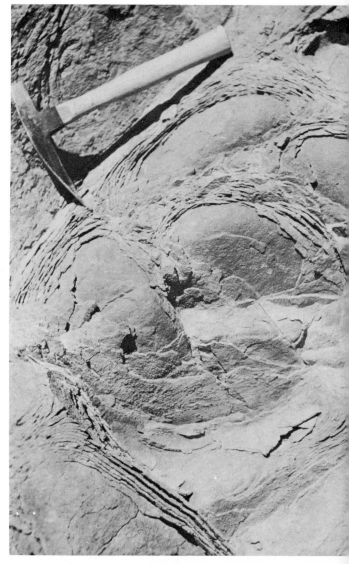

Figure 22.14 Spheroidal weathering, shown here, has produced many thin concentric shells in a basaltic igneous rock. (Photograph by Orlo Childs.)

stone, formed of the mineral clacite (calcium carbonate). The action of carbonic acid on lime-stone produces a salt (calcium bicarbonate) which is readily carried off in the flow of ground water and streams. Because limestone is a common rock, this process is of major importance in landform devel-opment. Surfaces of limestones are commonly deeply pitted and grooved (Figure 22.15). More important is the removal of vast amounts of rock in underground locations to produce cavern systems into which surface water disappears. The landforms associated with cavern development are explained in Chapter 29.

Those who have studied the rate at which car-

bonic acid acts have estimated that in a humid climate, such as that of the eastern United States, the ground surface of a limestone region may be lowered at the average rate of one foot in 10,000 years through this process alone. Because of their susceptibility to carbonic acid reaction, limestones in a humid climate normally have been lowered to produce valleys in contrast to surrounding uplands or ridges of other rock types. In arid climates, however, limestone resists weathering so effectively as to stand in prominent, high ridges or mesas.

In any soil rich in decaying plant matter, a variety of organic acids is formed in the soil solu-tion, and these also react with mineral surfaces to

Figure 22.15 Solution is active in cold climates, as evidenced by the intricate weathering forms in limestone at this locality in Alaska. (Photograph by Collier, U.S. Geological Survey.)

produce chemical weathering. The salts that are products of such reactions are carried down through the soil into the ground water zone, then eventually to streams.

The weathering processes reviewed above, both physical and chemical, work universally but produce few distinctive large landforms or spectacular activities that would draw the attention of the average person. Nevertheless, these processes are of enormous importance in slope development in that they prepare the bedrock for soil formation and for erosional removal by the agents of land sculpture. Without the weathering processes, vegetation could not thrive as we know it today, nor could the great continental land masses be easily reduced by the agents of denudation.

Mass wasting

Everywhere on the earth's surface, gravity pulls continually downward on all materials. Bedrock is usually so strong and well supported that it remains fixed in place, but should a mountain slope become too steep through removal of rock at the base, bedrock masses break free, falling or sliding to new positions of rest. In cases where huge masses of bedrock are involved, the result may be catastrophic

in loss to life and property in towns and villages in the path of the slide. Soil and mantle materials, being poorly held together, are much more susceptible to gravity movements. There is abundant evidence that on most slopes at least a small amount of downhill movement is going on at all times. Much of this is imperceptible, but sometimes the soil or mantle slides or flows rapidly.

Taken altogether, the various kinds of downslope movements occurring under the pull of gravity, which we have collectively termed mass wasting, constitute an important process in slope wasting and denudation of the lands. A few of the commoner kinds of gravity movements and resulting landforms are described here.

Soil creep

On almost any moderately steep, soil-covered slope, some evidence may be found of extremely slow downslope movement of the soil and mantle, a process called *soil creep*. Figure 22.16 shows some of the evidence that the process is going on. Joint blocks of distinctive rock types are found moved far downslope from the outcrop. In some layered rocks such as shales or slates, edges of the strata seem to bend in the downhill direction. This is not true plastic bending, but is the result of slight movement on many small joint cracks (Figure 22.17). Fence posts and telephone poles lean downslope and even shift measurably out of line. Retaining walls of road cuts lean and break outward under pressure of soil creep from above.

What causes soil creep? Heating and cooling of the soil, growth of frost needles, alternate drying and wetting of the soil, trampling and burrowing by animals, and shaking by earthquakes all produce some disturbance of the soil and mantle. Because gravity exerts a downhill pull on every such rearrangement that takes place, the particles are urged progressively downslope.

Creep affects rock masses enclosed in the soil or lying upon bare bedrock. Huge boulders which

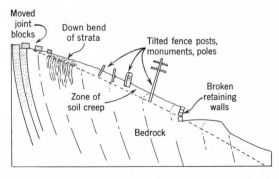

Figure 22.16 Slow, downhill creep of soil and weathered mantle is evident in various ways. (After C. F. S. Sharpe.)

have gradually crept down a mountain side in large numbers may accumulate at the mountain base to produce a boulder field containing blocks the size of a house. Creep also affects the rock pieces in a talus slope, causing the angle of the talus surface gradually to become flatter. In some alpine mountains, high above timberline, sheets of frost-shattered rock fragments creep slowly down the valleys, making curious tonguelike bodies which in many ways resemble a glacier of ice. These forms are called *rock glaciers* (Figure 22.18). Among the best examples are those from mountain ranges in Alaska, where a single rock glacier may be one to two miles long and a quarter of a mile wide.

Earth flow

In humid climate regions, if slopes are steep, masses of water-saturated soil, mantle, or weak bedrock may slide downslope during a period of a few hours in the form of *earthflows*. Figures 22.19 and 22.20 are sketches of earthflows showing how the material slumps away from the top, leaving steplike terraces bounded by arcuate scarps, and flows down to form a bulging "toe" in which wrinkles are curved convexly downslope.

Shallow earthflows, affecting only the soil and residual mantle, are common on sod-covered slopes that have been saturated by heavy rains. An earthflow may affect a few square yards, or it may cover an area of several acres. If the bedrock is rich in clay (shale or deeply weathered igneous rocks), earthflow sometimes include millions of tons of bedrock, moving by plastic flowage like a great mass of thick mud. The Slumgullion flow, pictured in Figure 22.21, originated as deeply weathered volcanic rock high on a mountain side. Once flowage began, the mass took the form of a tongue and did not stop until it had pushed six miles down the valley.

A special variety of earth flowage characteristic of arctic regions is *solifluction* (from Latin words meaning *soil* and *to flow*). In late spring and early summer, when thawing has penetrated the upper few feet, soil is fully saturated with water which cannot escape downward because of the underlying impermeable frozen mass (permafrost). Flowing almost imperceptibly, this saturated soil forms terraces and lobes that give the mountain slope a stepped appearance (Figure 22.22).

Mudflow

One of the most spectacular forms of mass wasting is the *mudflow*, a stream of fluid mud which pours down canyons in mountainous regions (Figures 22.23 and 22.24). In deserts, where vegetation does not protect the mountain soils, violent local storms produce rain much faster than it can

Figure 22.17 Slow creep has caused this downhill bending of vertical rock strata in Morgan County, West Virginia. (Photograph by Stose, U.S. Geological Survey.)

Figure 22.18 From the top of Mt. Sopris in the Rocky Mountains of Colorado, one can look down upon this rock glacier. Direction of motion is away from the observer. (Photograph by M. A. Melton.)

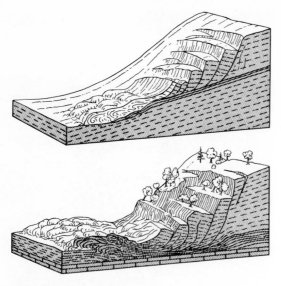

Figure 22.20 Earth flows in a mountainous region. (After W. M. Davis.)

Figure 22.19 Two varieties of earth flow. (After E. Raisz.)

Figure 22.21 This great earth flow in Slumgullion Gulch, in the San Juan Mountains of Colorado, dammed a river to produce Lake San Cristobal. (Photograph by C. W. Cross, U.S. Geological Survey.)

be absorbed by the soil. As the water runs down the slopes it forms a thin mud, which flows down to the canyon floors. Following stream courses, the mud continues to flow until it becomes so thickened that it must stop. Great boulders are carried along, buoyed up in the mud. Roads, bridges, and houses in the canyon floor are engulfed and destroyed. If the mudflow emerges from the canyon and spreads across a piedmont plain, property damage and loss of life can result, because in desert regions the plains lying at the foot of a mountain range which supplies irrigation water may be heavily populated.

Mudflows also occur on the slopes of erupting volcanoes. Freshly fallen volcanic ash and dust is turned into mud by heavy rains and flows down the slopes of the volcano. Herculaneum, a city at the base of Mt. Vesuvius, was destroyed by a mudflow during the eruption of 79 A.D., when the neighboring city of Pompeii was buried under volcanic ash.

Still other mudflows, usually of small size, occur in high mountains and in arctic tundra regions during periods of thaw when excess water is produced by melting of snow and soil ice (Figure 22.25). Unlike the mud flows of arid mountain regions, where the flow thickens as it travels, alpine and arctic mudflows may become more fluid as the flow progresses because of better mixing of soil and water.

Figure 22.22 Solifluction lobes cover this Alaskan mountain slope in the tundra climate region. (Photograph by P. S. Smith, U.S. Geological Survey.)

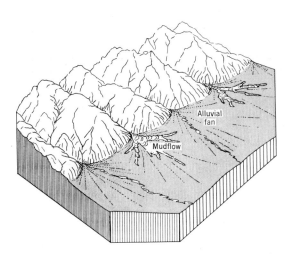

Figure 22.23 Thin streamlike mudflows commonly issue from canyon mouths in arid regions, spreading out upon the piedmont alluvial fan slopes.

Figure 22.24 Repeated mudflows from a small mountain ravine have built this steep debris fan into Upper Twin Lakes in the Sierra Nevada of California. The track of a mudflow which occurred in 1911 runs down to the right of center on the fan. (Photograph by Eliot Blackwelder.)

Figure 22.25 A small mudflow resulting from summer thaw in a tundra climate, De Salis Bay, Banks Island lat. 71½° N, long. 122° W). The inner channel is about two feet wide. (Photograph by A. L. Washburn, Arctic Institute of North America.)

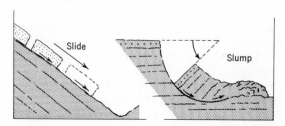

Figure 22.26 Landslides may involve (A) slip on a nearly plane surface or (B) slump with rotation on a curved plane.

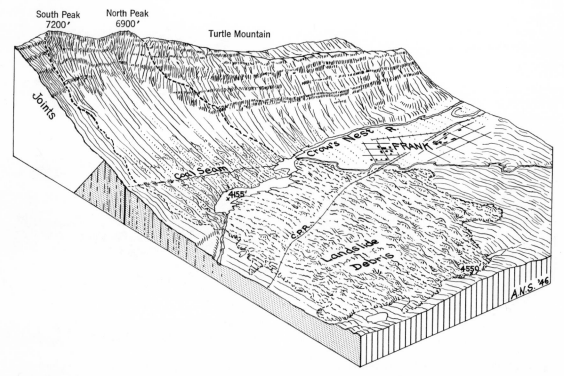

Figure 22.27 A classic example of a great, disastrous landslide is the Turtle Mountain slide, which took place at Frank, Alberta, in 1903. A huge mass of limestone slid from the face of Turtle Mountain between South and North peaks, descended to the valley, then continued up the low slope of the opposite valley side until it came to rest as a great sheet of bouldery rock debris. (After Canadian Geological Survey, Dept. of Mines.)

Landslide

Landslide is the rapid sliding of large masses of rock with little or no flowage of the materials in the early stages of the sliding, as characterized the previous types. Two basic forms of landslide are (*a*) *rockslide,* in which the bedrock mass slips on a relatively flat inclined rock plane, such as a fault or bedding plane, and (*b*) *slump,* in which there is backward rotation on a curved up-concave slip plane (Figure 22.26).

Wherever steep mountain slopes occur, there is a possibility of great and disastrous rockslides. In Switzerland, Norway, or the Canadian Rockies, for example, villages built on the floors of steep-sided valleys are sometimes destroyed and their inhabitants killed by the sliding of millions of cubic yards of rock, set loose without any warning (Figures 22.27 and 22.28). Certain kinds of artificial excavations, made in connection with the building of dams, railroads, or highways, may undermine rock masses, causing troublesome landslides. Aside from occasional great catastrophes, rockslides do not have strong geographical influences because of their sporadic occurrence in thinly populated mountainous regions. Small slides may, however, repeatedly block or break an important mountain highway or railway line.

Because rockslides are characteristic of over-steepened topography formed by glaciers, streams, and waves, and of regions having certain geologic characteristics, the basic reasons for the existence of steep slopes favorable to landsliding will be clarified in later chapters.

The second form of landslide produces *slump blocks,* great masses of bedrock or earth that slide downward from a cliff, at the same time rotating backward on a horizontal axis (Figure 22.29). Wherever massive sedimentary strata, usually sandstones or limestones, or lava beds, rest upon weak clay or shale formations, a steep cliff tends to be formed by erosion. As the weak rock is eroded from the cliff base, the cap rock is undermined. When a point of failure is reached, a large block breaks off, sliding down and tilting back along a curving plane of slip. Slump blocks may be as much as a mile or two long and several hundred feet thick. A single block appears as a ridge at the base of the cliff. A closed depression or lake basin may lie between the block and the cliff.

Slumping commonly occurs on a small scale wherever soil or mantle materials are cut away, hence is seen along caving river banks or along a sea cliff.

Rockfall and talus

Most rapid of all mass wasting processes is *rockfall,* the free falling or rolling of single masses of

Figure 22.28 The debris of a landslide in Yellowstone Park, Wyoming, consists of rock masses of all sizes tumbled in a disordered fashion. (Photograph by Douglas Johnson.)

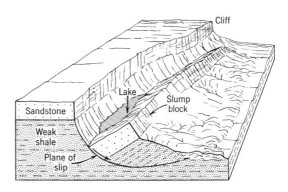

Figure 22.29 Slump blocks rotate backward as they slide from a cliff.

rock from a steep cliff. Individual fragments may be as small as sand grains, or as large as a city block, depending upon the overall scale of the cliff and the manner in which the rock breaks up. Large blocks disintegrate upon falling, strewing the slope below with rubble and leaving a conspicuous scar on the upper cliff face (Figure 22.30).

Where rockfall goes on continuously over long periods of time, yielding a rain of countless individual small fragments at the cliff base, these accumulate in a distinctive landform, the *talus cone,* already referred to as a by-product of rapid frost disintegration on exposed cliff faces at high altitudes or in arctic regions (Figure 22.3). A talus slope, or *scree slope,* as it is often called, has a

Figure 22.31 A talus slope on Specimen Mountain, Colorado. The angular slide rock fragments stand at an angle of about 35°.

Figure 22.30 This rock fall on the Palisades of the Hudson River, just north of the George Washington Bridge, took place in November 1955. About 1200 tons of broken rock fragments resulted from the fall of a large columnar joint block of diabase. (Photograph by *Bergen Evening Record.*)

remarkably constant slope angle of about 35° (Figure 22.31). So long as the talus slope is freshly formed and contains little very fine material mixed in with the coarse, the angle is surprisingly constant within one or two degrees of variation, regardless of the rock type or the shape of the blocks. Most cliffs are notched by narrow ravines which funnel the fragments into individual tracks, so as to produce cone-like talus bodies arranged side by side along the cliff (Figure 22.3). Where a large range of sizes of particles is supplied, the larger pieces, by reason of their greater momentum and ease of rolling, travel to the base of the cone, whereas the tiny

grains lodge in the apex. This tends to sort the fragments by size, progressively finer from base to apex. Most fresh talus slopes are unstable, so that the disturbance created by walking across the slope, or dropping of a large rock fragment from the cliff above, will easily set off a sliding of the surface layer of particles. The upper limiting angle to which coarse, hard, well-sorted rock fragments will stand is termed the *angle of repose*. Other examples of this critical angle of slope are seen in the leeward surfaces (slip faces) of sand dunes and on the side slopes of small volcanic cones.

Review Questions

1. What is the meaning of the term slope? In what way do slopes contribute to the functioning of the hydrologic cycle?

2. Define and distinguish between weathering and mass wasting. Into what two large groups can the weathering processes be divided?

3. Describe four common geometrical forms of rock breakup. For each, name two or three common rock types in which the particular form of breakup might be expected.

4. List the physical processes of weathering. Of these, which require water to be present? Which do not? Which are controlled by changes in air temperature? Which can act deep in the soil or bedrock? Which cannot?

5. What are felsenmeer and talus? Under what climatic environment would they be formed? What process of weathering dominates in such places?

6. How can the growth of salt crystals cause rock disintegration? What climatic conditions favor this process? What forms result?

7. Under what conditions can temperature changes alone cause rock disintegration? What evidence is available that the process is effective?

8. Explain how sheeting structure and exfoliation domes result from unloading. What rock type is most likely to exhibit such structure? Name a locality famous for the display of exfoliation domes.

9. Comment on the effectiveness of plant growth forces in producing the disintegration of rock.

10. What three groups of changes come under the general heading of chemical weathering processes?

11. What is the nature of changes in minerals when hydrolysis takes place? How does hydrolysis promote weathering? What rocks are most susceptible to this type of decay? What are some of the visible forms resulting from hydrolysis in granitic rocks? In basic rocks? How deep in the ground do the effects of hydrolysis extend?

12. How is carbonic acid formed and how does it act on rock? What type of rock is most susceptible? What surface forms are produced? What other acids are commonly found in soil water?

13. What role does mass wasting play in the denudation of the lands? List the evidences of soil creep. What general type of mechanism causes soil creep? Are large rock masses also affected by creep? Explain.

14. Describe an earthflow. How large are earthflows? Under what conditions of season and climate might earthflows be expected to take place? Describe and explain the special features of solifluction.

15. Under what topographic and climatic conditions do mudflows occur? Point out the similarities and differences between a mudflow and a stream.

16. To what kinds of movement and earth material is landslide restricted? Distinguish between rockslide and slump as two basic types of landslide. Describe the topographic and geologic conditions favorable to each of these types.

17. What is rock fall? What sizes of rock masses may be included? How is a talus cone produced and what angle of slope does it normally have? How may the particles of a talus cone be arranged in order of size from apex to base? Explain.

Exercises

Exercise 1. *Exfoliation Domes.* (Source: Yosemite National Park, Calif., U.S. Geological Survey topographic map; scale 1:24:000).

Explanatory Note: North Dome and Basket Dome, two great exfoliation domes of massive granitic intrusive rock rise above the northwest wall of Tenaya Canyon, a branch of Yosemite Valley. These domes are pictured in Figure 22.7, viewed from the south. In the southeastern part of this map is the floor of Tenaya Canyon, a deeply scoured glacial trough. Much rock was removed from the northwest wall of Tenaya Canyon by ice of the Wisconsin glacial stage, causing steep, irregular cliffs. North Dome and Basket Dome, lying above the level of this glacier, escaped modification.

The remarkable fidelity of contours on this map is a tribute to the great topographer-geologist, Francois E. Matthes, who not only surveyed the area and drew the contours, but who also published a comprehensive volume on the geologic history of Yosemite Valley, listed among the reading references.

QUESTIONS

1. (a) What contour interval is used on this map? **(b)** What is the difference in elevation between the summit of Basket Dome and the floor of Tenaya Canyon?

2. (a) Calculate the angle of slope of the southwest side of Basket Dome between 7300 and 7500 feet elevation. **(b)** Do the same for the steepest part of the northeast face of Basket Dome. **(c)** Can you give a geological reason for the fact that Basket Dome is highly unsymmetrical, whereas North Dome is highly symmetrical?

3. Explain the curious angular zigzag bends in the contours at 0.6–0.4[2] and 0.2–0.2. (Examine Figure 22.7 closely.)

4. Note that the topography of the wall of Tenaya Canyon, below 6500 feet elevation is steep, rough, and blocky in comparison with the smooth, broadly rounded slopes at higher elevation. Can you explain this contrast?

[2] On all maps used in the exercises of Chapters 22 through 31 a 1000-yard grid system is marked on the margins of the maps. Locations of places will be given in grid coordinates as explained on p. 52.

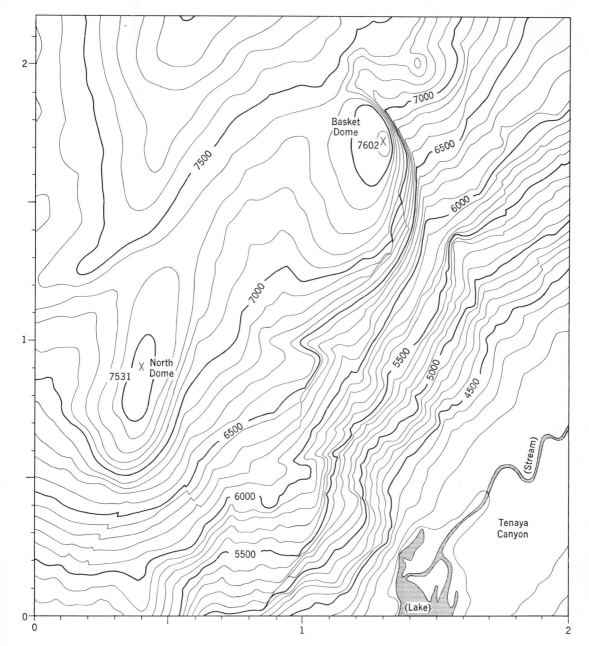

Exercise 1

Exercise 2. _Landslide._ (Source: Map 57*A*, Frank, Alta., Geological Survey of Canada; scale 1:9,600.)

Explanatory Note: The great Turtle Mountain landslide of April 29, 1903, is shown on this map, modified from a special large-scale map made during an investigation of the cause of the disastrous slide, which wiped out a part of the town of Frank, Alberta, taking the lives of 70 persons. Figure 22.27 is a block diagram of this area and gives a geological cross section. Between North Peak and South Peak, on Turtle Mountain, a great mass of limestone slid away, descending about 2500 feet to the Crow's Nest River. As the rock mass disintegrated into rubble a flowage movement developed; the momentum of the 35 to 40 million cubic yards of material was so great as to carry some debris 400 feet above river level on the east side of the valley.

On this map, limits of the slide are shown by a dashed line. Contour interval is reduced within the area of debris east of the river in order to show details of the topography. Series of dashed lines on Turtle Mountain in the vicinity of 0.3–0.7 represent open cracks, or fissures, in the limestone, which are fractures produced at the time of the landslide. (For further information on this slide see a report by R. A. Daly et al. listed among the reading references.)

QUESTIONS

1. (a) What two contour intervals are used on this map? **(b)** What is the length, in miles, of the landslide area, measured from South Peak (0.3–0.3) to 3.6–1.5?

2. (a) What is the elevation of the hachured contour located at 2.4–1.2? **(b)** at 3.3–1.4? **(c)** What is the summit elevation of the hill of landslide debris at 2.2–1.0?

3. Taking the volume of debris of the landslide east of the Crow's Nest River to be 30 million cubic yards, what average thickness has the landslide debris within the limits of the slide east of the river? To compute this roughly, draw in the 500-yard grid lines, then total the area of the squares and part squares included within the dashed line. For a more accurate answer, use 100-yard grid squares.

4. How steep is the east face of Turtle Mountain between the 6000-foot contour at 0.68–1.50 and the 5000-foot contour at 0.96–1.50? State this in feet per mile. **(b)** Draw a right triangle whose legs are scaled proportionately to the vertical and horizontal distances obtained in **(a).** Measure the angle of slope from this triangle with a protractor and state the answer in degrees.

5. Draw a profile from 0.0–0.4 to 3.8–1.5. Use a vertical scale equal to the horizontal scale of the map. Draw in the geological cross section as shown in Figure 22.27. Note that the joints in the limestone are inclined a little less than the slope of the mountain side and are probably the planes of fracture on which the block began to slide.

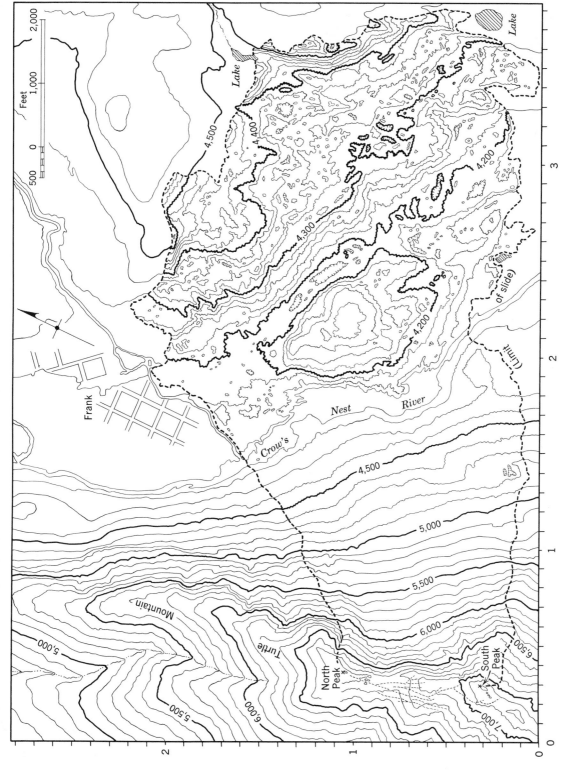

Exercise 2

CHAPTER TWENTY-THREE

Runoff

IN earlier chapters we followed the hydrologic cycle from the water vapor phase in air masses through precipitation and evapotranspiration to infiltration as subsurface water. The cycle is now completed by *runoff*, which consists of all surface water flow, both over the land slopes and in streams. Runoff may be derived directly from excessive precipitation which cannot infiltrate the soil, or it may originate as the outflow of ground water along lines where the water table intersects the earth's surface.

Seeking to escape to progressively lower levels and eventually to the sea, runoff becomes organized into *drainage systems*, which we may describe as more or less pear-shaped areas bounded by divides, within which ground slopes and branching stream networks are adjusted to dispose as efficiently as possible of the runoff and its contained load of mineral particles, and thus to lower the land surfaces progressively toward the ultimate goal of the processes of denudation—reduction to a nearly featureless plain close to sea level. Most drainage systems possess a constricted exit, normally the mouth of the master stream, where it meets a large

above: Running rapids of the Colorado River in Grand Canyon. Photograph by Eddy, from Ewing Galloway.

body of water. Thus, a drainage system is a converging mechanism funneling and integrating the weaker and more diffuse forms of runoff into progressively deeper and more intense paths of activity.

The study of drainage systems brings us in contact with two fields of science, hydrology and geology. Much of the study of the water itself, particularly as to the quantities of water involved in runoff and their variations in response to precipitation, is done by hydrologists, who are affiliated with the profession of civil engineering. The study of streams in eroding and transporting rock materials, so as to shape the landforms of drainage systems, is done by geologists. In the United States, both groups pool their efforts in the analysis and solution of problems of both runoff and ground water under the Water Resources Division of the U.S. Geological Survey, to which is given the responsibility for assessing the surface and ground water resources of the nation. Many facets of the work of that agency will be touched upon in this chapter; also the work of the Forest Service, which studies problems of runoff in the nation's forests, and the Soil Conservation Service, which is concerned with the effects of runoff in causing land erosion and related agricultural problems. Runoff problems concerned with the improvement of irrigation works and navigable waterways are dealt with by engineers and scientists of the Bureau of Reclamation and the U.S. Army Corps of Engineers.

Runoff and geography

For the geography student, runoff is a subject of vital concern as a basic natural resource upon which agricultural and industrial development are heavily dependent. Runoff held in reservoirs behind dams provides water supplies for great urban centers, such as New York City and Los Angeles; diverted from large rivers, it provides irrigation water for highly productive lowlands in arid lands, such as the Imperial Valley of California and the Nile Valley of Egypt. To these uses are added hydroelectric power, where the drop of the river is steep; or routes of inland navigation, where the drop is gentle.

As with ground water, the available sources of surface water are fast being fully exploited in heavily populated areas. More and more attention is being paid to reducing various forms of waste of useful water, making a larger proportion available for man's productive use. In underdeveloped lands, many proposed improvements in the agricultural and industrial economy require development of surface and ground water resources. A geographer analyzing the potential of such regions will need to understand the principles of runoff if he is to make realistic appraisals of the available water resources.

Forms of overland flow

Runoff that flows down the slopes of the land in more or less broadly distributed films, sheets, or rills is referred to as *overland flow* in distinction with *channel flow*, or *stream flow*, in which the water occupies a distinct narrow trough confined by lateral banks. Within this broad definition, overland flow can take many forms. It may be a continuous thin film, called *sheet flow*, where the soil or rock surface is extremely smooth, or a series of tiny rivulets connecting one water-filled hollow with another, where the ground is rough or pitted. On a grass-covered slope, overland flow is subdivided into countless tiny threads of water, passing around the stems. Even in a heavy and prolonged rain, overland flow in full progress on a sloping lawn may not be visible to the casual observer. On heavily forested slopes bearing a thick mat of decaying leaves and many fallen branches and tree trunks, overland flow may pass almost entirely concealed beneath this cover.

Intermediate in classification between overland flow and channel flow is flow in shallow *shoestring rills*, which may score the hillside surface as a system of long, parallel lines (Figure 23.4). In some cases, shoestring rills are merely seasonal features,

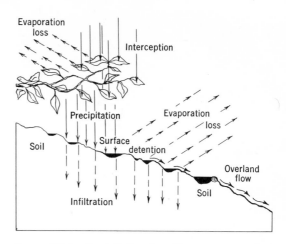

Figure 23.1 Precipitation is subject to evaporation, interception, and surface detention before infiltrating the soil surface or running off as overland flow.

developed during periods of torrential rain in the spring and summer, but healing over as ground frost heaves the soil during the winter season. Again, shoestring rills may actually represent a permanent change brought on by deforestation or cultivation, in which new stream channels are in the process of formation.

Progress of overland flow

Imagine that a hillside slope which has been thoroughly drained of moisture in a period of drought is subjected to a period of rain. What are the successive stages in the production of overland flow? If heavy vegetation such as forest is present, much of the rain at the beginning is held in droplets on the leaves and plant stems, a process termed *interception*. This water may be returned directly to the atmosphere by evaporation, so that if the rainfall is brief, little water reaches the ground. As explained in Chapter 21, the ground surface is capable of absorbing by infiltration even a heavy rain in the early stages of a rain period. Therefore, unless the rain continues for an hour or so, no overland flow may be expected. Soon, however, the soil passages are sealed or obstructed, dropping the infiltration rate to a low, but constant value. Any excessive precipitation now remains on the ground surface, first accumulating in small puddles or pools which occupy natural hollows in the rough ground surface or are held behind tiny check dams formed by fallen leaves and twigs (Figure 23.1). *Surface detention* is the term applied to the holding of water on a slope by such small natural containers. Assuming that the rain continues to fall with sufficient intensity, water then overflows from hollow to hollow, becoming true overland flow.

Figure 23.2 Overland flow running down an 8 per cent slope following a heavy thunderstorm. The ditch in the foreground receives the runoff and conducts it away as channel flow. (Soil Conservation Service photograph.)

Because any given square unit of ground on a hill side must receive the overland flow from the entire strip of ground of that width lying upslope of it, we may expect the rate of discharge (volume of water passing across a given line in a given unit of time) to increase in direct proportion to the length of the total path of flow. Depth of the flowing layer might therefore be expected to increase the farther downslope it progresses, but this increase may be small because the flow velocity will also be increasing down the slope. Figure 23.2 shows heavy runoff at the base of a long slope, where the accumulated overland flow has converged into broad shallow streams spreading across the slope.

At the base of a hill slope, overland flow is disposed of by passing into a stream channel or lake, or by sinking into the ground, should a highly permeable layer of sand, gravel, or blocky slide rock be encountered.

Overland flow is measured in inches of water per hour, just as for precipitation and infiltration. Therefore, a simple formula expresses the rate at which overland flow will be produced by a given unit of ground surface as follows:

Rate of production of overland flow = rate of precipitation − rate of infiltration

For example, if the rate of infiltration became constant at a value of 0.4 inches per hour, and the rate of rainfall was a steady 0.6 inches per hour (a heavy rain), the runoff would be produced at a rate of 0.2 inches per hour, assuming none to be returned to the atmosphere by evaporation.

Accelerated land erosion

Overland flow, by exerting a dragging force over the soil surface, picks up particles of mineral matter ranging in size from fine clay to coarse sand or gravel, depending on the speed of the flow and the degree to which the particles are bound by plant rootlets or held down by a mat of leaves. Added to this solid matter is dissolved mineral matter produced by acid reactions or direct solution. Such slow removal of soil is part of the natural geological process of land-mass denudation and is both inevitable and universal. Under stable, natural conditions, the erosion rate in a humid climate is slow enough that a soil with distinct horizons is formed and maintained, enabling vegetation to maintain itself. Soil scientists refer to this state of affairs as the *geologic norm*.

By contrast, the rate of soil erosion may be enormously speeded up through man-made activities or rare natural events to result in a state of *accelerated erosion*, removing the soil much faster than it can be formed. This condition comes about most commonly from a change in the conditions of vegetative cover and physical state of the ground surface. Destruction of vegetation by clearing of land for cultivation, or by forest fires, directly causes great changes in the relative proportions of infiltration to runoff. Interception of rain by foliage is ended; protection afforded by a ground cover of fallen leaves and stems is removed. Consequently the rain falls directly upon the mineral soil.

Direct force of falling drops (Figure 23.3) causes a geyserlike splashing in which soil particles are lifted and then dropped into new positions, a process termed *splash erosion*. It is estimated that a violent rainstorm has the ability to disturb as much as 100 tons of soil per acre. On a sloping ground surface, splash erosion tends to shift the soil slowly downhill. A more important effect is to cause the soil surface to become much less able to infiltrate water because the natural soil openings become sealed by particles shifted by raindrop splash. Reduced infiltration permits a much greater proportion of overland flow to occur from rain of given intensity and duration. The depth and velocity of overland flow then increase greatly, intensifying the rate of soil removal.

Another effect of destruction of vegetation is to reduce greatly the resistance of the ground surface to the force of erosion under overland flow. On a slope covered by grass sod, even a deep layer of overland flow causes little soil erosion because the energy of the moving water is dissipated in friction with the grass stems, which are tough and elastic. Similarly on a heavily forested slope, countless check dams made by leaves, twigs, roots, and fallen

Figure 23.3 A large raindrop (*above*) lands on a wet soil surface, producing a miniature crater (*below*). Grains of clay and silt are thrown into the air and the soil surface is disturbed. (Official U.S. Navy Photograph.)

tree trunks take up the force of overland flow. Without such vegetative cover the eroding force is applied directly to the bare soil surface, easily dislodging the grains and sweeping them downslope.

Summarizing these things, we may state that the eroding capacity of overland flow is directly proportional to the rate of precipitation and length of slope, but inversely proportional to both the infiltration capacity of the soil and the resistance of the surface. To complete this equation, we need only to add the effect of the steepness of ground slope. Obviously, the steeper the slope of ground, the faster is the flow and the more intense the erosion. We therefore add that the eroding capacity of overland flow increases directly with angle of

Figure 23.4 Shoestring rills on a barren slope indicate severe soil erosion. (Soil Conservation Service photograph.)

slope. As the slope angle approaches the vertical, however, erosion will become less intense from overland flow because the ground surface intercepts much less of the vertically falling rain.

Forms of accelerated erosion

When a plot of ground is first cleared of forest and ploughed for cultivation, little erosion will occur until the action of rain splash has broken down the soil aggregates and sealed the larger opening. Following this, overland flow begins to remove the soil in rather uniform thin layers, a process termed *sheet erosion.* Because of seasonal cultivation, the effects of sheet erosion are often little noticed until the upper horizons of the soil (*A* and *B* horizons) are removed or greatly thinned. Reaching the base of the slope, where the angle of surface is rapidly reduced to meet the valley bottom, soil particles come to rest and accumulate in a thickening layer termed *colluvium,* or simply *slope wash.* This, too, has a sheetlike distribution and may be little noticed, except where it can be seen that fence posts or tree trunks are being slowly buried. Material that continues to be carried by overland flow to reach a stream in the valley axis is then carried further down valley and may be built up into layers on the valley floor, where it becomes *alluvium,* a word applied generally to any stream-laid deposits. Colluvium and alluvium together are described as products of *sedimentation,* the opposite process from erosion. In many ways, sedimentation at the base of slopes and in valley bottoms is a process equally serious to erosion from the agricultural standpoint, because it results in burial of soil horizons under relatively infertile, sandy layers and may choke the valleys of small streams, causing the water to flood broadly over the valley bottoms.

Where slopes are exceptionally steep and runoff from storms is exceptionally heavy, sheet erosion progresses into a more intense activity, that of *rill erosion,* or *rilling* (Figure 23.4), in which innumerable, closely spaced channels, already referred to as *shoestring rills,* are scored into the soil and subsoil. If these rills are not destroyed by soil tillage, they may soon begin to integrate into still larger channels, termed *gullies.* This comes about as the more active rills deepen more rapidly than their neighbors and incorporate the adjacent drainage areas. Erosive action thus is concentrated into a few large channels which deepen into steep-walled, canyonlike trenches whose upper ends grow progressively upslope (Figure 23.5). Ultimately, a rugged, barren topography, resembling the badland forms of the arid climates (Chapter 25), may result from accelerated soil erosion allowed to proceed unchecked. Curative measures developed by the Soil Conservation Service have proved effective in stopping accelerated soil erosion and permitting the return to slow erosion rates approaching the geologic norm. These measures include construction of terraces to reduce slope angle and distance of overland flow, permanent restoration of overly steep slope belts to dense vegetative cover, and the healing of gullies by placing check dams in the gully floors.

Stream channels

The channel of a stream may be thought of as a long, narrow trough, shaped by the forces of flowing water to be most effective in moving the quantities of water and sediment supplied from the drainage basin or watershed. Channels may be so narrow that one can jump across them, or as wide as a mile or so for great rivers such as the Mississippi. Taking the entire range of natural channel widths as between one foot and one mile, a 5000-fold difference in size can exist.

Hydraulic engineers who must measure stream dimensions and flow rates have adopted a set of terms to describe channel geometry (Figure 23.6). *Depth,* in feet, is measured at any specified point in the stream as the vertical distance from surface to bed. Width is the distance in feet across the stream from one water's edge to the other. *Cross-sectional area, A,* is the area in square feet of a vertical slice across the stream at any specified place. *Wetted perimeter, P,* is the length in feet of the line of contact between the water and the channel, as measured from the cross section. An important characteristic of streams is the *hydraulic radius, R,* which is defined as the cross-sectional area, A, divided by the wetted perimeter, P, or $R = A/P$. Another important ratio expressing channel geometry is *form ratio,* defined as depth,

d, divided by width, w, or d/w. Form ratio is commonly stated as a simple fraction such as $\frac{1}{100}$ or $1:100$, meaning that the stream channel is 100 times as wide as it is deep. Finally, a most important measure is *slope*, S, (or *gradient*), which is the angle between the water surface and the horizontal plane. Slope can be stated in feet per mile. Thus a slope of five feet per mile means that the stream surface undergoes a vertical drop of five feet for each mile of horizontal distance downstream. Slope can also be given in terms of *per cent grade*, a common practice in engineering. A grade of 3 per cent, or 0.03, means that the stream drops 3 feet for every 100 feet of horizontal distance.

Stream flow

Gravity acts upon the water of a stream to exert pressure against the confining walls. A small part of the gravitational force is aimed downstream parallel with the surface and bed, causing flow. Resisting the force of downstream flow is the force of resistance, or friction, between the water and the floor and sides of the channel. As a result, water close to the bed and banks moves slowly; that in the deepest and most centrally located zone flows fastest. Figure 23.6 indicates by dotted lines the manner in which flow takes place, or the *velocity distribution*. We can imagine that each dot is a given drop of water and that we observe its subsequent positions at equal time intervals. The single line of highest velocity is located in midstream, if the channel is straight and symmetrical, but about one-third of the distance down from surface to bed.

The above statements about velocity need to be qualified. Actually, in all but the most sluggish streams, the water is affected by *turbulence*, a system of innumerable eddies that are continually forming and dissolving. Therefore, a particular molecule of water, if we could keep track of it, would actually describe a highly irregular, corkscrew path as it is swept downstream. Motions would include upward, downward, and sideward directions. Turbulence in streams is extremely important because of the upward elements of flow that lift and support fine particles of sediment. The murky, turbid appearance of streams in flood is ample evidence of turbulence, without which sediment would remain near the bed. Only if we measure the water velocity at a certain fixed point for a long period of time, say several minutes, will the average motion at that point be downstream and in a line parallel with the surface and bed. It is such average values that are shown by the arrows in Figure 23.6.

Because the average velocity at a given point in a stream differs greatly according to whether it is

Figure 23.5 This great gully, eroded into deeply weathered mantle material, was typical of certain parts of the Piedmont region of South Carolina and Georgia before remedial measures were applied. (Soil Conservation Service photograph.)

being measured close to the banks and bed, or out in the middle line, a single figure, the *mean velocity*, is computed for the entire cross section to express the activity of the stream as a whole. Mean velocity in streams is commonly equal to about six-tenths of the maximum velocity, but depends on the relative depth of the stream.

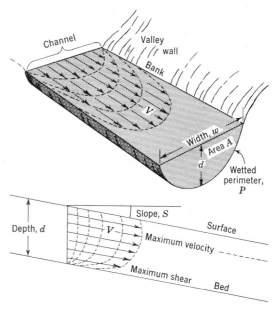

Figure 23.6 Geometry of a stream channel and relative speeds of water flow.

Figure 23.7 This stilling tower on Fish Greek, near Duarte, California, houses gages for recording stream flow. (U.S. Geological Survey photograph.)

The last and most important measure of stream flow is *discharge*, *Q*, defined as the volume of water passing through a given cross section of the stream in a given unit of time. Commonly, discharge is stated in cubic feet per second, abbreviated to *cfs*. Sometimes the hydraulic engineer simply states this quantity as *second feet*. Discharge may be obtained by taking the mean velocity, *V*, and multiplying it by cross-sectional area, *A*. This relationship is stated by the important equation, $Q = AV$.

Stream gaging

An important activity of the U.S. Geological Survey is the measurement, or gaging, of stream flow in the United States. In cooperation with states and municipalities this organization maintains over 6000 river-measurement stations on principal streams and their tributaries. The figures on discharge thus obtained are published by the Geological Survey in a series of *Water-Supply Papers*. Information on daily discharge and flood discharges is essential for planning the distribution and development of surface waters as well as for design of flood-protection structures and for the prediction of floods as they progress down a river system.

A stream gaging station requires a device for measuring the height of the water surface, or *stage* of the stream. Simplest to install is a *staff gage*, which is simply a graduated stick permanently attached to a post or bridge pier. This must be read directly by an observer whenever the stage is to be

recorded. More useful is an automatic-recording gage, which is mounted in a *stilling tower* built beside the river bank (Figure 23.7). The tower is simply a hollow masonry shaft filled by water which enters through a pipe at the base. By means of a float connected by cable to a recording mechanism above, a continuous ink-line record of the stream stage is made on a graph paper attached to a slowly rotating drum.

To measure stream discharge, it is necessary to determine both the area of cross section of the stream and the mean velocity. This requires that a *current meter* (Figure 23.8) be lowered into the stream at closely spaced intervals so that the velocity can be read at a large number of points evenly distributed in a grid pattern through the stream's cross section (Figure 23.9). A bridge often serves as a convenient means of crossing over the stream; otherwise a cable car or small boat is used. The current meter uses either a metal propellor or set of revolving cups whose rate of turning is proportional to current velocity. The Price current meter, pictured in Figure 23.8, is in general use by the Geological Survey and will measure velocities from one-fifth to 20 feet per second. As the velocities are being measured from point to point, a profile of the river bed is also made by sounding the depth. Thus, a profile is drawn and the cross-sectional area is measured from the profile. Mean velocity is computed by summing all individual velocity readings and dividing by the number of readings. Discharge can then be computed using the formula, $Q = AV$.

Because of the time and labor required to measure discharge repeatedly by current readings, it is practical to take instead only a limited set of such measurements over a wide range of discharges. From these measured discharges is constructed a *rating curve*, or *stage-discharge curve*, permitting discharge to be estimated directly from gage height. For the sample curve in Figure 23.10, eight points of discharge were actually measured by the current meter method. These were plotted on the graph against gage height in feet. A smooth curve was then drawn through the points. Thus if the gage height is known to be 20 feet, we can estimate that the discharge is occurring at a rate of about 16,500 cfs. Rating curves enable estimates of total discharge to be computed from stage records alone, despite wide fluctuations in stage.

A single rating curve may be useful only for limited periods of time because of changes in form of the river channel. Such changes may take place by channel erosion in floods. The rating curve is therefore recomputed and corrected as necessity demands.

Examples of channel characteristics

To illustrate the various geometrical and flow characteristics explained in the preceding paragraphs, two relatively large American streams are compared in Figure 23.11. The Columbia River at the International Boundary is chosen as an example of relatively deep river, in which the form ratio is large. The Platte River at Duncan, Nebraska, illustrates a broad, shallow stream channel in which the form ratio is small. Although of the same width as the Columbia River, the Platte is only one-fourth as deep at the deepest spot and has a hydraulic radius about one-eighth as great. The Columbia is a vastly greater stream in terms of its discharge, which is about 26 times greater than that of the Platte. A striking and important difference in these two rivers is the slope: 2.2 feet per mile for the Columbia, against 5.6 for the Platte. It is characteristic of broad, shallow channels engaged in carrying relatively large quantities of coarse sediment, that the gradients are markedly steeper than those of comparable deep-channel streams.

Of course, the comparisons shown in Figure 23.11 appy only to conditions on a given day. In the absence of a vast quantity of data on these and many other factors throughout the yearly cycle, we would not be safe in comparing the two rivers in a meaningful way.

Stream flow and precipitation

By studying the records of stream discharge in relation to precipitation on a given watershed, the hydrologist has developed a set of basic principles applying to the variations in stream discharge with different lengths and intensities of storms and with different sizes of watersheds.

Consider first a very small watershed, just over one acre in area, upon which a heavy rain fell in a total period of about an hour. Figure 23.12 is a graph showing what happened to the water from beginning to end of the storm. Rainfall was measured with the rain gage and is shown in terms of the intensity of rainfall, or quantity falling in

Figure 23.8 In gaging large rivers, the current meter is lowered on a cable by a power winch. Earphones, connected by wires to the meter, receive a series of clicks whose frequency indicates water velocity. (U.S. Geological Survey photograph.)

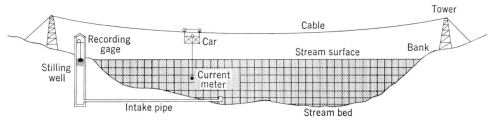

Figure 23.9 Idealized diagram of stream gaging installation.

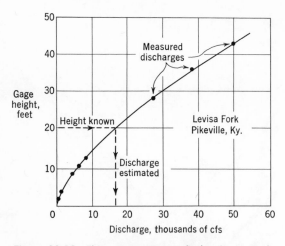

Figure 23.10 This rating curve applied to Levisa Fork, Kentucky, during the period October 1945 to January 1946. (After Hoyt and Langbein, *Floods.*)

COLUMBIA RIVER, Internat. Boundary 12 June 1948:

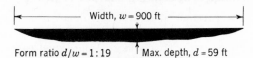

Form ratio $d/w = 1:19$ Max. depth, $d = 59$ ft

Cross-sectional area, $A = 42{,}300$ ft^2
Wetted perimeter, $P = 918$ ft
Hydraulic radius, $R = A/P = 46$ ft
Slope, $S = 2.2$ ft/mile
Discharge, $Q = 534{,}000$ cfs
Mean velocity, $V = 12.6$ ft/sec

PLATTE RIVER, Duncan, Neb., 25 June 1947:

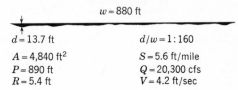

$d = 13.7$ ft	$d/w = 1:160$
$A = 4{,}840$ ft^2	$S = 5.6$ ft/mile
$P = 890$ ft	$Q = 20{,}300$ cfs
$R = 5.4$ ft	$V = 4.2$ ft/sec

Figure 23.11 Hydraulic characteristics of two rivers: a relatively deep river, the Columbia; a relatively shallow river, the Platte. (Data from A. O. Woodford, and U.S. Geological Survey.)

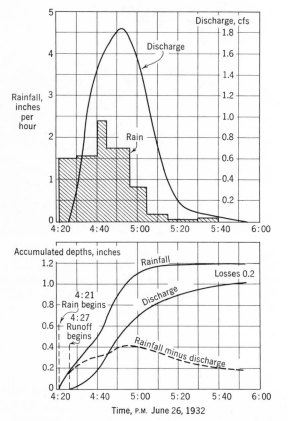

Figure 23.12 This hydrograph accounts for the receipt and outflow of water for a very small drainage area of about one acre near Hays, Kansas, during a rainstorm on June 26, 1932. (After E. E. Foster, *Rainfall and Runoff.*)

each 5- or 10-minute period. Rain began at 4:21 P.M. and was extremely heavy for nearly 40 minutes, after which it let up rapidly and ceased entirely by 5:40. Discharge, measured at the outlet point of the small watershed, is shown in Figure 23.12 by a smooth curve scaled in cubic feet per second. Because of the high initial infiltration capacity of the soil, all of the rain was at first absorbed by the soil or was detained in surface irregularities. About 6 minutes after the rain began, discharge set in and rose rapidly for a half hour, reached the peak just after 4:50, then declined again and became zero by 5:50 P.M.

The lower part of Figure 23.12 is another form of representation in which the quantities of rainfall and runoff are accumulated from beginning to end. Here both discharge and rainfall are scaled in terms of inches of water depth, so that the values can be directly subtracted. At the end of the storm, about 5:40 P.M., a total of 1.2 inches of rain had fallen, but only about 1.0 inch of water had been disposed of by runoff. This leaves 0.2 inches of loss through combined evaporation and infiltration. An important principle of this water graph, or *hydrograph*, as it is generally called, is that for a small watershed, the response of runoff to rainfall is rapid, with little time lag between. Let us now look at the hydrographs of larger areas over longer periods of time to see the effect of watershed size and storm duration on stream flow.

Figure 23.13 shows the hydrograph of Sugar Creek, Ohio, with a watershed area of 310 square

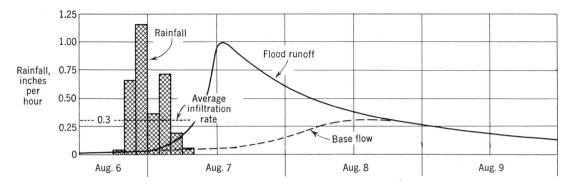

Figure 23.13 Four days of flow of Sugar Creek, Ohio, illustrate passage of a flood on a stream draining 310 square miles. (After Hoyt and Langbein, *Floods*.)

miles. Sugar Creek basin, a part of the much larger Muskingum River watershed, is outlined in Figure 23.14, a map showing by isohyetal lines the rainfall during the twelve-hour storm of August 6–7, 1935, for which the hydrograph was constructed. Over the area of Sugar Creek the average total rainfall was 6.3 inches for the entire storm, but the total quantity discharged by Sugar Creek was only 3.0 inches. This means that 3.3 inches, or more than half of the rainfall, was retained on the watershed, having infiltrated to become part of the soil and ground water, or had evaporated.

Studying the rainfall and runoff graphs in Figure 23.13, we see that prior to the onset of the storm, Sugar Creek was carrying a small discharge. This was being supplied by the seepage of ground water into the channel and is termed *base flow*. After the heavy rainfall began several hours elapsed before the stream gage at the basin mouth began to show a rise in discharge. This time interval is known as the *lag* and indicated that the branching system of channels was acting as a temporary reservoir, receiving inflow more rapidly than it could be passed down the channel system to the stream gage. The term *channel storage* is applied to runoff delayed in this manner during the early period of a storm.

The peak of flow in Sugar Creek was reached almost 24 hours after the rain began, or about 6 hours after the cessation of rainfall—a vastly greater delay than was observed in the one-acre plot previously studied (Figure 23.12). Note also that the rate of decline in discharge was much slower than the rate of rise. In general, then, we may reason that the larger a watershed, the larger is the lag of time between peak rainfall and peak discharge; the more gradual is the rate of decline of discharge after the peak has passed. Because much rainfall had entered the ground and had reached the water table, a slow but distinct rise is seen in the amount of discharge contributed by base flow.

Base flow and surface water flow

In regions of humid climates, where the water table is high and normally intersects the important stream channels, the hydrographs of larger streams will show clearly the effects of two sources of water: (*a*) *base flow* and (*b*) *surface water flow*. Figure 23.15 is a hydrograph of the Chattahoochee River, Georgia, a large river draining a watershed of some 3350 square miles, much of it in the humid southern Appalachian Mountains. The sharp, abrupt fluctuations in discharge are produced by overland flow, or surface flow, following rain periods of one to three days duration. These are each similar to the hydrograph of Figure 23.13, except

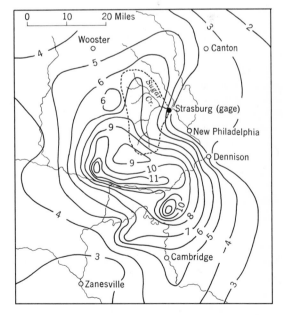

Figure 23.14 By means of isohyets the relation of total rainfall to Sugar Creek Watershed in Ohio can be seen for the rainstorm of Aug. 6–7, 1935. (After Hoyt and Langbein, *Floods*.)

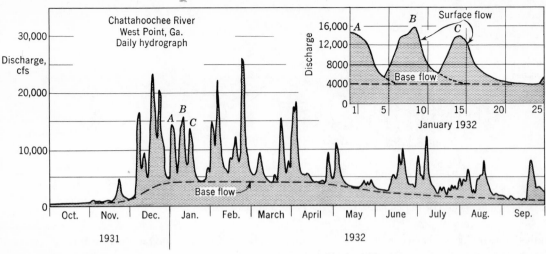

Figure 23.15 Individual rainstorms (*A*, *B*, and *C*) cause sharp peaks in the flow of the Chattahoochee River. (After E. E. Foster, *Rainfall and Runoff.*)

that they are here shown much compressed by the time scale.

After each rain period the discharge falls off rapidly, but if another storm occurs within a few days, the discharge rises to another peak. The enlarged inset graph, showing details of the month of January, shows how this effect occurs. Where a long period intervenes between storms, the discharge falls to a low value, the base flow, where it levels off. Throughout the year the base flow, which represents ground water inflow into the stream, undergoes a marked annual cycle. During the period of recharge (winter and early spring), water table levels are raised and the rate of inflow into streams is increased. For the Chattahoochee River, the rate of base flow during January, February, March, and April holds uniform at about 4000 cfs. As the heavy evapotranspiration losses of spring reduce soil water, and therefore cut off the recharge of ground water by downward percolation (See Chapter 21), the base flow falls steadily. The decline continues through the summer, reaching by the end of October a low of about 1000 cfs supplied entirely from base flow.

With a knowledge of climate characteristics and rock types to guide our reasoning, it may be guessed that base flow will be important in regions of ample, well-distributed rainfall, but unimportant or absent in semi-arid and arid regions.

Figure 23.16 shows comparative hydrographs for one-year periods for three watersheds of approximately the same areas. That of Ecofina Creek, Florida, is unusual in showing a large proportion of base flow and lack of strong discharge peaks.

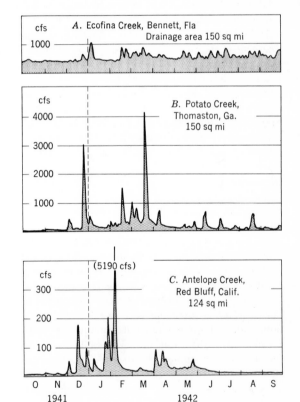

Figure 23.16 Hydrographs of three streams differ because of differences in climate, relief, and rock type. (After E. E. Foster, *Rainfall and Runoff.*)

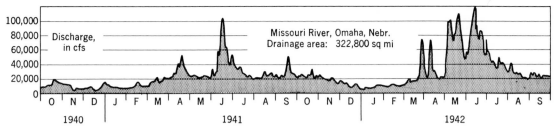

Figure 23.17 Annual fluctuations in discharge of the Missouri River follow a distinct cycle. (After E. E. Foster, *Rainfall and Runoff*.)

The explanation may lie partly in the low relief and gentle slopes of the watershed, but more particularly in the presence of cavernous limestone beneath the surface. Most of the excess rainfall enters the ground water system and is discharged copiously through solution passages. Potato Creek, Georgia, in a region of steep slopes, has occasional extreme peak flows that occur in winter and early spring when soil moisture is excessive and the proportion of surface runoff is high. Antelope Creek, gaged at Red Bluff, California, in the northern part of the state, likewise shows the extreme discharges typical of mountain watersheds, but the complete absence of peaks from June through October reflects the long summer drought of the Mediterranean-type climate, during which only base flow can be maintained.

Finally, examine the hydrograph of the Missouri River at Omaha, Nebraska, from October 1940, to September 1942 (Figure 23.17). This great river, draining 322,800 square miles of watershed, is a major tributary of the Mississippi River. Note that the discharge, ranging from 10,000 to over 100,000 cfs, is many times greater than the discharges of smaller streams considered thus far. High rates of flow are chiefly from snowmelt, which occurs on the High Plains in spring and in the Rocky Mountain headwater areas in early summer. This explains the sudden high discharges from April through June. During midwinter, when soil moisture is frozen and total precipitation small over the watershed as a whole, the discharge rises little above the base flow. Ground water recharge occurring in the spring raises summer levels of base flow to about 20,000 cfs, or two to three times the winter base flow.

Floods

In our modern day of newspapers, movies, and television, everyone has seen enough pictures of river floods to have a good idea of the appearance of flood waters and the havoc wrought by their erosive power and by the silt and clay that they leave behind. Nevertheless, even the hydraulic engineer may not be fully satisfied that he can exactly define the term *flood*. Perhaps it is enough to say that a condition of flood exists when the discharge of a river cannot be accommodated within the margins of its normal channel, so that the water spreads over adjoining ground upon which crops or forests are able to flourish. Most of our larger streams have a *flood plain*, a belt of low flat ground bordering the channel on one or both sides inundated by stream waters about once a year, at the season when abundant supplies of surface water combine with effects of a high water table and ample soil moisture to supply more runoff than can stay within the heavily scoured troughlike channel (Figure 23.18). Such annual inundation is considered a flood, even though its occurrence is expected and does not prevent the cultivation of crops after the flood has subsided, nor does it interfere with the growth of dense forests which are widely distributed over low, marshy flood plains in all humid regions of the world. Still higher discharges of water, the rare and disastrous floods which may occur as infrequently as a decade or longer, inundate ground lying above the flood plain, principally affecting broad steplike expanses of ground known as *terraces* (Figure 23.19).

Figure 23.18 The Kootenay River, near the 49th parallel of latitude in British Columbia, is seen here in a flood of 1922 that has inundated all of the flood plain except the natural levees. (Photograph by Bartlett, Geological Survey of Canada.)

Figure 23.19 The city of Hartford was partly inundated by the Connecticut River flood of March 1936. The river channel is to the left, its banks marked by a line of trees. (Official Photograph, 8th Photo Section, A. C., U.S. Army.)

For practical purposes, the U.S. Weather Bureau, which provides a flood-warning service, designates a particular stage or gage height at a given place as the *flood stage*, implying that the critical level has been reached above which overbank flooding may be expected to set in. Immediately at or below flood stage the river may be described as being in the *bankfull stage*, the flow being entirely within the limits of the heavily scoured channel.

Downstream progress of a flood wave

The rise of a river stage to its maximum height, or *crest*, followed by a gradual lowering of stage, is termed the *flood wave*. The flood wave is simply a large-sized rise and fall of river discharge of the type already analyzed in earlier paragraphs, and follows the same principles. Figure 23.20*A* shows

the downstream progress of a flood on the Chattooga-Savannah river system. In the Chattooga River near Clayton, Georgia, the flood peak or crest was quickly reached—one day after the storm—and quickly subsided. On the Savannah River, 65 miles downstream at Calhoun Falls, South Carolina, the peak flow occurred a day later, but the discharge was very much larger because of the larger area of watershed involved. Downstream another 95 miles, near Clyo, Georgia, the Savannah River crested five days after the initial storm with a discharge of over 60,000 cfs. This set of three hydrographs shows that (*a*) the time lag in occurrence of the crest increases downstream, (*b*) the entire period of rise and fall of flood wave becomes longer downstream, and (*c*) the discharge increases greatly downstream as watershed area increases.

Figure 23.20*B* is a somewhat different presentation of the same flood data, in that the discharge is given in terms of a common unit of area, the square mile, thus eliminating the effect of increase in discharge downstream and showing us only the shape or form of the flood crest. In other words, the time lag and sharpness of peaking of the flood wave are emphasized without respect to the total discharges involved.

Flood prediction

The U.S. Weather Bureau operates a River and Flood Forecasting Service through 85 selected offices located at strategic points along major river systems of the United States. Each office issues river and flood forecasts to the communities within the associated district, which is laid out to cover one or more large watersheds. Flood warnings are publicized by every possible means. Close cooperation is maintained with such agencies as the American Red Cross, the U.S. Army Corps of Engineers, and the U.S. Coast Guard, in order to plan evacuation of threatened areas, and the removal or protection of vulnerable property.

Long and intensive study of stream flow data enables the U.S. Weather Bureau to prepare graphs of flood stages telling the likelihood of occurrence of given stages of high water for each month of the year. Figure 23.21 shows expectancy graphs for four selected stations. The meaning of the strange-looking bar symbols is explained in the key. The Mississippi River at Vicksburg illustrates a great river responding largely to spring floods so as to yield a simple annual cycle. The Colorado River at Austin, Texas, is chosen to illustrate a river draining largely semi-arid plains. Summer floods are produced directly by torrential rains from invading moist tropical air masses. Floods of the late summer and fall are often attributable to tropical storms (hurricanes) moving inland from the Gulf of Mexico. The Sacramento River at Red Bluff, California, has a winter flood season when rains are heavy, but a sharp dip to low stages in late summer, which is the very dry period for the California coastal belt. The flood expectancy graph for the Connecticut River at Hartford shows two seasons of floods. The more reliable of the two is the early spring, when snowmelt is rapid over the mountainous New England terrain; the second, in the fall, when rare but heavy rainstorms, some of hurricane origin, bring exceptional high stages. Thus the exceptional maximum flood stage of the month of September was set by the hurricane of September 21–23, 1938, which added an enormous quantity of runoff to channels already carrying bankfull flows from heavy rains of September 18–20.

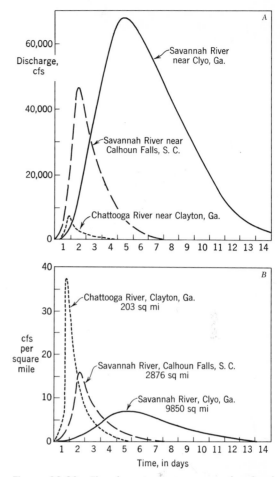

Figure 23.20 The downstream progress of a flood wave is shown on these hydrographs of the Savannah River in South Carolina and Georgia. (After Hoyt and Langbein, *Floods.*)

Flood control

In the face of repeated disastrous floods, vast sums of money have been spent on a wide variety of measures to reduce and control floods. The economic, social, and political aspects of flood control are beyond the scope of this book, but mention can be made of certain physical principles applied to the problem. Two basic forms of control are: (*a*) to detain and delay runoff by various means on the ground surfaces and in smaller tributaries of the watershed; (*b*) to modify the lower reaches of the river where flood-plain inundation is expected.

The first form of control is aimed at treatment of watershed slopes, usually by reforestation or planting of other vegetative cover so as to increase the amount of infiltration and reduce the rate of overland flow. This type of treatment, together

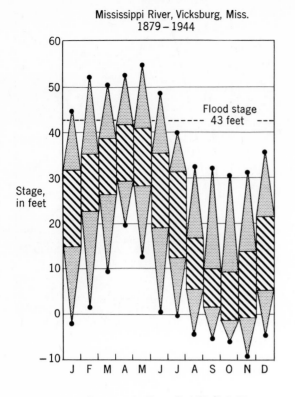

Mississippi River, Vicksburg, Miss.
1879 – 1944

Stage, in feet

Flood stage
43 feet

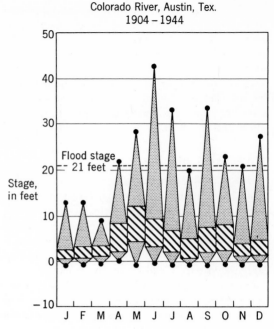

Colorado River, Austin, Tex.
1904 – 1944

Stage, in feet

Flood stage
21 feet

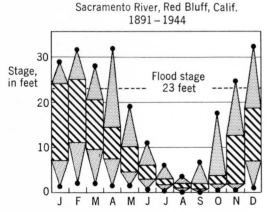

Sacramento River, Red Bluff, Calif.
1891 – 1944

Stage, in feet

Flood stage
23 feet

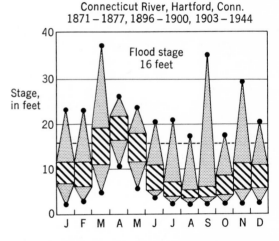

Connecticut River, Hartford, Conn.
1871 – 1877, 1896 – 1900, 1903 – 1944

Stage, in feet

Flood stage
16 feet

Key to flood expectancy graphs

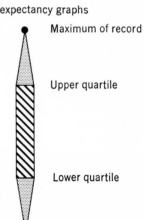

During 25% of the years of record the maximum monthly stage fell in this range

Maximum of record

Upper quartile

During 50% of the years of record the maximum monthly stage fell in this range

During 25% of the years of record the maximum monthly stage fell in this range

Lower quartile

Lowest monthly maximum of record

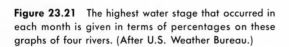

Figure 23.21 The highest water stage that occurred in each month is given in terms of percentages on these graphs of four rivers. (After U.S. Weather Bureau.)

Figure 23.22 This old photograph shows the artificial levee of the Mississippi River near Greenville, Mississippi, during the great flood of March 1903. A crevasse, or break, at the distant point, x, is discharging flood water into the lower flood plain on the left. (Mississippi River Commission photograph.)

with construction of many small flood-storage dams in the valley bottoms, may greatly reduce the flood crests and allow the discharge to pass into the main stream over a longer period of time.

Under the second type of flood control, designed to protect the flood-plain areas directly, two quite different theories can be practiced. First, the building of *levees*, or *dikes*, parallel with the river channel on both sides can function to contain the overbank flow and prevent inundation of the adjacent flood plain (Figure 23.22). Such levees are broad embankments build of earth and must be designed with great care, not only to possess the physical resistance to water pressures, but must be high enough to contain the greatest floods; otherwise they will be breached rapidly by great gaps, termed *crevasses*, at the points where water spills over (Figure 23.23). Under the control of the

Figure 23.23 This great rush of flood water through a crevasse in the Mississippi River levee occurred in April 1922, at Poydras, twelve miles south of New Orleans, Louisiana. (Photograph by E. Green.)

Mississippi River Commission, which began in 1879, a vast system of levees was built along the Mississippi River in the expectation of containing all floods. Figure 23.22 shows such a levee during the flood of 1903, when it was neccessary in Louisiana to add to the top of the levee by means of planks and sand-filled bags for a distance of 71 miles to prevent overflow. Levees have been continuously improved and now total more than 2500 miles in length and in places are as high as 30 feet. Additional levees on the lower, or deltaic, alluvial plain form floodways, by means of which excessive discharges can be diverted in time of flood and passed directly to the sea.

The second theory, practiced in more recent years on the Mississippi River by the U.S. Army Corps of Engineers, is to shorten the river course by cutting channels directly across the great meander loops to provide a more direct river flow. Shortening has the effect of increasing the river slope, which in turn increases the mean velocity. Greater velocity enables a given flood discharge to be moved through a channel of smaller cross-sectional area; the flood stage is correspondingly reduced. Channel improvement has had a measurable effect in reducing flood crests along the lower Mississippi and the levees are thus not in such great danger of being overtopped. Certain parts of the flood plain are also set aside as temporary basins into which the river is to be diverted according to plan to reduce the flood crest. This planned flooding can make use of the least populated parts of the flood plain.

Review Questions

1. What are the general characteristics of a natural drainage system? What is the shape of the drainage basin?

2. What branches of earth science deal with runoff and drainage systems? What governmental agencies take responsibility for various phases of this study? In what ways is a knowledge of principles of runoff of value to the student of geography?

3. Distinguish between overland flow and channel flow. To what extent is overland flow observable? How does flow in shoestring rills fit into this classification of types of flow?

4. Describe the development of overland flow, beginning with the onset of rainfall. What is interception? Surface detention? What equation relates overland flow to precipitation and infiltration?

5. How does the geologic norm of soil erosion differ from accelerated soil erosion? What is the role of splash erosion? What forms of land surface treatment bring about accelerated land erosion? Explain. How is the degree of ground slope a factor in intensity of soil erosion?

6. Describe the successively more severe forms of accelerated soil erosion. What happens to the eroded soil? Distinguish between *colluvium* and *alluvium*. In what ways is sedimentation harmful?

7. List the various geometrical elements of a stream channel, state how each is defined and measured. Explain the meaning of "per cent of grade."

8. Describe the manner in which velocity varies throughout a stream, both across the channel and in vertical section. Why is the velocity not the same in all parts of the stream?

9. What is stream turbulence? What role does it play in stream transportation?

10. What is the mean velocity of a stream? State and explain in words the equation relating discharge to area and mean velocity.

11. Describe the methods and equipment used in stream gaging. What governmental agency is responsible for stream gaging in the United States? How is mean velocity actually measured and computed? What use is made of a rating curve? How is it constructed?

12. What is a hydrograph? Describe the manner in which runoff occurs following a rainstorm on a very small watershed. Why is there a time lag between rainfall and runoff? For larger drainage basins, how do these relationships differ?

13. What is base flow? What supplies base flow? What is channel storage and how does it affect the hydrograph of a large watershed.

14. Describe the annual changes in base flow and surface water contributions in a watershed typical of the humid southeastern United States.

15. How is a flood defined? How can the normal channel of a river be distinguished from the adjacent flood plain? What is the bankfull stage of a stream flow?

16. Describe the progress of a flood crest down a large river. How does discharge change with increasing distance downstream? How does the form of the flood wave change?

17. What government agency supplies river and flood forecasts? How are its activities organized and what is their function?

18. How do flood expectancies differ for the Mississippi River at Vicksburg, Mississippi, and the Colorado River at Austin, Texas? Explain.

19. What basic forms of flood control are used? What principles lie behind each? What are the advantages and disadvantages of constructing extensive levee systems? How can channels be modified to reduce flood crests?

CHAPTER TWENTY-FOUR

Landforms made by streams

FAR from being mere systems for disposal of excess runoff, streams are important agents of land sculpture—the principal carriers of mineral matter from the lands to the oceans. Not only is this denudational role of interest to the geomorphologist, who studies the landforms produced, but also to the student of historical geology for whom the sedimentary strata of past geologic eras can be interpreted in many instances as the deposits brought by streams from ancient land masses.

Geologic work of streams

The geologic work of streams consists of three closely interrelated activities, *erosion, transportation,* and *deposition.* Erosion by a stream is the progressive removal of mineral material from the floor and sides of the channel, whether this be carved in bedrock, residual mantle, or transported mantle. Transportation consists of movement of the eroded particles by dragging along the bed, by suspension in the body of the stream, or in solution. Deposition is the progressive accumulation of transported particles upon the stream bed and flood plain, or on the floor of a standing body of water into which the stream empties. Obviously, erosion cannot occur without some transportation taking place, and the transported particles must

eventually come to rest. Therefore, erosion, transportation, and deposition are simply three phases of a single activity.

Stream erosion

Streams erode in various ways, depending on the nature of the channel materials and the tools with which the current is armed. The force of the flowing water alone, exerting impact and a dragging action upon the bed, can erode poorly consolidated alluvial materials such as sand, gravel silt, and clay, a process termed *hydraulic action.* Where rock particles carried by the swift current strike against bedrock channel walls, chips of rock are detached. The rolling of cobbles and boulders over the stream bed will further crush and grind smaller grains to produce an assortment of grain sizes. These processes of mechanical wear are combined under the term *corrasion,* or *abrasion,* which is the principal means of erosion in bedrock too strong to be affected by simple hydraulic action. Finally, the chemical processes of rock weathering—acid reactions and solution—are effective in removal of rock from the stream channel and may be designated as *corrosion.*

above: The Tennessee River near Calvert City, Kentucky.
Photograph, Ewing Galloway.

Figure 24.1 Potholes in a stream bed near Crater Lake, Oregon. (Photograph by A. K. Lobeck.)

Figure 24.2 A river in flood eroded this huge trench at Cavendish, Vermont, in November 1927. An area one mile wide and three miles long, once occupied by eight farms, was cut away by the flood waters. Damage was great because the material consisted of sand and gravel which offered little resistance. (Photograph by Wide World Photos.)

Effects of corrosion are most marked in limestone, which is a hard rock not easily carved by abrasion, but yielding readily to the action of carbonic acid in solution in the stream water.

One interesting form produced by stream abrasion is the *pothole*, a cylindrical hole carved into the hard bedrock of a swiftly moving stream (Figure 24.1). Potholes range in diameter from a few inches to several feet; the larger ones may be many feet deep. Often a spherical or discus-shaped stone is found in the pothole and is apparently the tool, or *grinder*, with which the pothole was deepened. A spiraling flow of water in the pothole causes the grinder to be rotated at the base of the hole, thus boring gradually into the rock. Many other features of abrasion, such as plunge pools, chutes, and troughs lend variety to the rock channel of a swift mountain stream.

Stream transportation

The load of a stream is carried in three forms; dissolved matter is transported invisibly in the form of chemical ions. All streams carry some dissolved salts resulting from rock decomposition. Clay and silt are carried in *suspension*, that is, held up in the water by the upward elements of flow in turbulent eddies in the stream. This fraction of the transported matter is termed the *suspended load*. Sand, gravel, and still larger fragments move as *bed load* close to the channel floor by rolling or sliding, and an occasional low leap.

The load carried by a stream varies enormously in the total quantity present and the size of the fragments, depending on the discharge and stage of the river. In flood, when velocities of 20 feet per second (13½ miles per hour) or more are produced in large rivers, the water is turbid with suspended load. Boulders of great size may be moving over the stream bed, if the river gradient is steep. Frederick S. Dellenbaugh, a member of Major Powell's boat party which descended the Grand Canyon of the Colorado River in 1871 and 1872, wrote that as the men rested beside the river at night they could feel and hear the dull, thundering impacts of huge boulders rolled over and over on the channel bottom in the swift rapids.

The hydraulic action of flood waters is capable of excavating enormous quantities of unconsolidated materials in a short time (Figure 24.2). Not only is the channel often greatly deepened in flood, but the undermining of the banks causes huge masses of alluvium to slump into the river where the particles are quickly separated and become a part of the stream's load. This process, known as *bank caving*, is an important source of sediment during high river stages, and is associated with rapid sidewise shifts in channel position on the outsides of river bends.

Suspended loads of large rivers

The load carried by a large river is of considerable importance in planning for construction of large storage dams and in the construction of canal systems for irrigation. Sediment will be trapped in the reservoir behind a dam, eventually filling the entire basin and ending the useful life of the reservoir as a storage body. At the same time, depriving the river of its sediment in the lower course below the dam may cause serious upsets in river activity. Resulting deep scour of the bed and lowering of river level may upset the grades of irrigation systems. In designing for canal systems, the forms of artificial channels must be adjusted to the size and quantity of sediment carried by the water, otherwise obstruction by deposition or abnormal scour may follow.

The table opposite gives comparative figures on the sediment loads of rivers in various stages.[1]

Although information is scanty on quantity of sediment moved as bed load, the proportion of suspended load is generally very high. For the Mississippi, 90 per cent of the total load is carried in suspension. The above table shows that rivers draining semi-arid or arid lands (Missouri and Colorado) have very high suspended loads because of the large expanses of barren soil from which sediment is easily swept by overland flow into the stream channels.

[1] Data from G. H. Matthes, "Paradoxes of the Mississippi," *Scientific American*, vol. 184, pp. 19–23, 1951.

How channels change in flood

We tend to think of a river in flood as changing largely through increase in height of water surface, which causes channel overflow and inundation of the adjoining flood plain. Because of the turbidity of the water we cannot see the changes taking place on the stream bed, but these can be determined by sounding the river depth during stream-gaging measurements (Figure 24.3). At first the bed may be built up by large amounts of bed load supplied to the stream during the first phases of heavy runoff. This is soon reversed, however, and the bed is actively deepened by scour as stream stage rises. Thus, in the period of highest stage, the river bed is at its lowest elevation. When the discharge then starts to decline, the level of the stream's surface drops and the bed is built back up by the deposition of alluvium. In the example shown in Figure

	Suspended sediment, parts per million	Fraction by weight
Mississippi River		
Yearly average	550 to 600	1/1800 to 1/1660
Flood stage (up to 2,000,000 cfs)	2,600	1/400
Low stage (70,000 cfs)	50 (water, blue, clear)	1/20,00
Missouri River		
Flood stage	20,000	1/50
Colorado River (before Hoover Dam)		
Flood stage (50,000 to 70,000 cfs)	40,000	1/25
Yellow River, China		
Flood stage	Weight of solids may be greater than weight of water	

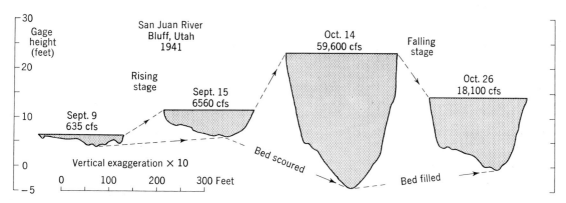

Figure 24.3 A series of cross sections shows changes in channel form of the San Juan River near Bluff, Utah, from early September to late October, 1941, during the progress of a flood. (After Leopold and Maddock, U.S. Geological Survey.)

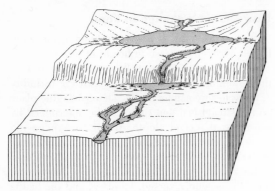

A. In the initial stage a stream has lakes, waterfalls, and rapids.

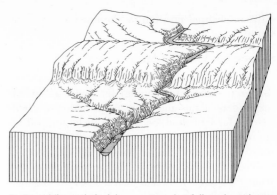

B. By middle youth the lakes are gone, but falls and rapids persist along the narrow incised gorge.

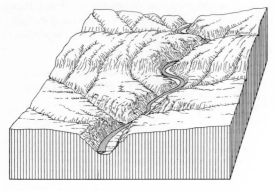

C. Early maturity brings a smoothly graded profile without rapids or falls, but with the beginnings of a flood plain.

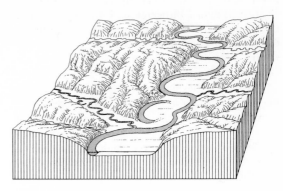

D. Approaching full maturity, the stream has a flood plain almost wide enough to accommodate its meanders.

E. Full maturity is marked by a broad flood plain and freely developed meanders. *L* = Levee; *O* = oxbow lake; *Y* = yazoo stream; *A* = alluvium; *B* = bluffs; *F* = flood plain.

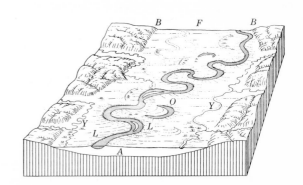

Figure 24.4 Stages in the life history of a stream. (After E. Raisz.)

24.3, about ten feet of thickness of alluvium was *reworked*, that is, moved about in the complete cycle of rising and falling stages.

Alternate deepening by scour and shallowing by deposition of load are responses to changes in the stream's ability to transport its load. The maximum quantity, or load, of debris that can be carried by a stream is a measure of the stream's *capacity*. Load is usually stated in terms of the weight of material moved through a given stream cross section in a given unit of time, commonly in units of

tons per day. Total load includes both the bed load and the suspended load.

If a stream is flowing in a channel of hard bedrock, it may not be able to pick up enough alluvial material to supply its full capacity for bed load. Such conditions exist in streams occupying deep gorges and having steep gradients, so that when flood stage occurs, the channel cannot be quickly deepened in response. In an alluvial river, however, where thick layers of silt, sand, gravel, and boulders underlie the channel, the rising river easily picks up and sets in motion all of the material that it is capable of moving. In other words, the increasing capacity of the stream for load is easily satisfied.

Capacity for load increases sharply with the stream's velocity, because the swifter the current the more intense is the turbulence and the stronger is the dragging force against the bed. Capacity to move bed load goes up about as the third to fourth power of the velocity. Thus, if a stream's velocity is doubled in flood, its ability to transport bed load is increased from eight to sixteen times. It is small wonder, then, that most of the conspicuous changes in the channel of a stream, such as sidewise shifting of the course, occur in flood stage, with very few important changes occurring in low water stages.

When the flood crest has passed and the discharge begins to decrease, the stream's capacity to transport load also declines. Therefore, some of the particles that are in motion must come to rest on the bed in the form of sand and gravel bars. First the largest boulders and cobblestones will cease to roll, then the pebbles and gravel; then the sand. Fine sand and silt carried in suspension can no longer be sustained, and settle to the bed. In this way the stream adjusts to its falling capacity. When restored to low stage the water may become quite clear, with only a few grains of sand rolling along the bed where the current threads are fastest.

With this introduction to the flow of streams and the manner in which they carry out their work of erosion, transportation, and deposition, we turn next to the way in which streams carve their valleys and shape a host of interesting landforms.

Life history of a stream

Throughout its life history, a stream passes through a series of stages, each with certain definite characteristics (Figure 24.4). The initial stage occurs as soon as a new land surface is created by uplift and dislocation of a portion of the earth's crust. It is assumed here for simplicity of discussion that the surface was formerly under ocean level and has now become exposed for the first time. The landscape is thus composed entirely of initial landforms. Rain falling upon the land will produce overland flow. This must flow down the initial slopes, whatever their form. Water flow will be concentrated where slight depressions exist in the slopes, thus causing the development of stream channels, which are quickly deepened by erosive action of the water and any loose rock particles it carries. Depressions will fill up with water, making lakes. Overflow at the lowest points on the rims of these lake basins will serve to make a connected system of drainage from higher to lower lakes.

Figure 24.5 The Royal Gorge of the Arkansas River in the Colorado Rockies illustrates well the canyon of a young river with a steep gradient. (Photograph by A. K. Lobeck.)

Thus the initial stream system comes into existence. It is characterized by falls, rapids, and lakes along its course (Figure 24.4A).

Once formed, the stream enters upon the stage of *youth*. Deepening of the channel is the principal activity of a young stream, whose capacity for load exceeds the load available to it. Lake outlets are cut through, draining the lakes and extending the stream across the old lake floors. Waterfalls are cut down at the lip until they are nothing more than rapids. A deepening *gorge* or *canyon* is perhaps the most striking landform associated with a young stream. The gorge is steep-walled and has a V-shaped cross section. The stream occupies all the bottom of the gorge. From the steep walls much weathered rock material is shed into the stream. Landslides occur frequently, large fallen masses sometimes temporarily damming the stream. Talus slopes of loose rock fragments may here and there extend down into the water. Because of rapid

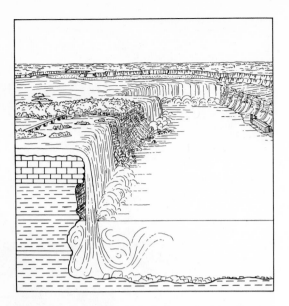

Figure 24.6 Niagara Falls is formed where the river passes over the eroded edge of a massive limestone layer. Continual undermining of weak shales at the base keeps the fall steep. (After G. K. Gilbert and E. Raisz.)

Figure 24.7 This air view of Victoria Falls of the Zambezi River shows that the river has excavated a long cleft in the bedrock, probably along a fault or other zone of weakness. (Photographer not know.)

denudation of the steep valley walls, bedrock outcrops are conspicuous, locally forming bold cliffs (Figure 24.4*B*).

The geographic importance of a young river valley can be readily imagined. There is no room for roads or railroads between the stream and the valley sides; hence road beds must be cut or blasted at great expense and hazard from the valley sides. Maintenance is expensive because of undercutting by the stream and the sliding and falling of rock, which can wipe out or damage the road bed. Yet a young gorge may afford the only passage through a mountain range. The Royal Gorge of the Arkansas River, in the Rocky Mountain Front Range of southern Colorado, is a striking example (Figure 24.5). Between 1870 and 1880, one of the bitterest contests of its kind was fought between rival railroad companies over right of way through the Royal Gorge. After a long series of court battles punctuated by fights between armed construction gangs along the route, the Santa Fe Railroad and the Denver & Rio Grande, Western Railroad reached a compromise in which the latter company took permanent possession of the gorge. It is now a part of the main line between Salt Lake City and Denver.

Another geographic consideration is that a young stream is not navigable, even though it might otherwise have a sufficient discharge.

The steep gradients of young streams, especially at waterfalls, sometimes make them important sources of hydroelectric power (Figures 24.6, 24.7). Most large young rivers, however, do not possess abrupt drops in gradient, and so it is necessary to build dams in order to create artificially the vertical drop necessary for turbine operation. An example is Hoover Dam, behind which lies Lake Mead occupying the canyon of the young Colorado River.

As a stream progresses through the stage of youth it removes falls and rapids from its course, creating a smooth, even gradient. Deepening of the valley becomes greatly retarded, allowing the canyon or gorge walls to be worn down to more moderate slopes (Figure 24.8).

Stream equilibrium

The stage of *maturity* is reached when the stream has completed its phase of rapid downcutting and has prepared itself a smoothly graded course. It is now in a state of balance, or *equilibrium*, in which the average rate of supply of rock waste to the stream from all its tributaries and their slopes is equal to the average rate at which the stream can transport the load. In other words, the stream's capacity is satisfied by the load supplied.

The longitudinal profile, representing the stream

channel from upper to lower end, is a profile of equilibrium (Figure 24.9). It may also be said that the stream is *graded*, which simply means that it possesses a profile of equilibrium.

It is important to understand that the balance between load and a stream's capacity exists only as an average condition over periods of many years. As already explained, streams scour their channels in flood and deposit load when in low stage. Thus in terms of conditions of the moment, a stream is rarely in equilibrium; but over long periods of time, the graded stream maintains its level by restoring those channel deposits temporarily removed by the excessive energy of flood flows.

Having attained this state of balance, the stream continues to cut sidewise on the outsides of banks. It cannot continue to cut down without destroying the equilibrium condition, but the lateral cutting does not materially affect the equilibrium (Figure 24.4*C*).

Flood-plain development

Immediate evidence of the earliest stage of maturity is the beginning of development of a flat valley floor. During enlargement of a bend, the river channel shifts toward the outer part of the bend, leaving a strip of relatively flat land, or *flood plain*, on the inner side of the bend (Figure 24.10). The flood plain is built of bars composed largely of sand and gravel brought as bed load scoured from the outsides of bends immediately upstream. Innundation of the flood plain approximately yearly in frequency allows finer silt and clay to settle out over the surface, adding to the flood-plain height and covering the coarser alluvium beneath.

As lateral cutting by the stream continues, flood-plain strips grow wider and presently join to form more or less continuous belts along either side of the stream (Figure 24.11). The stream bends are now larger and more smoothly rounded. When the bends are developed into smooth, sinuous curves

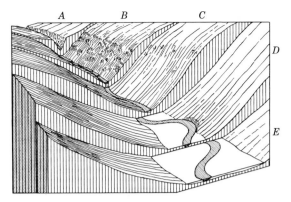

Figure 24.8 As a stream progresses from youth to maturity its valley walls become more gentle in slope and the bedrock is covered by soil and weathered rock mantle. (After W. M. Davis.)

they are termed *meanders*. As valley development progresses the flood plain becomes wide enough to accommodate the meanders without cramping their form. The stream has then passed from *early maturity* to *full maturity* (Figure 24.4*E*).

The stage of early maturity of a stream is significant geographically. The flood plain, though narrow, will accommodate roads or railroads. The graded stream profile assures low, smooth grades for the roadbeds. Agriculture, impossible on the steep walls of a young valley, can be practiced on the narrow flood-plain strips. With advanced maturity, the flood-plain valley assumes more and more importance as a productive belt and is occupied by relatively greater numbers of persons than the upland areas between the valleys.[2] Furthermore, the absence of rapids in the stream channels permits navigation, although streams in the early mature stage require locks to assure navigability.

[2] We are speaking figuratively here, because the changes in stage of a stream's life cycle take tens or hundreds of thousands of years.

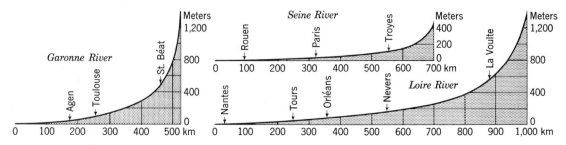

Figure 24.9 The longitudinal profiles of these French rivers show a smooth curve and rapidly increasing steepness toward the headwaters, as is typical of graded streams. (After E. de Martonne.)

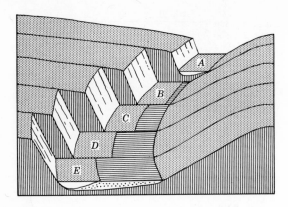

Figure 24.10 A graded stream cuts sidewise against the outside of a bend, leaving a flood-plain belt on the inside. (After W. M. Davis.)

After a stream has reached full maturity, its principal activity is to widen the flood plain. Eventually the flood plain attains a width several times as great as the meander belt. By *meander belt* is meant the area included by two lines, each one drawn on the side of the meandering stream in such a way as to connect the outermost points of the bends. Some students of landforms consider that a stream has reached a stage of *old age* when the flood plain is a definite number of times (such as five or eight times) as wide as the meander belt. Because this is an artificial distinction, little is to be gained by recognition of an old-age stage. Instead, it is common practice for the hydraulic engineer to apply the term *alluvial river* to a freely meandering stream with a broad flood plain.

The ultimate goal to which the stream profile is being lowered is an imaginary inland extension of a sea-level surface. Below this level, which the geologist calls *base level,* the valleys could not be deepened. The mouth of every stream that empties into the sea is at base level. Although theoretically the remainder of the stream might eventually reach base level, all alluvial rivers have a slight gradient, due to the fact that the lands within each drainage basin still stand well above sea level, and are shedding sediment which requires a sloping stream bed for transport.

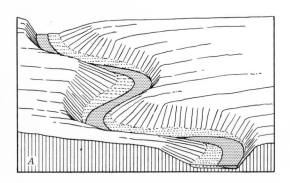

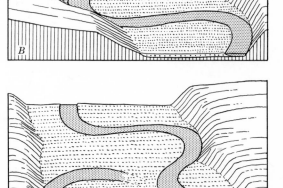

Figure 24.11 Widening of a valley by lateral cutting of a graded stream permits the free growth and cutoff of meander bends. (After W. M. Davis.)

Figure 24.12 The Mudjalik River in northern Saskatchewan has a flood plain replete with meanders, oxbow lakes, and swamps. Arcuate meander scarps border the flood plain. (Royal Canadian Air Force Photograph.)

Meanders of alluvial rivers

The flood plains of large alluvial streams have many special features of interest to the geographer (Figures 24.4*E* and 24.12). Meander bends grow as the stream undercuts the bank on the outside of the bend and deposits alluvium on the inside of the bend. These two sides of the bend are called the *undercut* and *slipoff slopes*, respectively. The bars of alluvium built on the slipoff slope are referred to as *point-bar deposits*.

The bends grow larger and larger until the channels meet, causing the intervening meander loop to be pinched off and abandoned. An occurrence of this type is called a *cutoff* (Figure 24.13). On a large river, such as the Mississippi, Missouri, or Arkansas, cutoffs are of considerable geographical importance. Where a state boundary is defined as the midline of a river, cutoffs cause portions of land within the cutoff bends to be transferred from one state to another, automatically altering the legal residences of persons who live on these lands and making them subject to laws and taxes of the other state. This difficulty can be overcome by fixing the boundary at a given time and maintaining it despite river changes. As a result, some maps show the old boundary meandering along a former river course quite different from the present course (Figure 24.14).

Along the Mississippi, towns grew up at many places along the steep undercut banks of meander bends. Here a river steamer could safely come close to the bank, dropping its gangplank directly upon the shore. If the meander bend was cut off the river took a new channel and the town immediately felt the effects of economic strangulation. Lakes formed by sealing off of the cutoff bend are called *oxbow lakes* (Figure 24.4*E*). Several oxbow lakes and marshes can be identified in Figure 24.12.

Natural levees

A flood plain, as the name implies, is normally inundated by flood stages. Unless protected by artificial levees (Chapter 23), a flood plain experiences inundation about once annually, at the season of highest runoff. Although the whole plain, from one valley wall, or *bluff*, to the other, is under water at such times (Figure 23.18), the water current is most rapid along the deep line of the river channel. Silt-bearing water, which spreads out and

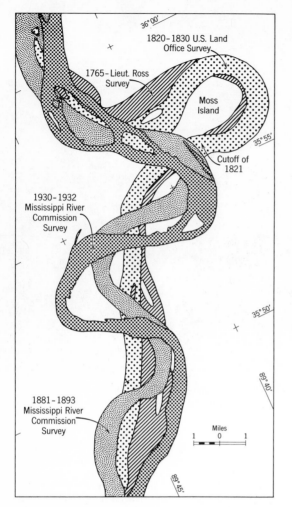

Streams entering upon the flood plain cannot directly join the main river because of the levees; hence they flow down valley, parallel to the river, considerable distances until a point of entry can be found. Streams of this type are called *yazoo streams* (Figure 24.4E), after the Yazoo River of the Mississippi River flood plain. Heightening of the natural levees by artificial levees may prevent the river from overflowing its banks in most floods. Once the water breaks through, however, it is difficult or impossible to control and the whole flood plain between levee and bluffs is inundated.

The extensive, flat lands of a broad flood plain are usually highly productive and densely populated agricultural regions. The natural levee slopes are intensively cultivated; ditches assisting in the natural surface water drainage away from the river bank. Farther from the river, in the lower parts of the flood plain and in oxbows and other sections of abandoned channels, are swamps that support a dense forest of trees adapted to the wet environment. Because of natural and artificial levees, the river channel is often slowly built up to appreciably higher level than the flood plain, making these "bottom lands," as they are called, subject to repeated inundations and consequent heavy loss of life and property. Flood plains of many of the world's great rivers present serious problems of this type. In China, in 1887, the Hwang Ho inundated an area of 50,000 square miles, causing the direct death of a million people and the indirect death of a still greater number through ensuing famine.

Braided streams and alluvial fans

When a stream is supplied with more rock waste than it can carry, the excess material is spread along the channel bottom. This is done by the stream to increase its gradient, which will in turn increase its velocity of flow and therefore increase its capacity to transport load. The process of building up the channel is termed *aggradation;* it is the opposite of *degradation*, the normal downcutting process so marked in young streams.

Aggradation gives a distinctive broad, shallow form to stream channels. The stream divides and subdivides into two, three, four, or more threads, which come together and redivide in a manner suggestive of the braided strands of rope. The term *braided stream* is, in fact, used to describe the pattern of an aggrading stream. The reason for braiding and constant shifting of the channels is that deposition of sand and gravel bars on the channel floor causes the stream to split into two or more channels which shift sideways toward lower adjacent ground. The stream thus forces itself out of its

Figure 24.13 A series of four surveys of the Mississippi River shows considerable changes in the position of the channel and the form of the meander bends. Note that one meander cutoff has occurred (1821) and new bends are being formed. (After U.S. Army Corps of Engineers.)

mingles with shallow flood waters on either side, quickly loses velocity, and much of the silt and mud settles out. Because the greatest amount of sediment settles out adjacent to the river channel there is built up by many such floods a belt of slightly higher ground, known as a *natural levee*, on both sides of the river (Figure 24.4E). The levee surface slopes gently downward away from the river to lower portions of the flood plain. Strangely enough, then, the highest ground on the flood plain is along the natural levees, immediately adjacent to the river. This narrow strip of ground may remain above water in all but the highest floods and is the safest place, aside from the flood-plain bluffs themselves, of any on the flood plain.

own channel. Aggrading streams are commonest in dry regions where stream flow is small, but where large quantities of rock waste are swept into stream valleys from relatively bare, unprotected valley slopes.

One very common landform built by braided, aggrading streams is the *alluvial fan*, a low cone of alluvial sands and gravels resembling in outline an open Japanese fan (Figure 24.15). The apex, or central point of the fan, lies at the mouth of a canyon, ravine, or gully and is built out upon an adjacent plain. Alluvial fans are of many sizes, ranging from tiny miniature fans a foot or two across, such as the ones seen alongside a roadcut, to huge fans many miles across.

Fans are built by young streams carrying heavy loads of coarse rock waste out from a mountain or upland region. Where the stream flows out upon the gentle slope of the plain, the current velocity is greatly reduced, thus forcing the stream to aggrade. The braided channel shifts constantly but, because it is firmly fixed in position at the canyon mouth, must sweep back and forth like the wagging tail of a gigantic dog. This fixed apex accounts for the semi-circular form and the downward slope in all radial directions from the apex (Figure 24.16).

Fans are of considerable geographic importance. In many mountainous regions, populations and cities are concentrated on the gentler outer fringes of alluvial fans near the base of a mountain range. Water for irrigation is diverted from the streams that issue from the canyon mouths. Artesian water can be had from wells drilled into the permeable alluvial material of which the fan is made. A striking example of fan utilization is found in the Los Angeles basin of southern California. (The map accompanying Exercise 6 of this chapter shows large fans formed along the base of the San Gabriel Range, east of the Los Angeles basin.) Flash floods have been a serious menace to such communities as Burbank, Glendale, Montrose, and Pasadena, whose favored residential districts are on the higher, inner slopes of these fans. These *debris floods*, as they are called by engineers, are distinctive in that the sediment load is very great and includes large cobbles and boulders as well as sand, silt, and clay. The floods arise on the steep slopes of mountain watersheds, especially where brush fires have destroyed protective vegetation.

Terraces

If a stream aggrades its valley for a long time the alluvial deposits may reach a thickness of many tens of feet, as Diagram *A* of Figure 24.17 shows. Among several possible causes of aggradation is the onset of a more arid climate, which reduces

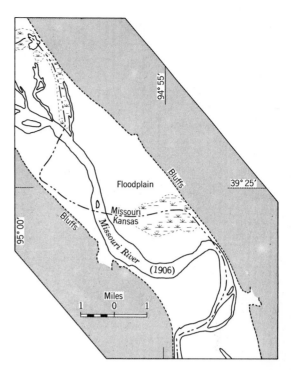

Figure 24.14 The Missouri-Kansas boundary was originally surveyed along the midline of the Missouri River, but the river has since shifted to a new course. (After U.S. Geological Survey.)

stream discharge and requires streams to steepen their gradients by building up their channels. A steeper gradient enables a stream to increase its ability to move coarse bed load shed from slopes unprotected by vegetative cover. Perhaps the commonest cause of aggradation in fairly recent geologic time in North America has been the advance and wasting away of great ice sheets. (See Chapter 26.) Melting water from the ice was heavily charged with rock debris, which caused virtually all streams near the ice front to fill their valleys with alluvium.

With return to normal conditions of reduced load, a stream will cut down through its alluvial deposit and eventually sweep most of it out of the valley. During this degradation a series of *alluvial terraces* is formed. A terrace is a relatively flat strip of ground bounded on one side by a steeply descending slope and on the other side by a steeply rising slope. A series of alluvial terraces resembles a flight of rather broad, low steps (Figure 24.18). As indicated in Diagrams *B* and *C* of Figure 24.17, terraces are made by the stream swinging from one side of the valley to the other as it slowly cuts down through the material. As each terrace is cut, the width of the next one above it is reduced.

Figure 24.15 A great alluvial fan in Death Valley, built of debris swept out of a large canyon. Note the braided stream channels. (Copyrighted Spence Air Photos.)

All older terraces would be destroyed were it not that bedrock of the valley wall here and there projects through the alluvium and protects higher terraces. In Diagram *C*, the valley alluvium has been largely removed, but some *rock-defended terraces* remain on the valley sides, protected from stream attack by the rock which outcrops at the points labeled *R*. Notice that the scarps separating terraces are curved in broad arcs concave toward the valley. The curvature is easily explained as the result of cutting of the scarps by curved meander bends.

Terraces are of geographical importance similar to that of river flood plains. The relatively flat terrace surfaces are suitable for cultivation and make good sites for towns and cities, highways, and railroads. In all these utilizations terraces have one advantage over flood plains: their surfaces may be well above the level of even the highest floods, whereas flood plains are normally subject to frequent inundation.

Deltas

The deposit of mud, silt, sand, or gravel made by a stream where it flows into a body of standing water is known as a *delta* (Figure 24.19). Deposition is caused by rapid reduction in velocity of the stream current as it pushes out into the standing water (Figure 24.20). The coarse particles settle out first; the fine clays continue out farthest and eventually come to rest in fairly deep water (Figure 24.21). Contact of fresh with salt water causes the finest clays to clot into larger aggregates which settle to the sea floor.

Deltas show a variety of shapes. The Nile delta, whose resemblance to the Greek letter "delta" suggested the name for this type of landform, has many *distributaries* which branch out in a radial arrangement (Figure 24.22*A*). Because of its broadly curving shoreline, causing it to resemble in outline an alluvial fan, this type may be described as an *arcuate* delta. The Mississippi River delta presents a very different sort of picture (Figure 24.22B). It is said to be of the *bird-foot* type because of the long, projecting fingers which grow far out into the water at the ends of each distributary. Where a river empties out upon a fairly straight shoreline along which wave attack is vigorous, the sediment brought out by the stream is spread along the shore in both directions from the river mouth, giving a pointed delta with curved sides. Because of its resemblance to a sharp tooth, this type is called a *cuspate* delta (Figure 24.22C). Where a river empties into a long, narrow estuary, the delta is confined to the shape of the estuary (Figure 24.22D). This type can be called an *estuarine* delta.

Deltas of large rivers have been of great geographic importance from earliest historical times because their extensive flat areas support dense agricultural populations. Important coastal cities, linking ocean and river traffic, are often situated on or near deltas, as Alexandria on the Nile, Calcutta on the Ganges-Brahmaputra, Amsterdam and Rotterdam on the Rhine, Shanghai on the Yangtze, Marseilles on the Rhone, and New Orleans on the Mississippi, to mention but a few. Delta growth is often rapid, ranging from a dozen feet per year for the Nile to 200 feet per year for the Po and Mississippi rivers. Thus, some cities and towns that were at river mouths several hundred years ago are today several miles inland. An important engineering problem is to keep an open channel for oceangoing vessels which have to enter the delta distributaries to reach port. The ends of the Mississippi River delta distributaries, known as *passes*, have been extended by the construction of jetties, between which the narrowed stream is forced to move faster, thereby scouring a deep channel (Figure 24.22B).

Rejuvenated streams and intrenched meanders

A mature stream, which has developed a graded profile with respect to a fixed sea level at its mouth, may experience a marked change if the land rises or the sea level falls. In either event, the base level of the stream is lowered and the stream is caused to begin rapid downcutting in order to reestablish its graded profile at a lower level. This process, termed *rejuvenation*, begins as a series of rapids at the stream's mouth, where the water passes from the former mouth down to the lowered sea level. The rapids quickly shift upstream, and soon the entire stream valley is being trenched to form a new, youthful valley.

If rejuvenation occurs when a stream has reached maturity, the effect is to give a steep-walled inner

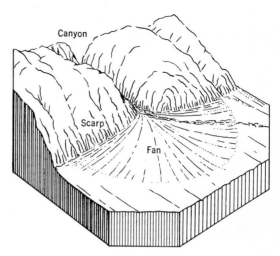

Figure 24.16 A simple alluvial fan.

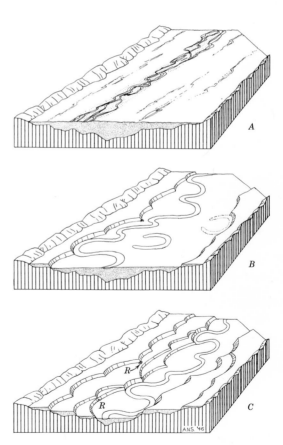

Figure 24.17 Alluvial terraces form when a graded stream slowly cuts away the alluvial fill in its valley.

Figure 24.18 Terraces of the Shoshone River near Cody, Wyoming, indicate former positions of the river flood plain. (Photograph by Frank J. Wright.)

Figure 24.19 This air view of the Kander delta in Switzerland shows a tongue of silt-ladened water being projected into Lake Thun. (Photograph by Comte, Mittel-holzer & Co., Zurich.)

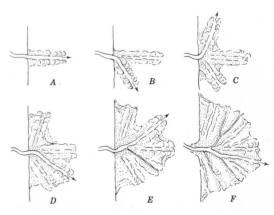

Figure 24.20 Stages in the formation of a simple delta. (After G. K. Gilbert.)

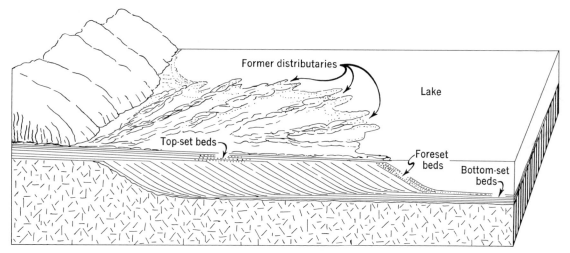

Figure 24.21 Structure of a simple delta shown in a vertical section. (After G. K. Gilbert.)

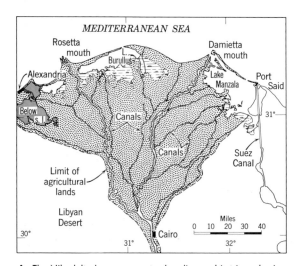

A. The Nile delta has an arcuate shoreline and is triangular in plan.

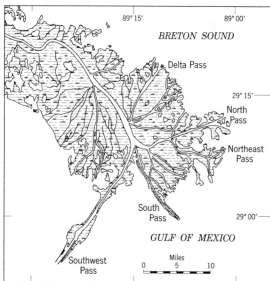

B. The Mississippi delta is of the branching, bird-foot type with long passes.

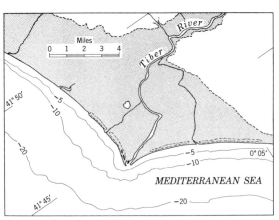

C. The Tiber delta on the Italian coast is pointed, or cuspate, because of strong wave and current action.

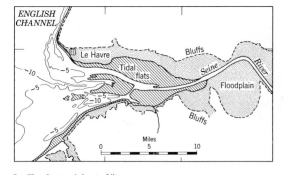

D. The Seine delta is filling in a narrow estuary.

Figure 24.22 Deltas.

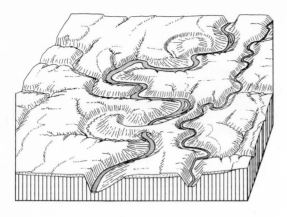

Figure 24.23 The winding valley of this stream resulted from intrenchment of the meandering river shown in Figure 24.4E. (After E. Raisz.)

Figure 24.24 The Goose-Necks of the San Juan River in Utah are intrenched river meanders in horizontal sedimentary strata. (Spence Air Photos.)

gorge, on either side of which lies the former flood plain, now a flat terrace high above river level (Figures 24.23 and 24.24). Meanders which the river had formed on its flood plain have now become impressed into the bedrock and give the inner gorge a meandering pattern. These sinuous bends are termed *intrenched meanders* to distinguish them from the common flood-plain meanders.

Although intrenched meanders are not free to shift about as flood plain meanders, they can enlarge slowly so as to produce cutoffs. Cutoff of an intrenched meander leaves a high, round hill surrounded on three sides by the deep abandoned river channel and on the fourth by the shortened river course. As might be guessed these hills form ideal natural fortifications. Many European fortresses of the Middle Ages were built on such cutoff meander spurs. A good example is Verdun, near the Meuse River.

Under unusual circumstances, where the bed rock includes a strong, massive sandstone formation, meander cutoff leaves a *natural bridge*, formed by the narrow meander neck (Figure 24.23). One well-known example is Rainbow Bridge at Navajo Mountain, in southeastern Utah; other fine examples can be seen in Natural Bridges National Monument at White Canyon in San Juan County, Utah.

Intrenched meanders do not offer ideal locations for railroads and highways, but in a few instances they have been the best available choices for arteries of travel. This point is illustrated well by

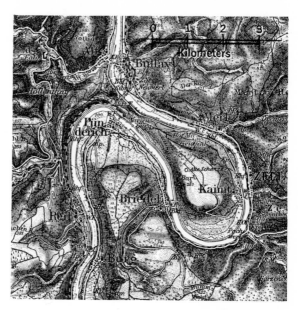

Figure 24.25 The Moselle River has a winding intrenched-meandering gorge through the Eifel district of Western Germany. (Portion of German 1 : 100,000 topographic map, 1890.)

the Moselle River, whose winding intrenched meanders through the Ardennes mountain upland of Belgium and Western Germany have been utilized (Figure 24.25). Engineers have even cut tunnels through the narrow meander necks to shorten the distance of travel.

Review Questions

1. What three geologic activities are carried on by a stream? Explain the ways in which stream erosion occurs. What is a pothole and how is it formed?

2. What are the modes of stream transportation? What sizes of particles are carried in each? When is bank caving of great importance?

3. How is the quantity of suspended sediment load of a stream stated? How does it vary in large rivers? Why?

4. Explain the changes in cross section of the channel of an alluvial river during a cycle of rising and falling discharge. Define stream capacity. What causes capacity to vary in a stream?

5. Describe the very first events in the formation of a new stream.

6. What features characterize the stage of youth of a stream? What is the geographical importance of young streams?

7. What event marks the attainment of the stage of maturity of streams? What is the profile of equilibrium? What is a graded stream? What is the form of the longitudinal profile of a graded stream?

8. Describe the flood plain and meanders of an alluvial river. What is the geographical importance of a flood plain?

9. Explain the following terms: undercut and slipoff slopes, point-bar deposits, cutoffs, oxbow lakes, natural levees, yazoo streams.

10. What is the lower limit to which a stream can eventually degrade its channel? What stage of stream development would be found on a peneplain?

11. When does aggradation take place in a stream? Does aggradation change the stream gradient? Explain. What is a braided stream?

12. Describe and explain the development of an alluvial fan. Where and why are alluvial fans of great importance to human beings?

13. Explain how stream terraces are formed. How did the advance and retreat of the continental ice sheet cause terraces to form in the northeastern United States?

14. Describe the stages in growth of a simple delta. What internal structures has a simple delta? How is the sediment sorted according to particle size?

15. Describe and explain the various forms commonly assumed by deltas of large rivers. Cite examples of the rates of growth of deltas.

16. How can a mature, graded river become rejuvenated? How do intrenched meanders form?

Exercises

Exercise 1. *Young Stream.* (Source: Colfax, Calif., U.S. Geological Survey topographic map; scale 1:125,000.)

Explanatory Note: The American River shown on this map is a young stream occupying a deep, V-shaped canyon in the west slope of the Sierra Nevada range.

QUESTIONS

1. (*a*) What contour interval is used on this map? (*b*) How deep is the canyon in the vicinity of 22–7?

2. (*a*) What is the average gradient in feet per mile of the river? (*b*) What is the gradient of the tributary stream flowing from 19–13 to 10–8?

3. (*a*) Measure the steepness of slope of the north wall of the main river canyon in the vicinity of 24–8. State this in feet per mile. (*b*) How many times steeper is this slope than the gradient of the river itself?

4. Make a topographic profile from 24–14 to 24–0. Use a vertical scale of 1 inch equals 5000 feet. What is the vertical exaggeration of this profile?

Exercise 2. *Stream in Early Maturity.* (Source: St. Albans, W. Va., U.S. Geological Survey topographic map; scale 1:62,500.)

Explanatory Note: The Kanawha River, shown on this map, has reached a stage of early maturity and has formed a flood plain between steep bluffs. (North is to the right on this map.) There is as yet insufficient width of flood plain to accommodate meanders.

QUESTIONS

1. (*a*) How wide is the river? (*b*) What is the contour interval of this map? (*c*) Give the elevation and location (in grid coordinates) of the highest point shown on this map.

2. (*a*) Is it possible to tell in which direction the Kanawha River is flowing? (*b*) Is it possible to determine the gradient of the river? (*c*) Draw in the 550-foot contour line as best you can to fit the assumption that the river flows from left to right.

3. Make a topographic profile from 7–0 to 7–7. Use a vertical scale of 1000 feet equals 1 inch. What is the vertical exaggeration of this profile?

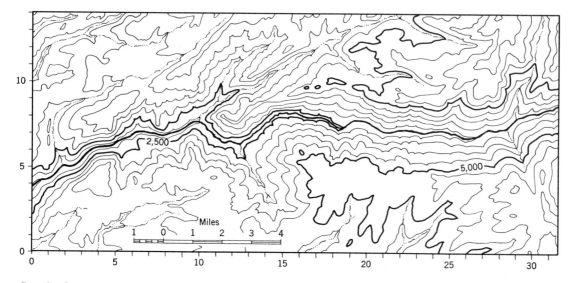

Exercise 1

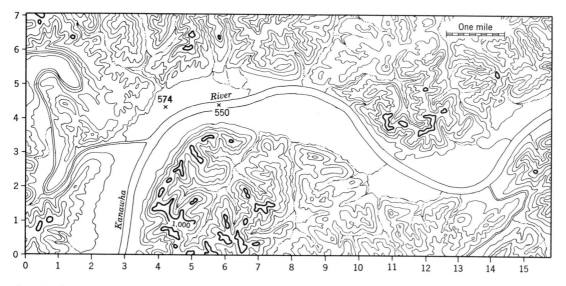

Exercise 2

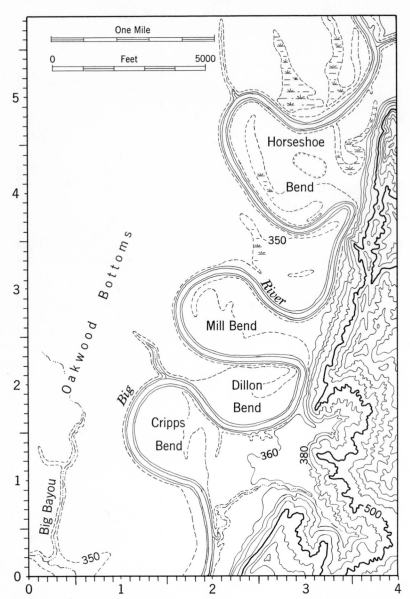

One Mile

0   Feet   5000

Horseshoe

Bend

350

Oakwood Bottoms

River

Mill Bend

Dillon

Bend

Big

Cripps

Bend

360

380

Big Bayou

500

350

Exercise 3. *Meandering Stream on Flood Plain.*
(Source: Gorham, Ill., U.S. Geological Survey topographic
map; scale 1:24,000.)

Explanatory Note: The Big Muddy River meander belt
lies close to valley bluffs on the east. To the west extends
a broad flat flood plain, Oakwood Bottoms. The innermost
pair of lines represents the river itself. The 350-foot contour line (dashed) reveals the existence of low natural
levees bordering the channel. Three contours are omitted
between 380 and 500 feet.

QUESTIONS

1. (*a*) What is the fractional scale of this map? (*b*) How
many times greater (or smaller) is this scale than that of
the map in Exercise 2?

2. (*a*) Measure the radius of curvature (in feet) of Mill
Bend and Cripps Bend. This is simply the radius of a
circle which best fits the meander curve along the midline

of the river channel. (*b*) Measure the width of the stream
channel (in feet), taking the average of several measurements along the stream. (*c*) How does the ratio of radius
of curvature to stream width for the Big Muddy River
compare with the corresponding ratio for the Mississippi
River, computed from the cutoff of 1821 in Figure 24.13?
State both ratios as whole numbers.

3. Place a sheet of thin tracing paper over the page and
redraw a portion of the map to show the river as having
cut off Dillon Bend, leaving an oxbow lake in its stead.
Take care to see that all contours are correctly redrawn.

4. The gradient of Big Muddy River cannot be computed
from this map alone. Suppose, however, that one regular
contour crosses the stream just after it leaves the map
area; that the next consecutive regular contour crosses the
stream just before it enters the map area. What then is the
river gradient in feet per mile?

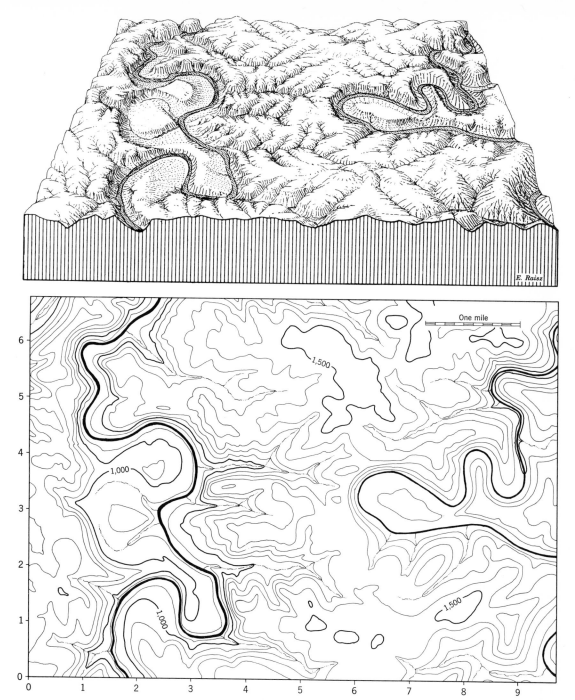

Exercise 4. Intrenched Meanders. (Source: Rural Valley, Pa., U.S. Geological Survey topographic map; scale 1:62,500.)

Explanatory Note: Mahoning Creek (left) and Redbank Creek (right) are intrenched meandering streams in the Appalachian Plateau of western central Pennsylvania. On this map north is to the right. For supplementary study refer to the intrenched meanders shown on one of the endpapers of this book.

QUESTIONS

1. (*a*) What contour interval is used on this map? (*b*) What is the fractional scale of this map? (*c*) What is the difference in elevation between the highest and lowest points shown on this map? Locate these points by grid coordinates.

2. The circular valley of an abandoned meander loop of Mahoning Creek is located in the vicinity of 1.7–2.8. (*a*) Draw in the former course of the stream around this bend. (*b*) By how many yards was the river shortened as a result of this cutoff?

3. (*a*) Make a profile from the point 2.3–3.7 to the point 2.3–4.8. (*b*) Why are the slopes of unequal steepness on the two sides of the stream at this place?

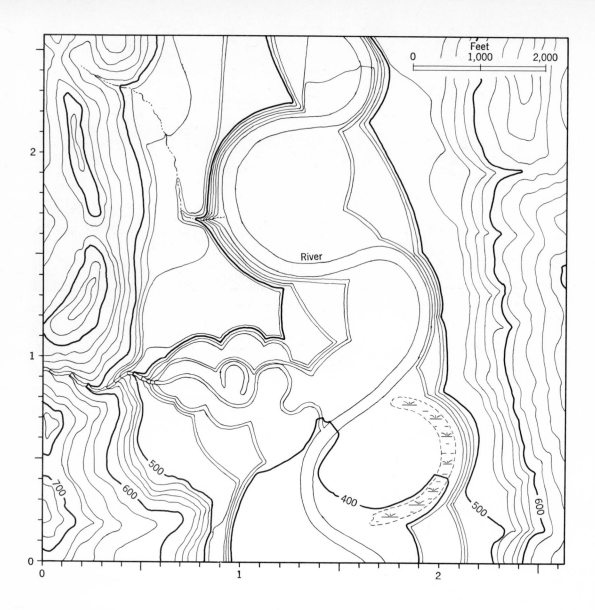

Exercise 5. *Alluvial Terraces.*

Explanatory Note: This is a synthetic map, not representing any real area, and should be thought of as a diagram on which features are idealized. A large stream has cut down through alluvial material (with which a bedrock valley had been filled during the glacial period), leaving terraces at different levels. Curved terrace scarps are of various heights and have a radius of curvature similar to that of the meander bends of the present stream.

QUESTIONS

1. (**a**) What is the fractional scale of this map? (**b**) How many times larger is this scale than that of the map in Exercise 3? (**c**) What contour interval is used on this map?

2. How high is the terrace scarp (**a**) at 1.1–2.2? (**b**) at 1.6–1.7? (**c**) at 1.4–1.0?

3. (**a**) Measure the radius of curvature of the large stream meander at 1.3–1.8. (This is the same as the radius of a circle which best fits the meander bend along the midline of the stream.) (**b**) Measure the radius of curvature of the small stream meander at 1.2–0.9. (**c**) Of these two streams, which one cut the curved terrace scarp at 1.2–1.05?

4. What is the origin of the semicircular swamp extending from 1.7–0.2 to 1.8–0.8?

5. Why does the small stream have such a deep gradient at 0.5–0.9 but such a low gradient at 0.9–0.8?

6. Why does the contour line at 1.95–1.9 bulge westward at this place instead of bending east in a sharp V as the higher contours do just east of it?

7. Make a topographic profile from 2.6–1.2 to 0.0–1.2. Use a vertical scale of 1 inch equals 200 feet.

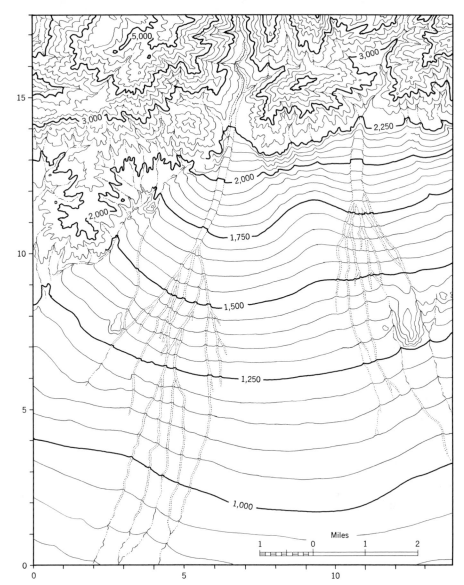

Exercise 6. *Alluvial Fans.* (Source: Cucamonga, Calif., U.S. Geological Survey topographic map; scale 1:62,500.)

Explanatory Note: The northern third of this map shows the southern slopes of the San Gabriel Mountain range of southern California, from which issue debris-laden streams of steep gradient. Large alluvial fans, covering the remainder of the map, have been built of gravels and bouldery debris by flood waters of these south-flowing streams. The sloping piedmont alluvial plain, therefore, consists of alluvial fans of various sizes arranged side by side. The contour interval on this map changes at the contact of the fans and mountain slopes because the difference in relief of the two types of topography is very great. For further details of these fans and the history of their development, see the paper by Rollin Eckis, listed among the reading references.

QUESTIONS

1. (*a*) What contour interval is used on the fan areas?
(*b*) What contour interval is used in the mountain areas?

(*c*) What is the fractional scale of this map?

2. The main stream located just west of the center line of the map is San Antonio Canyon. (*a*) What is the gradient (feet per mile) of this stream in the mountain canyon measured between the top edge of the map and the 2250-foot contour? (*b*) Why does the stream disappear at the canyon mouth, to be replaced by a broad channel shown by rows of dots? (The dotted lines mark boulder-strewn flood channels, cut somewhat below the level of the fan surface and normally dry.)

3. (*a*) What is the average gradient (feet per mile) of the fan surface between the 2000- and 1750-foot contours near 5.5–11.5? (*b*) What is the average gradient between the 1250- and 1000-foot contours near 7.0–4.0? (*c*) Make a profile of the fan of the San Antonio Wash from 6.5–14.0 to 2.0–0.0, using a vertical scale of 1 inch equals 1000 feet. (*d*) Why is the fan profile concave-up, steepening toward the fan apex?

CHAPTER TWENTY-FIVE

The cycle of land-mass denudation

THUS far, individual types of landforms produced by weathering, mass wasting, overland flow, and streams have been examined. Consider now the entire aspect of denudation of a large region under the combined attack of these agents. Imagine an area, such as a continent or a large portion of a continent, which is elevated by internal earth movements to provide a new land mass. This elevation will constitute the *initial stage* of a grand *cycle of land-mass denudation*, in which the region passes through youth, maturity, and old age. For the sake of simplicity, it must be assumed that the elevation of the land mass occurs rapidly and that further crustal deformation then ceases, leaving the denudational agents a long period of uninterrupted activity.

A single, ideal cycle of land-mass denudation will not cover all occurrences. There is a difference between landform development in humid climates and that in arid climates. It is consequently necessary to describe two cycles, one for each climate. Furthermore, some initial land masses are relatively smooth surfaced, representing an even sea floor broadly uparched by epeirogenic crustal move-

above: Appalachian landscape, Virginia.
Photograph, Fairchild Aerial Surveys, Inc.

ment. Others are mountainous because of breaking and bending of the rock during orogeny. For our purposes, two combinations will be discussed: (1) a smooth-surfaced land mass in a region of humid climate; (2) a rugged, mountainous landscape in an arid climate.

Cycle of land-mass denudation in a humid climate

A land mass formed by uparching of a relatively smooth sea floor would have gentle slopes dipping seaward from the high central area. A portion of this slope is shown in Block *A* of Figure 25.1; it is said to be in the *initial stage.* Overland flow upon the new surface would drain off in the most convenient downslope direction and would soon develop initial streams. In the manner already explained in connection with the life history of a stream, these would begin to trench youthful V-shaped valleys into the initial land mass. Marshes and lakes occupying shallow depressions in the initial surface would soon be drained.

Block *B* shows a stage of *early youth* in the cycle of land-mass denudation. The *relief* of the area—that is, the difference in elevation between valley bottoms and divide summits—is now in-

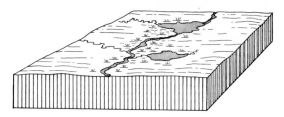

A. In the initial stage, relief is slight, drainage poor.

B. In early youth, stream valleys are narrow, uplands broad and flat.

C. In late youth, valley slopes predominate but some interstream uplands remain.

D. In maturity, the region consists of valley slopes and narrow divides.

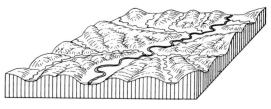

E. In late maturity, relief is subdued, valley floors broad.

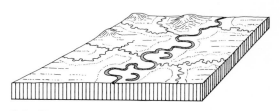

F. In old age, a peneplain with monadnocks is formed.

G. Uplift of the region brings on a rejuvenation, or second cycle of denudation, shown here to have reached early maturity.

Figure 25.1 The cycle of land-mass denudation in a humid climate. (After E. Raisz.)

creasing rapidly because the streams are cutting down rapidly, whereas between the streams there remain relatively flat portions of the initial land surface (Figure. 25.2). As the valleys deepen they also widen, because rock waste is swept down the valley sides into the streams. The unconsumed areas between valleys thus are reduced in proportionate area, while the steep valley slopes increase in extent. Small tributary valleys branch out from the larger streams, further cutting into the initial landmass.

Block *C* of Figure 25.1 shows remnants of the initial land surface, between which are well-developed valley systems, but the remnants shrink in area until the greater proportion of the region consists of steep valley slopes, a stage that may be termed *late youth*. Relief has been steadily increasing as the streams have been actively downcutting. Next, however, conditions show a marked change. When the larger streams become graded and begin to form their flood plains, the increase in relief is halted. The remaining flat remnants of the initial

Figure 25.2 The Grand Canyon of the Yellowstone River, viewed from over Inspiration Point, illustrates a youthful canyon carved into the initial surface of a lava plateau. (U.S. Army Air Service Photograph.)

surface are finally consumed, and the valley slopes intersect in narrow divides.

When relief has reached the maximum, the stage of *maturity* is attained (Block *D*, Figure 25.1 and Figure 25.3). From this time on, the valley floors are lowered with extreme slowness, whereas the interstream divides are rapidly lowered. Thus the relief of the region decreases steadily. Slopes become progressively lower in angle (Block *E*, Figure 25.1). Sheet wash and gravity movements no longer are so active as in previous stages.

Base level and peneplain

After a period of time much longer than was required for maturity to be reached, the landscape is reduced to a low rolling surface and may be said to have entered the stage of *old age* (Block *F*, Figure 25.1). By this time most of the streams have extremely low gradients and extensive flood plains. The ultimate goal, which would be reached if infinite time were available for its accomplishment, would be the reduction of the land to a surface

coinciding with sea level projected inland. To this imaginary surface is applied the word *base level*, for it is both a base toward which denudation is progressing and a water-level surface. Although the base level is attainable only in theory, a fairly close approach to it has been made in various parts of the world throughout eras of the geologic past. The word *peneplain* is given to a land surface of faint relief produced in the old-age stage of a cycle of denudation.

A peneplain is not perfectly flat but has gentle slopes. Because the streams are sluggish and the land slopes low, further denudation is extremely slow. It is not easy to set a particular figure for the number of years required for a region to pass from initial stage to old age, because this depends upon how high the land mass was elevated to begin with and how resistant the rocks are to weathering and erosion. Perhaps it would be safe to say that in known cases in the geologic record, several million years have been required to reduce a mountain mass to a peneplain.

Figure 25.3 This air view of a maturely dissected region shows a complex system of stream channels and small drainage basins. (Spence Air Photos.)

Sometimes a region contains zones or patches of rock far more resistant to weathering and erosion than the rock of the region as a whole. As the cycle progresses through maturity into old age, these harder rocks are left standing in prominent hills or isolated mountains, which rise conspicuously above the surrounding peneplain (Figure 25.4). To a residual hill or mountain of this type is given the name *monadnock*, named for Mount Monadnock in southern New Hampshire.

Rejuvenation

Once formed, a peneplain is usually elevated again by crustal movement. This follows the principle, stated earlier, that the internal earth forces act spasmodically, and that periods of extreme stability of a particular part of the world are ended by uparching or severe deformation.

A peneplain that is badly folded or fractured during orogeny is quickly obliterated in the erosion cycle that follows. If, however, the region is merely elevated by epeirogenic movements of a few hundred or a few thousand feet, remains of the pene-

plain persist for a considerable period. In Block *G* of Figure 25.1 this occurrence is illustrated. Similarity between this and the young stage illustrated in Block *C* is marked. The principal difference between the two is that the initial land surface in Block *C* is a former sea floor, whereas the "initial" surface in Block *G* is the uplifted peneplain. Drainage on the uplifted peneplain is already well established, so that the streams are merely rejuvenated and cut deep V-shaped valleys into their old shallow courses. When maturity of the second cycle is reached, the former peneplain is completely consumed, but its influence is seen generally in the accordant summits of hilltops over the region as a whole. There is no particular limit to the number of cycles a region can undergo. In some regions three or four previous cycles can be interpreted from a study of the topography.

Geographic aspects of the erosion cycle

The geographic importance of stage in the cycle of land-mass denudation is very great. Regions in the initial stage of the cycle are relatively flat

Geographic aspects of the erosion cycle | 373

Figure 25.4 Stone Mountain, on the Piedmont upland near Atlanta, Georgia, is a striking monadnock about 1½ miles long and rising 650 feet above the surrounding Piedmont peneplain surface (see Exercise 3). The rock is a light-gray granite, almost entirely free of joints, and has been rounded into a smooth dome by weathering processes. (Photograph by U.S. Army Air Service.)

plains on which drainage is poor and marsh lands often extensive. Sandy beach deposists left by waves as the land surface emerged from beneath the sea usually produce infertile soils. An excellent example is the coastal plain region of Georgia and northern Florida. The great Okefenokee Swamp occupies a shallow depression in the former sea floor whereas long sandy strips of higher land parallel the coast. The porous sands permit plant nutrients to be leached out of the soil.

Not all regions in an initial stage have emerged from the sea; some, such as the High Plains of eastern Colorado, western Kansas, and northern Texas, were built by aggrading streams and, although remarkably flat, are well drained and do not have extensive marshes. The High Plains possess a high productivity in wheat, not only because the soil and climate are favorable but also because the flatness of the land permits enormous grain fields to be cultivated and harvested by machines.

Still other areas of initial land surface are formed by lava flows, poured out profusely to inundate the previous topography and produce a high, undulating lava plateau. This is the origin of the plateau into which the Yellowstone River has carved its gorge (Figure 25.2 and Exercise 1). The Snake River Plain of southern Idaho is another example. A region in youth of the cycle supports its population on the relatively flat areas between deep V-shaped valleys. Because these valleys are in a young stage they have no flood plains; hence, roads, railroads, cities, and farms are situated on the uplands. A mature region, on the other hand, has no flat uplands remaining, hence is not favorable to habitation, agriculture, or transportation. Many of the world's mountain regions are in the stage of maturity in the erosion cycle. Extremely great relief and steep slopes are the result of recent, high uplift of those portions of the earth's crust. A coastal region, on the other hand, elevated only 200 or 300 feet above sea level, could never attain really mountainous relief because the streams can cut into the mass no more deeply than the mass itself rises above sea level. In some maturely dissected regions, the larger streams have already reached full maturity in their own individual life cycles and have sizable flood plains at the same time that the surrounding region is extremely rugged. Under such circumstances, human activity is concentrated in the valley floors.

Regions with a humid climate in late maturity or old age of the cycle are usually favorable to agriculture. Slopes are moderate or low and are well drained. Soils tend to be thick. Destructive soil erosion can be held in check. Roads and railroads cross the rolling surface without great difficulty or follow extensively developed flood plains.

Much of the Amazon Basin is a peneplain, but because of the heavy rainfall a dense forest vegetation renders the region passable only at the cost of great labor. Low, flood-plain areas bordering the mature rivers are forbidding morasses. Peneplains that have been uplifted and trenched by valleys in a new cycle are comparable geographically to regions in young stages of the cycle of land-mass denudation.

Drainage networks

Much of the earth's land surface consists of landforms produced in the cycle of denudation in a humid climate, although little is in the initial and early youth stages of the cycle because of the short duration of those stages. Thus, well-developed drainage systems characterize vast areas of the continents. Even in deserts, where a somewhat different cycle is followed by the land mass as a whole, the mountains and plateaus are dominated by drainage systems quite like those of the cycle in humid climates. It is therefore important to devote some attention to the form development, or *morphology*, of stream networks and the associated systems of slopes and drainage basins by which they are fed.

If we place a sheet of tracing paper over the topographic map of Exercise 2, the network of stream channels can be traced and examined, as in Figure 25.5. Only the larger streams are shown on topographic maps by actual lines, but most are clearly indicated by the sharp V-bends of contours. A larger-scaled map would probably show many more small finger-tip branches than are drawn on Figure 25.5, but even a generalized map illustrates the fundamental principles. Major divides have also

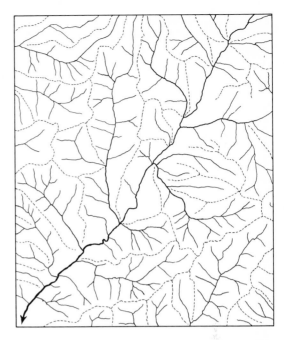

Figure 25.5 A drainage system consists of many small basins, each adjusted in size and shape to the magnitude of the stream it serves. Streams shown by solid lines; divides by dashed lines. This area is identical with that in Exercise 2.

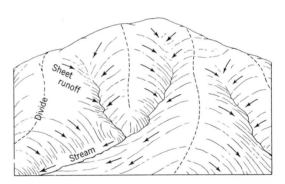

Figure 25.6 Overland flow from slopes in the head-water area of a stream system supplies water and rock debris to the smallest elements of the channel network.

been drawn (dashed lines) to show the outlines of the larger watersheds.

Ground slopes converge upon the head of each channel, bringing overland flow in sufficient quantities during heavy rains to produce channel flow and keep the channel well scoured, free of soil and vegetation which might otherwise tend to obstruct and obliterate the channel (Figure 25.6). Over a long period of time, as the land-mass cycle evolved through youth into maturity, the available ground has been apportioned to the individual small channels so that each receives the amount of

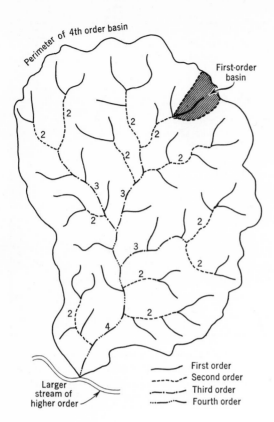

Figure 25.7 Orders of magnitude may be assigned to the segments of a branching stream system.

It was supposed that streams later occupied the valleys produced in this manner, hence, that the valleys came first and were not the work of the streams themselves.

To John Playfair, an English geologist, is attributed the first clear and convincing statement of beliefs universally accepted today concerning streams and their valleys. In 1802, he published the following statement, now know as *Playfair's law:*

Every river appears to consist of a main trunk, fed from a variety of branches, each running in a valley proportioned to its size, and all of them together forming a system of valleys connecting with one another, and having such a nice adjustment of their declivities that none of them join the principal valley either on too high or too low a level; a circumstance which would be infinitely improbable if each of these valleys were not the work of the stream which flows in it.

The three main points of this law, restated in abstract form, are: (1) valleys are proportioned in size to streams flowing in them; (2) stream junctions are accordant in level; (3) therefore, valleys are carved by the streams flowing in them, because both (1) and (2) would be "infinitely improbable" on the basis of chance alone. Exceptions occur in nature. Sometimes a tributary stream passes over a waterfall to reach the level of the master stream. Sometimes small streams occupy very large valleys. But for each of these exceptions, closer study reveals unusual or special conditions that have locally prevailed. Regions of homogeneous bedrock, which have been eroded by streams over a long period of time, invariably bear out the truth of Playfair's law.

Stream orders

Given a map of a complete stream channel network, we can subdivide the network into individual lengths of channel, or *channel segments*, according to a hierarchy of orders of magnitude, assigning a sequence of numbers to the orders as shown in Figure 25.7. Each finger-tip channel is designated as a segment of the *first order*. At the junction of any two first-order segments, a channel of the *second order* is produced and extends down to the point where it joins another second-order channel, whereupon a segment of *third order* results, and so forth. However, should a segment of the first order join a second- or third-order segment, no increase in order occurs at that point of junction. The trunk stream of any watershed bears the highest order number of the entire system. Channels of the first and second order usually carry flowing streams only in wet weather.

If large numbers of channel networks in a given region are divided into segments, each assigned an

runoff required to sustain it. Ground slopes and channel gradients have become mutually adjusted so that the rates of erosion are neither so rapid that a channel lengthens at the expense of its neighbors, nor is it so deficient in area of runoff that it becomes choked with debris of which it cannot dispose. Slow down-cutting of channels and slow lowering of slopes and divides continues, but with a general uniformity over the entire region.

Each finger-tip channel joins another, or enters a larger channel, in such a way that watersheds of increasing size are formed; exit channels are progressively larger in dimensions and discharge. Most stream junctions form acute angles, so that the discharge is carried in the general direction of the larger trunk streams in as direct a manner as possible and with as few channels as possible while, at the same time, providing each element of the stream network with an adequate area of surface runoff.

Playfair's law

Prior to about 1800 there was a widespread belief among naturalists that stream valleys and other landforms were the products of a great cataclysmic upheaval, or rending, of the earth's crust.

order according to the above rules, it will be possible to make some generalizations about the form and dimensions of the drainage network characteristic of that region. Consider first the distribution of numbers of segments of each order in a single watershed. In a carefully surveyed, large-scale map of a single drainage basin in the Big Badlands of South Dakota, all stream segments were assigned orders. The numbers of segments of each order were then counted to yield the following figures.[1]

Stream order	Number of stream segments	Bifurcation ratio
1	139	
		3.02
2	46	
		4.18
3	11	
		3.66
4	3	
		3.00
5	1	

[1] Data from K. G. Smith, Geological Society of America, *Bulletin*, vol 69, pp. 975–1008, 1958. See drainage map, Figure 14.

Consider the ratio between the number of stream segments of any given order to the number of segments of the next higher order, a proportion designated the *bifurcation ratio*. There are just over three times as many first-order segments as second-

order; over four times as many second-order segments as third-order; three and two-thirds times as many third-order as fourth-order; and three times as many fourth-order as fifth-order. The differences in these bifurcation ratios can be attributed to chance variations in the shape of any stream network.

Studies of many stream networks confirm the principle that in a region of uniform climate, rock type, and stage of development, the bifurcation ratio tends to remain constant from one order to the next. Values of bifurcation ratio between 3 and 5 are characteristic of natural stream systems. Theoretically, the lowest possible value would be exactly 2, if every segment divides to form two segments of lower order, but no other segments are present. From these studies, a *law of stream numbers* can be stated as follows. The numbers of stream segments of successively lower orders in a given basin tend to form a geometric series, beginning with a single segment of the highest order and increasing according to the bifurcation ratio. For example, if the bifurcation ratio is 3, and the trunk segment is of the sixth order, the numbers of segments will be 1, 3, 9, 27, 71 and 213.

Stream lengths and basin areas

Referring again to the drainage network map, Figure 25.7, it is apparent that the first-order channel segments have, on the average, the shortest length, and that segments become longer as order increases. The following table gives measurements for a part of the Allegheny River basin in McKean County, Pennsylvania.

ALLEGHENY RIVER DRAINAGE BASIN CHARACTERISTICS*

Stream order	Number of segments	Bifurcation ratio	Average length of segments, miles	Length ratio	Average watershed area, square miles	Average channel slope, per cent
1	5966		0.09		0.05	0.185
		3.9		3.3		
2	1529		0.3		0.15	0.091
		4.0		2.7		
3	387		0.8		0.86	0.054
		5.7		3.1		
4	68		2.5		6.1	0.022
		5.2		2.8		
5	13		7		34	0.008
		4.3		2.9		
6	3		20		242	0.0003
		3.0				
7	1		8 + (not complete)		550 (not complete)	0.0002

* Data by Marie E. Morisawa.

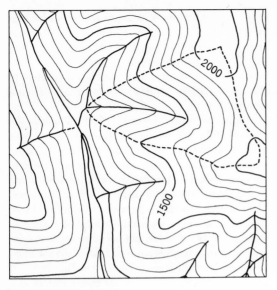

A. Low drainage density or coarse texture, Driftwood, Pennsylvania, Quadrangle.

B. Medium drainage density or medium texture, Nashville, Indiana, Quadrangle.

C. High drainage density or fine texture, Little Tujunga, California, Quadrangle.

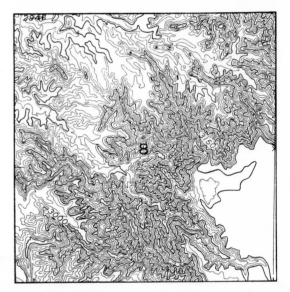

D. Extremely high drainage density or ultrafine texture, Cuny Table West, South Dakota, Quadrangle.

Figure 25.8 Four areas of one square mile each serve as representative examples of the natural range in drainage density. A dashed line shows the perimeter of a representative drainage basin of the first order. (From maps of the U.S. Geological Survey.)

The master stream of this basin is of the seventh order, but its entire length was not complete above the gaging station selected as the basin mouth. Therefore only the first six orders should be examined. The average length of stream segments, in miles, increases by a ratio of roughly three times with each increase in stream order. This proportion of length increase is known as the *length ratio*, and tends to be approximately constant for a given drainage system. Study of many drainage basins has led to the statement of the *law of stream lengths:* the average lengths of stream segments of successive orders tend to form a geometric series beginning with the average length of the first-order segments and increasing according to the length ratio.

The areas of individual small drainage basins are similarly related. Figure 25.7 shows the method of defining basin area. The area of a first-order basin is the entire surface draining into the first-order stream segment. The area of a third-order basin consists of the entire watershed contributing runoff to the third order segment, and includes also the areas of all second- and first-order basins above it. Study of many drainage basins shows that the increase of area with increase of stream order tends to follow a mathematical law.

Because most stream profiles are concave-up, decreasing in gradient from head to mouth, the average gradient of segments of each stream order will decrease as order increases. This decrease is clearly shown by the series of gradients given for the Allegheny River system in the above table (last column). Here again, the decrease in gradient with increasing order tends to follow a mathematical law quite similar to the law of stream numbers.

The mathematical laws governing stream numbers, lengths, areas, and gradients taken together, form an extension and verification of Playfair's law that the branches of a stream run in valleys proportioned to their sizes and have "a nice adjustment of their declivities." The measurement of physical properties of stream systems is a relatively recent development in the field of *quantitative geomorphology*, which uses mathematical and statistical analysis to describe landforms. The results thus obtained can be applied in the field of stream hydrology, to assist in understanding and predicting the discharges and flood characteristics of streams, because the shapes, sizes, and internal composition of drainage basins have a strong control over the stream flow characteristics.

Drainage density and texture of topography

If we study an area of badlands, the intricately eroded forms which develop in barren areas of soft clays in arid climates (Figure 25.9), we cannot fail to be impressed with the way that the landforms resemble miniature mountains. Innumerable tiny channels carve tiny valleys to reproduce on a small scale the same great canyon and ridge forms seen in a rugged mountain range, such as the San Gabriel Range of California, or the Great Smoky Mountains of North Carolina. Evidently nature follows the laws of stream numbers, lengths, areas, and gradients, regardless of whether the first-order drainage basin is so small that one can stand astride it, or whether it is a full mile across. Because such similarity of geometry prevails in maturely eroded land masses, it is necessary to have some means of describing and measuring the scale of magnitude of the forms.

If, for the drainage network maps of Figure 25.5, or 25.8 we should measure the total length in miles of all channels, and divide this figure by the total area in square miles of the entire map or watershed, the *drainage density* is found:

$$\text{Drainage density} = \frac{\text{total length of streams (miles)}}{\text{area (square miles)}}$$

Suppose that a drainage density value of 12 is obtained; this is interpreted as meaning that there are twelve miles of channel for every square mile of land surface. Area and length are measured from a map, which projects the sloping surfaces and channels upon a horizontal plane, so that the measured values are somewhat less than the true values, to a degree depending upon the amount of slope.

Figure 25.8 shows four topographic maps of the U.S. Geological Survey, each covering one square mile. A great range in drainage density is shown. Map *A* is from a region of *low drainage density*, averaging three to four miles of channel per square mile. This example comes from a region underlain by massive, hard, sandstone beds and is under heavy forest cover. Such a region of low drainage density may be described as having *coarse texture*, since the individual elements of the topography are very large, or gross. Map *B* shows a region of *medium drainage density*, averaging 12 to 16. This area is underlain by thin-bedded sandstones and thick shales, relatively easily eroded, but developed under a heavy deciduous forest cover. It is typical of large parts of the humid eastern United States where the stage of land-mass erosion is mature. This area may be described as of *medium texture*.

Map *C* shows *high drainage density*, or *fine texture*, developed in easily eroded, weak sedimentary strata in southern California, where vegetative cover is sparse. Drainage density runs from 30 to 40 under such conditions. Much higher values of drainage density are found in badlands, where there may be from 200 to 500 or more miles of channel per square mile. Such topography would

Figure 25.9 This vertical air photograph of an area of one square mile in the Big Badlands of South Dakota illustrates ultrafine texture. The topography is very similar but not identical to that shown in Figure 25.8D. North is toward the bottom of the page. (U.S. Dept. of Agriculture.

be described as *ultrafine texture*. Map *D*, taken from the badlands region of South Dakota, illustrates the appearance of badlands on maps of the same scale as the preceding three textures, but much intricate detail is lacking because it is impossible to draw the minute crenulations of the contours on a map of this scale. For this reason no drainage lines have been drawn in, but they can be seen in Figure 25.9, a portion of an air photograph covering one square mile at a nearby location within the Badlands National Monument, South Dakota.

What factors control drainage density? One highly important control is rock type. Hard, resistant rocks, such as intrusive granitic rock, gneiss, sandstone, and quartzite, tend to give low drainage density (coarse texture). This is because stream erosion is difficult and only a relatively large channel can maintain itself. Therefore, the first-order basins are large and provide large amounts of runoff to the channels. In weak rocks, such as shales and clays, even a small watershed can supply enough runoff for channel erosion. A second factor is the relative ease of infiltration of precipitation into the ground surface and downward to the water table (See Chapter 21). Highly permeable materials, such as sand or gravel, tend to give low drainage density because infiltration is great and little water is available as surface runoff to maintain channels. Clays and shales, on the other hand, have a high

proportion of surface runoff and this combines with their weakness to give high drainage density. A third major factor is the presence or absence of vegetative cover. A weak rock will have much lower drainage density in a humid climate, where a strong, dense, cover of forest or grass protects the underlying material, than in an arid region where no protective cover exists. For this reason, badlands are characteristic of arid climates, and the drainage density there tends to be markedly higher on all rock types, even the most resistant.

Cycle of land-mass denudation in an arid climate

The general appearance of desert regions is strikingly different from that of humid regions. This is a reflection of differences in both vegetation and landforms. It should be emphasized that rain falls in dry climates as well as in moist and that most landforms of desert regions are formed by running water. A particular locality in a dry desert may experience heavy rain only once in several years, but when it does fall, stream channels carry water and perform the same work as the constantly flowing streams of moist regions. Excess water runs off from the valley slopes into the streams, washing down rock particles into the channels, just as in the moister regions. We may even go further and say that, although running water is a rather rare phenomenon in dry deserts, it works with more spectacular effectiveness on the fewer occasions when it does act. This is explained by the meagerness of vegetation in dry deserts. The few small shrubs and plants that survive offer little or no protection to soil, mantle, or bedrock. Without a thick vegetative cover to protect the ground and hold back the swift downslope flow of water, excessive quantities of coarse rock debris are swept into the streams. A dry channel is transformed in a few minutes into a raging flood of muddy water, heavily charged with rock fragments.

From these statements it might be inferred that rainfall in desert regions is heavier and more violent than in moist regions. This is not true. In dry deserts, almost all rainfall is of the thunderstorm type, which is violent and heavy, affecting only a small area directly under the storm. In moist temperate regions, there are even more frequent and heavier thunderstorm downpours, but also many prolonged periods of steady, light rain during which the soil takes in moisture and becomes fully saturated. Furthermore, the air of humid regions tends to be moist, thus reducing evaporation from the ground. Under such conditions, vegetation can grow thickly and maintain its protective hold upon the ground. Water tables are high and streams are fed in part by base flow. It is true that in the humid tropics most of the rainfall is of the violent thunderstorm type, but this occurs so frequently that dense vegetation can flourish. In a dry desert the periods between rains are so prolonged that only a few species of extremely hardy plants can grow.

Because desert rainfall is so localized, a stream flowing into an adjacent dry area will evaporate rapidly, leaving its load upon the stream bed. One of the most important generalizations made about streams in desert regions is that "the streams are shorter than the slopes." Instead of long, continuously flowing streams extending to the sea, streams of desert regions are often short and terminate in alluvial fans and shallow, dry lake floors where rock waste accumulates.

A cycle of land-mass denudation in an arid region is illustrated in Figure 25.10. In this ideal cycle we imagine a mountainous region formed by folding or fracturing of the earth's crust and lying in an interior part of the continent (Block A). Relief is at the maximum in the initial stage and diminishes throughout successive stages. Numerous large depressions exist between mountain ranges. These do not fill up with water to form lakes, as in a moist climate, but remain dry because of excessive evaporation in the hot, dry climate. The flat central parts of such depressions provide the beds of temporary lakes and are known as *playas*. These lakes are shallow and fluctuate considerably in level, often disappearing entirely for long periods. Because they have no outlets, playa lakes contain salt water often more strongly saline than ocean water.

Throughout the erosion cycle, the intermontane depressions become filled with rock waste as alluvial fans are built out from the adjoining mountain masses (Figure 25.11). When the basins are filled with alluvium and the mountains masses are cut up into an intricate set of canyons, divides, and peaks, the region is said to be in the *mature stage* (Block B, Figure 25.10). As maturity progresses, the mountains are worn lower, at the same time shrinking in size as the alluvium of the fans encroaches progressively farther inward upon the mountain base.

When *old age* is reached the mountains are represented by small islandlike remnants of their former selves (Block C). Eventually even these remnants, which may be compared to monadnocks on a peneplain, are eroded away and a vast plain remains. This surface is a type of peneplain, but it has not been developed with reference to sea level as a base because no streams drain out to the sea,

and it may, therefore, even lie many hundreds of feet above sea level. It contains shallow depressions occupied by playas rather than by flood plains of meandering rivers. Wind action in a dry climate is effective in eroding shallow depressions and in making dunes of shifting sand.

Pediments

In most deserts, the sloping surfaces of boulders, gravel, and sand which extend from the abrupt base of steep mountain faces to the flat ground of the playas are alluvial fans, underlain by thick deposits of alluvium shed by the mountains. In some places, however, this alluvium, although outwardly taking the form alluvial fans, is nothing more than a veneer perhaps 10 to 20 feet thick, overlying a smooth sloping floor of solid bedrock. To such a rock surface, fringing a desert mountain range or cliff line, the term *pediment* is applied. On the right-hand cross section of Blocks B and C, Figure 25.10, pediment surfaces are shown in profile in a narrow zone between the thick basin alluvium and the rugged mountain masses.

Because the pediment gradient is approximately the same as that of the alluvial cover upon it, and because the alluvial cover is composed of the bed-load deposits of graded streams issuing from canyons in the mountain front, it is reasonable to suppose that the pediment is carved by water erosion. The larger streams will be actively down-cutting (youthful) in their upper reaches, deep within the mountain ranges. In their lower reaches, where the streams meet the flat basin floor, they are aggrading, or depositing. Therefore, in a narrow intermediate zone which lies close to the mouth of the canyon, the stream will be graded and can shift laterally to undercut the rock of adjacent mountain slopes, much as a saw blade might act if turned on its side. This process, termed *lateral planation*, is a normal activity of any stream and is the same process by which flood plains are widened by alluvial rivers of humid climates.

Other processes of removal are believed to be important in carving pediments, the relative importance of each depending upon the location and type of bedrock. Between the larger canyons are smaller streams, issuing from steep-walled narrow ravines, while still smaller channels, which may be termed *rills*, drain the mountain slope and are important in removing weathered rock and wearing back the slope. These forms of running water must also adjust their gradients to conform to the gradients of the larger streams which they join, hence, can extend the pediment as a continuous rock floor with only minor undulations.

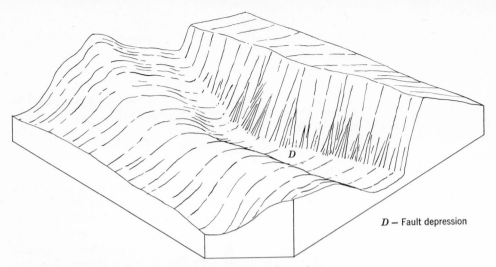

D — Fault depression

A. In the initial stage, relief made by crustal deformation is at the maximum.

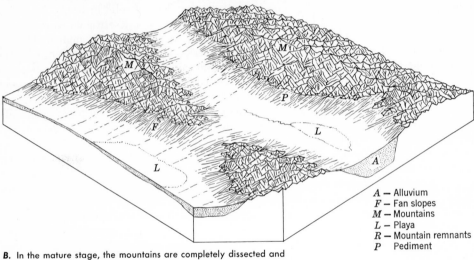

A — Alluvium
F — Fan slopes
M — Mountains
L — Playa
R — Mountain remnants
P   Pediment

B. In the mature stage, the mountains are completely dissected and the basins are filled with alluvial fan material and playa deposits.

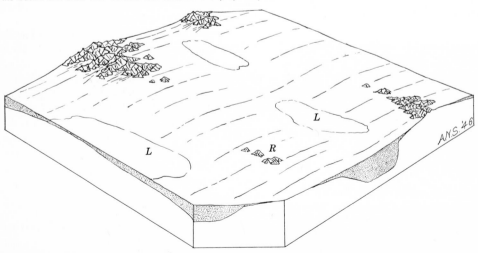

C. In the old stage, relief is low and alluvial deposits have largely buried the eroded mountain masses, whose remnants project here and there as islandlike groups.

Figure 25.10   The cycle of land-mass denudation in a mountainous desert.

Figure 25.11 This air view of Death Valley, California, shows a mature desert landscape comparable to that shown in Figure 25.10, Block B. (Copyrighted Spence Air Photos.)

Figure 25.12 Bedrock is widely exposed over this pediment surface at the foot of the Dragoon Mountains near Benson, Arizona. (Photograph by Douglas Johnson.)

Once a pediment or alluvial fan is formed, flood flows from the canyons easily fill the shallow, braided channels to overflowing and spread as a more or less uniform layer, termed a *sheetflood*, over the entire graded slope. Some geologists consider that the erosive power of sheetfloods is an important agent in shaping pediments.

Because a pediment is normally veneered by alluvium while it is being formed, the only way to be certain that a pediment exists is to see the bedrock widely exposed to view by later erosion. Thus, the pediment shown in Figure 25.12 has been cut into by stream action, exposing bedrock in numerous outcrops. The cause of stream rejuvenation in this case is not certain, but it may have been brought about by renewed faulting of the mountain block or by a climate change which upset the graded condition of the streams.

Geographical aspects of the arid cycle

The geographical aspects of mountainous deserts are well illustrated by the vast basin-and-range region which includes Nevada, southern California, western Utah, and the southern halves of Arizona and New Mexico. Here, excellent examples of various stages in the cycle can be observed as one travels through the desert on the main transcontinental highways, railroads, and airways. Sparseness of population goes hand in hand with sparseness of vegetation. In 1950, the state of Nevada, which lies wholly within this region, had only about 160,000 inhabitants in its 110,000 square miles. Contrast this with Pennsylvania, whose 45,000 square miles contained 10,500,000 persons. The vastness of waste land in this region can be partly appreciated when we realize that the explosion of the first test atom bomb was kept a secret within a single intermontane basin in New Mexico.

To the traveler, this landscape of mountainous deserts seems to be composed of three distinctive elements: (1) intensely rugged and inhospitable mountains; (2) huge sloping pediments and alluvial fans scored with innumerable shallow dry stream channels, or *washes;* and (3) perfectly flat playa lake floors, covered with shallow water or white salt deposits. In the rugged mountains occur valuable mineral deposits, which are an outstanding source of economic wealth. The alluvial fan slopes are virtually worthless except in the few places where wells bring in a flow of water for the needs of isolated communities. The playas provide mineral wealth of a different sort. Various salts of calcium, sodium, and potassium are often present in sufficient quantities to exploit.

Review Questions

1. Explain the concept of the cycle of land-mass denudation. What possible combinations of initial relief and climate may be considered?

2. Describe the various stages in the land-mass denudation cycle in a humid climate. Include discussion of the development of the drainage system, valley slopes and divides, and topographic relief. Which stage has greatest relief?

3. Describe the appearance of a peneplain. What is a monadnock? If elevation of the land causes a new cycle to begin, what happens to the peneplain?

4. Describe the appearance of a drainage network. How is it adapted to efficient discharge of runoff and sediment load?

5. State Playfair's law. What other view was held in Playfair's time. Does the law have any exceptions? Explain.

6. How is a stream network divided into orders? How do the numbers of segments of one order relate to the numbers of segments in higher orders? What is the bifurcation ratio? State the law of stream numbers and illustrate with a hypothetical example.

7. What law do lengths of stream segments follow in a given drainage basin? How do gradients change with increasing order of stream segments? What use is made of quantitative knowledge of stream morphology?

8. Define drainage density and give a series of typical values found in nature. Discuss the factors that control drainage density.

9. How does the role of running water in arid regions differ from that in humid climates? Contrast the forms of stream channels in humid and arid climates. Explain the statement that in deserts "streams are shorter than slopes."

10. Describe the stages of a land-mass cycle in mountainous deserts. Compare this cycle, stage by stage, with the cycle of land-mass denudation in a humid climate. Compare peneplains produced in the two cycles.

11. Describe a pediment. How does it resemble an alluvial fan? How does it differ from an alluvial fan? What processes are considered to produce pediments?

12. Discuss the economic geographical aspects of mountainous deserts. What physical factors in the environment tend to limit human occupation of such areas?

Exercises

Exercise 1. *Region in Stage of Youth.* (Portion of Yellowstone National Park topographic map, U.S. Geological Survey; scale 1:125,000.)

Explanatory Note: Much of the area of this map represents an undulating plateau surface at 8000 to 8500 feet elevation, which may be considered as an initial land surface built by repeated outpourings of lavas. Hot springs and geysers suggest the geologic recency of volcanic activity. Low stream gradients and marshes are typical of streams flowing across the undissected upland. In strong contrast with the initial upland is the deep, youthful Grand Canyon of the Yellowstone River downstream from the Upper and Lower Falls. Figure 25.2 is an oblique air photograph taken from a point just above the canyon, looking southwestward toward the falls.

QUESTIONS

1. (*a*) What contour interval is used on this map? (*b*) What is the fractional scale of the map? (*c*) Construct a graphic scale in miles for the map.

2. (*a*) Compute the gradient in feet per mile of the Yellowstone River in the Grand Canyon. (*b*) How does this gradient compare with the gradient of the Yellowstone River upstream from the Upper and Lower Falls?

3. Construct a topographic profile along the line from 15.0–0.0 to 15.0–13.3. Show the position of sea level with respect to the profile.

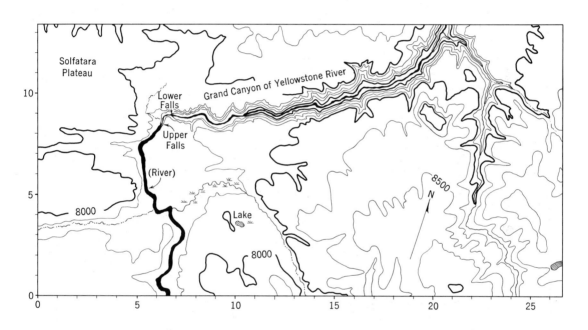

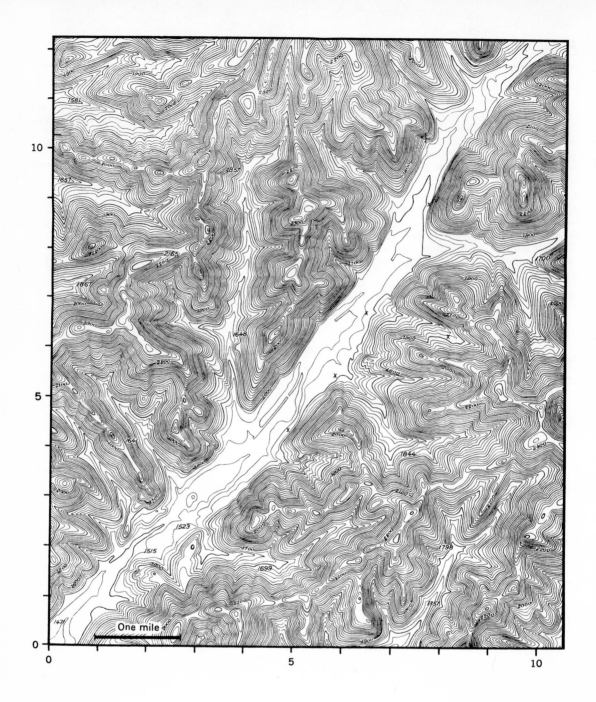

Exercise 2. *Region in Stage of Maturity.* (Portion of Belmont, N. Y., U.S. Geological Survey topographic map; scale 1:62,500.)

Explanatory Note: A maturely dissected region in a humid-temperate climate is shown without the drainage network. All the region has been formed into closely fitting drainage basins separated by narrow, rounded divides.

QUESTIONS

1. (a) What is the fractional scale of this map? **(b)** What contour interval is used? **(c)** What is the approximate average relief in this area? (Difference between elevations of divides and adjacent valley bottoms.)

2. Using a blue pencil, draw in the drainage network for this area. Indicate a stream channel wherever the contour lines form a series of sharply defined V's. (Use a tracing paper overlay for this exercise.)

3. Using a red pencil, outline all divides on this map. Carry the divide lines down the spurs to the valley bottoms in such a way as to enclose a single basin for each fingertip tributary of the drainage system. (Do this exercise on the same sheet of tracing paper used in Question 2.)

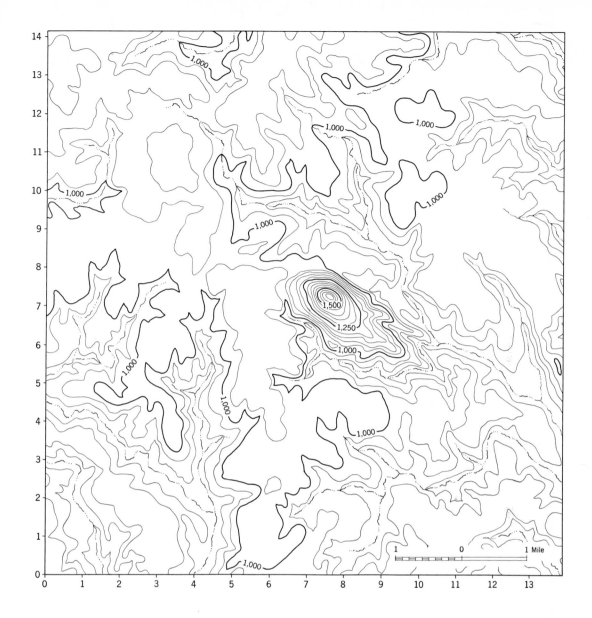

Exercise 3. *Monadnock on Peneplain*. (Source: Atlanta, Ga., U.S. Geological Survey topographic map; scale 1:125,000.)

Explanatory Note: The prominent knob in the center of the map is Stone Mountain, a small intrusive body of granite surrounded by ancient gneisses and schists. Because of its greater resistance to weathering and erosion, the Stone Mountain granite formed a conspicuous monadnock while the surrounding region was reduced to a peneplain, seen now in the broad, relatively flat divide areas between 950 and 1050 feet elevation. In a second erosion

cycle, stream valleys were cut into the peneplain surface, producing the present topography.

QUESTIONS

1. (**a**) What contour interval is used on this map? (**b**) How high does the summit of Stone Mountain rise above the peneplain surface one mile west of the summit?

2. Make a topographic profile through the summit of Stone Mountain, from 13.9–12.0 to 0.0–1.5. Use a vertical scale of 1 inch equals 1000 feet.

Exercise 4. *Mountainous Desert Landscape.* (Source: Avawatz Mountains, Calif., U.S. Geological Survey topographic map; scale 1:250,000.)

Explanatory Note: This map shows a portion of the Basin and Range physiographic province, the region used by Professor W. M. Davis to typify the land-mass denudation cycle in an arid climate. Death Valley, a downfaulted block, lies well below sea level despite filling with vast quantities of alluvium swept down from the Amargosa and Panamint Ranges, upfaulted blocks which bound the valley on either side. Figure 25.11 is an air photograph taken from a point above Death Valley, looking southeastward up the Amargosa River. Owl Lake and Lost Lake are ephemeral playa lakes occupying independent closed depressions considerably higher than Death Valley.

QUESTIONS

1. (*a*) How many square miles are covered by this map? (*b*) Give grid coordinate location and elevation of the highest and lowest points on this map.

2. By study of Figure 25.11, determine the position of the plane when the air photograph was taken. (*a*) Give grid coordinates of this position. (*b*) Give the azimuth of the line along which the camera axis was pointed.

3. (*a*) What is the maximum depth of the closed depression in which Owl Lake lies? (*b*) Give the grid coordinates of the lowest point on the rim of this depression. (*c*) What drainage changes are in progress there? (*d*) What is the relationship between Lost Lake and Owl Lake basins?

CHAPTER TWENTY-SIX

Landforms made by glaciers

MOST of us know ice only as a brittle, crystalline solid because we are accustomed to seeing it only in small quantities. Where a great thickness of ice exists, let us say 200 or 300 feet or more, the ice at the bottom behaves as a plastic material and will slowly flow in such a way as to spread out the mass over a larger area, or to cause it to move downhill, as the case may be. This behavior characterizes *glaciers*, which may be defined as any large natural accumulations of ice on land affected by present or past motion.

Conditions requisite to the accumulation of glacial ice are simply that snowfall of the winter shall, on the average, exceed the amount of melting and evaporation of snow that occurs in summer. (The term *ablation* is used by glaciologists to include both evaporation and melting of snow and ice.) Thus, each year a layer of snow is added to what has already accumulated. As the snow compacts, by surface melting and refreezing, it turns into a granular ice, then is compressed by overlying layers into hard crystalline ice. When the ice becomes so thick that the lower layers become plastic, outward or downhill flow commences, and an active glacier has come into being.

At sufficiently high altitudes, whether in high or low latitudes, glaciers form both because air temperature is low and mountains receive heavy orographic precipitation (Chapter 10). Glaciers that form in high mountains are characteristically long and narrow because they occupy previously formed valleys and bring the plastic ice from small collecting grounds high upon the range down to lower elevations, and consequently warmer temperatures, where the ice disappears by ablation (Figure 26.1). Such *valley glaciers*, or *alpine glaciers*, are distinctive types.

In arctic regions, prevailing temperatures are low enough that ice can accumulate over broad areas, wherever uplands exist to intercept heavy snowfall. As a result, areas of thousands of square miles may become buried under gigantic plates of ice whose thickness may reach several thousand feet. From the zone of most rapid accumulation the ice slowly spreads outward, enveloping all landforms it encounters and ceasing its spread only when the rate of ablation at its outer edge balances the rate at which it is spreading. This type of ice mass is called a *continental glacier*, *ice sheet*, or *icecap*.

The rate of flow of both alpine and continental

above: Mt. McKinley, Alaska.
Photograph by Bradford Washburn, from Fairchild.

389

Figure 26.1 Seen from the air, this large glacier flows westward along the northern edge of the Juneau Ice Field in Alaska. Dark bands are medial moraines. (U.S. Army Air Forces trimetrogon photograph.)

glaciers is very slow indeed, amounting to a few inches per day for large ice sheets and for the more sluggish valley glaciers, up to several feet per day for an active valley glacier. The upper few tens of feet of glacial ice is ordinarily greatly fractured and contains innumerable deep steep-sided *crevasses*, gaping cracks that render the glacier impassable or extremely dangerous to traverse.

Glacial erosion

Most glacial ice is heavily charged with rock fragments, ranging from pulverized rock flour to huge angular boulders of fresh rock. This material is derived from the rock floor upon which the ice moves, or in alpine glaciers, from material that slides or falls from valley walls. Glaciers are capable of great erosive work, both by *abrasion*, erosion caused by ice-held rock fragments that scrape and grind against the bedrock, and by *plucking*, in which the moving ice lifts out blocks of bedrock that have been loosened by freezing of water in joint fractures.

The debris thus obtained must eventually be left stranded at the outer edge or lower end of a glacier when the ice is dissipated. Thus there are two glacial activities to consider, erosion and deposition. Both result in distinctive landforms, which in some cases are further differentiated according to the type of glacier, whether alpine or continental.

A. Before glaciation sets in, the region has smoothly rounded divides and narrow, V-shaped stream valleys.

Figure 26.2 Landforms produced by alpine glaciers. (After W. M. Davis and A. K. Lobeck.)

Landforms made by alpine glaciers

Landforms made by alpine glaciers can best be studied by a series of diagrams (Figure 26.2), in which a previously unglaciated mountainous region is imagined to be attacked and modified by glaciers, after which the glaciers disappear and the remaining landforms are exposed to view.

Block *A* shows a mountainous region sculptured entirely by weathering, mass wasting, and streams. The mountains have a smooth, full-bodied appearance, with rather rounded divides. Although this is not always true, it is typical of the appearance of mountains in humid regions, for example, the Great Smoky Mountains of the southern Appalachians. Imagine now a climatic change in which the average annual temperature becomes several degrees lower and results in the accumulation of snow in the heads of most of the valleys high upon the mountain sides. An early stage of glaciation is shown at the right-hand side of Block *B*, where

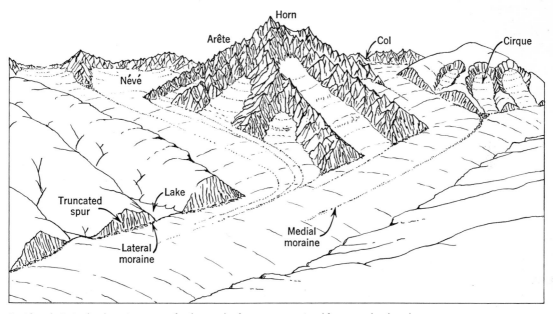

B. After glaciation has been in progress for thousands of years new erosional forms are developed.

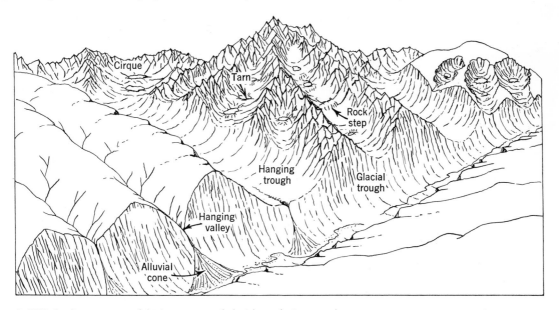

C. With the disappearance of the ice a system of glacial troughs is exposed.

Figure 26.2 continued

Figure 26.3 The Swiss Alps appear from the air as a sea of sharp arêtes and toothlike horns. In the foreground is a cirque. (Photograph by Schweitz Luftverkehrs A. G., Zurich.)

Figure 26.4 Lake Ellen Wilson in Glacier National Park, Montana, is a tarn, or glacial lake, in a rock basin. (Photograph by Douglas Johnson.)

Figure 26.5 A great landslide at S has formed a dam, D, in the floor of a glacial trough and has produced a lake, L. (After W. M. Davis.)

snow is collecting and bowl-shaped hollows are carved by the outward motion of the ice and by intensive frost shattering of the rock near the masses of compacted snow. These depressions developed in bedrock are termed *cirques*. They hold the *firn*, or *névé*, which is the snowfield of the glacier.

In Block *B*, glaciers have filled the valleys and are integrated into a system of tributaries that feed a trunk glacier just as in a stream system. Glaciers are, of course, enormously thicker than streams, because the extremely slow rate of ice motion requires a great cross section if a glacier is to maintain a discharge equivalent to a swiftly flowing stream. Tributary glaciers join the main glacier with smooth, accordant junctions, but, as we shall see later, the bottoms of their channels are quite discordant in level.

Vigorous freezing and thawing of melt water from snows lodged in crevices high upon the walls of the cirque shatters the bare rock into angular fragments, which fall or creep down upon the snowfield and are incorporated into the glacier. Frost shattering also affects the rock walls against which the ice rests. The cirques thus grow steadily larger. Their rough, steep walls soon replace the smooth, rounded slopes of the original mountain mass. Where two cirque walls intersect from opposite sides, a jagged, knifelike ridge, called an *arête*, results. Where three or more cirques grow together, a sharp-pointed peak is formed by the intersection of the arêtes. The name *horn* is applied to such peaks in the Swiss Alps (Figure 26.3). One of the best known is the striking Matterhorn. Where the intersection of opposed cirques has been excessive, a pass or notch, called a *col*, is formed.

Glacier flow constantly deepens and widens its channel so that after the ice has finally disappeared there remains a deep, steep-walled *glacial trough*, characterized by a relatively straight or direct course and by the U-shape of its transverse profile (Block *C*, Figure 26.2). Tributary glaciers likewise carve U-shaped troughs, but they are smaller in cross section, with floors lying high above the floor level of the main trough, so are called *hanging troughs*. Streams, which later occupy the abandoned trough systems, form scenic waterfalls and cascades where they pass down from the lip of a hanging trough to the floor of the main trough. These streams quickly cut a small V-shaped notch in the trough bottom.

Valley spurs that formerly extended down to the main stream before glaciation occurred have been beveled off by ice abrasion and are termed *truncated spurs* (Block *B*). Under a glacier the bedrock is not always evenly excavated, so that the floors of troughs and cirques may contain *rock basins* and *rock steps*. Cirques and upper parts of troughs thus are occupied by numerous small lakes, called *tarns* (Figure 26.4). The major troughs frequently contain large, elongate *trough lakes*, sometimes referred to as *finger lakes*. Landslides are numerous because glaciation leaves oversteepened trough walls. In glaciated countries such as Switzerland and Norway slides are a major type of natural disaster, because most towns and cities lie in the trough floors where they are readily destroyed by mudflows and landslides (Figure 26.5).

Debris may be carried by an alpine glacier within the ice, or it may be dragged along between the ice and the valley wall as a *lateral moraine* (Figure 26.2). Where two ice streams join, this marginal debris is dragged along to form a *medial moraine*, riding upon the ice in midstream (Figure 26.1). At the terminus of a glacier debris accumulates in a heap known as a *terminal moraine*, or *end moraine*. This heap is usually in the form of a curved embankment lying across the valley floor and bending upvalley along each wall of the trough to merge with the lateral moraines (Figure 26.6). As the end of the glacier wastes back, scattered debris is left behind. Should irregularities in the rate of glacier wasting cause the front temporarily to stand still, another moraine ridge will be built. Successive halts in ice retreat produce successive moraines, termed *recessional moraines*.

Glacial troughs and fiords

Many large glacial troughs now are nearly flat-floored because aggrading streams that issued from the receding ice front were heavily laden with rocks fragments. Figure 26.7 shows a comparison between a trough with little or no fill and another with alluvial-filled bottom. The deposit of alluvium extending down valley from a melting glacier is the *valley train*.

When the floor of a trough open to the sea lies below sea level, the sea water will enter as the ice front recedes, thus producing a narrow estuary known as a *fiord* (Figure 26.8). Fiords may originate either by submergence of the coast or by glacial erosion to a depth below sea level. Most fiords are explained in the second way because ice is of such a density that, when floating, from three-fourths to nine-tenths of its mass lies below water level. Therefore, a glacier several hundred feet thick could erode to considerable depth below sea level before the buoyancy of the water reduced its erosive power where it entered the open water. Fiords are observed to be opening up today along the Alaskan coast, where some glaciers are melting back rapidly and the fiord waters are being extended along the troughs. Fiords are found largely along mountainous coasts in latitudes 50° to 70° N and S. The explanation of this distribution lies in

climate and is treated under the discussion of marine west coast climate (Chapter 14).

Geographical aspects of alpine glaciation

In general, the ruggedness of fully glaciated mountains such as the Alps, Pyrenees, Himalayas, or Sierra Nevada makes for sparseness of population and difficulty of access. Land above timberline is useless for any purpose except summer pastures and the extraction of such minerals as may lie in the rocks. Below timberline, however, are rich forests. U-shaped glacial troughs provide broad, accessible strips of land at relatively low levels. These are utilized for town sites, for winter pasture, and as arteries of transportation. In the Italian Alps several great flat-floored glacial troughs extend from the heart of the Alps southward to the plain of northern Italy. These are important geographic controls because they provide smooth and easy access into the heart of the Alps and to the principal Alpine passes. The Brenner Pass lies at the head of a magnificent trough of this type, the Adige River valley.

The steep-walled troughs contain many waterfalls and rapids readily used for hydroelectric plants. Electrification of railroads and industry is highly advanced in Switzerland and Norway.

Because of restrictions upon travel and transportation, peoples of glaciated mountain regions tended to group into small political and national units.

Figure 26.6 Lateral and terminal moraines of a former valley glacier appear as looped embankments marking successive positions of the ice margins. (After W. M. Davis.)

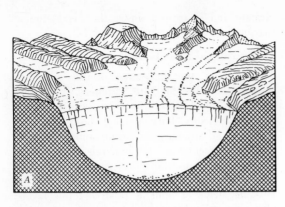

A. During maximum glaciation the U-shaped trough is filled by ice to the level of the small tributaries.

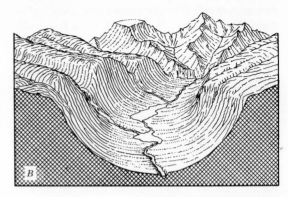

B. After glaciation the trough floor may be occupied by a stream and lakes.

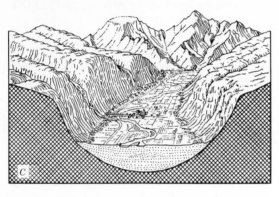

C. If the main stream is heavily loaded it may fill the trough floor with alluvium.

D. Should the glacial trough have been deepened below sea level, it will be occupied by an arm of the sea, or fiord.

Figure 26.7   Development of a glacial trough. (After E. Raisz.)

Ice sheets of the present

Two enormous accumulations of glacial ice are the Greenland and Antarctic icecaps. These may be imagined as huge plates of ice, several thousand feet thick in the central areas, resting upon land masses of subcontinental size. The Greenland cap has an area of 721,000 square miles and occupies about seven-eighths of the entire island of Greenland (Figure 26.9). Only a narrow, mountainous coastal strip of land is exposed.

The Antarctic icecap covers about 5,000,000 square miles and in places spreads out into the ocean to form floating *ice shelves.* One significant point of difference between these two icecaps is their position with reference to the poles. Whereas the antarctic ice rests almost squarely upon the south pole, the Greenland icecap is considerably offset from the north pole, with its center about at 75° N lat. (about 1035 miles from the pole). This illustrates a fundamental principle: that a large area of high land is essential to the accumulation of a great icecap. No land exists near the north pole; ice accumulation there is restricted to a thin layer of floating sea ice.

Contours drawn upon the surface of the Greenland icecap show that it is in the form of very broad, smooth domes. From a high point of about 10,000 feet elevation east of the center there is a gradual slope outwards in all directions. The rock floor of the icecap lies close to sea level under the central region, but is higher near the edges. Accumulating snows add layer upon layer of ice to the surface, while at great depth the plastic ice slowly flows outward toward the edges. At the outer edge of the sheet the ice thins down to a few hundreds of feet. Continual loss through ablation keeps the position of the ice margin relatively steady where it is bordered by a coastal belt of land. Elsewhere the ice extends in long tongues, called *outlet glaciers,* to reach the sea at the heads of fiords. From the floating glacier edge huge masses of ice break off and drift out to open sea with tidal

Figure 26.8 This Norwegian fiord has the steep rock walls of a deep glacial trough. (Photograph by Eneret Mittet and Co.)

currents. The breakup of the ice front is known as *calving* and is brought about by strains caused by the rise and fall of tide level as well as by the undercutting and melting at and below the water line. The calving of floating glacier fronts is an extremely rapid process compared to ablation of ice fronts on land. Consequently, icecaps are limited in their seaward extent and rarely extend far into the ocean beyond the limits of bays and shallow continental shelves.

Ice thickness in Antarctica is even greater than that of Greenland. For example, on Marie Byrd Land a thickness of 14,000 feet was measured, the rock floor lying 8200 feet below sea level. On Victoria Land Plateau at an elevation of 8900 feet above sea level, the ice was found to be 13,000 feet thick. This means that the rock floor over large parts of the Antarctic continent may lie below sea level.

An important glacial feature of Antarctica is the presence of great plates of floating glacial ice, termed *ice shelves* (Figure 26.9). The largest of these is the Ross Ice Shelf with an area of about 200,000 square miles and a surface elevation averaging about 225 feet above the sea. Ice shelves are fed by great outlet glaciers, but also accumulate new ice through the compaction of snow.

Ice sheets of the Pleistocene epoch

As if the vast ice sheets of Greenland and Antarctica do not seem fantastic enough, geologists have brought to light abundant and convincing evidence that much of North America and Europe and parts of northern Asia and southern South America were covered by enormous ice sheets in a period of time designated the Pleistocene epoch (see Chapter 20). Despite the fact that this period ended 10,000 to 15,000 years ago with the rapid wasting away of the ice sheets, the glacial epoch is the most recent major episode in geologic history. Landforms made by the last ice advance and recession are very little modified by erosional agents.

Figures 26.10 and 26.11 show the extent to which North America and Europe were covered at the maximum known spread of the last advance of the ice. In the United States, all the land lying north of the Missouri and Ohio rivers was covered, as well as northern Pennsylvania and all of New York and New England. In Europe, the ice sheet centered upon the Baltic Sea, covering the Scandinavian countries and spreading as far south as central Germany. The British Isles were almost covered by an icecap that had several centers on highland areas and spread outward to coalesce with the Scandinavian ice sheet. The Alps at the same time were heavily inundated by enlarged alpine glaciers, fused into a single icecap. All high mountain areas of the world underwent greatly intensified alpine glaciation at the time of maximum ice-sheet advance. Today, only small remnant alpine glaciers exist as vestiges of these great valley glaciers. In less favorable mountain regions no glaciers remain.

Proof of the former great extent of ice sheets has been carefully accumulated since the middle of the nineteenth century when the great naturalist Louis Agassiz first announced the bold theory. In general, the evidence of past glaciation lies in the recognition throughout North America and Europe of landforms identical with those now seen near the margins of the Greenland icecap and other glaciers. Although Agassiz's pronouncement was greeted with much skepticism a century ago, continental glaciation of the Pleistocene epoch is now universally accepted among scientists. Moreover, careful study of the deposits left by the ice has led to the knowledge that not one but four major advances and retreats occurred, spaced over a total period of about a million years. It is the deposits of the last advance, known as the *Wisconsin stage*, that form fresh and conspicuous landforms. For the most part, then, the discussion of glacial landforms will concern these most recent deposits.

Glacial stages

The four principal glacial stages of North America are matched by corresponding stages of Europe, as deciphered in the Alps. Together with the interglacial stages (periods of mild climate during which the ice sheets disappeared), these glacial stages in order of increasing age are:

North American stages (North-central U.S.)	European stages (Alps)
Wisconsin glacial	Würm glacial
Sangamon interglacial	Riss-Würm interglacial
Illinoian glacial	Riss glacial
Yarmouth interglacial	Mindel-Riss interglacial
Kansan glacial	Mindel glacial
Aftonian interglacial	Günz-Mindel interglacial
Nebraskan glacial	Günz glacial

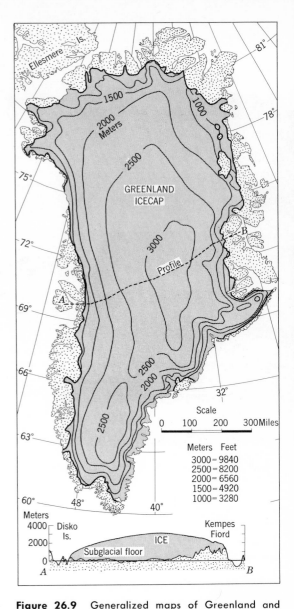

Figure 26.9 Generalized maps of Greenland and Antarctica. (After R. F. Flint, *Glacial and Pleistocene Geology*.)

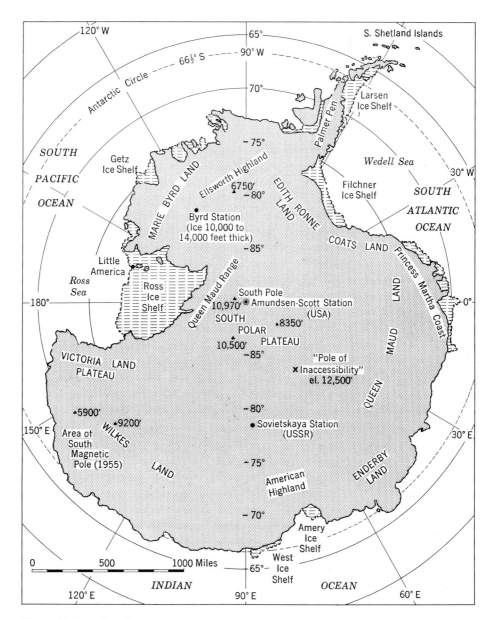

Figure 26.9 continued

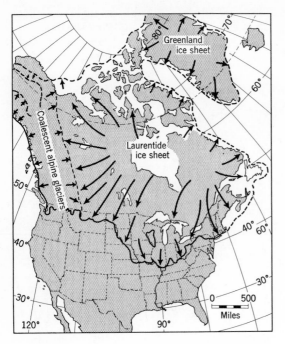

Figure 26.10 Pleistocene ice sheets of North America at their maximum spread reached as far south as the present Ohio and Missouri rivers. (After R. F. Flint.)

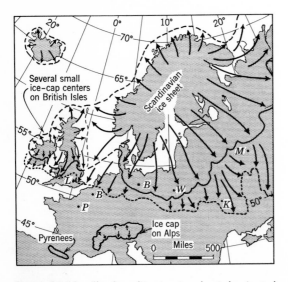

Figure 26.11 The Scandinavian ice sheet dominated northern Europe during the Pleistocene glaciations. Solid line shows limits of ice in the last glacial age; dotted line on land shows maximum extent at any time. (After R. F. Flint.)

Figure 26.12 shows the limit of southerly spread of ice of each glacial stage in the north-central United States. Where older limits were overridden by younger, the boundaries are conjectural. Notice that an area in Wisconsin (the *Driftless Area*) was surrounded by ice but never inundated.

The absolute age and duration in years of the Pleistocene epoch and its stages are extremely difficult to fix, even though the relative order of events is well established. The last ice disappeared 10,000 to 15,000 years ago from the north-central United States. The Wisconsin stage may have endured 30,000 years. The earliest onset of glacial advance (Nebraskan) may have occurred 300,000 to 600,000 years ago, although the beginning of the Pleistocene epoch of geologic time is commonly set by geologists as about one million years before present.

Cause of continental glaciation

It should not be inferred that the occurrence of an ice age as the last event of geologic history means that the earth as a planet is cooling off. There is excellent evidence in the form of rock deposits of similar periods of glaciation in the early part of the earth's geologic history. But, beyond the fact that glaciations are occasional events in geologic history, knowledge concerning the cause of glaciation is speculative. Obviously a prolonged period of cold climate with ample snowfall brings on the growth of icecaps.

One possible contributing cause of glaciation is a decrease in the quantity of solar radiation intercepted by the earth. It has been reasoned that, should this quantity of energy have diminished somewhat at the beginning of the Pleistocene epoch, the average temperature of the earth's atmosphere would have dropped to a lower level. Providing that this change did not also diminish the quantity of snowfall, the reduced ablation of snowfields would increase the quantity of snow turned into glacial ice, with resultant growth and spread of icecaps. A second factor, possibly working in harmony with the first, is the known increase in elevation of large parts of the continents during the Pliocene and early Pleistocene epochs as a result of widespread mountain making (orogenic uplift), as well as broad uparching of continental interiors (epeirogenic uplift). That mountains intercept large quantities of precipitation has already been explained (Chapter 10) in the discussion of orographic precipitation. The combined effects of reduced solar energy and increased altitude of continents would bring on colder climates with increased snowfall over favorable areas of the continents, such as the Laurentian Upland of eastern Canada and the Scandinavian peninsula. This com-

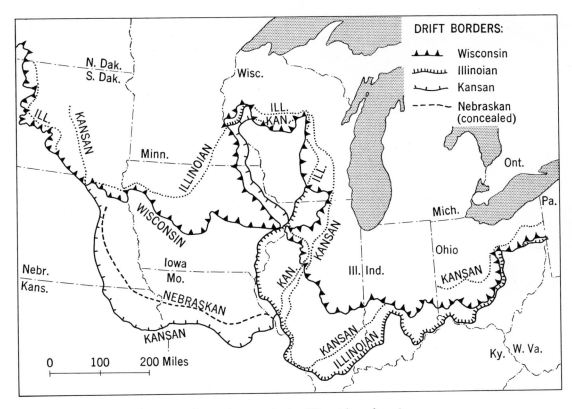

Figure 26.12 In each glacial stage the ice sheet reached a different line of maximum advance. (After R. F. Flint, *Glacial and Pleistocene Geology.*)

posite theory of cause of glaciation may be called the *solar-topographic theory.*

An important and widely held theory attributes glaciation to a reduction of the carbon dioxide content of the atmosphere. The role of carbon dioxide in absorbing long wave radiation and thus warming the atmosphere has been explained in Chapter 7. It is estimated that if the carbon dioxide content of the atmosphere, which is now 0.03 per cent by volume, were reduced by half that amount, the earth's average surface temperature would drop about 7° F. Such a reduction in carbon dioxide content might be postulated in combination with increased continental altitude to bring on the growth of icecaps.

Other theories invoke quite different mechanisms. It has been postulated that increased quantities of volcanic dust in the atmosphere might bring about a glacial period because more solar energy would be reflected back into space, permitting less to enter the lower atmosphere. Along with the reduced air temperature would be the increase in numbers of tiny dust particles to serve as nuclei for the condensation of moisture, thus favoring increased precipitation. Another group of theories

propose shifts in the positions of the continents with respect to the poles, bringing various parts of the land masses into favorable geographical positions for the growth of ice sheets. Still another theory requires that changes in oceanic currents, specifically the diversion or blocking of such warm currents as the Gulf Stream, would have brought colder climates to the subarctic regions. Variations in the earth's orbit, causing changes in the amounts of solar energy received by the earth, have also been considered as the cause of glacial periods.

Erosion by ice sheets

Like alpine glaciers, ice sheets are effective eroding agents. The slowly moving ice may scrape and grind away much solid bedrock, leaving behind smoothly rounded rock masses bearing countless minute abrasion marks. Scratches, or *striations*, trend in the general direction of ice movement (Figure 26.13), but variations in ice direction from time to time often result in intersecting lines. Certain kinds of rock were susceptible to deep grooving. Outstanding are the beautifully formed grooves in limestone of Kelley's Island near the south shore of Lake Erie (Figure 26.14).

Figure 26.13 Glacial striations and fracture marks, mostly crescentic gouges, cover the smoothly rounded surface of this rock knob. These marks were made by the East Twin Glacier, Alaska. The ice moved in a direction away from the photographer. (Photograph by Maynard Miller.)

Figure 26.14 Unusually smooth, deep glacial grooves were carved in limestone by the ice action on Kelley's Island near the south shore of Lake Erie. (Photograph by Orlo Childs.)

Where a strong, sharp-pointed piece of rock was held by the ice and dragged over the bedrock surface, there resulted a series of curved cracks fitted together along the line of ice movement. These *chatter marks*, and closely related *crescentic gouges*, whose curvature is the opposite, are good indicators of the direction of ice movement (Figure 26.13). Some very hard rocks have acquired highly polished surfaces from the rubbing of fine clay particles against the rock. The evidences of ice erosion described here are common throughout the northeastern United States. They may be seen on almost any exposed hard rock surface. Once understood, they may be recognized by any alert observer.

Commonly bearing the above abrasion marks is a type of conspicuous knob of solid bedrock that has been shaped by the moving ice (Figure 26.13). One side, that from which the ice was approaching, is characteristically smoothly rounded and shows a striated and grooved surface. This is termed the *stoss* side. The other, or *lee* side, where the ice plucked out angular joint blocks, is irregular, blocky, and steeper than the stoss side. The quaint term *roches moutonnées* has long been applied by glaciologists to such glaciated rock knobs because of the "fancied resemblance to Eighteenth Century wigs slicked down with mutton tallow."[1]

Vastly more important than the minor abrasion forms are enormous excavations that the ice sheets made in some localities where the bedrock is of a weak variety and the ice current was accentuated by the presence of a valley paralleling the direction of ice flow. Under such conditions the ice sheet behaved much as a valley glacier, scooping out a deep, U-shaped trough. As fine examples may be cited the Finger Lakes of western New York State. Here a set of former stream valleys lay parallel to southward spread of the ice, which scooped out a series of deep troughs. Blocked at the north ends by glacial debris the basins now hold elongate lakes. Many hundreds of lake basins were created in a similar manner all over the glaciated portion of North America and Europe. Countless small lakes of Minnesota, Canada, and Finland occupy rock basins scooped out by ice action (Figure 26.15). Irregular debris deposits left by the ice are also important in causing lake basins.

Deposits left by ice sheets

The term *glacial drift* has long been applied to include all varieties of rock debris deposited in close association with glaciers. Drift is of two major types: (1) *Stratified drift* consists of layers of sorted and stratified clays, silts, sands, or gravels deposited

[1] R. F. Flint, *Glacial and Pleistocene Geology*, John Wiley and Sons, New York, 1957, p. 64.

by melt-water streams or in bodies of water adjacent to the ice. (2) *Till* is a heterogeneous mixture of rock fragments ranging in size from clay to boulders and is deposited directly from the ice without water transport. Moraines of valley glaciers, previously described, are composed largely of till, whereas the valley train is composed of stratified drift.

Over those parts of the United States formerly covered by Pleistocene ice sheets, glacial drift averages from 20 feet thick over mountainous terrain such as New England, to 50 and more feet thick over the lowlands of the north-central United States. Over Iowa, drift is from 150 to 200 feet thick; over Illinois, it averages more than 100 feet thick. Locally, where deep stream valleys existed prior to glacial advance, as in Ohio, drift may be several hundred feet deep.

In order to understand the form and composition of deposits left by ice sheets, it is desirable to consider the conditions prevailing at the time of existence of the ice, as shown in Figure 26.16. Block *A* shows a region partly covered by an ice sheet with a relatively stationary front edge. This condition occurs when the rate of ice ablation balances the amount of ice brought forward by spreading of the ice sheet. Any increase in ice movement would cause the ice to shove forward to cover more ground; an increase in the rate of wasting would cause the edge to recede and the ice surface to become lowered. Although the Pleistocene ice fronts did advance and recede in many minor and major fluctuations, there were considerable periods when the front was essentially stable. This condition is represented in Block *A*.

The transportational work of an ice sheet may be likened to that of a great conveyor belt. Anything carried on the belt is dumped off at the end and if not constantly removed will pile up in increasing quantity. Rock fragments brought within the ice are deposited at the edge as the ice evaporates or melts. There is no possibility of return transportation.

Glacial till that accumulates at the immediate ice edge forms an irregular, rubbly heap known as a *terminal moraine*. After the ice has disappeared, as in Diagram *B*, the moraine appears as a belt of knobby hills interspersed with basinlike hollows, some of which hold small lakes. The term *knob and kettle topography* is often applied to morainal belts (Figure 26.17). Terminal moraines tend to form great curving patterns, the convex form of curvature being directed southward and indicating that the ice advanced as a series of great lobes, each with a curved front (Figure 26.18). Where two lobes came together, the moraines curved back and fused together into a single moraine pointed

Figure 26.15 Seen from the air this esker in the Canadian shield area appears as a narrow embankment crossing the terrain of glacially eroded lake basins. (Photograph by Canadian Department of Mines, Geological Survey.)

northward. This is termed an *interlobate moraine* (Figure 26.16, Block *B*). In its general recession accompanying disappearance, the ice front paused for some time along a number of lines, causing morainal belts similar to the terminal moraine belt to be formed. These belts, known as *recessional moraines* (Figures 26.16 and 26.18), run roughly parallel with the terminal moraine but are often thin and discontinuous.

Figure 26.16, Block *A*, shows a smooth, sloping plain lying in front of the ice margin. This is the *outwash plain*, formed of stratified drift left by braided streams issuing from the ice. Their deposits are in reality great alluvial fans upon which are spread layer upon layer of sands and gravels. The adjective *glaciofluvial* is often applied to stream-laid stratified drift.

Large streams issue from tunnels in the ice, particularly when the ice for many miles back from the front has become stagnant, without forward movement. Tunnels then develop throughout the ice mass, serving to carry off the melt water. After the ice has gone (Block *B*, Figure 26.16) the outwash plain remains in its original form, but may be bounded on the iceward side by a steep slope which is the mold of the ice against which the outwash was built. Such a slope is called an *ice-contact slope*. Farther back, behind the terminal moraine, the position of a former ice tunnel is marked by a long, sinuous ridge known as an *esker*. The esker is the deposit of sand and gravel formerly laid upon the floor of the ice tunnel. Inasmuch as ice formed the sides and roof of the tunnel, its disappearance left merely the stream-bed deposit, which

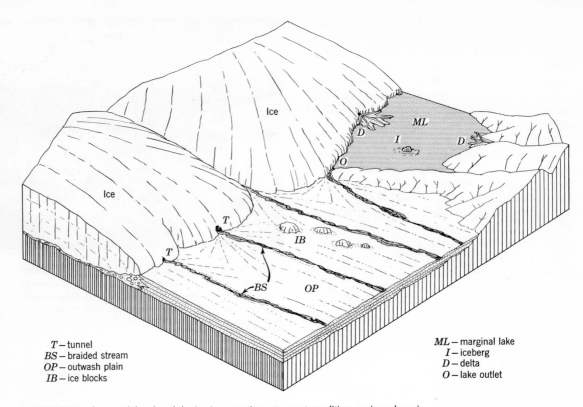

T – tunnel
BS – braided stream
OP – outwash plain
IB – ice blocks

ML – marginal lake
I – iceberg
D – delta
O – lake outlet

A. With the ice front stabilized and the ice in a wasting, stagnant condition, various depositional features are built by meltwaters.

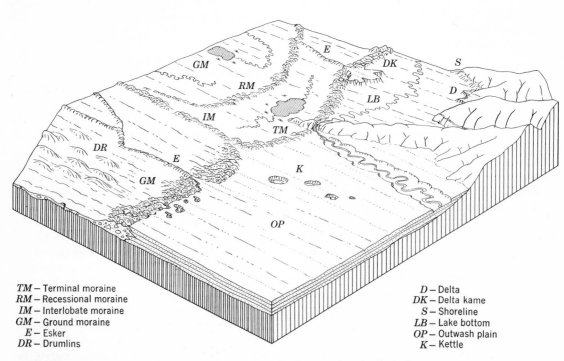

TM – Terminal moraine
RM – Recessional moraine
IM – Interlobate moraine
GM – Ground moraine
E – Esker
DR – Drumlins

D – Delta
DK – Delta kame
S – Shoreline
LB – Lake bottom
OP – Outwash plain
K – Kettle

B. After the ice has wasted completely away, a variety of new landforms made under the ice is exposed to view.

Figure 26.16 Marginal landforms of continental glaciers.

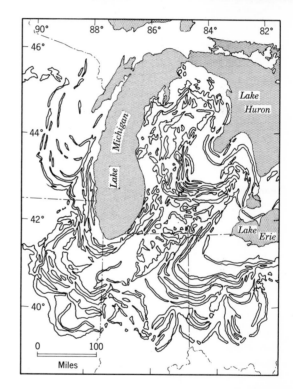

Figure 26.17 Morainal topography consists of many small hills and depressions. (Photograph by Douglas Johnson.)

Figure 26.18 Moraine belts of the north-central United States have a festooned pattern left by ice lobes. (After R. F. Flint and others, *Glacial Map of North America*, 1945.)

Figure 26.19 This esker near Belgrade, Maine, is being excavated as a source of sand and gravel.

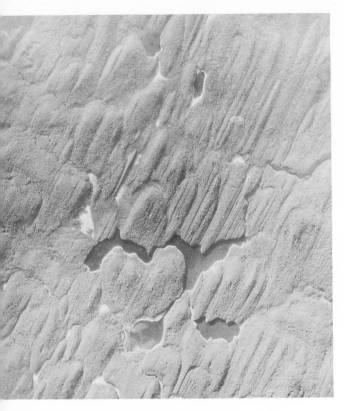

Figure 26.20. Viewed from high altitude, these drumlins in northern British Columbia show clearly the general trend of ice movement from upper right to lower left. The individual drumlins are ½ to 1½ miles long, ¼ mile wide or less, and 50 to 75 feet high. (U.S. Army Air Forces trimetrogon photograph.)

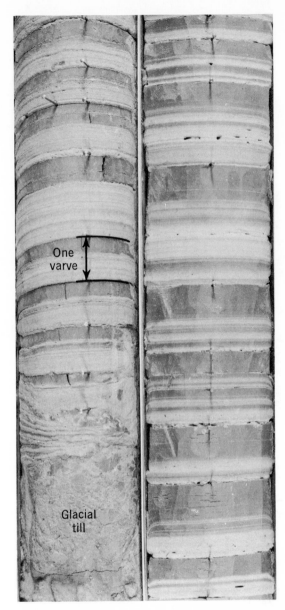

Figure 26.21 Samples of varved clays from glacial lake beds near New York City. Each varve consists of an upper dark layer and a lower light layer. The columns measure about ten inches from top to bottom of the photograph. (Photograph by C. A. Reeds. Courtesy of the American Museum of Natural History.)

now forms a ridge (Figure 26.19). Eskers are often many miles long; in parts of Maine a few are more than 100 miles long. Some have branches just as streams do. Because the esker is made of highly porous sand and gravel, the rapid draining away of water from the crest may prevent the growth of trees along the top of some eskers, which look as if artificially cleared of forest (Figure 26.15).

Another curious glacial form is the *drumlin*, a smoothly rounded, oval hill resembling the bowl of an inverted teaspoon. It consists of glacial till (Figure 26.20). Drumlins invariably lie in a zone behind the terminal or recessional moraines. They commonly occur in groups or swarms, which may number in the hundreds. The long axis of each drumlin parallels the direction of ice movement, and the drumlins thus point toward the terminal moraines and serve as indicators of direction of ice movement. From a study of the composition and structure of drumlins, it has been generally agreed that they were formed under moving ice by a kind of plastering action in which layer upon

layer of bouldery clay was spread upon the drumlin. This would have been possible only if the ice were so heavily choked with debris that the excess had to be left behind. Furthermore, some sort of knob or surface irregularity may have been required to start the plastering action and localize its occurrence.

Between the terminal, recessional, and interlobate moraines, the surface left by the ice is usually overspread by a cover of glacial till known as *ground moraine.* This cover is often inconspicuous because it forms no prominent or recognizable topographic feature. Nevertheless, the ground moraine may be thick and may obscure or entirely bury the hills and valleys that existed before glaciation. Where thick and smoothly spread, the ground moraine forms an extensive, level *till plain,* but this condition is likely only in regions already fairly flat to start with. In more dissected regions, the preglacial valleys and hills retain their same general outlines despite glaciation.

Deposits built into standing water

Where the general land slope is toward the front of an ice sheet, a natural topographic basin is formed between the ice front and the rising ground. Valleys that may have opened out northward are blocked by ice. Under such conditions, *marginal glacial lakes* form along the ice front (Figure 26.16, Block *A*). These lakes overflow along the lowest available channel, which lies between the ice and the ground slope or over some low pass along a divide. Into marginal lakes streams of melt water from the ice build *glacial deltas,* similar in most respects to deltas formed by any stream flowing into a lake. Streams from the land likewise build deltas into the lake. When the ice has disappeared the lake drains away, exposing the bottom upon which layers of fine clay and silt have been laid. These fine-grained strata, which have settled out from suspension in turbid lake waters, are called *glaciolacustrine* sediments and are a variety of stratified drift. The layers are commonly of banded appearance, with alternating dark and light layers, termed *varves.* Each pair, or individual varve, is interpreted as being the deposit of one year, the thicker light-colored band being composed of coarser-textured warm season deposits; the thin, dark band is fine clay that settles out in winter, then the lake is sealed over by an ice cover and becomes stilled (Figure 26.21). Glacial lake plains are extremely flat, with meandering streams and extensive areas of marshland.

Deltas, built with a flat top at what was formerly the lake level, are now curiously isolated, flat-topped landforms known as *delta kames.* Delta and stream channel deposits built between a stagnant ice mass and the wall of a valley become *kame terraces,* whose steep scarps are ice-contact slopes (Figure 26.22). Kame terraces are difficult to distinguish from the uppermost member of a series of alluvial terraces, but most kames have undrained depressions or pits produced by the melting of enclosed ice blocks. Built of very well-washed and sorted sands and gravels, kames commonly show the steeply dipping foreset beds characteristic of deltas (Figure 26.23).

Geographical aspects of glacial landforms

Because much of Europe and North America was glaciated by the Pleistocene ice sheets, landforms associated with the ice are of fundamental geographical importance in influencing the activity of human beings. Agricultural influences of glacia-

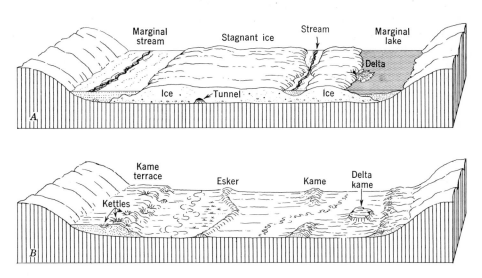

Figure 26.22 Kames may originate as stream or lake deposits laid between a stagnant ice mass and the valley sides. (After R. F. Flint.)

Figure 26.23 These cross-bedded, sorted sands were laid down in a glacial delta near North Haven, Connecticut. (Photograph by R. J. Lougee.)

Figure 26.24 Thick layers of outwash sands and gravels such as these on the north shore of Long Island are excavated in great quantities for use in highway and building construction. The dark layer at the top is a bed of glacial till, left by a glacial advance. Boulders in the foreground are glacial erratics which have rolled down from the till bed. (Photograph by A. K. Lobeck.)

tion are both favorable and unfavorable, depending on preglacial topography and whether the ice eroded or deposited heavily. In hilly or mountainous regions, such as New England, the glacial till is thinly distributed and extremely stony. Cultivation is made difficult by countless boulders and stones in the soil. Along morainal belts the steep slopes, irregularity of topography, and abundance of boulders and stones in the till are unfavorable to cultivation. These same features, however, make morainal belts extremely desirable as suburban residential areas. A pleasing variety of hills, depressions, and small lakes makes ideal locations for large estates.

Extensive till plains, outwash plains, and lake plains, on the other hand, make for some of the most productive agricultural land in the world. In this class belong the prairie lands of Indiana, Illinois, Iowa, Nebraska, and Minnesota.

Glaciofluvial deposits are of great economic value. The sands and gravels of outwash plains, kames, and eskers provide the aggregate necessary for concrete and other building purposes (Figure 26.24). The purest sands may be used for molds needed for metal castings. Huge quantities of ground water are contained in glaciofluvial deposits. Where deep, preglacial valleys were filled with such materials, large quantities of water can be pumped from wells penetrating the deposit. In this way, many large cities and industrial plants in Ohio, Pennsylvania, and New York obtain their water supplies.

Review Questions

1. What is a glacier? What conditions are necessary for the formation of glaciers? Define ablation. What is firn? What is the distinction between alpine and continental glaciers? How fast does glacial ice flow?

2. How do glaciers erode their channels? Compare alpine glaciers with streams in regard to erosion and transportation activities.

3. How do alpine glaciers modify mountain topography? Describe and explain the following features: cirque, arête, horn, col, glacial trough, hanging trough, rock basin, rock step, tarn, finger lake.

4. What is the form of a glacial trough? How does this form differ from that of a normally eroded stream valley? Explain how a fiord is formed. Where are fiords found?

5. Describe the various kinds of deposits made by a valley glacier. What are the location and form of the following types of moraines: medial, lateral, terminal, and recessional? What is a valley train?

6. Where are the ice sheets of the world today? About how thick is the ice in the central parts of these ice sheets? Explain how an icecap is fed and how the ice moves. What is calving of a tide-water glacier?

7. Describe the extent of ice sheets of the Pleistocene epoch in North America and Europe. Describe the southern glacial limit in the United States. What great scientist was largely responsible for convincing the scientific world that the Pleistocene glaciation actually occurred?

8. Name in order the glacial and interglacial stages of North America. How long ago did the last glacial ice disappear from the United States?

9. Review the principal theories that attempt to explain the occurrence of glacial periods.

10. What erosional features on rock surfaces give evidence of the former presence of an ice sheet? How can the direction of ice movement be inferred?

11. How can the direction of ice movement be inferred from the shape of a glaciated rock knob (roche moutonnée)? How were the Finger Lakes of western New York State formed?

12. What is glacial drift? What is the distinction between stratified drift and till?

13. Describe and explain the various depositional forms associated with the margin of an ice sheet.

14. What kinds of moraines are left by ice sheets? Describe the topography of an outwash plain.

15. What is a glacial outwash plain? Describe the surface topography of an outwash plain.

16. How is an esker formed? How long are eskers? Of what material are they composed?

17. What is a drumlin? Of what material is it composed? How is it formed? Where are most drumlins found in relation to the terminal moraine?

18. What is a till plain? How is it formed?

19. Explain how marginal glacial lakes are formed. What types of deposits are formed in them? What is a delta kame? a kame terrace? What are varves?

Exercises

Exercise 1. _Young Stage of Alpine Glaciation._
(Source: Cloud Peak, Wyo., U.S. Geological Survey topographic map; scale 1:125,000.)

Explanatory Note: Steep-walled cirques have been cut into the broadly rounded summit of the Big Horn range in northern Wyoming, but much of the preglacial surface remains. The cirques contain lakes (cross-ruled), which form chainlike groups extending down the glacial troughs which lead from the cirques.

QUESTIONS

1. (**a**) Determine the fractional scale of this map. (**b**) What is the contour interval? (**c**) Give location (grid coordinates) and the approximate elevation of the highest point on this map.

2. What is the depth of the cirque located at 3.1–2.3, measured from the lake at this point to the upland surface at 2.9–2.0?

3. Cirques heading on the east side of the range seem to have eaten back closer to the main divide running down the center of the map than those heading on the west side of the range. Can you give an explanation for this?

4. Lay out the shortest possible route for a trail over this range from 5.5–2.3 to 0.0–1.5 in such a way that the gradient nowhere exceeds 1600 feet per mile. Avoid all cirques and troughs.

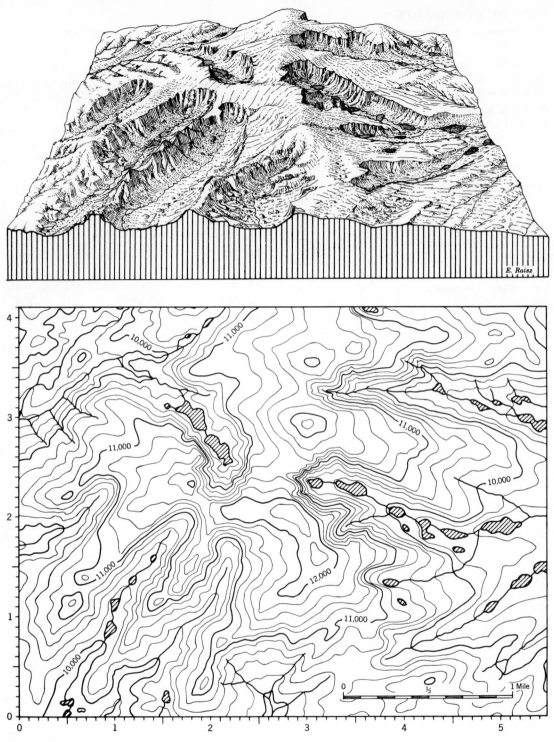

E. Raisz

Exercise 1

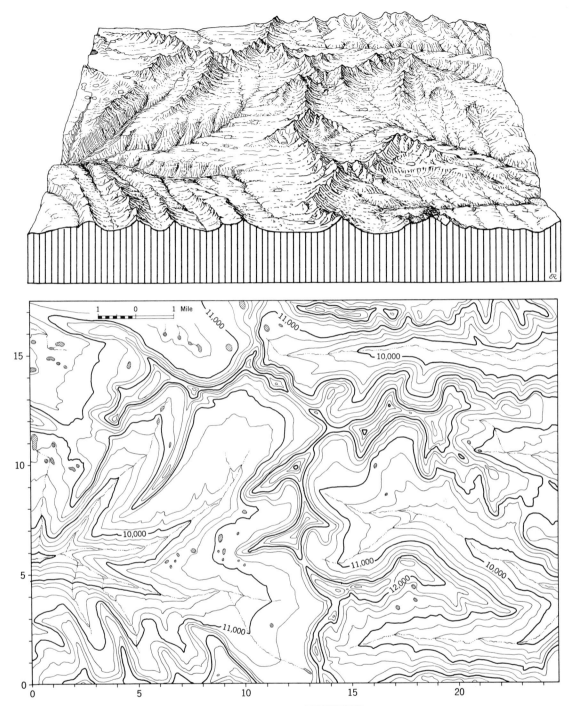

Exercise 2. *Mature Stage of Alpine Glaciation.*
(Source: Hayden Peak, Utah, U.S. Geological Survey
topographic map; scale 1 : 125,000.)

Explanatory Notes: The map and block diagram show a
maturely glaciated portion of the great Uinta Mountain
range of northern Utah. North is toward the right. Broad,
relatively flat-floored cirques are separated by narrow,
steep-walled divides, consisting of pointed horns connected
by sharp arêtes. Streams have cut deep V-shaped canyons
into the cirque mouths. For further details on the glacial
features of this area see a report by W. W. Atwood (1909),
listed among the reading references.

QUESTIONS

1. Make a topographic profile from 14.0–17.5 to 2.0–0.0,
using a vertical scale of 1 inch equals 2000 feet.

2. On a sheet of thin tracing paper laid over this map,
write the word *cirque* on all cirques that you can identify.
Label all good examples of arêtes, horns, and cols.

3. On another sheet of tracing paper laid over this map,
color blue all areas which you would imagine to be covered
by glaciers at a stage of maximum glaciation. Add arrows
to show directions of ice movement. In another color,
draw in all medial moraines which you might expect.

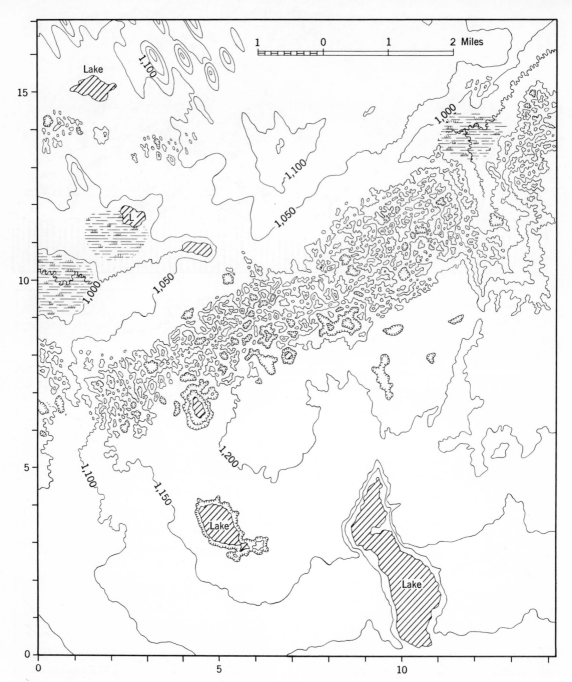

Exercise 3. *Moraine and Pitted Outwash Plain.*
(Source: St. Croix Dalles, Wis.-Minn., U.S. Geological Survey topographic map; scale 1:62,500.)

Explanatory Note: Running across this map from northeast to southwest is a terminal moraine belt composed of innumerable small hills and depressions. To the southeast of this moraine is a sloping outwash plain containing iceblock lakes. North of the moraine is a lower area with marshes and drumlins, which was beneath the ice and has a cover of thin ground moraine.

QUESTIONS

1. (*a*) What is the contour interval used on this map?

(*b*) How wide is the terminal moraine belt in the center of the map?

2. (*a*) How deep is the closed depression at 8.5–8.8? **(*b*)** What is the elevation of the surface of the lake at 4.5–6.5? **(*c*)** What is the slope (feet per mile) of the outwash plain surface between 6.0–7.5 and 9.0–0.0?

3. Give the compass bearing or azimuth on which the ice was moving, as indicated by the orientation of the drumlins at 4.0–16.0 and by the trend of the moraine belt.

4. Did the ice advance over the area now covered by the outwash plain? What is the evidence?

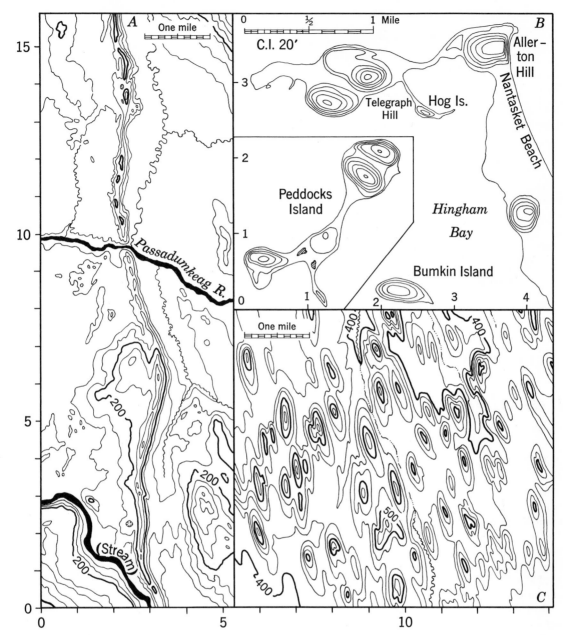

Exercise 4. *Esker and Drumlins.* (Source: Map *A*, Passadumkeag, Maine, 1:62,500. Map *B*, Hull, Mass., 1:31,680. Map *C*, Weedsport, N. Y. 1:62,500. U.S. Geological Survey topographic maps.)

Explanatory Note: Map *A* shows an esker ridge, named Enfield Horseback, running from north to south down the center of the map. Maps *B* and *C* show drumlins from two well-known drumlin localities, Boston Bay and western New York State, respectively. Note that the scale of Map *B* differs from that of the other two and therefore has a grid system of its own. A portion of the Weedsport map is reproduced on one of the endpapers of this book.

QUESTIONS

Map A: **1.** (*a*) How wide (yards) is this esker, approximately? (*b*) How high (feet) is the esker crest above the surrounding lowland, just north of the Passadumkeag River?

2. (*a*) Why does the esker crest rise and fall in elevation? (*b*) Explain the closed depressions at 2.3–13.9.

Map B: **3.** Give the length, width, and height of four drumlins on this map, locating each by grid coordinates.

4. Why has Allerton Hill such a steep slope on the east?

Map C: **5.** How many drumlins are shown on this map? Count all hills represented by one or more closed contours.

6. Which drumlins are higher, those on Map *C* or those on Map *B?* Compare the highest three on each map.

7. In which direction did the ice move when forming the drumlins on Map *C?* Give compass bearing. Compare with direction of movement indicated by drumlins in Map *B*. Compare the shapes of drumlins on the two maps.

CHAPTER TWENTY-SEVEN

Landforms made by waves and currents

OCEAN waves work unceasingly to transform the shores of the continents and islands. The origin, form, and mode of travel of ocean waves was treated in Chapter 9. Waves travel across the deep ocean with only gradual loss of energy, but when shallow water is reached, the wave form changes radically and new water motions are developed. These take the form of powerful surges and currents capable of performing great erosive and transportational work.

Most shorelines have a rather smooth, sloping bottom extending out beneath the water level. As waves approach this shallow zone, wave velocity becomes less and wave crests become more closely spaced (Figure 27.1). Wave height and steepness increase rapidly until the crest rolls forward to make a *breaker* (Figure 27.2). After the breaker has collapsed, a foamy, turbulent sheet of water rides up the beach slope. This *swash,* or *uprush,* is a powerful surge causing a landward movement of sand and gravel on the beach. When the force of the swash has been spent against the slope of the beach, the return flow, the *backwash,* pours down the beach, but much disappears by infiltration into

above: Pemaquid Point, Maine.

Photograph, Charles P. Cushing.

the permeable beach sand. Sands and gravels are swept seaward by the backwash.

Wave erosion

In times of relative calm or moderate winds, waves do little erosional work but tend instead to build beaches and other deposits out of sand and gravel. In times of storm, when enormous waves break and throw tons of water against the shoreline, erosion is rapid (Figure 27.3). The violent uprush hurls cobbles and boulders against exposed bedrock along the shore, causing fragments to be broken free. A continual crushing and grinding action goes on as the stones are jostled together. The products of this breaking up are sorted according to size. Fine particles are carried out to sea, where they eventually come to rest in deep, quiet water to form mud layers. Sands and gravels remain close to shore, forming beaches and bars.

Should the shoreline consist of hard rock, erosion will be slow and the storms of many years' time will make little visible change. Where soft materials, such as glacial moraines or outwash plains, form the shoreline, erosion is very rapid. The force of the water alone is sufficient to erode such deposits, and the sea cliff may recede many feet in a single storm (Figure 27.4). Some of the

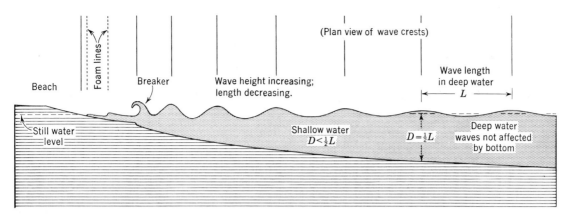

Figure 27.1 As waves enter shallow water the form changes until breaking occurs.

Figure 27.2 Breaking of a wave generates a forward swash; gravity reverses the flow to make the backwash. (After W. M. Davis.)

Figure 27.3 Tremendous forward thrust is evident in these storm waves breaking against a sea wall at Hastings, England.

Figure 27.4 Storm waves breaking against a coast underlain by weak sand quickly undermined this shore home at Seabright, New Jersey. The barrier of wooden pilings (right) proved ineffective in preventing cutting back of the cliff. (Photograph by Douglas Johnson.)

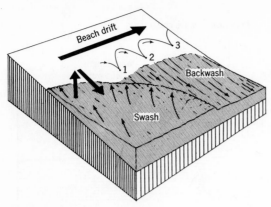

Figure 27.5 When waves approach a shore obliquely, the swash and backwash move sand and gravel particles along the beach in a series of arched paths.

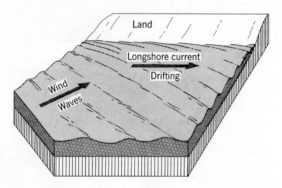

Figure 27.6 When waves approach a shoreline obliquely, a longshore current is set in motion in the shallow-water zone where waves are breaking.

particular forms produced by wave erosion are described and explained in a later paragraph.

Shore and beach drifting

The unceasing alternate shifting of materials with swash and backwash of breaking waves results not only in movements of rock fragments in seaward and landward directions on the beach, but also in a sidewise movement known as *beach drifting* (Figure 27.5). Wave fronts usually approach the shore with a slight obliquity rather than directly head on. The swash is therefore directed obliquely up the beach, and the sand, gravel, and boulders are consequently moved obliquely up the slope. After the water has spent its energy, the backwash flows down the slope of the beach, being controlled by the pull of gravity which urges it in the most direct downhill direction. The particles are therefore dragged directly seaward and come to rest at a position to one side of the starting place. Because

on a particular day, wave fronts approach consistently from the same direction this movement is repeated many times. Individual rock particles thus travel a considerable distance along the shore. Multiplied many thousands of times to include the numberless particles of the beach, this form of mass transport is a major process in shoreline development.

Although the word *beach* is in common language use, it would be well at this point to define a beach as a deposit of sand, gravel or cobbles formed inshore from the zone of breaking waves by the action of swash and backwash. If the sand is arriving at a particular section of the beach more rapidly than it can be carried away, the beach is widened and built shoreward, a change called *progradation*. If sand is leaving a section of beach more rapidly than it is being brought in, the beach is narrowed and the shoreline moves landward, a change called *retrogradation*.

A process related to beach drifting is *longshore drifting*. When waves approach a shoreline under the influence of strong winds, the water level is slightly raised near shore by a slow shoreward drift of water. There is thus an excess of water pushed shoreward, which must escape. A *longshore current* is set up parallel to shore in a direction away from the wind (Figure 27.6). When wave and wind conditions are favorable, this current is capable of moving sand along the sea bottom in a direction parallel to the shore.

Both beach drifting and longshore drifting move particles in the same direction for a given set of onshore winds and oblique wave fronts and therefore supplement each other's influence in sediment transportation.

Tidal currents are still another type of water movement that causes the transportation of rock particles. The nature of these currents was explained in Chapter 6. They are particularly effective in narrow bays and estuaries, but of little importance where a shoreline is fairly straight.

Wave refraction

The phenomenon of change in direction, or bending, of wave fronts as they approach the shore is known as *wave refraction*. This is illustrated in Figure 27.7, which shows a shoreline with bays and promontories. Successive positions of a wave are indicated by the lines numbered 1, 2, 3, etc. In deep water the wave fronts are parallel. As the shore is neared, the retarding influence of shallow water is felt first in the areas in front of the promontories. Shallowing of water reduces speed of wave travel at those places, but in the deeper water in front of the bays the retarding action has not yet occurred. Consequently, the wave front is bent, or *refracted*, in rough conformity with the shoreline. If the shoreline pattern consists of broad, open curves, the waves may break everywhere along the shore at the same time, but this is unusual. The wave ordinarily will break first upon the promontory and on the bay head last, as indicated in Figure 27.7.

Particularly important in understanding the development of embayed shorelines is the distribution of wave energy along the shore. On Figure 27.7, dashed lines (lettered *a*, *b*, *c*, *d*, etc.) divide the wave at position 1 into equal parts, which may be taken to include equal amounts of energy. As the wave is followed into shore, the dashed lines indicate what happens to each unit of energy. Along the headlands the energy is concentrated into a short piece of shoreline; along the bays it is spread over a much greater length of shoreline. Consequently, the breaking waves act as powerful erosional agents on the promontories, but are relatively weak and ineffective at the bay heads. The important principle thus revealed is that headlands and promontories are rapidly eroded back, tending to produce a simple, straight shoreline as an ultimate form.

Wave refraction also occurs where oblique waves approach a perfectly straight shore (Figure 27.8). They are turned so as to break almost parallel with the beach. Wave-refraction patterns can be studied from air photographs and may provide valuable information regarding the form of the bottom in the vicinity of the shoreline.

Development of sea cliffs

Where a steeply sloping land surface descends below the water the development of steep cliffs bordering the shoreline is especially favored. Such a condition may come about by a sinking of the land or a rise of ocean level, bringing the water line against what were formerly the steep slopes of mountains or hills.

Figure 27.9 illustrates the development of sea cliffs. Block *A* shows an early stage, termed the *nip stage*, in which wave attack has carved out a small cliff in the hard bedrock. At the base of the cliff is a small rock platform sloping seaward and lying just below water level. Disintegrated rock fragments are swept seaward because wave energy is excessive and will not permit sand and gravel to remain as a beach.

Block *B* shows a cliff developed to considerable height, because, as the cliff is cut back, the rise of land slope causes its height to increase. The waves have sought out points of comparative weakness in the rock, penetrating to form crevices and *sea caves*. Some more solid portions of rock project

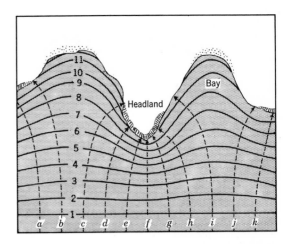

Figure 27.7 Wave refraction along an embayed coast causes energy to be concentrated on the headlands.

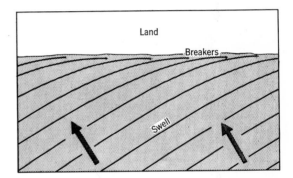

Figure 27.8 On a straight shoreline, wave refraction tends to bend the wave front toward the beach.

seaward. Where attached to the mainland they may form *sea arches;* where detached, they rise as *stacks* (Figure 27.10). At this stage, the cliff line has reached its greatest degree of irregularity. It is still being vigorously undercut, as evidenced by a wave-cut *notch* at the cliff base. The sloping rock-floored platform at the cliff base, known as the *abrasion platform* is now relatively wide. The inner edge is covered by water only at times of high tide or storm. A beach of sand or cobblestones may be present, but is transitory and may disappear during a single storm, to be built back very slowly. At the outer edge of the rock-abrasion platform, the slope is extended in a deposit of sand and larger rock particles known as the *shore-face terrace,* derived from ground-up rock that the waves have eroded from the cliff.

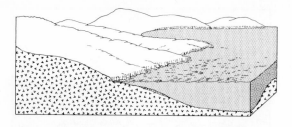

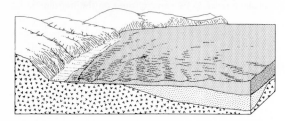

A. Breaking waves first cut out a small cliff, or *nip*.

B. As the cliff is cut back it develops undercut notches, arches, stacks, and crevices. At the same time, an abrasion platform is cut and a terrace built. A = arch; S = stack; C = cave; N = notch; P = abrasion platform; T = shore face terrace; B = beach; R = crevice.

C. When equilibrium has been reached a broad platform is present and the cliff is no longer actively undermined.

Figure 27.9 Development of sea cliffs. (After E. Raisz.)

Figure 27.10 The chalk cliffs of Normandy, along the French channel coast, show stacks, arches, and sea caves.

Streams that formerly flowed to the sea in valleys whose lower ends were at sea level may now be shortened and left as *hanging valleys* (Figure 27.11), having been unable to deepen their valleys with sufficient rapidity to keep pace with the retreating sea cliff. If the rock material is of an unstable variety, large masses may slump or slide from the cliff (Figure 27.12).

A late stage in the development of sea cliffs, shown in Block *C* of Figure 27.9, may be considered the *mature stage*. The abrasion platform has been so greatly widened that all, or almost all, wave energy is expended in friction as the waves travel over the shallow platform, and in shifting sand across the beach. Consequently, wave attack upon the cliff base is greatly reduced. Weathering and rainbeat acting upon the cliff face wear it down to a lower slope. Irregularities such as sea caves and crevices disappear. The beach may now be broad and deep with little bedrock appearing at the surface.

The geographical influence of marine cliffs is felt in several ways. The coast may be inaccessible because of the high cliffs. In military operations this is especially significant, because a landing is hazardous and a beachhead difficult to expand where a sheer cliff parallels the beach. If the stream valleys are hanging, there are few points where access may be had to the coastal region. Along such coasts, which tend to be fairly straight, the only natural harbors are at the mouths of large streams that have been able to cut down to an accordant junction with the sea (Figure 27.10 and 27.11). This condition prevails along parts of the French channel coast.

A shore bordered by a marine cliff may be of limited value for summer beach use because of the inaccessibility of the shore from the land back of the cliff and because the beach may be thin or rocky even if present. At high tide, the abrasion platform is sometimes inundated to the cliff base, making the shore a dangerous place where bathers can be trapped by rising tide.

Shoreline classification

Because shorelines display a wide variety of forms, it is desirable to have a classification to group them according to their origin and development. Five major classes of shorelines have been found to include virtually all known types (Figure 27.13).

1. *Shorelines of submergence.* Wherever a sinking down of the earth's crust occurs near the border of a land area, or there is a world-wide rise of sea level, the new shoreline takes a position along what was approximately a former contour of the land surface. Below this level all the surface

Figure 27.11 When a marine cliff is cut back rapidly, hanging valleys appear as notches in the cliff. The large stream at the right has been able to maintain an accordant junction with the sea level and provides a small harbor. (After W. M. Davis.)

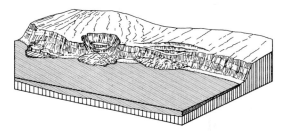

Figure 27.12 Coastal landslides in weak sedimentary strata are the result of oversteepening of a marine cliff by wave attack. (After W. M. Davis.)

formerly exposed to the air is now submerged beneath the sea. In this way, the term *shoreline of submergence* is applicable.

It is possible to subdivide shorelines of submergence into subgroups, depending on the type of topography that existed before the submergence. Wherever a region was dissected by streams into a system of valleys and divides, submergence produces a highly irregular, embayed shoreline termed a *ria shoreline.* Former valleys become deep embayments; former hilltops produce islands; former divides between valleys produce promontories or peninsulas. Variations in ria shoreline form depend on the stage of dissection and relief of the land immediately before submergence. Two possibilities, one a mountainous region (1*A*), the other a coastal plain of very low relief (1*B*), are illustrated in Figure 27.13.

Some coastal regions have been heavily eroded by valley glaciers, whose troughs were excavated below sea level. After the glaciers have disappeared, *a fiord shoreline* results (Figure 27.13, 1*C*). (See also Chapter 26.) Such shorelines are distinctive because of the steepness of the fiord walls, the great depth of water, and the great inland extent of the fiords.

Other subtypes of shorelines of submergence result from the submergence of landscapes formed by continental glaciation (Figure 27.13, 1*D*).

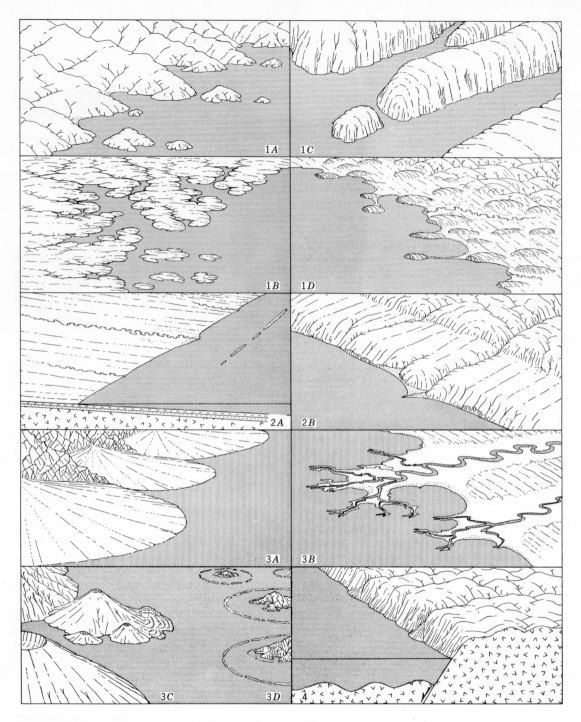

Figure 27.13 Classification of shorelines. (1) *Shorelines of Submergence:* 1A, submerged mountainous coast; 1B, submerged coastal plain, low relief; 1C, fiord coast; 1D, submerged glacial deposits (drumlins). (2) *Shorelines of Emergence:* 2A, coastal plain type, low relief; 2B, steeply sloping type, strong relief. (3) *Neutral Shorelines:* 3A, alluvial fan shoreline; 3B, delta shoreline; 3C, volcano shoreline; 3D, coral reef shoreline. (4) *Fault Shorelines.*

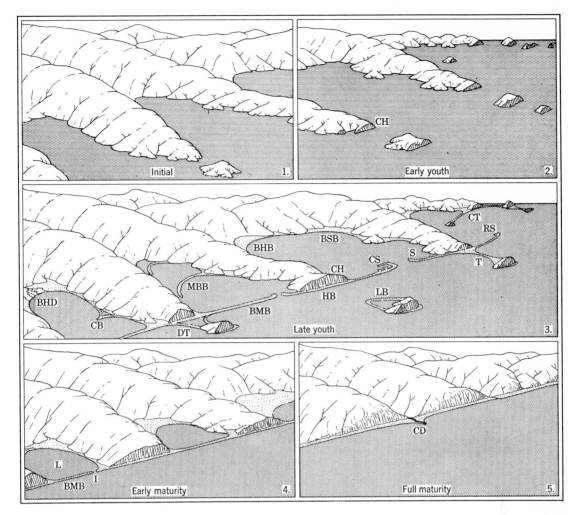

Figure 27.14 Development of the shoreline of submergence. T = tombolo; S = spit; RS = recurved spit; CS = complex spit; CT = complex tombolo; LB = looped bar; CH = cliffed headland; DT = double tombolo; HB = headland beach; BMB = baymouth bar; CB = cuspate bar; BHB = bayhead beach; BSB = bayside beach; BHD = bayhead delta; L = lagoon; I = inlet; CD = cuspate delta.

2. *Shorelines of emergence.* Wherever a rising of the earth's crust has occurred near the border of a continent, or the sea level has fallen, a *shoreline of emergence* is created. The water line takes a position against what was formerly a slope of the sea floor. Above the new shoreline lies a new coastal land belt which has emerged from the sea. Withdrawal of water to form extensive continental ice sheets is an effective cause of sea-level lowering. It is likely that shorelines of emergence were widely distributed during the time of maximum glacier advance in the Pleistocene epoch.

Most sea floors that have been submerged for a long period of geologic time near the margins of continents have been receiving layered deposits of muds, sands, and gravels derived from erosion of the lands and distributed by ocean currents. These continental shelves have a relatively smooth surface and gentle slope away from the continents. (See Chapter 20.) When a continental shelf is exposed by emergence it produces a low, smooth, gently sloping coastal plain, bounded by a simple, even shoreline, which may be termed a *coastal-plain shoreline* (Figure 27.13, 2A).

Along some coastal belts, the submarine topography contains steep slopes. The shoreline of emergence here differs from that of the coastal-plain shoreline in that deep water lies close off-shore and the coastal belt may be relatively mountainous to within a short distance of the shore (Figure 27.13, 2*B*). No simple name has been given to this subtype, but it may be designated a *steeply sloping shoreline of emergence*. Old wave-cut cliffs and benches at various levels above the sea indicate that emergence was spasmodic.

3. *Neutral shorelines.* Wherever a shoreline has been formed as a result of new materials being built out into the water, it is classified as a *neutral shoreline*. The word "neutral" implies that there has been no relative change between the level of the sea and the coastal region of the continent.

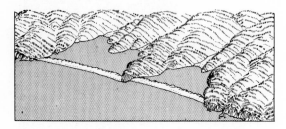

Figure 27.15 These baymouth bars have sealed off two bays and greatly simplified the outer shoreline. (After W. M. Davis.)

Figure 27.16 Two tombolos have connected this island with the mainland. (After W. M. Davis.)

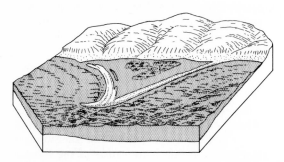

Figure 27.17 This cuspate bar, which has enclosed a triangular lagoon, receives drifted beach materials from both sides. (After E. Raisz.)

Several types of neutral shorelines are known. Each type is easily understood when referred to the agent responsible for building out the material into the water (Figure 27.13, 3*A*, 3*B*, 3*C*, 3*D*). An *alluvial fan shoreline*, curved in outline, is built by braided streams building a fan in the manner already explained in Chapter 24. Very similar are shorelines formed by building of a glacial outwash plain into the sea where the ice front stood near the shore. A *delta shoreline* is built of material brought out by a stream system (Chapter 24). Where a volcanic eruption has occurred, the slope of a volcano or the edge of a lava flow may compose the shore, which is then classified as a *volcano shoreline*. A *coral-reef shoreline* is built by marine organisms in the shallow-water zones of tropical seas.

4. *Fault shorelines.* An unusual type of shoreline is produced by faulting of the earth's crust in such a way that there is a dropping down of a segment of the crust on the seaward side of the break and corresponding rising up of the landward side. Should the downdropped block subside below sea level, the shoreline will come to rest against the steeply sloping land surface which is the surface of the plane of faulting, and can be termed a *fault shoreline* (Figure 27.13, 4). A similar result would be obtained where a crustal mass bounded by fault planes arises from beneath the sea.

5. *Compound shorelines* are those that show the forms of two of the previous classes combined, for example, submergence followed by emergence, or vice versa.

Life history of a shoreline of submergence

A shoreline of submergence of the ria type passes through a series of developmental stages, as illustrated in Figure 27.14. In the initial stage, submergence has just occurred to modify the shoreline. The coast is deeply bayed, with long peninsulas or promontories. Numerous islands lie offshore.

In the stage of early youth, wave attack is vigorous upon the headlands and upon the seaward sides of islands. Wave refraction brings maximum attack to these points. Wave-cut cliffs form such minor features as sea caves, stacks, and arches. The term *cliffed headland* is applied to the beveled peninsulas. Rock abrasion platforms develop at the cliff base, but beaches are thin or absent.

In the stage of late youth, the cliffs have increased in height and have been cut back considerably. Some of the smaller islands have been entirely planed off by wave abrasion and the larger ones have lost considerable area. In this stage, large numbers of depositional forms begin to appear. They are built of sand and gravel by the processes of beach and longshore drifting, described earlier, and represent a series of sequential landforms built out of the waste products of wave abrasion against the cliffs.

Fronting the cliffed headlands are *headland beaches*. From these the beach materials have drifted out across the bay mouths to produce *spits*, long slender sandbars whose ends extend into open water. Spits usually bend landward at their ends and may be termed *recurved spits*. Continued growth may add new curved portions to the end of a recurved spit, forming a *compound recurved spit*. Should waves generated within the waters of the bay break upon the spit on its landward side, a secondary spit may be built by shore drifting, forming a *complex spit*. Some large spits, such as Sandy Hook (Exercise 4), are both compound and complex.

When a spit has been extended so as to be joined to the opposite side of the bay, or to be separated by only a very narrow opening, it becomes a *baymouth bar* (Figure 27.15). Generally speaking, a bar is attached to land at both ends, whereas a spit has one end free in open water. A variety of other types of bars also forms along the coast. A bar connecting an island with the mainland is termed a *tombolo*. It may serve as the location of a road or railroad connecting the island with the mainland. Between the island and mainland may lie a harbor suitable for small craft. Sometimes a double tombolo is formed, enclosing a lagoon of quiet water between island and mainland (Figure 27.16). A *looped bar* may grow along the landward side of an island as a result of the drift of materials around the lee side of the island from the cliffed portion on the seaward side. Along the sides and ends of the bays are formed *bayside beaches* and *bayhead beaches*. These grow as a result of the drift of sand along the shore from the headlands. Because the bay heads are places of minimum wave attack, the sand tends to accumulate there. If the bays are long and narrow, curving bars will be built across the bay. If located in the middle portion of the bay, they are called *midbay bars;* if near the bay heads, *bayhead bars*. These bars are always smoothly curved, the concave part of the curve facing seaward and merging smoothly with the line of the bayside beaches. A *cuspate bar*, whose sharply pointed outline resembles a shark's tooth, sometimes forms along the side of a bay or on the outer shoreline (Figure 27.17) and seems to be caused by the meeting of drift materials brought from opposite directions. At bay heads, deltas may be built into water, thus aiding in the process of filling the bays.

As the stage of youth draws to a close, the outlying islands are completely consumed and the cliffed headlands begin to form a fairly straight

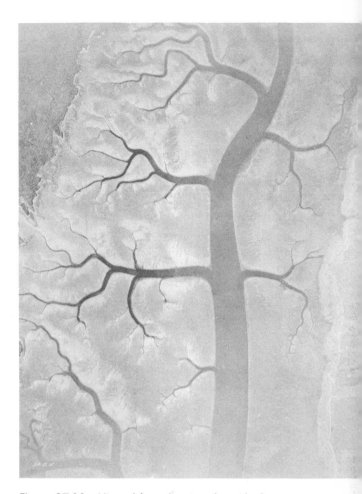

Figure 27.18 Viewed from the air at low tide these tidal mud flats near Yarmouth, Nova Scotia, show a well-adjusted branching system of tidal streams. The area shown is 1½ miles wide. (Royal Canadian Air Force Photograph.)

line. Baymouth bars develop until bays are almost sealed off.

With the attainment of a simple, smooth shoreline the stage of early maturity is reached. This coast consists alternately of cliffed headlands and baymouth bars. The point of fundamental importance is that throughout the life cycle thus far described, a highly irregular shoreline has been replaced by a nearly straight shoreline. The bays now become filled in by delta materials supplied by streams and by deposition of silts as the tide rises and falls, and the tide-induced currents flow in and out through narrow passes in the baymouth bars. Some small bays lack any passes in the baymouth bars, but the permeability of the sand is sufficient to permit runoff to escape into the sea. When completely silted in, the bay area will be a *tidal flat* or *tidal marsh*, whose surface is at the level of mean high tide (Figure 27.18). A network of tiny serpen-

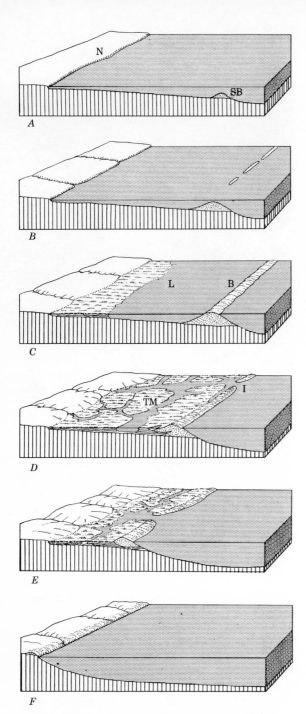

Figure 27.19 Stages in the development of a shoreline of emergence of the coastal-plain type. N = nip, SB = submarine bar, L = lagoon, B = barrier island, I = inlet, TM = tidal marsh. (After E. Raisz.)

tine *tidal streams* serves to flood and drain the tidal flat alternately.

Throughout early maturity the shoreline continues to retreat landward. The sea cliffs are progressively cut back while the baymouth bars are pushed back to keep in a straight line. Eventually a position is reached where the shoreline coincides with the original line of the bay heads. The baymouth bars and all other depositional features except the outer beach disappear, and the cliff of bedrock extends along the entire shoreline, which is then said to have attained *full maturity* (Figure 27.14). No further major development occurs, aside from the continued landward retreat of the shoreline. This retrogression will, however, become a very slow process, as the increased relief of the land causes the cliffs to be heightened and to supply more detritus to the shore.

Geographical aspects of shorelines of submergence

The influence of shorelines on human activity is strong, especially that of shorelines of submergence. The deep embayments of the youthful shoreline make splendid natural harbors. Much of the shoreline of Scandinavia, France, and the British Isles is thus provided with harbor facilities. Consequently, these peoples have a strong tradition of fishing, shipbuilding, ocean commerce, and marine activity generally. Mountainous relief of ria and fiord coasts makes agriculture difficult or impossible, forcing the people to turn to the sea for a livelihood. Rich forests and cheap hydroelectric power have, however, stimulated lumbering and manufacturing. New England and the Maritime Provinces of Canada have a youthful shoreline of submergence with abundant good harbors. The influence of this environment has been to foster the same development of fishing, whaling, ocean commerce, shipbuilding, and manufacturing seen in the British Isles and Scandinavian countries.

A mature shoreline of submergence has few natural harbors but extensive sheer marine cliffs. Portions of the channel coast of France illustrate this development (Figure 27.10).

Development of shorelines of emergence

Development of a coastal-plain type of shoreline of emergence is illustrated by the diagrams of Figure 27.19. In the stage of earliest youth (*Block A*), an uplift of the land or fall of sea level has brought the shoreline to rest against what was formerly a part of the sea bottom. The shoreline is relatively straight, the water extremely shallow near shore and deepening only gradually in a seaward direction. Large waves approaching the shore encounter the shallow zone at a considerable distance out and break before reaching the shoreline. In early youth, two activities begin to occur in the zone of breaking waves: deepening of the bottom by wave and current scour, and the building of an embankment, known as *submarine bar*, on the shoreward side of the deepened zone. Small waves reaching shore erode a small cliff, which, like the first cliff of a shoreline of submergence, is termed the *nip*.

As the submarine bar is built progressively higher, it begins to appear above the water surface in various places along its length (Block *B*). Thus a chain of low-lying islands is formed. When these have joined to make a fairly continuous belt of land, a *barrier island*, or *barrier beach*, has been formed (Block *C*). This stage may be designated as middle youth, although various authorities disagree on what shall be termed early, middle, or late youth in this series. Behind the barrier beach lies a *lagoon*, or belt of quiet water.

Into the lagoon mud, silt, and sand are brought by streams that drain the land. Tidal currents moving in and out of narrow openings of inlets in the barrier beach also bring sediment into the lagoon to form tidal deltas (Figure 27.20). Gradually the lagoon becomes filled to the level of high tide, and a tidal marsh, or salt marsh, replaces the open water of the lagoon (Blocks *C* and *D*).

The spacing of tidal inlets in a barrier beach depends in part on the average range of tides along the coast, being more closely spaced where the range is great. In heavy storms, new inlets may be breached by wave action (Figure 27.20). Tidal currents in and out of the lagoon will tend to keep the inlets open, but shore drifting of sand along the seaward side of the beach may seal them off permanently. Among these opposing activities a sort of balance is maintained, so that neither too many nor too few inlets exist.

The barrier island or beach is developed both by storm waves and by wind. Storm waves toss new deposits of sand and gravels upon the inner edge of the beach, often to a height several feet above mean sea level. Onshore winds shift the sand toward the landward side of the beach, creating dunes which may rise 20, 50, or more feet above sea level.

Although eventually the barrier beach will be pushed landward, it may temporarily be built out by the addition of successive beach deposits. This would occur if a considerable supply of sediment were being brought from the land and carried out by tidal currents for distribution along the shore. The successive wave-tossed deposits form *beach ridges*, separated by long, shallow troughs called *swales*. Building of beach ridges is not restricted to barrier beaches, but may occur along any coast where excessive quantities of debris are being

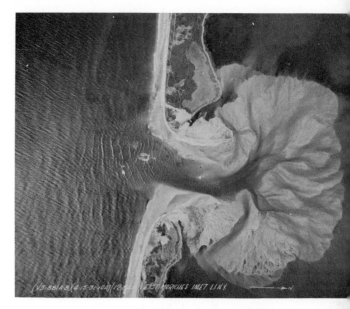

Figure 27.20 East Moriches Inlet was cut through Fire Island, a barrier island off the Long Island shoreline, during a severe storm in March 1931. This aerial photograph, taken a few days after the breach occurred, shows the underwater tidal delta being built out into the lagoon (right) by currents. The entire area shown is about a mile long. North is to the right; the open Atlantic Ocean on the left. (U.S. Army Air Forces Photograph.)

dumped into the ocean by rivers. Many miles of new land may be built in this way. Such land has a sandy corrugated surface but is only a few feet above sea level. At certain places along a shoreline which is being built out by addition of beach ridges, the accumulation is concentrated to produce prominent capes or forelands. These appear on the map as toothlike projections along the shore and have been called *cuspate forelands*. Cape Canaveral on the Florida coast and Dungeness Foreland on the coast of southern England are fine examples (Figure 27.21).

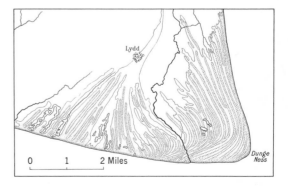

Figure 27.21 Dungeness Foreland, on the Dover Straits of southeastern England, is a large cuspate foreland with curving beach ridges.

As middle youth passes into late youth the barrier beach is gradually driven landward, encroaching upon the area of the lagoon, which itself has become filled with sediment (Figure 27.19, Block *E*).

As soon as the barrier beach is pushed back to the position of the original shoreline of the initial stage, the shoreline has entered maturity (Block *F*). As this position will not be attained at all parts of the coast simultaneously, the stage of early maturity may be applied when the barrier beach is still seaward of this line in some places; full maturity is attained when the barrier beach as a separate zone has disappeared, being replaced by a beach attached directly to the mainland. From this stage on there is no significant change in the nature of the shoreline. The cliff continues to be eroded and to be pushed back into the land. As most coasts bordering a coastal-plain type of shoreline are nearly level plains of low elevation, the cliff will never be very high. Should a hilly or mountainous topography lie a short distance inland, however, the cliff may cut into the steep slopes and produce a shoreline similar to that of the mature shoreline of submergence.

If a shoreline of emergence of the type described above begins and ends with a stage in which the shoreline is even and nearly straight, we may well ask what fundamental change has been accomplished throughout the development cycle. Although the initial and mature shorelines are similar in outward form, there is a significant difference in the underwater profile bordering upon the shoreline. Whereas in the initial stage the water was so shallow that the waves broke far from shore, in the mature stage the water is much deeper close to shore, permitting waves to reach close to the shoreline before breaking. The entire process of barrier beach formation and shoreward movement was but a by-product of the process of bottom deepening carried out by the waves and wave-induced currents.

Geographical aspects of shorelines of emergence

Shallow water and evenness of shoreline result in generally poor harbors, or no harbors at all, along coastal-plain shorelines of emergence, especially in the initial and mature stages. In the stages where a lagoon exists, the lagoon itself may serve as a harbor if channels and dock areas are dredged to sufficient depths. Ships enter and leave through one of the passes in the barrier island, but these require artificial sea walls and jetties to confine the current and thereby keep sufficient channel depth. Frequently the major port cities are located where a large river empties into the lagoon.

One of the finest examples of a barrier island and lagoon is along the Gulf Coast of Texas. Here the island is unbroken for as much as 100 miles at a stretch and passes are few. The lagoon is five to ten miles wide, indicating that the original slope of the sea bottom was very slight. Galveston is built upon the barrier island adjacent to an inlet connecting Galveston Bay with the sea. Most other Texas ports, however, are located on the mainland shore. The Texas coast is not a simple example of a young shoreline of emergence because a slight submergence has been the most recent event in the history of the shoreline. This submergence has not altered the barrier island-lagoon relationships but has caused an embayed inner shoreline with extensive estuaries marking the mouths of the larger streams. Corpus Christi, Rockport, Texas City, Lavaca, and other ports are located along the shores of these embayments. (See Figure 29.10.)

Still another good illustration of the shoreline of emergence is along the Atlantic coast of New Jersey, Delaware, Maryland, Virginia, and North Carolina (see Exercise 3). Virtually the entire coast from Sandy Hook to Cape Lookout is bordered by a barrier beach. Like the Texas coast, this portion of the Atlantic shoreline has experienced a recent submergence, which has caused vast embayments such as Chesapeake Bay and Delaware Bay. Along the New Jersey coast, however, the old inner shoreline is remarkably straight and still shows vestiges of the original nip. The lagoon is largely filled now and forms a flat plain through which wander sinuous tidal creeks. The barrier beach makes a splendid resort and has been fully utilized with the building of such cities as Barnegat City, Atlantic City, and Ventnor.

Figure 27.22 This elevated wave-cut cliff and bench was carved by waves of ancient Lake Bonneville, which occupied the Great Salt Lake basin during the glacial period. Weathering and sheet erosion have begun to obscure the wave-eroded forms. (Photograph by Douglas Johnson.)

Elevated shorelines

A shoreline may, at any stage in its development, be raised above water level so as to become a land feature. At the same time, a new shoreline, which is a true shoreline of emergence, is produced at the new position of the water line. The raised shoreline, or *elevated shoreline*, is not a shoreline of emergence; in fact, it is not a true shoreline at all because it is no longer associated with wave and current action. Having once been elevated, it is attacked by weathering, mass wasting, and streams and will eventually be destroyed.

Elevated shorelines result either from crustal uplift along a coastal belt such as the California coast, which is subject to faulting and earthquakes, or from a falling of sea or lake level.

Lake Bonneville, the ancestor of the present Salt Lake in Utah, rose to a maximum level in the Pleistocene epoch when rainfall was greater and evaporation less than now. Excellent illustrations of elevated shorelines are to be found on the lower slopes of the mountain ranges in the Salt Lake region (Figure 27.22). From a study of these ancient wave-cut benches with their associated beaches, spits, and bars, it has been possible to reconstruct the history of the old lake and to make inferences as to climates of the past.

Where lake level falls steadily, or coastal regions rise steadily, the elevated shorelines become *strand lines* resembling natural contours of the land (Figure 27.23).

Where elevated wave-cut platforms stand but a few feet above mean sea level, as they do on many islands of the Pacific (Figure 27.24), we have difficulty in deciding whether there has been a rise of land level or a sinking of sea level, inasmuch as the result would be the same in either event.

Extreme emergence of a coast may expose a wide belt of former sea floor (Figure 27.25). This new land is a coastal plain (Chapter 29) and is veneered with recently formed mud and sand layers. The new shoreline is a typical shoreline of emergence of the coastal-plain type.

Coral-reef shorelines

As a variety of neutral shoreline, coral-reef shorelines are unique in that the addition of new land is made by organisms: corals, which secrete lime to form their skeletons, and *algae*, plants that also make limy encrustations. Corals are colonial types of animals, that is, they occur in large colonies of individuals. As coral colonies die, new ones are built upon them, thus developing a coral limestone made up of the strongly cemented limy skeletons. Coral fragments torn free by wave attack and pulverized may be deposited to form beaches, spits, and bars, which later are cemented into a limestone.

Figure 27.23 These elevated shorelines indicate continuously rising land near Cape Adelaide Regina on the Boothia Peninsula, Northwest Territories. Mottled surface in foreground is new ice (September). (Royal Canadian Air Force Photograph.)

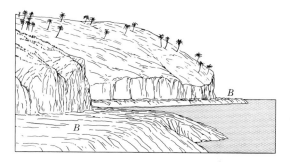

Figure 27.24 This wave-cut rock bench (*B*) on the shore of Tutuila in the Samoan Islands is about ten feet above mean sea level and may indicate a recent drop of sea level or a recent rise of the island. (After W. M. Davis.)

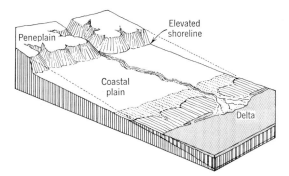

Figure 27.25 A coastal-plain strip 40 miles wide and more than 1000 miles long indicates emergence along the east coast of peninsular India. The present shoreline is a young shoreline of emergence; the former shoreline, now of the elevated type, appears as a steep mountain front rising abruptly from a plain. (After W. M. Davis and S. W. Cushing.)

Figure 27.26 A fringing reef on the south coast of Java forms a broad bench between surf zone (left) and a white coral-sand beach. Inland is tropical rainforest. (Photograph by Luchtvaart-Afdeeling, Bandoeng.)

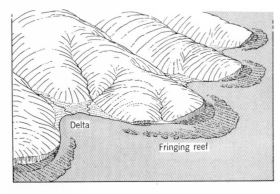

Figure 27.27 Fringing reefs are widest in front of headlands and may be absent near the mouths of streams. (After W. M. Davis.)

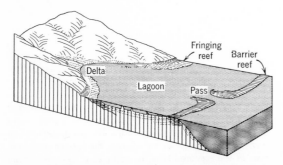

Figure 27.28 A barrier reef is separated from the mainland by a shallow lagoon. (After W. M. Davis.)

Coral-reef shorelines occur in warm, tropical water between the limits 30° N and 25° S lat. Water temperatures above 68° F are necessary for dense reef coral growth. Furthermore, reef corals live near the water surface, down to limiting depths of about 200 feet. Water must be clean and well aerated for vigorous coral growth; hence corals thrive in positions exposed to wave attack from the open sea. Because muddy water prevents coral growth, reefs are missing opposite the mouths of muddy streams. Coral reefs are remarkably flat on top (Figure 27.26) and have a level approximately equal to the upper one-third mark of the range of tide. Thus they are exposed at low tide and covered at high tide.

Three general types of coral reefs may be recognized: (1) fringing reefs, (2) barrier reefs, and (3) atolls. *Fringing reefs* are built as platforms attached to shore (Figure 27.27). They are widest in front of headlands where wave attack is strongest, and the corals receive clean, fresh water with abundant food supply. Fringing reefs are usually absent near the mouths and deltas of streams, where the water is muddy. This is a fact of great military importance where the problem is to find reef-free places for landing of troops and supplies. Fringing reefs may be from one-fourth to one-half mile wide, even up to one and a half miles wide, depending on the length of time that the reef has been developing.

Barrier reefs lie out from shore and are separated from the mainland by a lagoon which may range from one-half mile to ten miles or more wide (Figure 27.28). The reef itself may be from 20 to 3000 feet wide. The lagoon is shallow and flat-floored, usually 20 to 40 fathoms (120 to 240 feet) deep. There are, however, many towerlike columns of coral in the lagoon. *Passes,* which occur at intervals in barrier reefs, are narrow gaps through which excess water from breaking waves is returned from the lagoon to the open sea. They sometimes occur opposite deltas on the mainland shore, because of the inhibiting effect of mud on coral growth. Passes are of geographical and military importance because they provide the only means of entrance by ship into the lagoon.

Atolls are more or less circular coral reefs enclosing a lagoon, but without any land inside (Figure 27.29). In all other respects they are similar to barrier reefs. On large atolls, parts of the reef have been built up by wave action and wind to form low island chains, connected by the reef. A cross section of an atoll shows that the lagoon is flat-floored and shallow (10 to 40 fathoms), and that the outer slopes are steep, often descending thousands of feet to great ocean depths.

Several plausible theories have been advanced

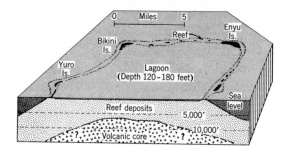

Figure 27.29 Bikini Atoll in the Pacific, scene of early atom bomb tests, is thought to consist of a great thickness of reef deposits resting on a sea mountain of volcanic rock. (After M. Dobrin et al.)

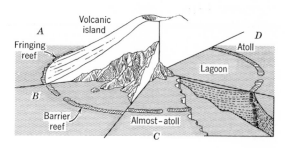

Figure 27.30 The subsidence theory of barrier-reef and atoll development is shown in four stages, beginning with a fringing reef attached to a volcanic island and ending with a circular reef. (After W. M. Davis.)

for the origin of atolls and barrier reefs. To explain each one and discuss the advantages and disadvantages of each would take many pages. One interesting theory of origin, which has been popular since it was first outlined by a great scientist, Charles Darwin, in 1842, may be called the *subsidence theory* (Figure 27.30). He supposed that small islands, such as volcanoes, slowly subsided in a general downwarping of the earth's crust over parts of the ocean basin. Coral reefs, which were originally fringing reefs attached to the island shores, continued to build upward as the island subsided. Thus the area of the island shrank and a lagoon formed, creating a barrier reef. Finally the island sank out of sight, but the reef persisted, maintained at sea level by vigorous coral and algal growth.

The geographical aspects of atoll islands are unique in some respects. First, there is no rock other than coral limestone, composed of calcium carbonate. This means that trees requiring other minerals, such as silica, cannot be cultivated without the aid of fertilizers or some outside source of rock from a larger island composed of volcanic or

other igneous rock. The palm tree is native to atoll islands because it thrives on brackish water, and the seed, or palm nut, is distributed widely by floating from one island to another. Native inhabitants have cultivated the coconut palm to provide food, clothing, fibers, and building materials. Fresh water is scarce on small atoll islands because there is not enough surface area for the collection of rainfall, and the land is so low that a high water table of fresh water is not present to supply springs, streams, and wells. Rainfall must be caught in open vessels or catchment basins and carefully conserved. Fish and other marine animals are an important part of the diet on atoll islands. Calm waters of the lagoon make a good place for fishing and for beaching canoes. Coral islands of the western Pacific stand in continual danger of devastation by tropical cyclones (hurricanes or typhoons). Breaking waves wash in over the low-lying ground sweeping away palm trees and native houses and drowning the inhabitants. There is no high ground for refuge. (See Chapter 11.) In the same way, great seismic sea waves of unpredictable occurrence may inundate atoll islands (Chapter 9).

Review Questions

1. Why do breakers form in shallow water? What do the terms *swash* and *backwash* mean? How are beach materials moved by these currents?

2. Under what conditions do waves do the greatest amount of shore erosion? When are beaches built?

3. Explain beach drifting and longshore drifting. What forms are built by these processes? What is a longshore current, and how is it caused?

4. Describe the phenomenon of wave refraction. Why does refraction occur? When waves are refracted along an embayed coast where is the energy of wave erosion concentrated? Where is it least? What important result does this have on the form of the shoreline?

5. Describe the development of sea cliffs, beginning with a newly submerged slope and continuing through to a mature sea cliff. Explain the following terms: nip, sea cave, sea arch, stack, wave-cut notch, abrasion platform, beach, shore-face terrace, hanging valley.

6. How can shorelines be classified? Name the five principal classes.

7. What kinds of shorelines of submergence are recognized? Name and explain the subdivisions.

8. What two types of shorelines of emergence can be recognized? How do they differ?

9. Name several types of neutral shorelines. What characteristic do they have in common?

10. Explain how a fault shoreline is formed.

11. Describe the successive stages in the development of a ria shoreline of submergence, beginning with the initial stage and continuing through to the mature stage. List all possible forms of beaches, bars, and spits that may develop during the youthful and early mature stages.

12. How are bays filled in with sediment? What is a tidal marsh?

13. How have shorelines of submergence exerted an influence on human activities?

14. Describe the successive stages in the development of a shoreline of emergence of the coastal-plain type. Include mention of the following features: nip, submarine bar, barrier beach, lagoon, tidal inlet, beach ridges, swales. What is a cuspate foreland? Give an example.

15. Discuss the geographical aspects of shorelines of emergence. Compare harbor facilities of a young shoreline of emergence with those of a young shoreline of submergence.

16. What is meant by an elevated shoreline? How does it differ from a shoreline of emergence? Where may some excellent elevated shorelines be seen today?

17. How are coral reefs formed? Under what conditions do reef-building corals flourish?

18. What three general types of reefs are formed? Describe each type. Explain Darwin's subsidence theory of atolls.

Exercises

Exercise 1. *Shoreline of Submergence, Stage of Early Youth.* (Source: Brest, France, topographic sheet No. 21; scale 1:200,000.)

Explanatory Note: The coastal region around the port of Brest lies in the peninsula of Brittany, which projects westward into the Atlantic Ocean. The coast here is deeply embayed and represents a shoreline of submergence modified appreciably by wave erosion only where the shore is exposed to waves of the open sea. This coastline resembles in many ways the Maine coast of the United States, but lies much farther north (48° N) and was never modified by intensive glacial action, as was the Maine coast. Submarine contours are shown as dashed lines for depths of 1, 5, 10, 20, 30, 40, and 50 meters. Contour interval on land is 20 meters.

QUESTIONS

1. Place a sheet of tracing paper over the map. In red pencil line mark all parts of the shoreline where a marine cliff is well developed. In blue pencil shade all probable sand beaches.

2. (*a*) Why are there few prominent cliffs along the shoreline of the Harbor of Brest? (*b*) Study the peninsula ending at 11–4. Which side seems to have undergone the greatest marine erosion? What is the topographic evidence? Is this what you would expect, knowing that the open Atlantic lies to the west, a bay 15 miles wide to the southeast?

3. On the same tracing sheet used in Question 1, draw in black lines a reconstruction of the drowned stream system, which may have occupied the Harbor of Brest before the region was submerged.

4. To what stage of development would you assign the shoreline between 25–22 and 31–21? Between 22–10 and 34–0?

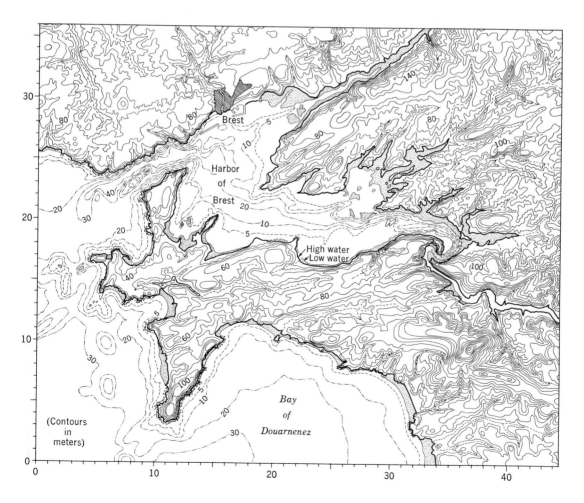

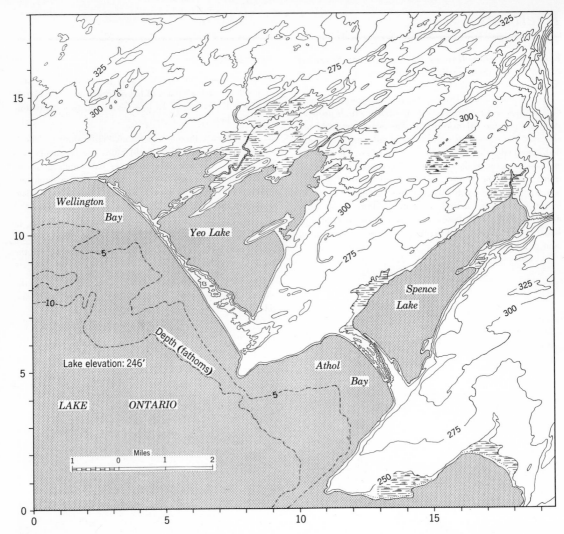

Lake elevation: 246'

LAKE ONTARIO

Wellington Bay

Yeo Lake

Spence Lake

Athol Bay

Depth (fathoms)

Miles

Exercise 2. *Young Shoreline of Submergence with Bars.* (Source: Wellington, Ont., topographic map; scale 1:63,360. Geological Survey of Canada.)

Explanatory Note: The north shore of Lake Ontario is a shoreline of submergence on a topography developed first by normal stream erosion and associated weathering and mass wasting processes, then heavily glaciated by the Pleistocene ice sheets. A baymouth bar separates Yeo Lake from Wellington Bay, and a midbay bar has cut off the inner part of Athol Bay to produce Spence Lake.

QUESTIONS

1. (*a*) What fractional scale has this map? (*b*) What is the height (feet) above lake level of the small hills at 6.8–8.0?

(*c*) Is it more likely that these hills are sand dunes or that they are beach-ridge deposits thrown up by storm waves? Explain.

2. (*a*) What is peculiar about the form of the outlet channel through the bar between Spence Lake and Athol Bay? Explain in terms of the beach drifting process. (*b*) Are tidal currents responsible for keeping this channel clear?

3. On a thin sheet of tracing paper laid over this map, redraw the shoreline as a smooth, simple shoreline of early maturity passing approximately through 0.0–14.0, 6.0–11.0, 10.0–8.0, 16.0–4.0 and 19.0–0.0. Imagine all headlands to be cut back to this line. Redraw the contours to show the cliffed headlands and baymouth bars.

Exercise 3. *Young Shoreline of Emergence with Barrier Island.* (Source: Accomac, Va., U.S. Geological Survey, topographic map; scale 1:62,500.)

Explanatory Note: A barrier island represented by Metomkin Island and Cedar Island is separated from the mainland by a lagoonal belt consisting of expanses of open

water, Metomkin Bay and Floyd's Bay, and of salt marsh with sinuous tidal creeks. Immediately after emergence, but before the appearance of the barrier island, the shoreline lay just east of the ten-foot contour line on the seaward side of Parker Neck, Bailey Neck, Joynes Neck, and Custis Neck.

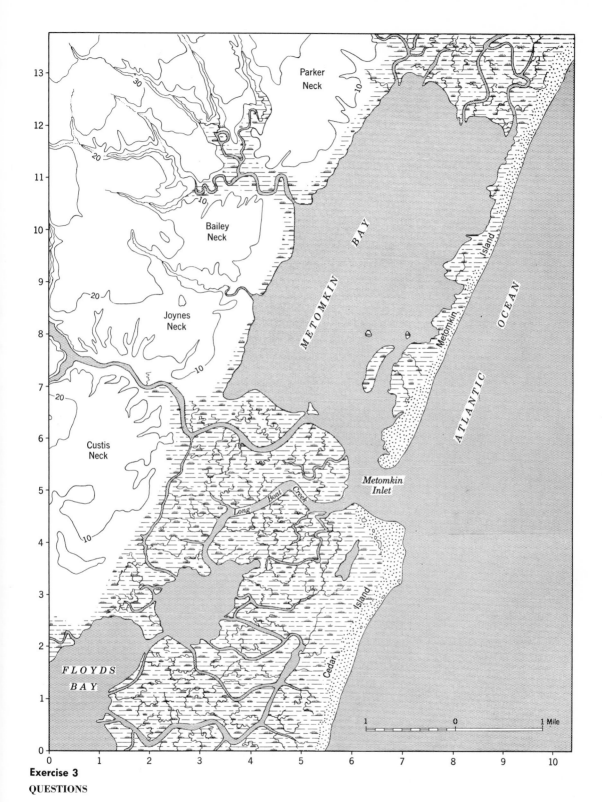

Exercise 3

QUESTIONS

1. (**a**) How far (miles) seaward of the initial shoreline does the barrier island lie in the vicinity of the northern end of Metomkin Bay? (**b**) in the vicinity of Cedar Island? (**c**) Why does this distance increase toward the south? Give two possible explanations.

2. (**a**) Why are the ends of Cedar Island and Metomkin Island offset at Metomkin Inlet? (**b**) In which direction do you think materials are being moved along this coast by shore drifting processes? What is the evidence?

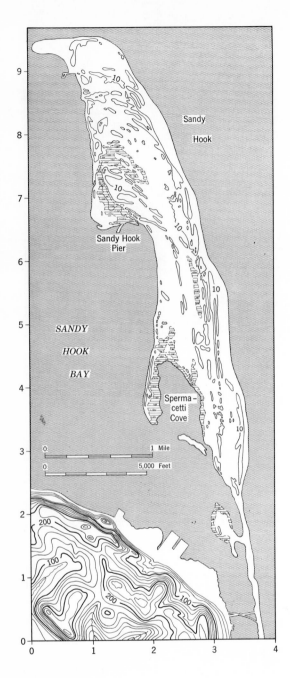

Exercise 4. *Sandy Hook Spit.* (Source: Navesink, N. J., topographic map; scale 1:24,000. State of New Jersey, Department of Conservation and Development.)

Explanatory Note: Sandy Hook is a large spit extending north from Navesink Highlands into the Atlantic Ocean and forming a part of the enclosure of Lower Bay of New York Harbor. It is formed of sand carried northward along the New Jersey coast by shore drifting processes. Numerous beach ridges show various stages in the growth of the spit. The tendency of these ridges to recurve westward or landward is typical of complex spits. The tip of the spit is said to have grown about one mile since 1764, one-half mile since 1865.

QUESTIONS

1. (a) What contour interval is used on the spit? **(b)** on the mainland?

2. (a) What is the origin of the small spit enclosing Spermacetti Cove on the west? **(b)** In what direction do beach materials generally drift on the west shore of Sandy Hook? **(c)** Is this the same direction as prevailing shore drifting on the eastern (Atlantic Ocean) shore? Explain.

3. Would you expect to find sand dunes on Sandy Hook spit? If so, give the grid coordinates of possible dune forms shown by contour lines.

4. What is the origin of the marsh in the vicinity of 1.4–7.6?

5. Do the Navesink Highlands (mainland) show any topographic forms produced by wave erosion? If so, describe and locate the forms.

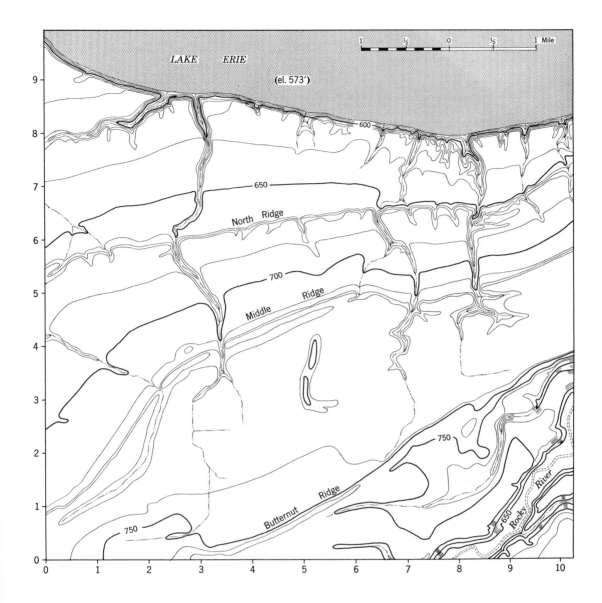

The map shows contour lines with elevations marked: LAKE ERIE (el. 573'), 600, 650, North Ridge, 700, Middle Ridge, 750, Butternut Ridge, 650 Rocky River. Scale bar showing 1, ½, 0, ½, 1 Mile. Grid coordinates 0 to 10 horizontally and 0 to 9 vertically.

Exercise 5. *Elevated Shorelines and Beach Ridges.* (Source: Berea, Ohio, U.S. Geological Survey topographic map; scale 1:62,500.)

Explanatory Note: Lake Erie, whose present shoreline is located in the northern part of this map, formerly stood higher than at present. Three ridges mark previous higher stands of the water level; Butternut Ridge, the highest, is also the oldest; Middle Ridge and North Ridge mark progressively lower stages. On both Middle Ridge and Butternut Ridge a well-developed beach ridge is indicated by the contours, whereas North Ridge is simply a low, wave-cut escarpment. The present shoreline of Lake Erie is a good example of a mature shoreline with a continuous wave-cut scarp and numerous hanging valleys.

QUESTIONS

1. Make a topographic profile across the map from north to south, starting at 4.0–9.0. Use a vertical scale of 1 inch equals 100 feet. Label the three ridges.

2. On the profile draw horizontal lines to show the lake level at the time each of the three elevated shorelines was formed. Note that Middle Ridge and Butternut Ridge may have been barrier beaches typical of a shoreline of emergence.

3. At 5.2–3.5 is a curious curved ridge. Could this be some type of depositional shore feature? Explain.

4. (*a*) How high is the present scarp along the shore of Lake Erie? (*b*) Make an enlarged contour sketch map of a sea cliff with a hanging valley similar to those shown on the map.

CHAPTER TWENTY-EIGHT

Landforms made by wind

WIND, the fourth of the agents of erosion thus far discussed, produces a variety of interesting sequential landforms, both erosional and depositional. In terms of total mass of material thereby removed or deposited, however, it ranks below mass wasting, running water, waves, and ice, except in certain desert regions especially favorable to its action. In humid regions, with ample soil moisture and dense vegetative cover, there are few evidences of the work of wind. These usually are coastal sand dunes. Elsewhere, vegetation holds the ground in place unless man has laid it bare.

Erosion by wind

Wind performs two kinds of erosional work. Loose particles lying upon the ground surface may be lifted into the air or rolled along the ground. This process is *deflation*. Where the wind drives sand and dust particles against an exposed rock or soil surface, causing it to be worn away by the impact of the particles, the process is *abrasion*. Abrasion requires cutting tools carried by the wind; deflation is accomplished by air currents alone.

above: Dunes near Qatif, Saudi Arabia.
Photograph by courtesy of Arabian American Oil Company.

Deflation acts wherever the ground surface is thoroughly dried out and is littered with small, loose particles derived by rock weathering or previously deposited by running water, ice, or waves.

Thus, dry river courses, beaches, and areas of recently formed glacial deposits are highly susceptible to deflation. In dry climates, virtually the entire ground surface is subject to deflation because the soil or rock is everywhere bare. Wind is selective in its deflational action. The finest particles, those which constitute mud, clay, or silt, are lifted most easily and raised high into the air. Sand grains are moved only by moderately strong winds and tend to travel close to the ground. Gravel fragments and pebbles up to two or three inches in diameter may be rolled over flat ground by strong winds but do not travel far. They become easily lodged in hollows or between their fellows. Consequently, where a mixture of sizes of particles is present on the ground, the finer sizes are removed; the coarser particles remain behind.

The principal landform produced by deflation is a shallow depression termed a *blowout*, or *deflation hollow*. This depression may be from a few yards to a mile or more in diameter, but is usually only a few feet deep. Blowouts form in plains regions in

Figure 28.1 This blowout hollow on the plains of Nebraska contains a remnant column of the original material, thus providing a natural yardstick for the depth of material removed by deflation. (Photograph by N. H. Darton, U.S. Geological Survey.)

dry climates. Any small depression in the surface of the plain, particularly where the grass cover is broken through, may develop into a blowout. Rains fill the depression, creating a shallow pond or lake. As the water evaporates the mud bottom dries out and cracks, forming small scales or pellets of dried mud which are lifted out by the wind. In grazing lands, cattle may trample the margins of the depression into a mass of mud, breaking down the protective grass-root structure and facilitating removal when dry. Thus the depression is progressively enlarged (Figure 28.1). Blowouts are also found on rock surfaces where the rock is being disintegrated by weathering.

In the great deserts of southeastern California, Arizona, and New Mexico, the floors of intermontane basins are subject to deflation. The flat floors of the vast, shallow playas have in some places been reduced by deflation as much as several feet over areas of many square miles.

Where deflation has been active on a ground surface littered with loose fragments of a wide range of sizes, the pebbles that remain behind tend to accumulate until they cover the entire surface (Figure 28.2). By rolling or jostling about as the fine particles are blown away, the pebbles may become closely fitted together, forming a *desert pave-*

ment. In North Africa such a pebble-covered surface is called a *reg.* The precipitation of calcium carbonate, gypsum, and other salts near the surface, as ground water is drawn to the surface and evaporated in dry weather, tends to cement the pebbles together, forming a highly effective protection against further deflation.

The sandblast action of wind against exposed rock surfaces is limited to the basal few feet of a cliff, hill, or other rock mass rising above a relatively flat plain, because sand grains do not rise high into the air. Wind abrasion produces pits, grooves, and hollows in the rock. Where a small rock mass projects above the plain it may be cut away at the base to make a *pedestal rock*, delicately balanced upon a thin stem. Most pedestal rocks, or *mushroom rocks*, are, however, produced by weathering processes.

Dust storms and sand storms

In dry seasons over plains regions, strong, turbulent winds lift great quantities of fine dust into the air, forming a dense, high cloud called a *dust storm.* The dust storm is generated where ground surfaces have been stripped of protective vegetal cover by cultivation or grazing, or where they naturally carry no vegetation cover because of ex-

Figure 28.2 This flat gravel surface near the Colorado River at Yuma, Arizona, is covered by pebbles left behind when winds swept away the fine sands and silts of a river bar. (Photograph by Frank J. Wright.)

Figure 28.3 Front of an approaching dust storm, Coconino Plateau, Arizona. (Photograph by D. L. Babenroth.)

treme aridity of the climate. A dust storm approaches as a great dark cloud extending from the ground surface to heights of several thousand feet (Figure 28.3). Within the dust cloud deep gloom or even total darkness prevails. Visibility is cut to a few yards, and a fine choking dust penetrates everywhere.

It has been estimated that as much as 4000 tons of dust may be suspended in a cubic mile of air. On this basis, a dust storm 300 or 400 miles in diameter might be carrying more than 100 million tons of dust—enough to make a hill 100 feet high and 2 miles across the base.[1] A region that supplied the dust for thousands of such storms would thus lose a considerable mass over a span of thousands of years. Whether during the same period streams would remove more material from the same area is difficult to say, but in all probability they would remove much more.

Dust travels enormous distances in the air. That of individual dust storms is often traceable as far as 2000 or 2500 miles. Volcanoes erupt much extremely fine dust into the air. The renowned eruption of the volcano Krakatoa in the Dutch East Indies in 1883 cast out an enormous quantity of dust, some of which was caught by atmospheric circulation at high levels and carried around the entire earth. It is said that unusually brilliantly colored sunsets occurred in the British Isles in the years following 1883 as a result of the presence of the Krakatoa dust in the atmosphere. These were referred to as the "Chelsea sunsets," and were a favorite subject for paintings by English artists of the period.

The true desert *sandstorm* is a low cloud of moving sand that rises only a few inches (or at most, five or six feet) above the ground. It consists of sand particles driven by a strong wind. Those who have experienced sandstorms report that a man standing upright may have his head and shoulders entirely above the limits of the sand cloud. The reason why the sand does not rise higher is that the individual particles are engaged in a leaping motion, termed *saltation* (Figure 28.4). Grains describe a curved path of travel and strike the ground with considerable force but at a low angle. The impact causes the grain to rebound into the air. At the same time, the surface layer of sand grains creeps downwind as the result of the constant impact of the bouncing grains.

The erosional effect of blown sand is thus concentrated on surfaces a few inches or a foot or two above the flat ground surface. Telephone poles on wind-swept sandy plains are quickly cut through at

[1] A. K. Lobeck, *Geomorphology*, McGraw-Hill, New York, 1939, 731 pp., p. 380.

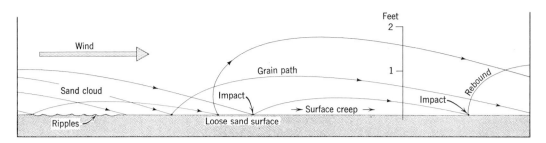

Figure 28.4 Sand particles travel in a series of long jumps. (After R. A. Bagnold.)

the base unless a protective metal sheathing or heap of large stones is placed around the base.

Sand dunes

A *dune* is any hill or accumulation of sand shaped by the wind. Dunes may be active, or *live*, when bare of vegetation and constantly changing form under wind currents. They may be inactive, or *fixed*, dunes, covered by vegetation that has taken root and serves to prevent further shifting of the sand.

Several common varieties of dunes are treated here. The *crescentic dune*, or *barchan* (also spelled barcan, barkhan, or barchane), is an isolated dune, which in plan view resembles a blunted crescent (Figure 28.5). The broadly rounded ends of the crescent point downwind and indicate the direction of dune motion and prevailing winds. On the windward side of the crest the sand slope is gentle, being the slope up which the sand grains move. On the lee side of the dune, within the crescent, is a steep curving dune slope, the *slip face*, which

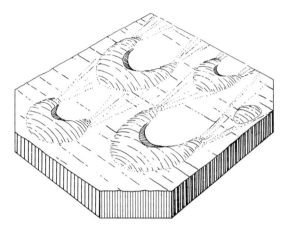

Figure 28.5 Barchan, or crescentic dunes.

Figure 28.6 Barchan dunes at Biggs, Oregon. (Photograph by G. K. Gilbert, U.S. Geological Survey.)

Figure 28.7 This air photograph of a sand dune field between Yuma, Arizona, and Calexico, California, shows a sand sea of transverse dunes in the background and a field of crescentic barchan dunes in the foreground. (Copyrighted Spence Air Photos.)

maintains an angle of about 35° from the horizontal (Figure 28.6). Sand grains fall or slide down the steep face after being blown free of the crest. When a strong wind is blowing, the flying sand makes a perceptible cloud at the crest. The term *smoking crest* has been used for this feature. Crescentic dunes rest upon a flat, pebble-covered ground surface. The sand may originate as a drift in the lee of some obstacle, such as a small hill, rock, or clump of brush. Once a sufficient mass of sand has formed it begins to move downwind, taking the form of a crescent dune. Thus the dunes are commonly arranged in chains extending downwind from the source drifts.

Where sand is so abundant that it completely covers the ground, dunes take the form of wavelike ridges separated by troughlike furrows. The dunes are called *transverse dunes* because their crests trend at right angles to direction of wind (Figure 28.7). The entire area may be called a *sand sea*, for it resembles a storm-tossed sea suddenly frozen to immobility. The term *erg*, referring to any large

expanse of dunes in the Sahara Desert, has been adopted by geographers for this type of landscape. Individual sand ridges have sharp crests and are asymmetrical, the gentle slope being on the windward, the steep slope on the lee side. Deep depressions lie between the dune ridges. Sand seas require huge quantities of sand, often derived from weathering of a sandstone formation underlying the ground surface, or from adjacent alluvial plains. Still other transverse dune belts form adjacent to beaches which supply abundant sand and have strong onshore winds (Figure 28.10).

Another group of dunes belong to a family in which the curve of the dune crest is bowed convexly downwind, the opposite of the curvature of crests in the barchan and transverse dunes. These may be described as *parabolic* in form. A common representative of this class, the *coastal blowout dune*, is formed adjacent to beaches, where large supplies of sand are available and are blown landward by prevailing winds (Figure 28.8*A*). A saucer-shaped depression is formed by deflation;

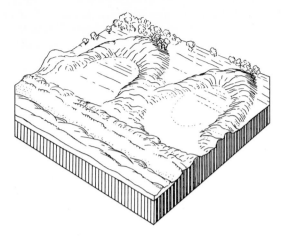

A. Coastal blowout dunes with saucerlike depressions.

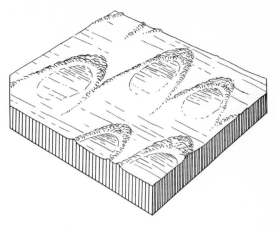

B. Parabolic blowout dunes on an arid plain.

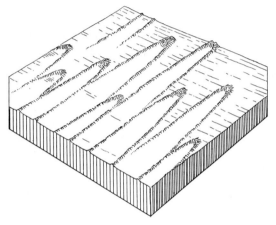

C. Parabolic dunes of hairpin form.

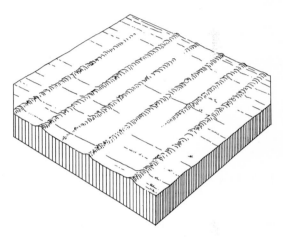

D. Longitudinal dune ridges on a desert plain.

Figure 28.8

Figure 28.9 At Cape Henry, Virginia, dunes of beach sand are migrating landward, inundating a forest. Note that the dune height is about the same as treetop height. (Photograph by Douglas Johnson.)

the sand is heaped in a great curving ridge resembling a horseshoe in plan. On the landward side is a steep slip face which advances over the lower ground and buries forests, killing the trees (Figure 28.9). Coastal blowout dunes are well displayed along the southern and eastern shore of Lake Michigan, those of the southern shore being set aside for public use as the Indiana Dunes State Park (Exercise 3).

In arid plains and plateaus, where vegetation is sparse and winds strong, groups of *parabolic blowout dunes* develop to the lee of shallow deflational hollows (Figure 28.8*B*). Sand is caught by low bushes and accumulates in a broad, low ridge. These dunes have no steep slip faces, and may remain relatively immobile. In some cases, however, the dune ridge migrates downwind, drawing the parabola into a long, narrow form with parallel sides (Figure 28.8*C*). This form resembles a hairpin in plan; hence has been named a *hairpin dune*, although it is a member of the parabolic family. Hairpin dunes stabilized by vegetative growth are seen in Figure 28.10.

Still another class of dunes is described as *longitudinal* because the dune ridges run parallel with the wind direction. On desert plains and plateaus, where sand supply is meager but winds are strong from one direction, *longitudinal dune ridges* are formed (Figure 28.8*D*). These are usually only a few feet high, but may be several miles long. In some areas, at least, the longitudinal dune is produced by extreme development of the hairpin dune, such that the parallel side ridges become the dominant form.

Also longitudinally oriented with respect to the wind, but not a true dune, is the *sand drift*, which is a long, tapering sharp-crested ridge of sand extending downwind from some topographic obstacle, such as a hill that might rise above a desert plain (Figure 28.11). Sand moving in saltation passes over or around the obstacle, lodging to the leeward and gradually building the drift until the zone of quiet air is filled.

Although the dunes described above are representative of types found in the United States, many other types have been described. In the vast deserts of North Africa, Arabia, and southern Iran are large, complex dune forms apparently not represented in the United States. One of these is the *seif dune*, or *sword dune*, which is a huge tapering sand ridge whose crestline rises and falls in alternate peaks and saddles and whose side slopes are indented by crescentic slip faces. Seif dunes may be a few hundred feet high and tens of miles long. Another Saharan type is the *star dune*, *pyramidal dune*, or *heaped dune*, a great hill of sand whose base resembles a many-pointed star in plan. Radial ridges of sand rise toward the dune center, culminating in sharp peaks as high as 300 feet or more above the base. Star dunes seem to remain fixed in position for centuries and can serve as reliable landmarks for desert travelers. In the great desert of central Australia a predominating dune form is the *longitudinal sand ridge*, which trends parallel with the prevailing wind and is essentially the same as the longitudinal dune described above (Figure 28.8*D*), except that the ridges are irregular, or wavy, in plan.

Loess

In several parts of the world the ground is underlain by deposits of wind-transported silt, which has settled out from dust storms over many thousands of years. The material thus formed is known as *loess*. It generally has a uniform buff color and lacks any visible layering or other banding. Loess has a tendency to break, or *cleave*, along vertical cliffs wherever it is exposed by the cutting of a stream or by man (Figure 28.12). The cleavage is possibly produced by a slight shrinkage of the entire mass as it has compacted after being laid down.

The greatest deposits of loess are in China, where thicknesses over 100 feet are common and a maximum of 300 feet has been measured. It covers many hundreds of square miles in northern China and appears to have been derived from interior Asia, out of which blow dry winter winds. Loess deposits are also important in central Europe, Argentina, and New Zealand, but not so extensive or thick as in China.

Figure 28.10 The arrows on this photograph point to elongate blowout dunes of hairpin form, which once advanced from the beach and have since become stabilized by vegetation. Active transverse dunes are overriding the blowout dunes in a fresh wave, San Luis Obispo Bay, California. (Spence Air Photos.)

Figure 28.11 Longitudinal sand drifts appear on this air photograph as sharp-crested, bladelike streamers of sand drawn out to the lee of a hill. Several barchan dunes are present in the lower left-hand corner. Width of area shown is about three-fourths of a mile. Air photomosaic of portion of Chao-Virú-Moche area, Peru. (Courtesy Ministerio de Fomento.)

Figure 28.12 This perpendicular road cut in loess south of Vicksburg is typical of thick glacial loess accumulations on the eastern bluffs of the Mississippi River. (Photograph by Orlo Childs.)

In the United States, important loess deposits lie in the Mississippi River valley (Figure 28.13). Much of the prairie plains region of Illinois, Iowa, Missouri, Nebraska, and Kansas is underlain by a loess layer ranging in thickness from a few feet to 100 feet. There are also extensive deposits along the lands bordering the lower Mississippi River flood plain on its east side, throughout Tennessee and Mississippi (Figure 28.12). Still other loess deposits are in northeast Washington and western Idaho. The American and European loess deposits are directly related to the continental glaciers of the Pleistocene epoch. At the time when the ice covered much of North America and Europe, it is possible that a generally dry winter climate prevailed in the land bordering the ice sheets and that strong winds blew southward and eastward over the bare ground, picking up silt from the flood plains of braided streams which discharged the melt water from the ice. This dust settled upon the ground between streams, gradually building up to produce a smooth, level ground surface. The loess is particularly thick along the eastern sides of the valleys because of prevailing westerly winds, and is well exposed along the bluffs of most streams flowing through the region today (Figure 28.14).

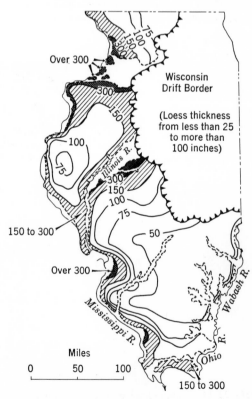

Figure 28.14 This map of Illinois shows thickness of loess in inches. (After R. F. Flint.)

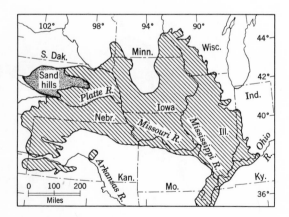

Figure 28.13 Loess deposits of the central United States are important within the shaded area. (After E. T. Apfel.)

The importance of loess in world agricultural resources cannot be easily overestimated. Loess plains and plateaus have developed rich, black soils especially suited to cultivation of grains. The highly productive plains of southern Russia, the Argentine pampa, and the rich grain region of north China are underlain by loess. In the United States, corn is extensively cultivated on the loess plains in those states, such as Iowa and Illinois, where rainfall is sufficient; wheat is grown farther west on loess plains of Kansas and Nebraska and in the Palouse region of eastern Washington where the climate is drier.

Because loess forms vertical walls along valley sides and is able to resist sliding or flowage, but at the same time is easily dug into, it has been widely used for cave dwellings both in China and in Central Europe. In China, old trails and roads in the loess have become deeply sunken into the ground as a result of the pulverization of the loess of the road bed and its removal by wind and water (28.15).

Figure 28.15 Road sunken deeply into loess, Shensi, China. (Photograph by Frederick K. Clapp.)

Review Questions

1. Explain the processes of deflation and abrasion by wind.

2. What conditions favor deflation? What topographic forms are produced?

3. What is a desert pavement? How does it form? What is a reg?

4. What forms does wind abrasion produce?

5. How do dust storms originate? How much material might be carried in a single dust storm? How far does the dust travel?

6. How do sand grains travel in a sandstorm? How high do the grains rise? At what level is abrasion concentrated?

7. What are sand dunes? What is the distinction between live dunes and fixed dunes?

8. Describe a crescentic dune. In which direction does it move?

9. What are transverse dunes? What is a sand sea? What is the source of the sand? What places would be most favorable for the development of dune areas? What is an erg landscape?

10. Describe a coastal blowout dune, a parabolic blowout dune and a hairpin dune. How does each develop?

11. Describe longitudinal sand dunes and drifts. What do they indicate as to the direction of prevailing winds?

12. What is loess? How is it formed? What structure has loess?

13. Describe the distribution of loess throughout the world. What origin has the loess of northern China?

14. What states of the Mississippi-Missouri river region have loess deposits? Of what economic importance is loess?

Exercises

Exercise 1. *Crescentic (Barchan) Dunes.* (Source: Sieler, Wash., U.S. Geological Survey topographic map; scale 1:24,000.)

Explanatory Note: The isolated, crescent- shaped hills on this map are barchan dunes similar in appearance to those shown in Figures 28.5 and 28.6 and in the lower right hand corner of Figure 28.7. They lie near the easternmost fringe of a large dune field in the vicinity of Moses Lake, Washington. On many of these barchan dunes, a low ridge curves westward from each end of the crescent, reversing the normal curvature of the barchan. This results from a tendency of the dunes to take the parabolic form (Figure 28.8) which has become superimposed on the barchan form. The parabolic form is well shown in dunes at 0.1–1.3, 0.6–1.2, and 0.1–0.6.

QUESTIONS

1. (*a*) What contour interval is used on this map? (*b*) What is the fractional scale of this map?

2. (*a*) On a sheet of tracing paper placed over the map, outline in pencil the base of at least twelve well-developed barchan dunes. (*b*) Indicate by an arrow the direction of prevailing wind. (*c*) Choosing the three highest, best-formed dunes, measure the length and height of each in feet and write this information directly beside the dune outline. (*d*) Mark the slip faces of these three selected dunes with hachures to show the extent and form of the slip face.

3. What evidence is there that the ground water table lies close to the surface between dunes? What effect might this have on dune development?

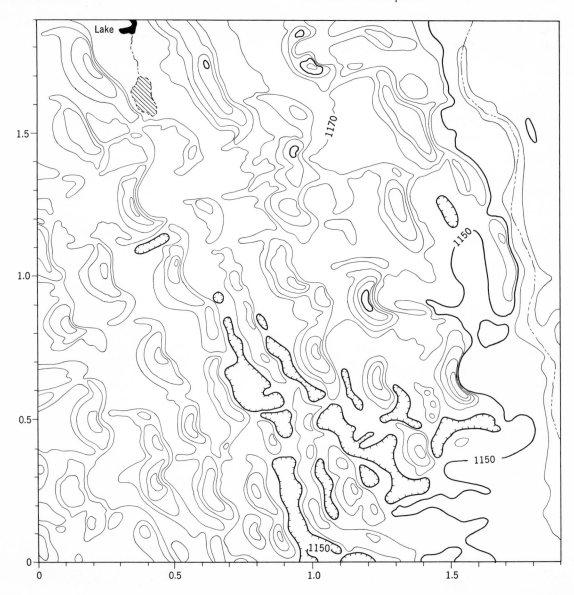

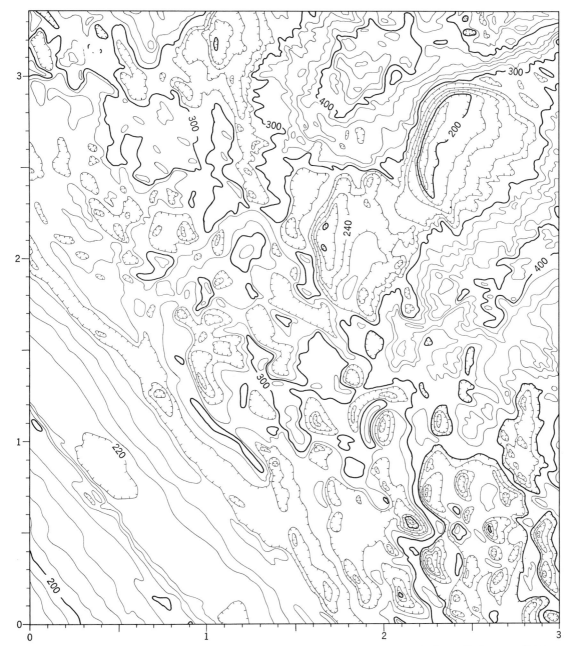

Exercise 2. *Sand Sea of Transverse Dunes.* (Source: Glamis Southeast, Calif., U.S. Geological Survey topographic map; scale 1:24,000).

Explanatory Note: Near Yuma, Arizona, in the dry, hot Sonoran Desert, is the largest active sand dune belt of the United States. The portion shown here consists of barren dunes of loose, pale-yellow sand separated by irregular depressions. An air view of this dune belt is shown in Figure 28.7. Although the area of the map lies north of the photo area, the dune topography is very similar to that pictured in the middle distance of the photograph, which is a view toward the west. A series of parallel dune ridges, seen cutting diagonally across the southwest corner of the map, forms the southwestern border of the dune belt. Over most of the map, however, the sand is formed into great

ridges separated by deep hollows. High, steep slip faces dip toward the southeast and east.

QUESTIONS

1. Compare map scale and contour interval with those of the map of Exercise 1. **(a)** What is the maximum relief of this dune belt, measuring from the highest dune peak to the deepest point in a dune depression? **(b)** Give elevations and grid coordinates of the highest dune peak and lowest point in the deepest closed depression.

2. In what way do the shapes of the dune ridges and depressions indicate direction of prevailing winds? What is this direction?

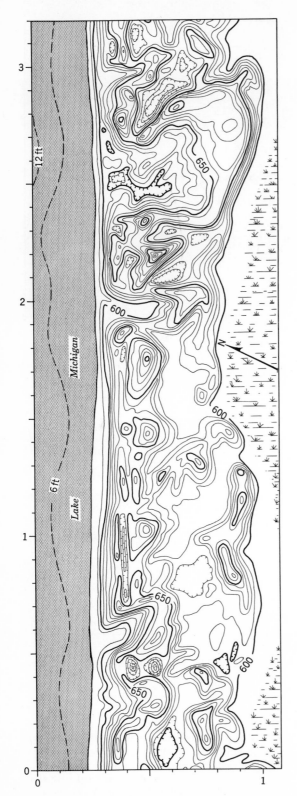

Exercise 3. *Coastal Blow-Out Dunes.* (Source: Dune Acres, Ind., U.S. Geological Survey topographic map; scale 1:24,000.)

Explanatory Note: This map shows a part of the southern coast of Lake Michigan, set aside for public use as the Indiana Dunes State Park. Abundant supplies of beach sand have accumulated here by shore drifting toward the southern end of Lake Michigan. Strong onshore winds, from northerly and northwesterly directions, have produced a series of large coastal blowout dunes of the type shown in Figure 28.8*A*.

QUESTIONS

1. (*a*) State the contour interval on this map. (*b*) Give the grid coordinates of all points of elevation greater than 700 feet. (*c*) What is ground distance in miles, represented by the long dimension of this map? (*d*) Give the width in miles of the dune belt at its widest point.

2. Place a tracing sheet over this map. Outline in pencil the well-developed blowout dunes at 0.8–2.7, 0.7–2.0, and 0.5–0.6. Show the form of each of these dunes by hachures drawn on the slopes.

3. What type and distribution of vegetation would you expect over this coastal dune belt?

Exercise 4. *Hairpin Dunes.* (Source: Idaho Falls South, Idaho, U.S. Geological Survey topographic map; scale 1:24,000.)

Explanatory Note: Long narrow dune ridges on this map trend southwest to northeast. Here and there a ridge is doubled back on itself to produce the characteristic hairpin form of highly elongated parabolic blowout dunes, such as those illustrated in Figures 28.8*C* and 28.10. The ends of several of the hairpin dunes have been built up into prominent dune masses.

QUESTIONS

1. (*a*) Compare the contour interval of this map with that of Exercise 3. **(*b*)** Which of the two exercise maps has the larger scale?

2. On a sheet of tracing paper laid over this map, outline the base of all dunes, connecting the individual ridge and hill elements so as to produce and emphasize the outlines of a few simple hairpin dunes. Show by arrow the direction of north on the map. Use another arrow to show prevailing wind direction required for development of these dune forms.

CHAPTER TWENTY-NINE

Coastal plains, horizontal strata, domes

THE foregoing chapters on landforms produced by weathering, mass wasting, streams, ice, waves, and wind have given little or no account of the manner in which variations in rock composition and structure are capable of exerting a powerful control upon the shapes and sizes of landforms. Instead, by assuming that all bedrock is of uniform composition throughout, it has been possible to describe the simple, ideal erosional landforms produced by each agent of denudation. There are, it is true, large land areas where bedrock is fairly uniform throughout, and it is in such areas that the denudational agents can produce the ideal forms. Elsewhere, sedimentary rocks are tilted, folded, domed, or faulted; metamorphic rocks are arranged in belted patterns; intrusive igenous rocks have solidified in a variety of bodies. It is with such structures and their topographic expression that these chapters deal.

Classification of land masses

As illustrated in Figure 29.1, land masses fall into several groups, distinguished according to the structure and composition of the bedrock comprising the mass.

above: The Mitten Buttes, Monument Valley, Arizona.

A. **Undisturbed structures.**
1. **Coastal plains.** Recently emerged coastal belts underlain by sedimentary rock layers which lap over older rocks of the continents.
2. **Horizontal strata.** Sedimentary strata, essentially horizontal in attitude, which have been raised over a large area, but not otherwise seriously disturbed. Horizontal lava flows of great thickness and extent may be included in this group.

B. **Disturbed structures.**
3. **Domes and basins.** Circular or oval zones of uplift or depression causing sedimentary layers to be convexly or concavely bent.
4. **Folds.** Sedimentary strata that have been deformed by mountain-making crustal movements into long belts of wavelike folds. The folds may be broad and open or tightly compressed, depending on the degree of crustal compression.
5. **Fault blocks.** Crustal masses of any rock type or structure broken by faulting into sharply cut blocks that have been displaced in relation to one another. Some tilting usually accompanies the faulting.
6. **Homogeneous crystallines.** Masses of intrusive igneous rock or metamorphic rock which are essentially uniform throughout as regards their resistance to weathering and erosion.
7. **Belted metamorphics.** Narrow zones of metamorphic rocks forming parallel mountain and valley belts (Figure 19.16).

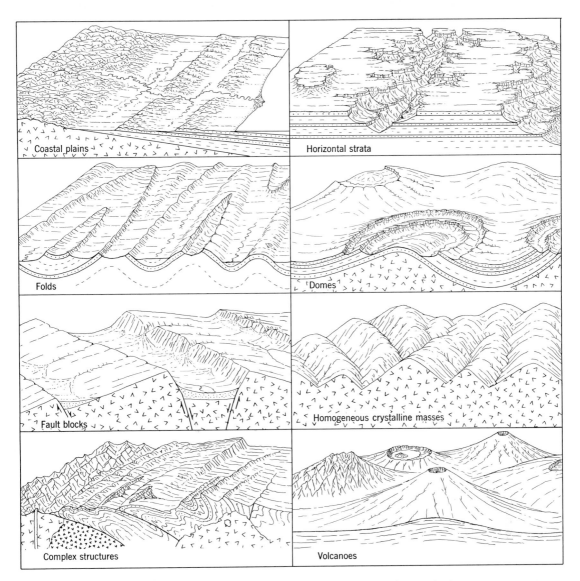

Coastal plains

Horizontal strata

Folds

Domes

Fault blocks

Homogeneous crystalline masses

Complex structures

Volcanoes

Figure 29.1 Land masses can be classified according to the groups illustrated here. Belted metamorphics are shown in Figure 19.16. Classification is based on variety and structure of rock.

8. **Complex structures.** Crustal masses that have suffered a combination of folding, faulting, or intrusion by igneous rocks so as to make a mass of irregular and complicated structures.

C. **Volcanoes and related forms.**

All types of rock masses resulting from the extrusion of molten rock. These include various types of volcanoes and lava flows.

There is a significant difference in the initial appearance of the undisturbed and the disturbed structures. The former have surfaces of low relief (plains or plateaus) before erosional modification sets in. The disturbed structures and volcanic forms, on the other hand, usually have bold, mountainous relief in the initial stage. Relief is greatest at the beginning of their life history, and the masses are ultimately reduced to surfaces of faint relief.

Each one of the structural types described above passes through an orderly series of erosional stages, patterned after the general cycle of land-mass denudation already explained. For regions of horizontal strata or homogenous crystalline rocks, this cycle is very similar to the ideal general cycle because these rock masses are of uniform composition and structure in every direction horizontally. Folds, fault blocks, domes, and volcanoes, however, have life cycles quite different, not only from the ideal cycle, but also from one another, because the rock variations or initial shapes have a dominant control upon the denudational rates.

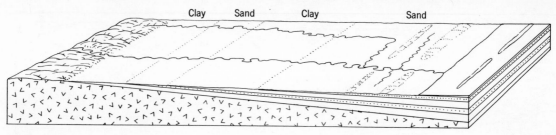

Clay   Sand   Clay   Sand

A. Initial stage; plain recently emerged.

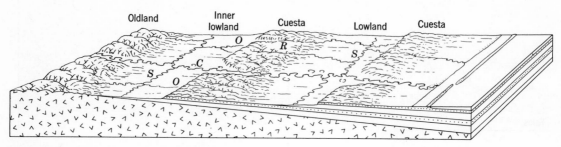

Oldland   Inner lowland   Cuesta   Lowland   Cuesta

B. Mature stage; cuestas and lowlands developed. *S* = subsequent; *C* = consequent; *O* = obsequent; *R* = resequent.

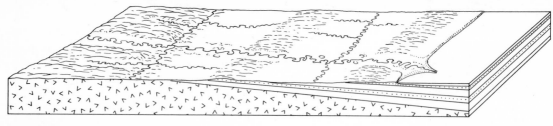

C. Late mature or old stage; relief very low.

Figure 29.2 Development of a broad coastal plain. (After A. K. Lobeck.)

Coastal plains

Coastal plains pass through a series of stages illustrated in Figure 29.2. In Block *A* the region has recently emerged from beneath the sea, where it was formerly a shallow continental shelf accumulating successive layers of sediment brought from the land and distributed by currents. On the initial surface, streams flow directly seaward, down the slope of the new surface. A stream of this origin is a *consequent stream*, defined as any stream whose course is controlled by the initial slope of a land surface. Consequent streams occur on many landforms, such as volcanoes, fault blocks, or beds of drained lakes. Streams that formerly drained the land surface inland from the coastal plain, but that now have become extended across it to reach the new shoreline, are called *extended consequent streams*. The term *oldland* is applied to the area of older rock lying inland from the coastal plain. If the oldland had prominent hills upon its surface before the submergence which allowed sediments to be deposited, the hills may project through the coastal-plain layers as *mendips* (named after the Mendip Hills of southern England), or *inliers*.

In the mature stage of coastal-plain development a new series of streams and topographic features has developed (Block *B*). Where more easily eroded strata (usually clay or shale) are exposed, denudation is rapid, making *lowlands*. Between them rise broad low ridges or belts of hills comprising *cuestas*. The lowland lying between the oldland and the first cuesta is called the *inner lowland*. Cuestas are commonly underlain by sand, sandstone, limestone, or chalk. They have a fairly steep slope on the landward side, or *inface*, because the edge of the eroded layer is exposed on this side. The seaward slope, or *backslope*, of the cuesta is gentle because it follows the top surface of the gently inclined harder layer. Where the resistant layer is very hard and is underlain by a weak layer, the cuesta face is often steep with occasional rock cliffs, as in the limestone cuesta near Rheims, France (Figure 29.3). More commonly, however, the cuesta is merely a belt of low hills.

Figure 29.3 This sharply defined cuesta in the Paris basin of northern France has its steep face to the east (left), a very gentle slope westward from the crest. (Photograph by Douglas Johnson.)

Streams that develop along the trend of the lowlands, parallel with the shoreline, are of a class known as *subsequent* streams. They take their position along any belt or zone of weak rock and therefore follow closely the pattern of rock exposure. Subsequent streams occur in many regions and will be mentioned frequently in the discussion of folds, domes, and fault blocks.

Streams that flow down the inface of a cuesta to join the subsequent stream in a lowland are *obsequent streams.* Their direction of flow is opposite to the seaward slope of the strata, as well as opposite to the direction of flow of the consequent streams. Streams that came into existence on the backslopes of cuestas, but which were not originally present as consequent streams, are termed *resequent streams.* They flow in the same direction as the original consequent streams, but develop only as the backslope of the cuesta comes into being by removal of the weaker overlying layers (Figure 29.4).

The drainage lines on a maturely dissected coastal plain combine to form a *trellis* pattern (Figure 29.4), consisting of consequent, subsequent, obsequent, and resequent streams.

Diagram *C,* Figure 29.2, shows the coastal plain reduced to a peneplain in the stage of old age. The trellis drainage pattern persists, and the cuestas still show as faint hills rising above the nearly flat lowlands.

Coastal plains of the United States and England

Splendid examples of coastal plains are present along the Atlantic and Gulf coasts of the United States, in southeastern England, and in the Paris Basin region of north-central France.

The coastal plain of the United States is by far the largest of these, ranging in width from 100 to 300 miles and extending for 2000 miles along the Atlantic and Gulf coasts. Strata are of Cretaceous and Tertiary age, the former being exposed nearest to the inner margin of the coastal plain because they lie directly upon the oldland rocks of Paleozoic and pre-Cambrian age. The coastal plain starts at Long Island, which is a partly submerged cuesta, and widens rapidly southward so as to include much of New Jersey, Delaware, Maryland, and

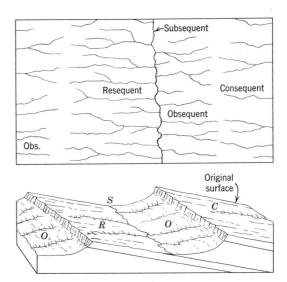

Figure 29.4 Four kinds of streams are associated with eroded dipping sedimentary layers. These form a trellis drainage pattern.

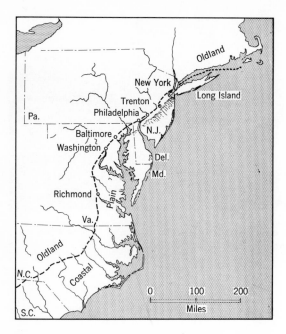

Figure 29.5 The coastal plain of the Atlantic seaboard states shows little cuesta development except in New Jersey. The inner limit of the coastal plain is marked by a series of fall-line cities. (After A. K. Lobeck.)

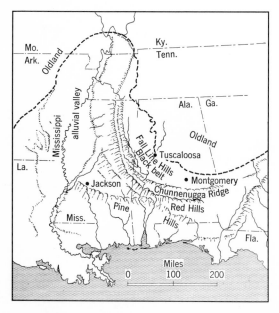

Figure 29.6 The Alabama-Mississippi coastal plain is belted by a series of sandy cuestas and shale or marl lowlands. (After A. K. Lobeck.)

Virginia (Figure 29.5). Throughout this portion the coastal plain has but one cuesta, that which forms the Atlantic Highlands, Mt. Laurel, Pine Hills, and similar hill groups. The cuesta is underlain by a porous sand formation of Tertiary and Cretaceous age, which resists erosion by absorbing rainwater rapidly and thereby minimizing overland flow. The inner lowland is a continuous broad valley developed on a weak clay formation of Cretaceous age.

In Alabama and Mississippi the coastal plain is maturely dissected in all but the coastal area, which has recently emerged from the sea. Cuestas and lowlands run in belts roughly parallel with the coast (Figure 29.6). Hence the term *belted coastal plain* is applied to these regions. The cuestas tend to be underlain by sandy formations and support a growth of pines. Limestone forms fertile lowlands such as the Black Belt in Alabama. The principal streams cross the belted topography with little regard for lowlands and cuestas, suggesting that they originated as extended consequents. The shoreline of the Gulf Coast is one of fairly recent emergence, as explained in an earlier chapter.

The entire southeastern portion of England is a mature coastal plain (Figure 29.7). Two cuestas dominate the topography. The innermost is of Jurassic limestone and is locally named the Cotswold Hills. In England, the term *wold* is applied to a cuesta, *vale* to an intercuesta lowland. The outer or southeastern cuesta is of white chalk of Cretaceous age and includes the Chiltern Hills. Between cuestas is a lowland in which lie Oxford and Cambridge; hence, it is called the Educational Lowland. An extensive inner lowland runs between the inner cuesta and the oldland rock masses of Cornwall, Wales, and the Pennine Range. In the inner lowland are the important cities Bristol, Gloucester, Birmingham, Nottingham, Lincoln, and York, as well as extensive farm lands. This lowland is drained by a number of subsequent streams, the Severn, Avon, Trent, and Ouse.

Geographical aspects of coastal plains

Broad coastal plains, such as those of the eastern United States and southeastern England, show intensive agricultural development because of the fertility and easy cultivation of broad lowlands. Although important seaport cities have developed on coastal plains there was not the same impelling necessity toward marine occupations that was induced by mountainous coastal belts bordered by shorelines of submergence.

Cuestas provide valuable forests, as in England and Europe and in the southern United States. Where excessively porous sands occur, as in the New Jersey coastal plain, pine and oak are supported.

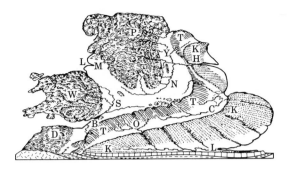

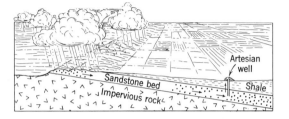

Figure 29.7 Southeastern England is a broadly curved, mature coastal plain. L = London; K = Cretaceous chalk cuesta; C = Cambridge; O = Oxford; H = Humber River; Y = York; N = Nottingham; S = Severn River; B = Bristol; D = Dartmoor; W = Wales; M = Manchester; L = Liverpool; P = Pennine Range; T = Jurassic limestone cuesta. (After W. M. Davis.)

Figure 29.8 An artesian well requires a dipping sandstone layer. (After E. Raisz.)

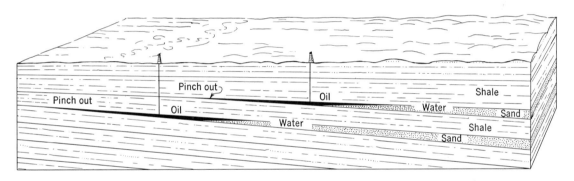

Figure 29.9 Oil pools can form in the fringes of sand formations which pinch out in the up-dip direction.

Transportation tends to follow the lowlands and to connect the larger cities located there. For example, important roads and railroads connect New York with Trenton, Philadelphia, Baltimore and Washington, all of which are situated in an inner lowland. Cuesta topography, however, is rarely so rugged as to interfere seriously with the location of communication lines.

The seaward dip of sedimentary strata in a coastal plain provides a structure favorable to the development of artesian water wells. Water penetrates deeply into a sandy cuesta stratum, which is overlain by shales or clays impervious to the flow of underground waters. When a well is drilled into the sand formation considerably seaward of its surface exposure, water under hydraulic pressure reaches the surface (Figure 29.8). Artesian water in large quantities is available in many parts of the Atlantic and Gulf coastal plains, although it is no longer sufficient to supply the demands of densely

populated and industrialized localities.

The Gulf Coastal Plain of the United States contains petroleum and natural gas accumulations of enormous economic value. Oil occurs in *stratigraphic traps*, which are layers or lenses of permeable sand or sandstone capped by impermeable shales or clays. One kind of stratigraphic trap is the *pinch out*, illustrated in Figure 29.9. A sandstone formation in the coastal plain sequence of strata thins in the updip (landward) direction to a feather edge, where it disappears, whether through lack of deposition, or by later erosion that preceded deposition of the next younger beds. Capped above by impermeable beds, the sandstone wedge forms a trap for oil migrating updip. Figure 29.10, shows two curving bands of oil *pools* of this type in the Gulf Coast of Texas.

Another quite different type of oil pool common in coastal plains and other regions of thick sedimentary strata occurs on *salt domes*, or *salt plugs*

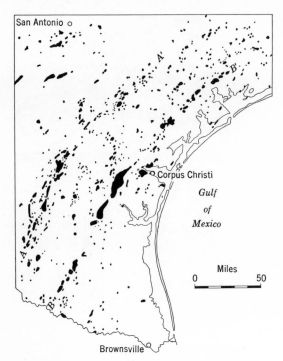

Figure 29.10 Two zones of oil pools on up-dip pinch-outs of sands of Eocene age (*AA'*) and Oligocene age (*BB'*). (After A. I. Levorsen.)

(Figure 29.11). These strange, stalklike bodies of rock salt project upward through coastal plain strata. Apparently they were forced up by slow plastic flowage from thick salt formations lying in deep lower layers of the coastal plain. Surrounding strata are sharply bent up and faulted against the side of the salt plug, making traps for petroleum. Salt plugs commonly have a cap rock of limestone resting upon a plate of gypsum and anhydrite. Oil may collect in cavities in the limestone. Distribution of salt domes of the Gulf Coast is shown in Figure 29.12. The salt dome should not be confused with sedimentary domes discussed later in this chapter.

Other mineral deposits of economic importance in coastal plains include: *sulfur,* occurring in the coastal plain of Louisiana and Texas; *phosphate* beds, found in Florida; *lignite* (a low-grade, woody coal), used as a fuel in Alabama, Mississippi and Texas; and *clays,* used in manufacture of pottery, tile, and brick in New Jersey and the Carolinas.

Horizontal strata

Considerable areas of the continental shields are covered by thick sequences of sedimentary-rock layers, which at one time in the geologic past were the bottom deposits of shallow inland seas or were stream deposits spread over vast alluvial plains. Strata of all three post-Cambrian geologic eras are represented. When uplifted with little disturbance other than a faint warping or minor faulting, these

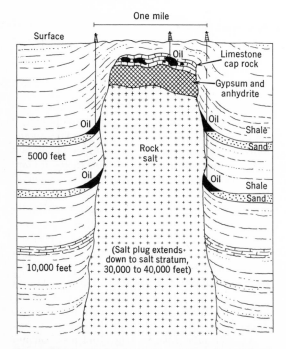

Figure 29.11 Idealized structure section of a salt dome.

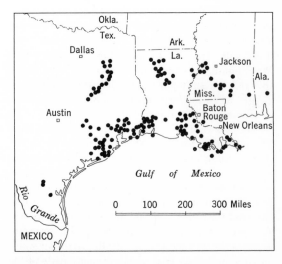

Figure 29.12 Distribution of salt domes of the Gulf Coast region is indicated by dots. (After K. K. Landes.)

sedimentary strata pass through a series of stages of erosion such as those illustrated in the series of block diagrams of Figure 29.13.

In the initial stage the land is fairly smooth and is drained by consequent streams following the gentle slope of the surface. If the elevation of the initial surface is high, these streams soon cut deep canyons, leaving plateau surfaces between. Should the region have initially low elevation above sea level, the streams are prevented by the base level from cutting deeply, and hence strong relief can never develop in the region. Throughout the stage of youth, the region, whether of great or small relief, is dissected by streams whose valley network develops at the expense of the initial land surface.

When the initial land surface is entirely or almost entirely consumed and the region has reached its most rugged character, the stage of maturity has been reached. Throughout the remainder of the erosion cycle the relief diminishes and the slopes perhaps tend to become more gentle. In old age the region is reduced to a rolling plain upon which the larger streams have broad, flat flood plains. A few remnants of harder rock strata may remain as monadnocks.

The horizontal attitude of the rock layers gives rise to distinctive landforms where the layers are of alternately weak and resistant nature (Figure 29.14). The resistant layers, usually of sandstone and limestone (the latter particularly in arid climates), form *cliffs* or steep slopes. The weak layers, usually of shale, clay, or marl, are easily washed away from beneath the lower edges of the resistant layers, hence serving to accentuate the cliffs above them and form smoothly descending slopes at each cliff base. In dry climates, where vegetation is scant and the action of rainwash especially effective, sharply defined topographic forms develop. They comprise what may be described as *scarp-slope-shelf* topography, because the normal sequence of forms is a cliff, or scarp, at the base of which is a smooth slope. This in turn flattens out to make a shelf, terminated at the outer edge by the cliff of the next lower set of forms. In the walls of the great canyons of the Colorado Plateau region in Colorado, Utah, Arizona, and New Mexico, these forms are wonderfully displayed (Figure 29.15).

In plateau regions underlain by horizontal strata, the erosion processes tend to strip successive layers from the plateau surface. Cliffs, capped by hard rock layers, retreat as near-perpendicular surfaces because the weak clay or shale formations exposed at the cliff base are rapidly washed away by storm runoff and channel erosion. Thus undermined, the rock in the upper cliff face repeatedly breaks away along vertical fractures. Where a cliff has thus retreated a considerable distance from a canyon,

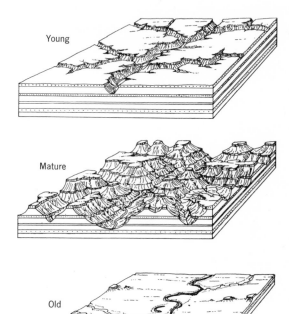

Figure 29.13 Erosional development of horizontal sedimentary strata. The development of cliffs is accentuated here, as typical of an arid climate. (After E. Raisz.)

there remains a broad, flat bench which is the exposed surface of the next layer below. The bench so formed is termed an *esplanade* (Figure 29.15). Should the entire plateau surface be formed by the complete or almost complete removal of a rock series, leaving a plateau capped by a resistant layer, the plateau is termed a *stripped surface* or *stratum plain*.

In the later stages of erosion the landscape in an arid region has many *mesas* (Figure 29.14), table-topped hills or mountains bordered on all sides by

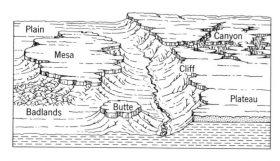

Figure 29.14 In arid climates, a distinctive set of landforms develops in flat-lying sedimentary formations.

Figure 29.15 This panoramic drawing by the noted geologist-artist, W. H. Holmes, published in 1882, shows the Grand Canyon at the mouth of the Toroweap. In this part of the canyon, rarely seen by tourists, a broad bench called The Esplanade is well developed. (From Dutton, *Atlas to accompany Monograph II*, U.S. Geological Survey.)

cliffs and representing the remnant of a formerly extensive layer of resistant rock. Often a mesa is capped by a lava flow, which is generally more resistant than the sedimentary rocks over which it once flowed. As a mesa is reduced in area by retreat of the cliffs that border it, it maintains its flat top and altitude. Before its complete consumption the final stage is a small, steep-sided hill or peak known as a *butte* (Figure 29.16).

Where extremely weak clays or shales, lacking a protective vegetative cover, are exposed to rainwash and gully erosion in dry regions, a very rugged topography resembling miniature mountains develops. Such areas are termed *badlands* (Figures 29.14 and 29.17).

In humid climates the elements described above, namely, scarp-slope-shelf topography, stripped surfaces, mesas, and buttes, are present only in greatly subdued aspect. This is due to the thick cover of vegetation that protects the ground from rapid rainwash and permits a layer of soil and mantle to cloak the bedrock. Nevertheless, occasional lines

of cliffs do form, and mesalike hills and mountains are developed. Vast areas in western Pennsylvania and New York, Ohio, West Virginia, Kentucky, Tennessee, and Alabama consist of maturely dissected horizontal strata. Much of this land is mountainous and heavily forested.

In a maturely dissected region of horizontal strata the stream system forms a *dendritic drainage pattern*, in which the smaller streams show no predominant directional orientation or control (Figure 25.5). This pattern has been likened to the branching of an apple tree. Usually the larger trunk streams show a rough parallelism, because they were the original consequent streams which followed a perceptible slope of the region as a whole. The smaller streams, whose pattern is dendritic, are said to be *insequent* in origin. An insequent stream is controlled in its growth by very minor inequalities of rock resistance and slope which are not themselves systematically oriented. On the whole, therefore, the direction of branching is very much a matter of chance.

Figure 29.16 This early photograph shows a butte of horizontal red sandstones capped by a gypsum layer, near Cambria, Wyoming. (Photograph by N. H. Darton, U.S. Geological Survey.)

In addition to regions underlain by sedimentary rocks, the regions of horizontal strata may be made to include thick accumulations of lava flows. In some parts of the world, such as the Columbia Plateau region of eastern Washington and Oregon, or the Deccan Plateau of western India, the vast outpourings of highly fluid basalt lavas now cover thousands of square miles and are several thousand feet thick. Interbedded with the lavas are lake and stream deposits of sands, gravels, and clays, as well as much volcanic ash and dust. Consequently, the structure exhibits alternately weak and resistant layers in which erosion produces landforms very similar to those of sedimentary strata.

Geographical aspects of horizontal strata

Generalizations cannot readily be made about the utilization of areas underlain by horizontal strata because of the great variations in surface relief that exist. On initial and old surfaces, where the topography is plainlike, agriculture is widely developed. On the high plains of western Kansas and Nebraska, eastern Wyoming and Colorado, New Mexico, and Texas, wheat farming is the predominant activity. Here the plain is in its initial or very early stage of erosion. Despite elevations of 3000 to 5000 feet, the plain is trenched only by a few major through-flowing streams.

Some regions of horizontal strata in the interior United States, including much of Illinois, Indiana,

Figure 29.17 Badlands, such as these in the Petrified Forest National Monument, Arizona, are like miniature mountain topography on bare clay formations. (Photograph by B. Mears, Jr.)

Figure 29.18 Seen from the air, the maturely dissected Allegheny Plateau of West Virginia appears largely forested. Relief of 700 to 800 feet is here developed on shales of Devonian age. (Photograph by J. L. Rich. Courtesy of the *Geographical Review*.)

Ohio, Missouri, Montana, Kansas and Iowa, are maturely dissected, but a mantle of glacial drift has reduced relief so that slopes are gentle and are highly cultivated. Where relief is strong, as in the mountain areas of the Alleghenies or the Cumberland Mountains, cultivation is limited to a few small tracts, such as the flood-plain belts of larger streams, despite the favorable humid climate (Figure 29.18). In the canyon lands of the Colorado Plateau an extremely low population density exists, not only because the high relief and aridity do not favor agriculture, but also because human access is virtually impossible across the network of sheer-walled canyons.

As with coastal plains, regions of horizontal strata have only those minerals and rocks of economic value that are associated with sedimentary rocks (or lavas). Building stone, such as the Bedford limestone in Indiana or the Berea sandstone in Ohio, is a valuable product. Limestone may be quarried for use in manufacture of Portland cement or as a flux in iron smelting. Some important deposits of lead, zinc, and iron ores occur in sedimentary rocks. For example, the lead and zinc mines of the Tristate district (Missouri, Kansas, Oklahoma) are in horizontal limestones.

Perhaps the greatest mineral resources occurring in sedimentary strata are coal and petroleum. Where the strata are undisturbed, coal is of the *bituminous*, or soft, variety and lies in horizontal layers from a few inches to several feet thick and hundreds of square miles in extent. Where the relief of the region is great, coal seams outcrop along the valley walls into which mine openings termed *drifts* can be tunneled to obtain the coal. This is common practice in the bituminous fields of western Pennsylvania, eastern Ohio, and West Virginia. Where the coal seams are not exposed at the surface they must be reached by vertical shafts, as in the Illinois coal fields. Anywhere that a rich coal seam outcrops in a hillside or lies near the surface it can be reached by removing the overburden of rock and mantle with powerful earth-moving machines. This process, termed *strip mining*, leaves great gashes and adjacent embankments of rock debris.

Petroleum occurs within permeable sandstone layers, in which the oil is trapped by overlying impermeable shales. Because the strata are not perfectly horizontal, but are affected by minor warpings and faults as well as by changes in thickness and character of the sandstone layers, there are many structures in which petroleum is localized into pools. Stratigraphic traps, similar in principle to those of coastal plains, form important pools. Traps also result from faulting, which offsets the edges of the strata (Figure 30.16).

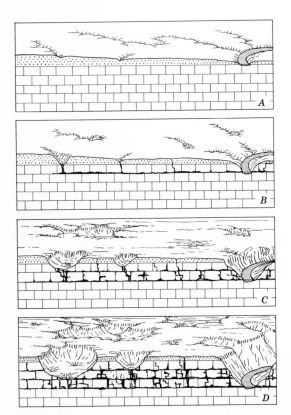

Figure 29.19 As a cavern system develops, surface stream flow is diverted to underground flow. (After A. K. Lobeck.)

Limestone caverns

Limestone, composed of calcium and magnesium carbonate, is readily dissolved by weak solutions of carbonic acid present in soil and ground water. Ground waters carry away the dissolved carbonates, leaving elaborate systems of subterranean caverns. Most persons are familiar with the names of famous caverns, such as Mammoth Cave, Carlsbad Caverns, Luray Caverns, or Cave of the Winds, and many Americans have visited one or more of these famous tourist attractions. Although caverns may develop in folded, faulted, and steeply dipping limestone layers, most caverns occur in areas of flat-lying strata, so that it is appropriate to take up the subject at this point.

The development of a cavern system is illustrated in Figure 29.19. According to one widely held theory of cavern formation, it is necessary that a thick limestone formation be present and that the region be an elevated one with the valleys of the larger rivers deeply cut so as to provide topographic relief. At first (Stage *A*) the limestone is solid and is covered by a sandstone layer. The water drains off by means of surface streams. As the large river cuts more deeply, underground water flows through joint cracks in the limestone to emerge at the river bank (Stage *B*). The passageways in the limestone become larger and deeper as time goes on (Stage *C*). By now, all surface water pours down into cavities known as *sinkholes* (Figure 29.20). These are usually filled at the surface by broken rock and soil through which the water filters. Occasionally they are enlarged by collapse so as to make a gaping hole. In Stage *D* the sinkholes are enlarged into small valleys and the cavern system is fully developed, with many passageways and shafts. On the lowest level run underground rivers, which emerge at the banks of the main river. Abandoned caves at higher levels may be dry except for the localized dripping of water.

Cave deposits (or "formations," as they are usually called by tourist guides in our American caverns) are encrustations of calcium carbonate or gypsum formed after the cavern is fully enlarged and is no longer the site of rapid solution. The slow drip of water from the ceilings is accompanied by evaporation so that a small amount of calcium carbonate is left behind. Many beautiful forms result. Some of these are pictured in Figure 29.21. Spikelike forms hanging from the ceilings are *stalactites* (*D*); blunt columns growing up from the floor are *stalagmites* (*B*). Where the water drips from a long joint crack on the ceiling, a *drip curtain* results (*C*). Stalactites and stalagmites join to form *columns;* and rows of columns formed under a large joint crack may coalesce to make a

Figure 29.20 Outcrops of horizontal limestone strata show in the walls of this deep sinkhole on the Kaibab Plateau of northern Arizona. Because of high elevation (8500 feet), the climate here is cool and humid, favoring limestone solution.

wall. Among the blocks of stone that litter the cavern floor, pools of water overflow from one to another, making *travertine terraces* (*D*).

The geographical importance of caves is felt in several ways. Throughout man's early development, caves were an important habitation. Now we find the skeletal remains of these people, together with their implements and cave drawings, preserved through the centuries in caves in many parts of the world. Today, with increasing destructiveness of weapons of warfare, caverns are achieving importance as possible sites for storage of valuable materials, as living quarters, and as factories for important types of production.

Caverns have provided some valuable deposits of *guano*, the excrement of birds or bats, which is rich in nitrates and is used in the manufacture of fertilizers and explosives. Bat guano was taken from Mammoth Cave for making gunpowder during the war of 1812. Much more recently a valuable guano deposit in a limestone cavern in the wall of the Grand Canyon of the Colorado River has been mined and lifted to the Canyon rim by cable car.

A. Entrance to caves.

B. A stalagmite.

C. A drip curtain.

D. A travertine terrace.

Figure 29.21   The Jenolan Caves of New South Wales, Australia, have remarkably fine displays of cavern deposits. (Courtesy N. S. W. Government Printer.)

Karst landscapes

Where limestone solution has been especially active there results a landscape with many unique landforms. This is especially true along the Dalmatian coastal area of Yugoslavia, where the topography is termed *karst*. The term may be applied to the topography of any limestone area where sinkholes are numerous and small surface streams nonexistent. Four stages of development of a karst landscape are shown in Figure 29.22. Exposed limestone surfaces are deeply grooved and fluted into *lapiés* (*A*) (Figure 22.15). Deep, steep-walled funnel-like sinkholes, called *dolines* (*B*), are numerous (Figure 29.20). In places, these have coalesced to make open, flat-floored valleys termed *poljes* (*C*). Here surface streams flow and the soil may be suitable for agriculture.

Some other regions of karst or karstlike topography are the Mammoth Cave region of Kentucky, the Causses region of France, the Yucatan Peninsula, and parts of Cuba and Puerto Rico.

Domes and basins

Sedimentary layers in many places show a warping into broad domelike or basinlike structures, which may range from 25 to 100 or even 200 miles in diameter, but in which the strata are nowhere inclined more than 1° or 2° from the horizontal. Such domes and basins tend to form concentric cuestas when dissected. An example is the Weald Uplift of southeastern England (Figure 29.23). As the central part of the dome is eroded away, older rock layers are exposed. As each layer is cut through, it is eroded back from the center. Thus the cuestas have their steep inface toward the center of the dome and retreat away from the center. An example of a broad, shallow basin structure is the Paris Basin. The cuestas have their steep infaces outward, and as erosion progresses the cuestas retreat toward the center of the basin.

Domes may also be steep-sided and high, differing from the broad, low type in that the strata on the flanks dip outward at angles up to 25° or more. Thus the dome forms a conspicuous hill or mountain and, when maturely dissected, may constitute a truly rugged mass of peaks. To distinguish this type of dome it will be referred to as a *mountainous dome*. Basins of comparable development are not known because, although the strata may be strongly domed up by the intrusion of molten rock under great pressure, there is no geologic mechanism by which the strata can be sharply punched down.

The erosion of a mountainous dome is shown in

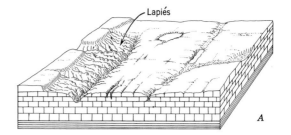

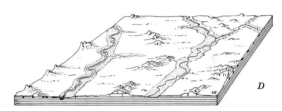

Figure 29.22 Stages of evolution of a karst landscape show increased relief and cavern development followed by decreasing relief and the removal of the limestone mass. (Drawn by E. Raisz.)

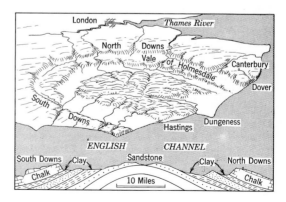

Figure 29.23 The Weald region of southeastern England is a broad dome of sedimentary strata from which the top has been removed. (After A. K. Lobeck.)

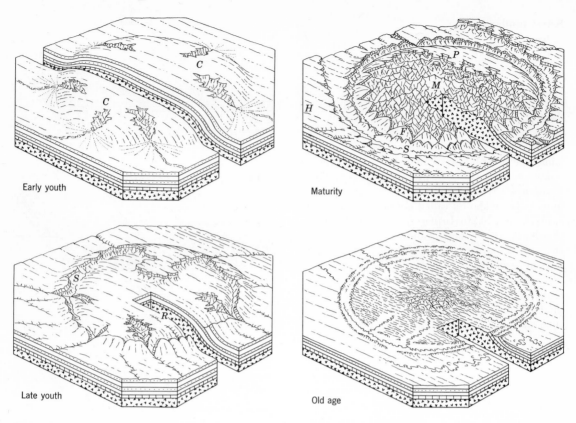

Early youth

Maturity

Late youth

Old age

Figure 29.24 Stages in the development of a mountainous dome. C = consequent stream; S = subsequent stream; F = flatiron; P = plateau in center of dome; M = mountains of crystalline rock; H = horizontal strata surrounding dome; R = resequent stream.

Figure 29.25 This early photograph shows a remarkably fine hogback of dipping sandstone beds four miles east of Gallup, New Mexico. Today U.S. Highway 66 runs through this gap. (Photograph by Darton, U.S. Geological Survey.)

the diagrams of Figure 29.24. In the stage of early youth a series of consequent streams drains outward in a *radial* drainage pattern. These streams intrench the flanks of the dome and quickly expose the underlying layers. As erosion progresses, the resistant strata begin to stand out as sharp-crested ridges, or *hogbacks*, encircling the dome (Figure 29.25). Hogbacks are very striking landforms; they owe their development to the rapid removal of weaker shale or clay beds on either side (Figure 29.26). A concentric arrangement of alternate hogback ridges and valleys develops on the mature dome. Streams occupying the weak rock valleys are subsequent in origin, forming a concentric, or *annular*, drainage pattern (Figure 29.27). Tributaries that flow down from the intervening hogback ridges are resequent and obsequent streams, the former flowing outward, the latter inward.

As dome erosion progresses, older and deeper rocks are exposed in the center. If geologic conditions are favorable, erosion may reveal in the center a core of intrusive igneous rock representing material that was forced up to produce the dome. In this event the igneous rock is younger than the sedimentary rock of the dome. One variety of intrusive dome is the *laccolith*, a convex but flat-bottomed mass of igneous rock which came up between strata and spread out, forcing the overlying layers to rise (Figure 29.28). In other domes the central core is of ancient rock, much older than even the sedimentary layers, and represents the rock upon which those sediments were deposited. It shows through in the dome core because the strata are not thick enough to cover it when the dome is fully dissected.

The last sedimentary rock layer to be stripped from the central core of crystalline rock clings to the sides of the core in triangular patches known as *flatirons*. The flatirons cap the ends of mountain spurs and are separated by V-shaped canyons (Figure 29.24).

In the old-age stage, a mountainous dome has been reduced to a peneplain on which the hogback ridges are represented by faint rows of hills. In the central core, a few monadnock masses may rise conspicuously above the peneplain level.

Geographical aspects of domes

For broad, low domes and basins the human-geographic and economic features are essentially those of coastal plains or regions of horizontal strata. Mountainous domes, however, have some unique features. These are illustrated by the great Black Hills dome of western South Dakota and eastern Wyoming (Figure 29.29).

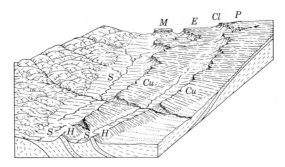

Figure 29.26 Hogbacks may gradually merge into cuestas, the cuestas into plateaus and esplanades, if the dip of the strata becomes less from one place to another. S = subsequent stream; H = hogback ridge; Cu = cuesta; M = mesa; E = esplanade; Cl = cliff; P = plateau. (After W. M. Davis.)

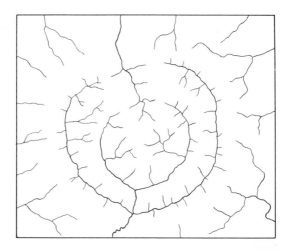

Figure 29.27 The drainage pattern on a maturely eroded dome combines annular and radial elements. It resembles a trellis pattern bent into a circle.

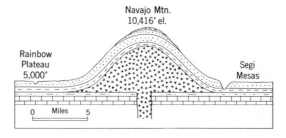

Figure 29.28 Navajo Mountain, Utah, is thought to be a laccolith whose igenous rock core is still covered by sedimentary strata. (After H. E. Gregory.)

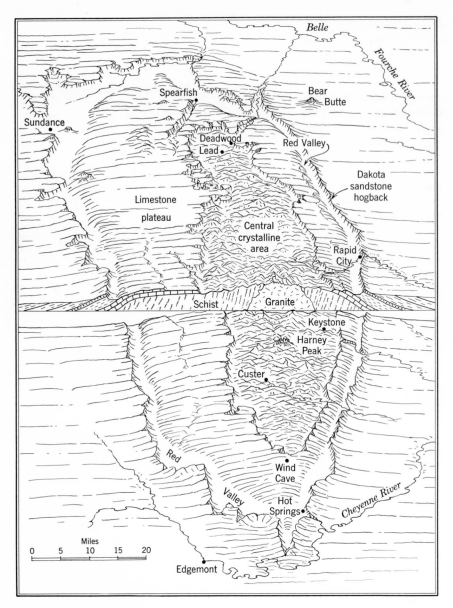

Figure 29.29 The Black Hills consist of a broad, flat-topped dome, deeply eroded to expose a core of crystalline rock.

The annular subsequent valleys that encircle the dome are splendid locations for railroads and highways. Thus it is natural that towns and cities should grow in these valleys. In the Black Hills dome, one annular valley in particular, the Red Valley, is continuously developed around the entire dome and has been termed the Race Track because of its shape. It is underlain by a weak shale which is easily washed away. In the Red Valley lie such towns as Rapid City, Spearfish, and Sturgis. On the outer side of the Red Valley is a high, sharp hogback of Dakota sandstone, known simply as the Hogback Ridge. It rises some 400 or 500 feet above the level of the Red Valley. Farther out toward the margins of the dome the strata are less steeply inclined and form a series of cuestas. Artesian water is obtained from wells drilled in the surrounding plain.

The eastern central part of the Black Hills consists of a mountainous core of intrusive and metamorphic rocks. These mountains are richly forested, whereas the intervening valleys are beautiful open parks. Thus the region is attractive as a summer resort area. Harney Peak, elevation 7242 feet, is highest of the peaks of the core. In the northern part of the central core, in the vicinity of Lead and Deadwood, are valuable ore deposits. At Lead is the fabulous Homestake Mine, one of the world's richest gold-producing mines. In the southern part of the central crystalline area, at Pennington, is the Etta Mine, known widely for its enormous pegmatite crystals of spodumene, a source of lithium. These occurrences illustrate the principle that the interior cores of mature domes may be favorable places for mineral deposits.

The western central part of the Black Hills consists of a limestone plateau deeply dissected by streams. The original dome has a flattened summit. The limestone plateau represents one of the last remaining sedimentary rock layers to be stripped from the core of the dome.

The subject of economic importance of domes cannot be passed by without mention of the important accumulations of oil and gas in many domes of sedimentary strata. Although not illustrated in the Black Hills themselves, many domes of the Rocky Mountain region have been important petroleum producers, for example, the Rock Springs Dome and Teapot Dome in Wyoming. Oil tends to accumulate in the domed sandstone layers which are overlain by impervious shales. An example of a very low dome in the initial stage of development, which is a valuable producer of oil, is the Dominguez Hills dome in the Los Angeles Basin (Figure 29.30).

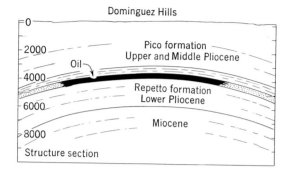

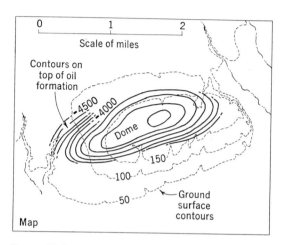

Figure 29.30 The Dominguez Hills, a low dome in an early stage of erosion has beneath it a valuable oil pool. (After H. W. Hoots and U.S. Geological Survey.)

Review Questions

1. What groups of geologic structures make up the bedrock land masses of the earth? Name and describe briefly each variety.

2. What is the basic difference in surface relief of the undisturbed and disturbed structural groups of land masses in the initial stages of their respective erosion cycles?

3. How is a coastal plain formed? By what rock types is it underlain? What is a consequent stream? Where and how does it form on a new coastal plain?

4. What is the oldland? What is a mendip?

5. Describe the topography of a mature coastal plain. Name the component parts as they appear along a profile line beginning on the oldland and extending to the sea.

6. What is a subsequent stream? an obsequent stream? a resequent stream? Show by a sketch map how these stream types are related in a trellis drainage pattern.

7. Describe the coastal plain of the Atlantic and Gulf coast states. What is notable about the drainage pattern of the Gulf coastal plain? What kind of shoreline is associated with the Gulf coastal plain?

8. Briefly state the salient features of the coastal plain topography of southeastern England.

9. How are agriculture and transportation influenced by coastal-plain topography? Explain how artesian wells can function on a coastal plain.

10. What are some of the mineral products of coastal plains? Which of these is most important in the United States?

11. Describe the stages of erosional development of a region of horizontal strata. What determines the maximum relief that can occur?

12. What special features develop during erosion of horizontal layers of shale and sandstone in an arid climate? Explain the following: mesa, butte, esplanade, stripped surface (stratum plain), badlands.

13. What is a dendritic drainage pattern? Of what kind of streams is it composed? How does a dendritic drainage pattern develop?

14. How can horizontal lava flows result in topography

similar to that on horizontal sedimentary strata? Where are great lava plateaus found today?

15. How does the topography of a region of horizontal strata in the various stages of the erosion cycle influence agriculture and human settlement? What are the principal economic mineral products of region of horizontal strata?

16. In what kind of rock are caverns formed? Why? What are sinkholes? Describe stalactites, stalagmites, drip curtains, and columns. What is travertine? What is guano?

17. What is karst? From what region does this term originate? Describe lapiés, dolines, and poljes. Name some regions of karst topography.

18. Describe the various kinds of dome and basin structures that occur in regions underlain by sedimentary rock formations. What variations may be found in the sizes of these structures and the steepness of dip of the strata?

19. Outline the systematic changes in topography that occur as a mountainous dome is eroded through the stages of youth, maturity, and old age. What type of drainage pattern is formed? Of what kinds of streams is this pattern composed? Compare this pattern with that of a coastal plain.

20. What is a hogback? How is it formed? What are flatirons?

21. Describe a laccolith. How does it differ from a batholith?

22. Describe briefly the important structural and topographical features of the Black Hills. In what ways are these features related to the economic products of the Black Hills?

23. How can domes act as traps for petroleum? Give examples of domes that have become valuable oil producers.

Exercises

Exercise 1. *Cuestas of the Paris Basin.* (Source: France; scale 1:200,000; Chalons Sheet.)

Explanatory Note: This map shows a part of two cuestas of the Paris Basin in the region east of Paris, France. The Argonne cuesta, supporting the Argonne Forest of World War I fame, runs down along the eastern side of the map. It is a deeply dissected, rugged sandstone cuesta with steep scarps on the east side. The Hills of Champagne (Monts de Champagne) comprise a lower but well-defined cuesta running through the western part of the map, with divide summits rising to slightly over 200 meters. Between the two cuestas is a lowland on weak marls and clays, the Wet Champagne (Champagne Humide) in which flows the Aisne River. West from the Hills of Champagne the cuesta backslope descends gradually to form the Dry Champagne (Champagne Pouilleuse), a chalk plain with few surface streams. For a detailed discussion of the topography, geology, and military geography of this region, see the volume by Douglas Johnson (1921) listed among the reading references.

QUESTIONS

1. (*a*) State the scale of this map in miles to the inch, and construct a graphic scale in miles. (*b*) State the contour interval of this map in feet.

2. On a sheet of thin tracing paper laid over this map, copy off the principal streams, whether indicated on the map by a line or merely by contour indentations. Use the following color scheme: subsequent streams, blue; resequent streams, red; obsequent streams, green. The result will be a trellis pattern typical of a mature coastal plain.

3. On a sheet of thin tracing paper laid over the map, draw the boundaries separating the zones underlain by various types of rock as shown in the structure section above. First mark off the boundaries along the line of Section AB on the map, then extend the lines north and south as best fits the topography. Color chalk and limestone areas blue; clay and marl green; sandstone yellow.

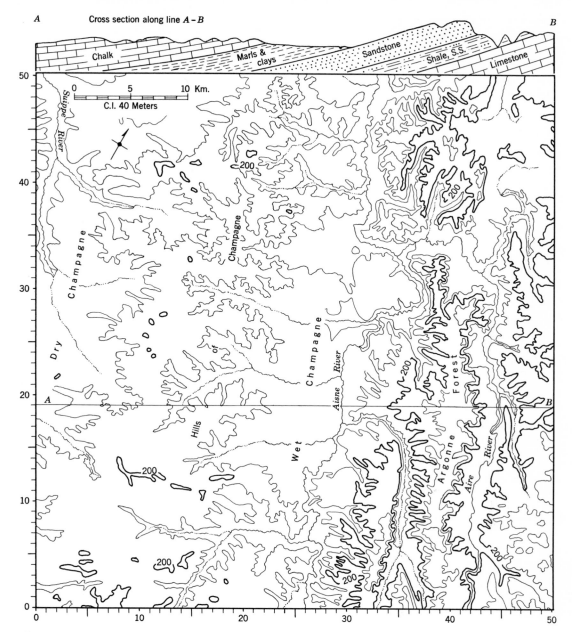

A   Cross section along line A – B   B

Chalk   Marls & clays   Sandstone   Shale, S.S.   Limestone

C.I. 40 Meters

Exercise 1

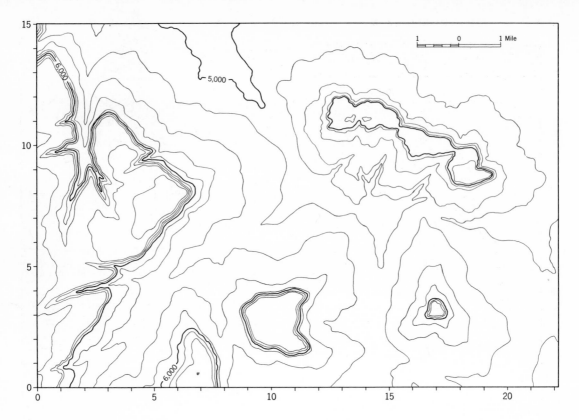

Exercise 2. *Mesas, Buttes, and Canyons.* (Source: Marsh Pass, Ariz., U.S. Geological Survey topographic map; scale 1:250,000.)

Explanatory Note: Erosion of a resistant sandstone layer underlain by a weak shale formation has produced the steep-sided flat-topped mesas, buttes, and plateaus shown on this map of a semi-arid part of northern Arizona. Refer to Figure 29.14 for terminology.

QUESTIONS

1. (*a*) What contour interval is used on this map? (*b*) Locate by grid coordinates and give the elevation of the highest point on the map. (*c*) How high is the cliff at 4.5–5.5?

2. On a sheet of thin tracing paper laid over this map, label one good example of each of the following forms: mesa, butte, plateau, canyon, cliff.

3. On the same sheet of paper used in Question 2, draw in a complete drainage system for this area, showing channels wherever indicated by the contours.

4. Make a topographic profile from 22.0–3.0 to 0.0–3.0, using a vertical scale of 1 inch equals 2000 feet. Then show on the profile the sandstone and shale formations in a manner similar to that in Figure 29.14. For those who wish to do so, a block diagram of the map area may be extended behind the completed profile.

5. Assuming the sandstone cap rock to be of uniform thickness wherever it now remains, have we any reason to think that the layer is not horizontal, but instead that it is slightly tilted or bent? Cite evidence bearing on this question.

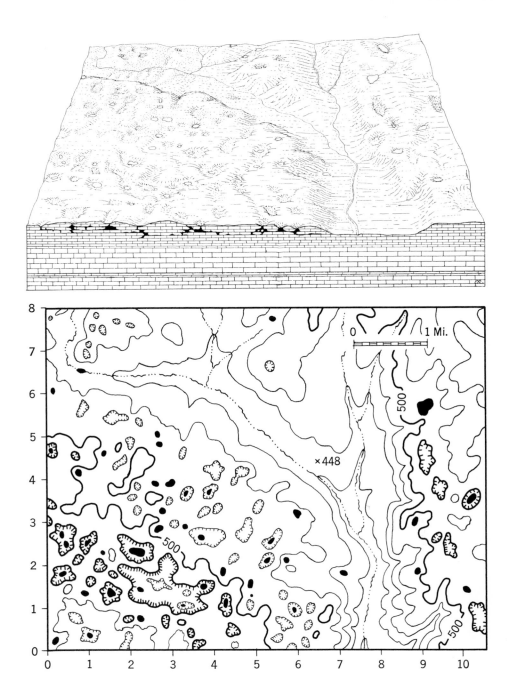

Exercise 3. Sinkholes. (Source: Princeton, Ky., U.S. Geological Survey topographic map; scale 1:62,500.)

Explanatory Note: Numerous small sinkholes, some containing lakes (solid black), are represented by the closed hachured contours. This topography indicates a limestone formation beneath the surface.

QUESTIONS

1. What contour interval has been used on this map? (Refer to the numbered heavy contour and to the spot height located at 6.5–4.4).

2. Estimate the depth of each of the sinkholes whose loca-

tion is given by the grid coordinates listed below. By "depth" is meant the difference in elevation between the lowest outlet point on the rim of the depression and the deepest point on the bottom of the depression. **(a)** 2.7–1.5. **(b)** 2.2–2.3. **(c)** 9.1–4.5.

3. Draw an east-west topographic profile across the map from 10.6–1.6 to 0.0–1.6. Use a vertical scale of 100 feet equals 1 inch.

4. On the broad divide located at 6.5–5.5 draw in contours to show a sinkhole whose depth is more than 40 but less than 80 feet. Label the contours with their correct elevations.

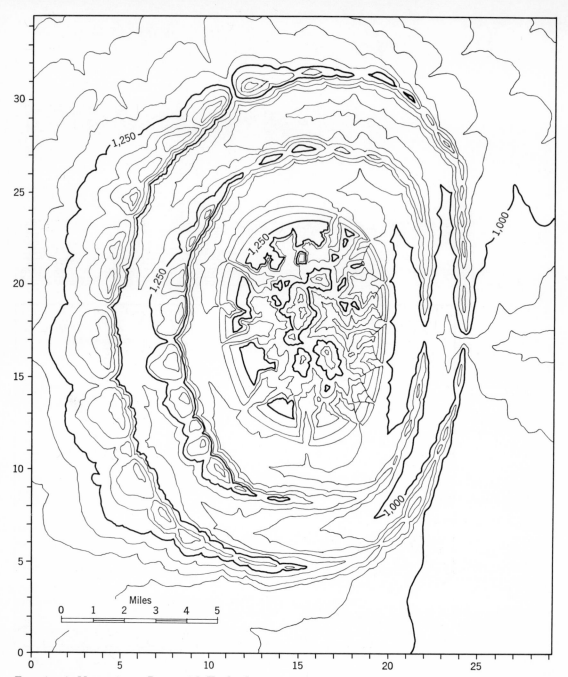

Exercise 4. *Mountainous Dome with Hogbacks.*

Explanatory Note: This is a synthetic map, not representing any real area, and should be regarded as an idealized diagram for illustrating landforms typical of a maturely dissected dome, such as those shown in Figures 29.24 and 29.29.

QUESTIONS

1. On a sheet of thin tracing paper laid over this map, label good examples of the following: hogback, flatiron, subsequent valley, central crystalline area, watergap.

2. On the same sheet used in Question 1, draw in a complete drainage system, showing all streams indicated by the contours. Use the following color scheme: subsequent streams, blue; resequent streams, red; obsequent streams, green; insequent streams, black.

3. Make a topographic profile from 29–19 to 0–19, using a vertical scale of 1 inch equals 1000 feet. Then draw in sandstone and shale layers to fit the topography, using Figures 29.24 and 29.29 as a guide to your interpretation. Indicate crystalline rocks in the core of the dome.

4. Assuming the sandstone formations that make the two hogback ridges to be of uniform thickness where present over this region, why are the hogback ridges broad and cuestalike on the west side? Does your answer also explain why the major streams drain out through gaps in the east side of the dome?

CHAPTER THIRTY

Folds, faults, and fault blocks

REGIONS of sedimentary strata that have been compressed into sets of parallel, wavelike folds pass through a series of stages illustrated in the diagrams of Figure 30.1. Consequent streams drain the flanks of the folds to join major consequent streams that follow the axes of the troughs. In geological terminology, a downfold is known as a *syncline;* an upfold, an *anticline* (Block *A*). It may help in remembering these terms to know that the root word *clino* means "lean," as, for example, in the word *incline.* The prefix *syn* means "together." Hence, a syncline is a structure in which strata dip toward the center line of the trough. *Anti,* meaning against or opposite, implies that in an anticline the layers dip away from the center line. In the initial stages of the development of folds, anticlines are identical with the mountains, or ridges; synclines, with the valleys.

Block *A* (Figure 30.1) shows erosion of anticlines occurring during the last stages of folding. Synclines are being filled with alluvial fan materials swept down from the adjacent anticlines. After folding has ceased the upper layers of soft, unconsolidated rock are removed until, as shown in Block *B,* a hard, well-cemented sandstone layer is exposed, reflecting the full amplitude of the folding. Coinciding with synclines are *synclinal valleys;*

with anticlines, *anticlinal mountains.*

Streams that drain the flanks of the anticlines quickly cut deep ravines, exposing the underlying layers. The breaching spreads rapidly to the crest of the anticline, where a long, narrow valley is opened out along the summit (Block *B*). This valley is occupied by a subsequent stream excavating a belt of weak rock and is known as an *anticlinal valley,* because it lies upon the center line of the anticline. As this valley grows in length, depth, and breadth it replaces the original anticlinal mountain. A reversal of topography thus occurs. The synclinal valley, which originally contained the major stream, is now shrunken between the growing anticlinal valleys on either side. Moreover, the anticlinal valleys are the more rapidly deepened because of the core of weak rock exposed to attack, so that eventually the syncline becomes a mountain ridge, termed a *synclinal mountain* (Block *C*). This might well bring to mind the words of the prophet, Isaiah, "Every valley shall be exalted, and every mountain and hill shall be made low." At this stage, which is that of maturity of the folds, the original topography has been completely reversed.

above: Sheep Mountain, near Greybull, Montana. Photograph by Barnum Brown, American Museum of Natural History.

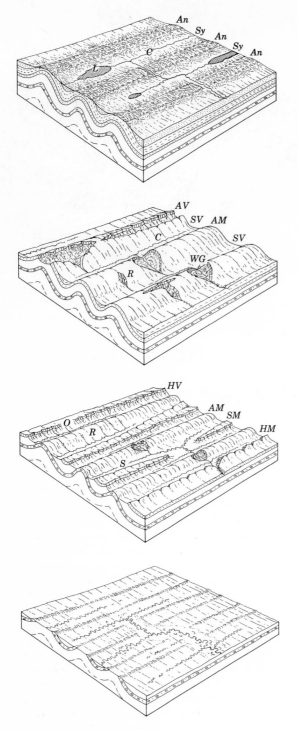

A. While folding is still in progress, erosion cuts down the anticlines; alluvium fills the synclines, keeping relief low. An = anticline; Sy = syncline; C = consequent stream; L = lake.

B. Long after folding has ceased, erosion exposes a highly resistant layer of sandstone or quartzite. AV = anticlinal; SV = synclinal valley; C = consequent stream; WG = watergap; R = resequent stream.

C. Continued erosion partly removes the resistant formation but reveals another below it. AM = anticlinal mountain; SM = synclinal mountain; HM = homoclinal ridge; HV = homoclinal valley; O = obsequent stream; S = subsequent stream.

D. Peneplanation reduces the fold belt to low relief, but the hard-rock ridges still show.

Figure 30.1 Stages in the erosional development of folded strata.

The drainage pattern is a trellis type, similar in most respects to the trellis pattern of a mature coastal plain, but different in that the major subsequent streams are more closely spaced and the obsequent and resequent tributaries are shorter (Figure 30.2).

Here and there in a belt of folds, a principal stream crosses several folds at nearly right angles, passing through the sharply defined ridges by narrow *watergaps*. These streams are likely to have existed previously to the folding and to have maintained themselves as the folds were formed. The term *antecedent* has been applied to such streams. Some are illustrated in Block *B* of Figure 20.11, crossing the series of folds produced in the Appalachian revolution of Permian time.

As the dissection of the folded strata progresses, there is a continuous change in the form and position of the various types of ridges and valleys. Following the reversal of topography shown in Block *C*, Figure 30.1, the synclinal ridges will be completely removed by erosion. Meanwhile, new ridges are appearing in the centers of the anticlinal valleys. These form as a result of the uncovering of still older resistant strata which were folded along with the rest, but which previously lay below the general level of the land surface. These new ridges, which may be thought of as second-generation *anticlinal ridges*, grow in height as the weak rock is stripped from both sides. In time the anticlinal ridges, like the original anticlines of the initial land surface, are breached by streams and finally are transformed into anticlinal valleys. Thus an inversion of topography is again accomplished. The hard sandstone layers stand as narrow, sharp ridges separated by long, parallel valleys. Where the strata in a ridge dip in one direction only, representing one flank of an anticline or syncline, the ridge is termed a *homoclinal ridge* (Block *C*). Likewise, a valley of weak shales or limestones in which the layers all dip in one direction is termed a *homoclinal valley*.

In summary, mature topography developed on alternately resistant and weak sedimentary strata may have three types of ridges, or mountains: anticlinal, synclinal, and homoclinal; and three types of valleys: anticlinal, synclinal, and homoclinal.

Ultimately the belt of folds is reduced to a peneplain (Figure 30.1, Block *D*). Even here, the ridges rise as rows of low hills and the streams maintain their trellis drainage pattern.

Zigzag ridges and plunging folds

The folds illustrated in Figure 30.1 are continuous and even-crested, hence produce ridges that are approximately parallel in trend and continue for great distances. In some fold regions, however,

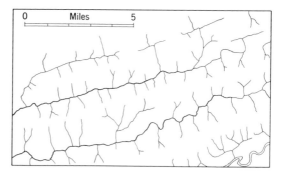

Figure 30.2 A trellis drainage pattern on folds. This resembles Figure 29.4, but opposing sets of tributaries are shorter and of more nearly equal length than on cuesta topography.

the folds are not continuous and level-crested but instead have crests that rise or descend from place to place. When maturely dissected, such folds give rise to a zigzag line of ridges (Figure 30.3).

The topographic form of a syncline whose trough descends, or *plunges*, differs from that of an anticline which plunges in the same direction, when both are maturely dissected. Figure 30.3 compares the two forms. The plunging syncline is represented by a ridge with a slightly concave summit but steeply descending cliffs on the end and sides. Along the direction of plunge of the fold center line, or *axis*, this ridge develops an increasing concavity, then separates into two diverging homoclinal ridges. The plunging anticline is represented by a ridge that points in a direction opposite to the plunging synclinal mountain. The end is smoothly rounded and descends gradually to the level of the valley in the direction of plunge. In the opposite direction the mountain splits into two homoclinal ridges. Enclosed is a valley bounded by steep cliffs (Figure 30.3). The end of this valley, where the cliff line swings around, is often termed an *anticlinal cove*. In comparing the two forms it is apparent that the cliff slope faces outward on a plunging syncline, but faces inward in a plunging anticline.

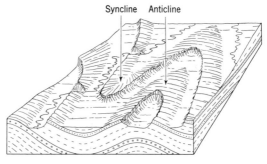

Figure 30.3 Folds with crests which plunge downward give zigzag ridges when maturely eroded. (After E. Raisz.)

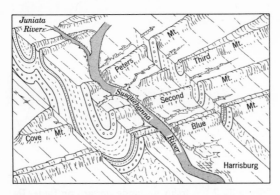

Figure 30.4 A great synclinal fold involving three resistant quartzite-conglomerate formations and thick intervening shales has been eroded to form bold ridges through which the Susquehanna River has cut a series of watergaps. (After A. K. Lobeck.)

Geographical aspects of fold regions

Some of the human-geographical and economic aspects of maturely dissected fold regions are illustrated by the Appalachians of south-central and eastern Pennsylvania (Figure 30.4). The ridges, of resistant sandstones and conglomerates, rise boldly to heights of 500 to 2000 feet above broad lowlands underlain by weak shales and limestones. Major highways run in the valleys, crossing from one valley to another through the watergaps of streams that have cut through the ridges. Important cities may be situated near the watergaps of major streams. An example is Harrisburg, where the Susquehanna River issues from a series of water-

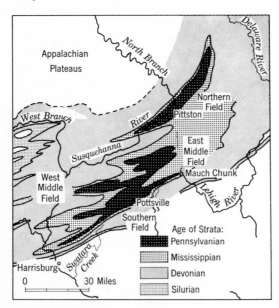

Figure 30.5 Anthracite coal basins of central Pennsylvania correspond with areas of Pennsylvanian strata (dark shading), downfolded into long synclinal troughs.

gaps cut in Blue Mountain, Second Mountain, and Peters Mountain (Figure 30.4). Where no water-gaps are conveniently located, the roads must climb in long, steep grades over the ridge crests. The ridges are heavily forested; the valleys are rich agricultural belts. Fire towers are situated upon the ridge crests and command splendid views of distant ridges.

In various fold regions of the world, for example, in the Pennsylvania Appalachians, an important resource is *anthracite*, or hard coal (Figure 30.5). This occurs in strata that have been folded and squeezed. Pressure has converted the coal from bituminous into anthracite. Because of extensive erosion, all coal has been removed except that which lies in the central parts of synclines. The coal seams dip steeply; workings penetrate deeply to reach the coal that lies in the bottoms of the synclines. Seams near the surface are worked by strip mining.

Broad, gentle anticlinal folds may form important traps for the accumulation of petroleum. The principle is the same as in low domes of sedimentary strata (Figure 29.30). Oil migrates in permeable sandstone beds to the anticlinal crest, where it is trapped by an impervious cap rock of shale. Many of the oil and gas pools of western Pennsylvania, where petroleum production first succeeded, are on low anticlines.

Pressures which created folds also changed shales into slates of considerable commercial value. The slate quarries of Pennsylvania occur in rows paralleling the base of a great sandstone ridge. Limestone, if of satisfactory quality for the manufacture of portland cement, is quarried along narrow belts where a steeply dipping bed appears at the surface.

Not all fold regions contain as extensive agricultural valleys as the Pennsylvania Appalachians. In parts of Maryland, West Virginia, and Virginia the ridges are predominant and form a great rugged mountain belt difficult to cross and thinly populated.

Other fold regions somewhat like the Appalachians are the Ouachita Mountains of Arkansas and the Jura Mountains of the Swiss and French Alps region (Figure 30.6). The Jura Mountains consist almost entirely of anticlinal limestone ridges. Good illustrations of fold belts likewise occur in North Africa, principally in Tunisia and Algeria, and in the Union of South Africa, not far north of Capetown.

Faults and fault blocks

A *fault* is a break in the brittle surficial rocks of the earth's crust as a result of unequal stresses. Faulting is accompanied by a slippage or displacement along the plane of breakage. Faults are often of great horizontal extent, so that the *fault line* can

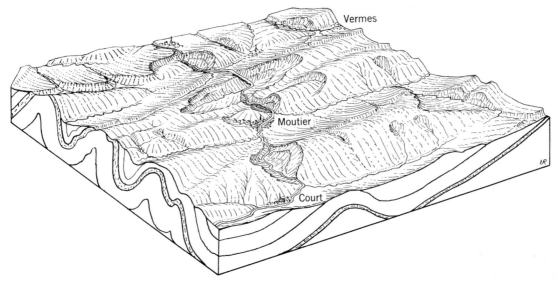

Figure 30.6 The Jura Mountains of France and Switzerland, a foothill range lying northwest of the Alps, are formed of a series of folded limestones. Almost all the mountains are anticlinal. Streams have cut valleys through these ridges to make deep watergaps. (Drawn by E. Raisz.)

be traced along the ground for many miles, sometimes even 100 miles or more. Little is known of what happens to faults at depth, but in all probability they extend down for at least several thousands of feet.

Faulting occurs in sudden slippage movements which generate *earthquakes*, the wavelike ground tremors that start in the zone of maximum movement. A particular fault movement may result in a slippage of as little as a few inches or as much as 25 or 50 feet. Successive movements may occur many years apart, even many tens or hundreds of years apart, but aggregate total displacements of hundreds or thousands of feet. This is known from the fact that clearly recognizable sedimentary rock layers are sometimes offset on opposite sides of a fault and the amount of displacement can be accurately measured.

According to the nature and relative direction of the displacement, several types of faults can be recognized (Figure 30.7). A *normal fault* has a steep or nearly vertical *fault plane*. Movement is

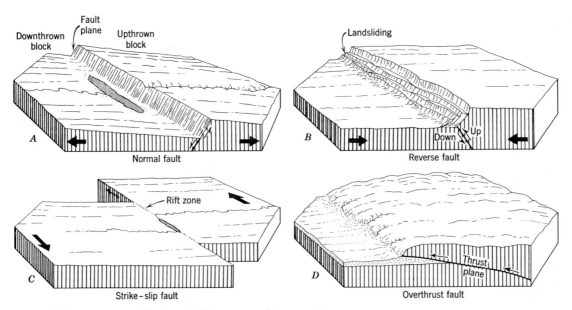

Figure 30.7 Four types of faults and their topographic expression.

Figure 30.8 The grass-covered scarp in the foreground is a fault-scarp made by a single fault movement. The amount of displacement is equivalent to the difference in height between the lower ground on which the trees are growing and the level on which the man is standing. In the background is the Wasatch Range of Utah, raised by earlier fault movements and considerably worn back by long erosion. (Photograph by Douglas Johnson.)

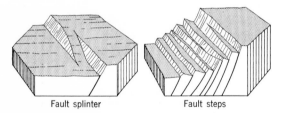

Fault splinter   Fault steps

Figure 30.9 Normal faults are often complicated by splinters and steps.

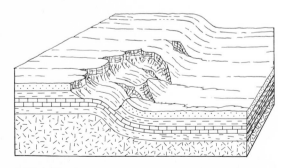

Figure 30.10 A monocline is basically similar to a normal fault, but the strata have bent instead of fracturing.

predominantly in a vertical direction, so that one side is raised or *upthrown* relative to the other, which is *downthrown*. A normal fault results in a steep, straight *fault scarp*, whose height is an approximate measure of the vertical element of displacement (Figure 30.8). Fault scarps range in height from a few feet to a few thousand feet. Their length is measurable in miles; often they attain lengths of 100 to 200 miles. Normal faulting is an expression of tension in the earth's outer crust. It is an evident geometric observation that sliding upon an inclined surface of the type indicated in Figure 30.7*A* must result in a spreading apart of points situated on opposite sides of the fault.

In a *reverse fault* the inclination of the fault plane is such that one side rides up over the other and a crustal shortening occurs (Figure 30.7*B*). Reverse faults produce fault scarps similar to those of normal faults, but the possibility of landsliding is greater because an overhanging scarp tends to be formed.

A strike-slip fault is unique in that the movement is predominantly in a horizontal direction (Figure 30.7*C*). Hence no scarp results, or a very low one at most. Instead, only a thin line is traceable across the surface. Streams sometimes turn and follow the fault line for a short distance. Sometimes a narrow trench, or *rift*, marks the fault line (Figure 30.17).

A *low-angle overthrust fault* (Figure 30.7*D*) likewise involves predominantly horizontal movement, but the fault plane is in a horizontal position and one slice of rock rides up over the adjacent ground surface. A thrust slice may be a few hundred or thousand feet thick but up to 25 or 50 miles wide. Overthrusting of this type is generally associated with strong crustal compression in which intense folding also occurs. The scarp produced by low-angle overthrusting is not straight or smooth, as in normal and reverse faults; instead it may be irregular in plan.

Normal faults are not always simple, clean breaks. The fault may be split in such a manner that the end of one fault is overlapped by the end of another (Figure 30.9). Between the overlapping ends a sloping ramp, or *fault splinter*, is formed. Paradoxically, it is thus possible to go from the downthrown to the upthrown block without crossing any fault!

Normal faults may occur as a series of parallel, closely set fractures between which the rock is broken into thin slices (Figure 30.9). At the surface a series of steplike levels occurs, giving rise to the term *step faulting* for this multiple-fault arrangement.

Closely related to normal faulting is *monoclinal flexing* (Figure 30.10), in which sedimentary layers are sharply bent between the upthrown and downthrown sides instead of being fractured. Many monoclines turn into true faults at greater depth or pass into faults along their lengths. Limestone strata, in particular, seem to have bent readily to form monoclines, whereas sandstones are more brittle and have broken into true faults under similar conditions of stress. A monocline passes through a series of stages of erosion quite similar to an anticline, except that only half the anticline is represented.

Faults rarely are isolated features. More often they occur in multiple arrangements, commonly as a parallel series of faults. This gives rise to a grain or pattern of rock structure and topography. A narrow block dropped down between two normal faults is a *graben* (Figure 30.11). A narrow block elevated between two normal faults is a *horst*. Grabens make conspicuous topographic trenches, with straight, parallel walls. Horsts make blocklike plateaus or mountains, often with a fairly flat top, but steep, straight sides.

Erosional development of a fault scarp

Some of the various stages and forms attained by normal faults throughout the erosional period that follows their formation are illustrated in Figure 30.12. At the rear part of the block is the original fault scarp, produced directly by crustal movement, and therefore belonging to the group of initial landforms. Stage *A* is a *young fault scarp* in which the scarp is still straight and smooth, with only a few stream-cut canyons and some talus cones and alluvial fans built along the scarp base.

Stage *B* is a *mature fault scarp*. Weathering and erosion have caused the scarp to retreat from the original line and to become highly irregular in plan. In the particular instance illustrated, this has been facilitated by the presence of a resistant sandstone cap-rock layer underlain by a weak shale formation.

In Stage *C* the resistant capping formation on the upthrown side of the fault has been entirely stripped away, allowing the thick shale below to be rapidly removed and bringing the surface level lower than on the downthrown side, where the resistant cap rock remains intact. In this stage the scarp results entirely through erosion and is designated a *fault-line scarp* in order to distinguish it from a fault scarp produced directly by crustal movement. Furthermore, this erosional scarp faces in a direction opposite to that of the original fault scarp, hence is termed an *obsequent fault-line scarp*.

In Stage *D* the region has been reduced to a peneplain and the scarp obliterated entirely. The land surface on both sides of the fault is at the same general level. This stage might not occur if a

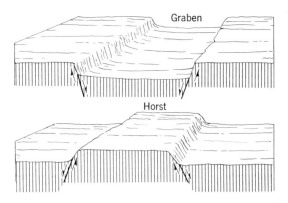

Figure 30.11 Graben and horst are simply down-dropped and uplifted fault blocks, respectively.

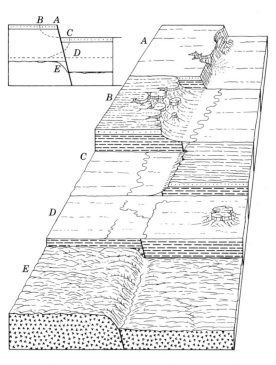

Figure 30.12 Most fault lines in horizontal strata evolve through a series of erosional stages in which scarps are successively obliterated and redeveloped on deeper rocks.

Figure 30.13 This resequent fault-line scarp makes a remarkably straight line. Although this area was heavily glaciated by the Pleistocene ice sheets, the scarp was not obliterated. The large lake whose shore rests against the scarp is MacDonald Lake, near Great Slave Lake, Northwest Territories, Canada. This area lies between 60° and 65° N lat. and is in the northern fringe of the coniferous forest belt, near the arctic tundra. (Royal Canadian Air Force Photograph.)

region were high above base level, and it might occur at some other stage in the erosional history of a fault.

In Stage *E* further erosion has revealed still another fault-line scarp. It appears because the weak shale formation has been stripped from both sides of the fault, revealing a basement of resistant igneous rocks upon which the shale was once deposited. Because the new erosional scarp faces in the same direction as the initial fault scarp, it is termed a *resequent fault-line scarp* (Figure 30.13).

Fault-block mountains

In regions where normal faulting is on a grand scale, with displacements up to several thousands of feet, huge mountain masses are produced. In general, these faulted mountain blocks can be classed as *tilted* and *lifted* (Figure 30.14). A tilted block has one steep face, the fault scarp, and one gently sloping side. The initial divide lies near the top of the fault scarp and is hence situated over to one side of the block. A lifted block, which is a type of horst, is bounded by steep slopes on both sides.

Figure 30.15 shows stages in the life history of a tilted fault block. Most numerous good examples of fault-block ranges are in the desert of the western United States. It should not be supposed, however, that block mountains and arid climates necessarily go hand in hand.

In youth, the fault block is asymmetrical and has generally even sides, despite the presence of numerous small stream valleys that have been developing as the fault block was elevated.

In maturity (Figure 30.15), the range is dissected into a great number of divides, spurs, and peaks separated by deep canyons. The main crest line of the range is now pushed back to a more nearly central position and the simple blocklike aspect of the mountain range has disappeared. Along the base of the fault scarp, between canyon mouths, remain some parts of the original fault scarp. These make *triangular facets*, aligned nicely along the base line (Figure 30.15). Fans are more extensive than in early youth. The adjoining basins are filled higher with alluvium. If in a humid climate, a rolling landscape of moderate relief develops in late maturity, whereas in old age the range is reduced to a subdued peneplain surface. The fault line is completely buried under alluvium, and no triangular facets or other surface indications of the fault remain. In a desert climate, pediments would spread across the fault block, but the retreating mountain slopes would remain steep to the end.

Geographical aspects of faults and block mountains

Faults are of economic and human-geographic significance for both geologic and topographic reasons. Fault planes are usually zones along which the rock has been pulverized, or at least considerably fractured. This has the effect of permitting ore-forming chemical solutions to rise along fault planes. Many important ore deposits lie in fault planes or in rocks that faults have broken across.

Another related phenomenon is the easy rise of underground water along fault planes. Springs, both cold and hot, are commonly situated along fault lines. They occur along the bases of young fault-block mountains, as, for example, Arrowhead

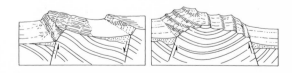

Figure 30.14 Fault-block mountains may be of tilted type (left) or lifted type (right) and may be composed of almost any kind of rock or structure. (After W. M. Davis.)

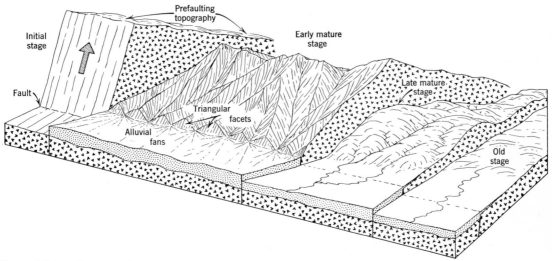

Figure 30.15 Stages in the erosion of a tilted fault block are shown from left to right. (After W. M. Davis.)

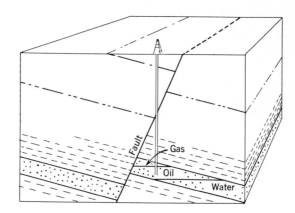

Figure 30.16 An oil pool has accumulated in the permeable sandstone beds and is prevented from escaping by the impermeable shales faulted against the edge of the sandstone layer.

Springs along the base of the San Bernardino Range and Palm Springs along the foot of the San Jacinto Mountains, both in southern California.

Petroleum, too, finds its way along fault planes where the rocks have been rendered permeable by crushing, or it becomes trapped in porous beds that have been faulted against impervious shale beds (Figure 30.16). Some of the most intensive searches for oil center about areas of faulted sedimentary strata because of the great production that has been achieved from pools of this type.

Fault scarps and fault-line scarps may form imposing topographic barriers across which it is difficult to build roads and railroads. The great Hurricane Ledge of southern Utah is a feature of this type, in places a steep wall 2500 feet high. On the downthrown side of such a fault, alluvium may have accumulated to produce a favorable belt for

agriculture, whereas the upthrown side is rocky and deeply cut by stream valleys.

Active faults, those on which repeated fault movements are in progress, may impose serious threat of earthquake damage to cities, bridges, aqueducts, and other structures located on or near the fault lines. The California coastal belt is faced with such problems. Through the San Francisco Bay area passes the famed San Andreas fault (Figure 30.17). The devastating earthquake of 1906 resulted from slippage along this fault, which is of the strike-slip type. The San Andreas fault, 600 miles long, extends southward and is in places represented by a rift valley, elsewhere by a normal fault bordering the San Bernardino mountain block. Where the Los Angeles aqueduct crosses this fault line and is particularly vulnerable to breakage through fault movement, special structures

Figure 30.17 The valley followed by the road is the San Andreas Rift, California, marking a strike-slip type of fault along which earthquake-generating movements occur from time to time. In the foreground is Grant Lake. The view is southeast toward Palo Prieto Pass. (Spence Air Photos.)

have been prepared to assure rapid repair in the event of damage. Vulnerability of the urban communities in the San Francisco and Los Angeles areas to earthquake shock is especially great because the alluvial materials of the plains shake with great violence in an earthquake which might otherwise cause little disturbance to solid bedrock.

Grabens may be of such size as to form broad lowlands. An illustration is the Rhine graben of Western Germany. Here a belt of rich agricultural land, 20 miles wide and 150 miles long, lies between the Vosges and Black Forest ranges, both of which are block mountains faulted up by contrast with the downdropped Rhine graben block.

Block mountains and associated basins of arid regions have essentially the same geographical and economic features as mountainous deserts already described under the land-mass cycle of denudation in arid climates. The mountain masses may contain rich mineral deposits, depending on the nature of the rocks and minerals existing before faulting. Forests may be rich at sufficiently high elevations in desert regions. In humid climates, the Vosges and Black Forest ranges of France and Germany illustrate the important forest resources of block mountains. Mature block mountains are sometimes great obstacles to transportation and are generally avoided by railroads, which require low grades. Highways must ascend steep, often tortuously winding grades, to surmount the ranges. The Vosges mountain block, whose steep face is toward the east, served as a barrier to the westward advance of German armies in the First World War, and defied repeated heavy attacks.

Review Questions

1. What is an anticline? a syncline? How are these features related in a series of folds?

2. What is an anticlinal valley? a synclinal valley? How does reversal of topography normally occur in the process of erosion of a fold region?

3. How are watergaps formed in a fold region? Of what geographic importance are watergaps? What is an antecedent stream? How might antecedent streams develop in a fold region?

4. What type of drainage pattern is developed in a maturely dissected region of folds? Of what types of streams is this pattern composed?

5. How do homoclinal ridges and valleys differ from anticlinal and synclinal ridges and valleys? Show all these types by simple cross-sectional diagrams.

6. What effect does a downplunge of fold axes have upon the forms of ridges and valleys? How can a plunging synclinal mountain be distinguished from a plunging anticlinal mountain?

7. Discuss the geographical aspects of fold regions of rugged ridge-and-valley topography. What economic mineral products are important in fold regions?

8. What is a fault? What is a fault line? Explain how earthquakes are related to faults.

9. Describe a normal fault, and explain how it differs from a reverse fault. What kind of topographic feature is produced by these types of faulting? Explain how fault splinters and fault steps are associated with normal faults.

10. What is a strike-slip fault? How does it differ in topographic expression from a normal fault? What is a rift? Describe the San Andreas fault of California. Is this an active fault line at the present time?

11. Describe a low-angle overthrust fault. With what kind of crustal deformation is it associated? What topographic expression does an overthrust fault have?

12. How does monoclinal flexing differ from faulting? Are the two structures basically related?

13. Distinguish between a graben and a horst. Briefly describe the Rhine graben region as an illustration of graben and horst forms.

14. Why is it necessary to distinguish between a fault scarp and a fault-line scarp? Which form comes first? What varieties of fault-line scarps are recognized?

15. What kinds of block mountains can be formed? Compare the stages of youth and maturity of a large, tilted fault-block mountain. What are the triangular facets? How do they differ from flatirons?

16. In what ways do faults influence the occurrence of ground water and springs? How is petroleum concentrated by fault structures? Why are fault zones favorable for occurrences of ore minerals?

Exercises

Exercise 1. *Mountains Developed on Folded Strata.*

Explanatory Note: This is a synthetic map, not representing any real topography, and should be regarded as an idealized diagram illustrating the ridge and valley forms typical of a maturely dissected region of folded strata. Refer to Figures 30.1 and 30.3 for aid in understanding the relation between structure and topography on this map.

A portion of a U.S. Geological Survey topographic quadrangle showing ridge and valley forms is reproduced on one of the endpapers of this book and should be compared with the exercise map.

QUESTIONS

1. On a sheet of thin tracing paper laid over this map, label each ridge and valley with the names *anticlinal ridge, synclinal ridge, homoclinal ridge, anticlinal valley,*

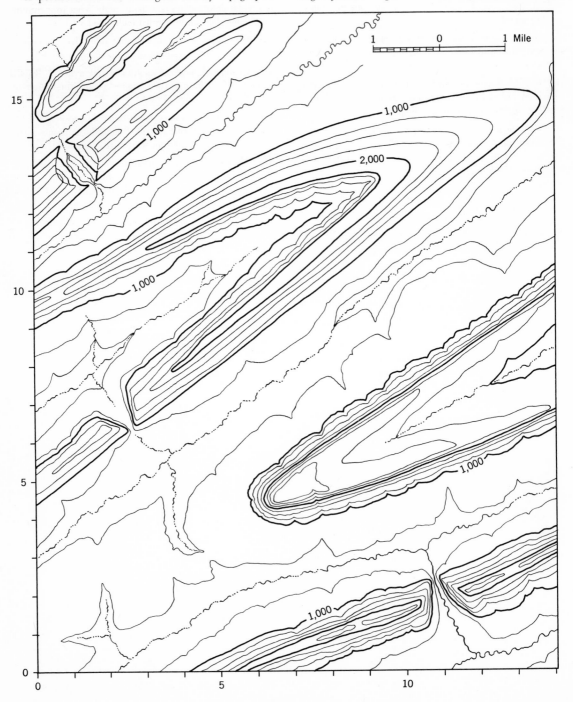

synclinal valley, or *homoclinal valley*. To help you do this, study Figures 30.1 and 30.3, comparing the forms shown on the map with the labeled forms on the block diagrams.

2. On the same sheet of paper used in Question 1, draw in a complete drainage system using the following color scheme: subsequent streams, blue; resequent streams, red; obsequent streams, green.

3. Make a topographic profile from the upper left-hand corner of the map to the lower right-hand corner. Use a vertical scale of 1 inch equals 2500 feet. Draw in sandstone and shale formations in such a way as to fit the interpretation of topography in your answer to Question 1. Be guided by the cross sections in Figures 30.1 and 30.3.

4. Explain the fact that the deep gap in the ridge at 2.5–6.5 now contains no through-flowing stream, although it resembles the watergap at 11.0–2.0. What drainage change seems to have occurred here?

Exercise 2. *Fault scarps and graben.* (Source: Klamath, Oregon, U.S. Geological Survey topographic map; scale 1:250,000.)

Explanatory Note: The steep, simple scarps trending northwest to southeast on this map are fault scarps. Upper Klamath Lake occupies a graben and is bounded by fault scarps on both sides. Swan Lake Valley is a downtilted block with a fault scarp on the east side only.

QUESTIONS

1. On a sheet of thin tracing paper laid over this map, mark all fault lines which you can safely interpret from the topographic forms. Write the letter *D* and *U* on opposite sides of each fault line to indicate which side went down, which went up.

2. Make a topographic profile across the map from 0.0–8.0 to 40.0–8.0, using a vertical scale of 1 inch equals 2000 feet. Then indicate the positions of the faults as in Figure 30.11.

3. At 32.0–13.0 is a fault splinter such as is illustrated in Figure 30.9. Label this feature on your tracing sheet prepared for Question 1.

4. Why is the floor of Swan Lake Valley so flat?

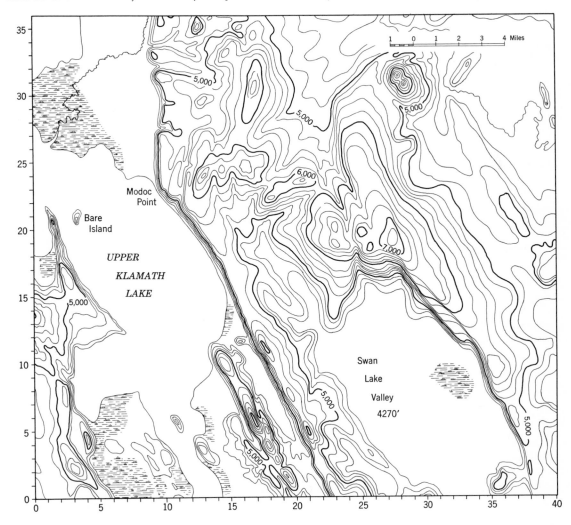

CHAPTER THIRTY-ONE

Crystalline masses and volcanic forms

THE term *crystalline rock* is useful in referring collectively to intrusive igneous rock and the metamorphic rocks, such as schists and gneisses. It is of value in understanding regional landform assemblages to recognize the range of land-mass types possible under the general class of crystalline rocks, even though distinct subgroups cannot always be separated.

Homogeneous crystallines

Intrusive igneous rocks, such as granites (Figure 19.3), generally occur in enormous batholiths. One batholith in Idaho is exposed over an area of 16,000 square miles, a region almost as large as New Hampshire and Vermont combined. The rock seems to extend down many thousands of feet, and for practical purposes may be considered bottomless. A smaller body of igneous rock less than 40 square miles in surface extent is termed a *stock*.

Batholiths and stocks do not reach the surface of the earth when formed, hence produce no initial landforms and have no initial stage in the erosional development cycle. They appear only after pro-

longed erosion has stripped away the older, overlying rock when the land mass is in a mature or old stage of denudation (Figure 31.1). An additional illustration of the process of exposure of deep-seated rocks was given in the discussion of the manner in which the central core of a dome becomes exposed (Chapter 29).

Topography developed on batholiths varies somewhat according to texture and composition of the rock and whether or not the mass has been faulted. Where the rock is quite uniform and free of strong faults, it is eroded into a maze of canyons and ravines which follow no predominant trend (Figure 31.2). The drainage pattern is dendritic and is composed of insequent streams just as for horizontal sedimentary strata. In fact, the two patterns may be virtually indistinguishable.

Where faulting has occurred, making a series of intersecting zones of crushed and weakened rock, the drainage follows the fault lines and forms a rectangular pattern (Figure 31.3). The streams are of subsequent type because they developed in the zones of weakness.

Certain areas of metamorphic rocks, such as gneisses and schists, also develop a dendritic drainage pattern of insequent streams because the variations in rock texture and composition seem to

above: Volcan de Agua, near Guatemala City.
Photograph, Fairchild Aerial Surveys, Inc.

have little influence upon valley development. The topography of such areas may be identical with that of batholiths. Therefore it is convenient to use the term *homogeneous crystallines* to include both the igneous intrusive and metamorphic rock masses.

Belted metamorphics

Regions of metamorphic rock normally show a strong grain in the topography. Ridges tend to be elongate in one direction and to be separated by long, roughly parallel valleys (see Figure 19.16). Neither ridges nor valleys have the sharpness of folded sedimentary strata, but the drainage pattern is clearly of trellis or rectangular form. Regions of this type may be classed as *belted metamorphics* because the topography is a reflection of different rates of denudation of parallel belts of metamorphic rocks, such as schist, slate, quartzite, and marble. Marble tends to form distinctive valleys; slate and schist make belts of medium to strong relief; quartzite usually stands out boldly and may produce conspicuous narrow hogback ridges. Furthermore, most metamorphic rocks have been broken by reverse and overthrust faults which run parallel with the different belts and often separate one rock type from another. Subsequent stream valleys occupying these fault lines help bring out the grain

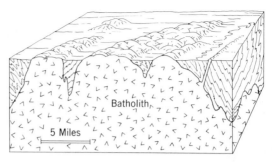

Figure 31.1 Deep-seated igneous rocks appear at the surface only after long-continued erosion has removed thousands of feet of overlying rocks. (After Longwell, Knopf, and Flint.)

Figure 31.2 This dendritic drainage pattern is developed on the maturely dissected Idaho batholith.

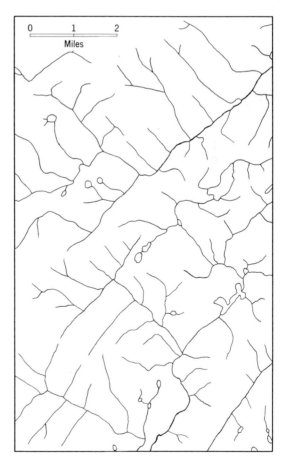

Figure 31.3 This rectangular drainage pattern in a batholith reveals an intersecting pattern of faults breaking the igneous rock.

Figure 31.4 Complexly folded and faulted strata of pre-Cambrian age are exposed in this steep mountain face in the northern Rockies of Glacier National Park, Montana. (Photograph by Chapman, U.S. Geological Survey.)

of the topography. Much of New England, particularly the Taconic and Green Mountains, illustrates these principles well. The larger valleys trend north and south and are underlain by marble. These are flanked by ridges of gneiss, schist, slate, or quartzite. The highlands of the Hudson and of northern New Jersey continue this belted pattern southward where it joins the Blue Ridge. Near Harpers Ferry, Maryland, quartzite ridges rise prominently above broad valley belts of schist.

Areas of complex structure

Some parts of the earth's crust, particularly the continental shields, have undergone several periods of folding, faulting, intrusion, and volcanism. As each event occurred, new rocks or new structures were added to the mass, so that it may appear today as a region of *complex structure* (Figure 31.4). Because of the variety of rock types and structures, the landforms show a variety of forms.

Figure 31.5 shows by a series of diagrams the cycle of erosion in a geologically complex region.

In the initial stage, mountains result from faulting, folding, doming, and volcanic activity. In the mature stage, a highly irregular drainage pattern develops. The rugged topography consists of fault and fault-line scarps, hogbacks, old volcanoes, and other landform types. Intrusive and sedimentary rocks of various ages and shapes are exposed. In the old-age stage, the region is reduced to a peneplain, but the harder rock masses stand out as monadnocks.

Geographical aspects of batholiths, metamorphic belts, and complex areas

Regions of intrusive igneous rock, metamorphic rock, and complex structure are often rich in mineral wealth. Where igneous intrusion occurred repeatedly, metallic ores were deposited. Examples from the Rocky Mountains are the copper, silver, gold, and lead of Butte, Montana; the silver and lead of the Coeur d'Alene District in Idaho; and the lead, zinc, and silver of Leadville, Colorado.

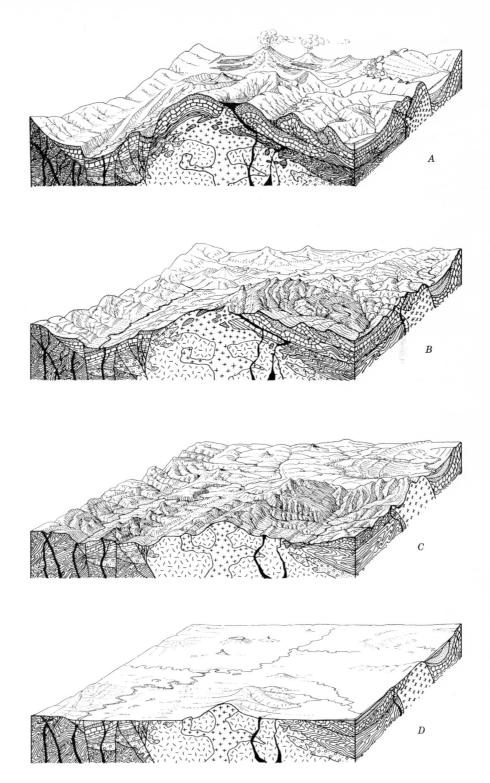

Figure 31.5 Stages in the development of a region of highly complex structure. (Drawn by E. Raisz.)

Figure 31.6 Amboy Crater, a cinder cone surrounded by its lava flows, lies in the middle of the desert in southeastern California. Running water from desert cloudbursts has already begun to cut ravines in the sides of the cone. (Copyrighted Spence Air Photos.)

Metamorphic rocks, such as slates, quartzites, marbles, and schists, are not likely to contain metallic ores of importance, unless intrusive rocks have penetrated them. They do, however, have economic value for the slate or marble which can be quarried from them. Vermont has these rocks, along with intrusive granites which are quarried as well.

Among the foreign examples of valuable metallic mineral deposits occurring in igneous, metamorphic, and complex rocks might be cited the tin deposits of the Katanga District, Belgian Congo.

Much of the batholithic, metamorphic, and complex areas of the world are mountainous, hence, heavily forested and thinly populated. Examples are the Salmon River Mountains, underlain by the great Idaho batholith; the Great Smoky Mountains of South Carolina, Georgia, and Tennessee, underlain by intrusive and metamorphic rocks in generally complex arrangement; or the Taconic and Green mountain ridges of belted metamorphics in Vermont and Massachusetts. Lumber is thus an important resource of these regions, in addition to their mineral wealth. At the same time, transportation is often difficult, and in the absence of agricultural land the population is thinly distributed if not actually absent from large areas.

Other extensive regions of intrusive or metamorphic rocks are of low relief, having been reduced to peneplains and only slightly dissected in the present erosion cycle. Much of eastern Canada is of this type of topography, as are parts of Sweden and Finland. Geologists refer to these stable masses of ancient rock as the *Canadian shield* and *Fenno-Scandian shield* (Chapter 20). Not only are they similar in rock conditions, but all these regions because of glaciation have countless lakes, and because of similar climate support an evergreen coniferous forest.

In the United States, the outstanding example of

a peneplain on intrusive and metamorphic rocks is the Piedmont Upland of Virginia, the Carolinas, and Georgia. A rolling landscape of monotonously uniform hill-top level extends in a vast belt between the Blue Ridge Mountains on the west and the Coastal Plain on the east. Above this surface rise a few monadnocks. On the Piedmont, soils are thick, slopes are low enough to permit agriculture, and transportation is easy between most points.

Volcanoes and associated landforms

Volcanoes are built by the eruption of molten rock and heated gases under pressure from a relatively small pipe, or *vent*, leading from a magma reservoir at depth. Both explosive and quiet types of eruption occur, the forms built differing for the two types.

Volcanoes of explosive eruption are *cinder cones* and *composite cones;* those formed by relatively quiet outflow of lava are *lava domes.* Quiet eruption of lava, if issuing from extensive cracks, or *fissures,* in sufficient quantities may make great plains or plateaus of lava, classified with horizontal strata (Chapter 29).

Cinder cones

Smallest of the volcanoes are the cinder cones, built entirely of pieces of solidified lava thrown from a central vent. They form where a high proportion of gas in the molten rock causes it to froth into a bubbly mass and to be ejected from a vent with great violence. The froth breaks up into small fragments which solidify as they are ejected and fall as solid particles near the vent (Figure 31.6). The fragments resemble clinkers and ash taken from a coal furnace. Large pieces up to several tons in weight are *volcanic bombs;* they may be somewhat plastic when ejected. Smaller pieces, a fraction of an inch up to an inch or two in size, are *cinders;* these make up the bulk of the cinder cone. Still finer particles are termed *ash* and *volcanic dust.* The ash falls like snow upon the ground within a few miles of the eruption (See Figure 31.9). Finer dust is carried by winds to distant regions and may settle out only after years of drifting in the atmosphere.

Cinder cones rarely grow to more than 500 or 1000 feet in height. Growth is rapid. Monte Nuovo, near Naples, Italy, grew to a height of 400 feet in the first week of its existence. Paricutin, in Mexico, started as a cinder cone and reached a height of 1000 feet in the first three months. The angle of slope of a recently formed cinder cone ranges between 26° and 30°. So loose is the material that it absorbs heavy rain without permitting surface run-off. Erosion is thus delayed until weathering produces a soil which fills the interstices.

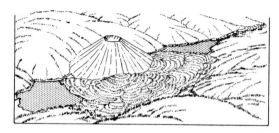

Figure 31.7 A cinder cone with its lava flows has dammed a valley, making a lake. Farther downvalley, in the distance, another lava mass has made a second dam. (After W. M. Davis.)

Cinder cones normally have large central craters (Figure 31.6). The rim is often much higher on one side than the other, as the prevailing wind blows the finer cinders and ash to one side of the vent.

Lava flows sometimes issue from the same vent as a cinder cone. They may burst apart the side of the cone but more commonly do not alter its form. Cinder cones may erupt in almost any conceivable topographic location, on ridges on slopes and in valleys, (Figure 31.7). Cinder cones usually occur in groups, often many dozens in an area of a few tens of square miles. They sometimes show an alignment parallel with fault lines in the underlying rock.

Composite volcanoes

Most of the world's great volcanoes are composite cones. They are built of layers of cinder and ash alternating with layers of lava, and for this reason have been called *strato-volcanoes* by some

Figure 31.8 A small young volcano on the island of Java. (Photographer not known.)

A. This distant view of Sakurajima shows the great cauliflower cloud of volcanic gases and condensed steam.

B. A blocky lava flow is advancing slowly over a ground surface littered with volcanic bombs and ash.

C. Reaching the sea the hot lava makes clouds of steam.

D. Volcanic ash has buried this village.

Figure 31.9 Sakurajima, a Japanese volcano, erupted violently in 1914. These pictures show various scenes from the eruption. (Photographs by T. Nakasa.)

writers. The steep-sided form is governed by the angle at which the cinder and ash stands, whereas the lava layers provide strength and bulk to the volcano (Figure 31.8). Among the outstanding examples of recently formed composite volcanoes are Fujiyama in Japan, Mayon in the Philippines, Mt. Hood in Oregon, and Shishaldin in the Aleutians. Other famous ones, less perfectly formed, are Vesuvius, Etna, and Stromboli in Italy and Sicily. Heights of several thousand feet and slopes of 20° to 30° are characteristic.

Many composite volcanoes lie in a great belt, the *circum-Pacific ring*, extending from the Andes in South America, through the Cascades and the Aleutians, into Japan; thence south into the East Indies and New Zealand. (See Figure 20.8). There is also an important Mediterranean group, mentioned above, which includes active volcanoes of

Italy and Sicily. Otherwise, Europe has no active volcanoes.

The eruption of large composite volcanoes is usually accompanied by explosive issue of steam, cinders, bombs, and ash, and by lava flows (Figure 31.9). The crater may change form rapidly, both from demolition of the upper part and from new accumulation.

Calderas

One of the most catastrophic of natural phenomena is a volcanic explosion so violent as to destroy the entire central portion of the volcano. There remains only a great central depression, termed a *caldera*. Whether the upper part of the volcano is largely blown outward in fragments or subsides into the ground beneath the volcano is not certain. Although calderas have been formed in historic

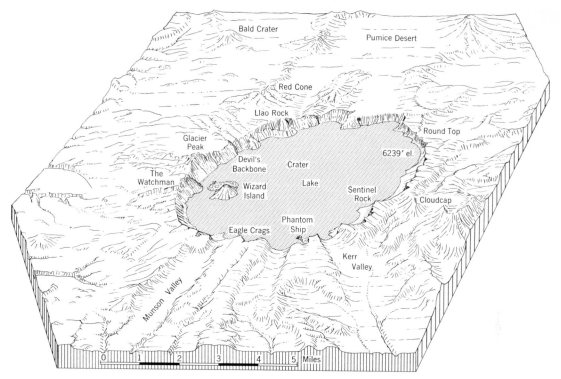

Figure 31.10 Crater Lake, Oregon, is an outstanding illustration of a caldera, now holding a lake. A great composite volcano which existed here was destroyed in prehistoric time by violent explosion. (After E. Raisz.)

time, conditions near the volcano do not permit observation of the process. Vast quantities of ash and dust are emitted and fill the atmosphere for many hundreds of square miles around.

Krakatoa, a volcanic island in the Dutch East Indies, exploded in 1883, leaving a great caldera. It is estimated that eighteen cubic miles of rock disappeared during the explosion. Great sea waves, or *tsunamis*, generated by the explosion killed many thousands of persons living on low coastal areas of Java and Sumatra. Another historic explosion was that of Katmai, on the Alaskan Peninsula, in 1912. A caldera more than two miles wide and 2000 to 3700 feet deep was produced at this time. The explosion was heard at Juneau, 750 miles distant, while at Kodiak, 100 miles away, the ash formed a layer ten inches deep.[1]

A classic example of a caldera produced in prehistoric time is Crater Lake, Oregon (Figure 31.10). Mt. Mazama, the former volcano, is estimated to have risen 4000 feet higher than the present rim. Valleys previously cut by streams and glaciers into the flanks of Mt. Mazama were beheaded by the explosive subsidence of the central portion and now form distinctive notches in the rim. Wizard

[1] A. K. Lobeck, *Geomorphology*, McGraw-Hill, New York, 1939, p. 685.

Island, a recent volcano with associated flows, has since grown in the floor of the caldera.

Erosion cycle of volcanoes

Figure 31.11 shows successive stages in the erosion of volcanoes, lava flows, and a caldera. In the first block are active volcanoes in the process of building. These are in their initial stage. Lava flows issuing from the volcanoes have spread down into a stream valley, following the downward grade of the valley and forming a lake behind the lava dam.

In the next block some changes have taken place, the most conspicuous of which is the destruction of the largest volcano to produce a caldera. A lake occupies the caldera, and a small cone has been built inside. One of the other volcanoes, formed earlier, has become extinct. It has been dissected by streams, losing the initial form, and may be said to be in a stage of late youth. Smaller, neighboring volcanoes are still active, and the contrast in form is marked. The examples of large, beautifully formed composite volcanoes cited above are all in their initial or very young stage.

The drainage pattern of streams upon a volcanic cone is of necessity *radial* in pattern. Because these streams take their positions upon a slope of an initial land surface they are of consequent

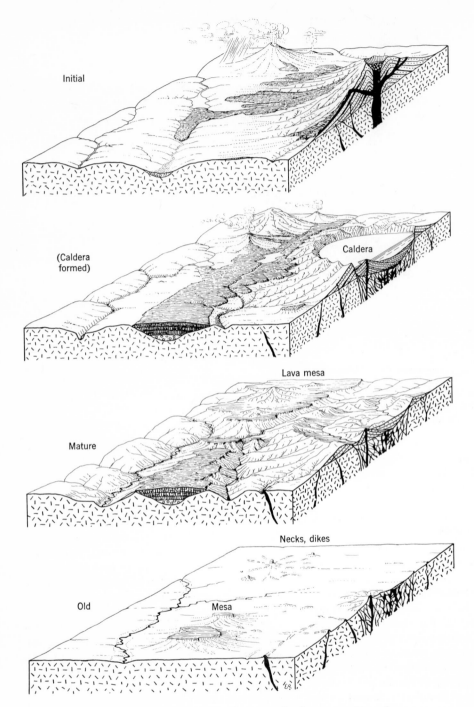

Figure 31.11 Stages in the erosional development of volcanoes and lava flows. (Drawn by E. Raisz.)

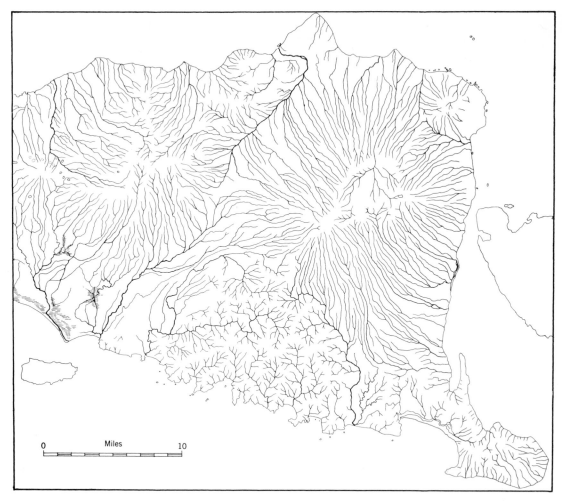

Figure 31.12 Radial drainage patterns of volcanoes in the East Indies. (After Verbeek and Fennema.)

origin. It is often possible to recognize volcanoes from a drainage map alone (Figure 31.12) because of the perfection of the radial pattern. Where a well-formed crater exists, small streams flow from the crater rim toward the bottom of the crater. Here the water is absorbed in the porous layers of ash within the cone, or is conducted outward by means of a single gap in the crater rim. This inward drainage, described as *centripetal*, often adds to the certainty of interpreting a volcano from a drainage pattern.

In the third block, Figure 31.11, all volcanoes are extinct and have been eroded into the stage of maturity. The caldera lake has been drained and the rim worn to a low, circular ridge. The lava flows which formerly flowed down stream valleys have been able to resist erosion far better than the rock of the surrounding area and have come to stand as mesas high above the general level of the region.

An example of a maturely dissected volcano is Mt. Shasta in the Cascade Range (Figure 31.13). A smaller subsidiary cone of more recent date, named Shastina, is attached to the side of the mountain.

Figure 31.11 shows the old-age stage of erosion of volcanoes. There remains now only a small sharp peak, or *volcanic neck,* representing the solidified lava in the pipe, or neck, of the volcano. Radiating from this are wall-like *dikes,* formed of lava, which previously filled fractures around the base of the volcano. Perhaps the finest illustration of a volcanic neck with radial dikes is Ship Rock, New Mexico (Figure 31.14). Because the central neck and radial dikes extend to great depths in the rock below the base of the volcano, they may persist as landforms

Figure 31.13 Mt. Shasta in the Cascade Range is a maturely dissected volcano. The bulge on the left-hand slope is a more recent subsidiary cone, Shastina. (Infrared photograph by Eliot Blackwelder.)

Figure 31.14 Shiprock, New Mexico, is a volcanic neck. Radiating from it are dikes. (Spence Air Photos.)

long after the cone and its associated flows have been removed.

Lava domes or shield volcanoes

A very important type of volcano, differing greatly in form from those already discussed, is the *lava dome* or *shield volcano*. The best examples are from the Hawaiian Islands, which consist entirely of lava domes (Figure 31.15).

Lava domes are characterized by gently rising, smooth slopes which tend to flatten near the top, producing a broad-topped volcano. The Hawaiian domes range to elevations up to 13,000 feet above sea level, but including the basal portion lying below sea level they are more than twice that high. In width they range from 10 to 50 miles at sea level and up to 100 miles wide at the submerged base.

Lava domes, as the name implies, are built by repeated outpourings of lava. Explosive behavior and emission of fragments are not important, as they are for cinder cones and composite cones. The lava, which in the Hawaiian lava domes is of a dark basaltic type, is highly fluid and travels far down the low slopes, which do not usually exceed 4° or 5°.

Instead of the explosion crater, lava domes have a wide, steep-sided *central depression*, or *sink*, which may be two miles or more wide and several hundred feet deep. These large depressions are a type of caldera produced by subsidence accompanying the removal of molten lava from beneath. Molten basalt is actually seen in the floors of deep *pit craters*, steep walled depressions one-fourth to one-half mile wide or smaller, which occur on the floor of the sink or elsewhere over the surface of the lava dome. Most lava flows issue from cracks, or *fissures*, on the sides of the volcano.

Lava domes of the Hawaiian islands are in various stages of erosion (Figure 31.15). Active volcanoes such as Kilauea and Mauna Loa are in the initial stage and have smooth slopes. Others, such as East Maui, are partly dissected by deep canyons but still possess sizable parts of the original surface. Still others, such as West Maui, are fully dissected. Rising from the sea are some steep-walled stacks representing the last vestiges of old domes; and there exist submarine banks some 250 feet below sea level, representing the final stage in destruction.

Geographical aspects of volcanoes

Volcanic eruptions count among the earth's great natural disasters. Wholesale loss of life and destruction of towns and cities are frequent in the history of peoples who live near active volcanoes. Loss occurs principally from sweeping clouds of

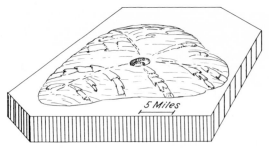

A. Initial dome with central depression and fresh flows issuing from radial fissure lines.

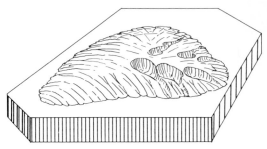

B. Young stage with deeply eroded valley heads.

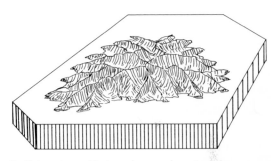

C. Mature stage with steep slopes and great relief.

Figure 31.15 Lava domes in various stages of erosion make up the Hawaiian Islands. (Data from Stearns and Macdonald.)

incandescent gases that descend the volcano slopes like great avalanches; from lava flows whose relentless advance engulfs whole cities; from the descent of showers of ash, cinders, and bombs; from violent earthquakes associated with the volcanic activity; and from mudflows of volcanic ash saturated by heavy rain. For habitations along low-lying coasts there is the additional peril of great seismic sea waves, generated by submarine earth faults. These do not necessarily accompany volcanic activity and may occur without warning in the ocean basins which are bordered by belts of active mountain making (Chapter 9).

The surfaces of volcanoes and lava flows remain barren and sterile for long periods after their formation. Certain types of lava surfaces are extremely rough and difficult to traverse; the Spaniards who encountered such terrain in the southwestern United States named it *malpais* (bad ground). Most volcanic rocks in time produce highly fertile soils that are extensively cultivated.

Volcanic ash may have a remarkably beneficial effect upon productivity of soil where the ash fall is relatively light. The eruption of Sunset Crater, near Flagstaff, Arizona, about 800 A.D., spread a layer of sandy volcanic ash over the barren reddish soil of the surrounding region and caused it to become highly productive because of the moisture-conserving effect of the ash, which acted as a mulch in the semi-arid climate. Because Hopi Indian corn grows well in sand, this development attracted Indians, who settled the area thickly. As the ash was gradually washed off of the slopes by heavy summer rains or blown into thick dunes by wind, the fertility declined and after about 200 years of occupation the region was abandoned to its previous state.

Young and mature volcanoes possess most of the geographical attributes of rugged mountains of any sort. Steep slopes prevent extensive agriculture, although providing valuable timber resources. Thus the San Francisco Mountains, a group of maturely dissected volcanoes in northern Arizona, are clothed in what is perhaps the finest known western yellow pine forest (ponderosa pine). A lumber industry centered about the towns of Flagstaff and Williams has flourished for many years.

As scenic features of great beauty, attracting a heavy tourist trade, few landforms outrank volcanoes. National parks have been made of Mt. Rainier, Mt. Lassen, and Crater Lake in the Cascade Range. Mt. Vesuvius and Fujiyama also attract many visitors.

Mineral resources, particularly the metallic ores, are conspicuously lacking in volcanoes and lava flows, unless later geologic events have resulted in the injection or diffusion of ore minerals into the volcanic rocks. The gas-bubble cavities in some ancient lavas have become filled with copper or other ores. The famed *kimberlite* rock of South Africa, source of diamonds, is the pipe of an ancient volcano.

As a source of crushed rock for concrete aggregate or railroad ballast, and other engineering purposes, lava rock is often extensively used. Thus the ancient lava layers that make up the Watchung ridges of northern New Jersey have in places been virtually leveled in quarrying operations continued over several decades.

Review Questions

1. What is a batholith? a stock? How large are these features? Of what kind of rock is a batholith composed? What kind of topography does it produce in a mature stage?

2. What is the meaning of a rectangular drainage pattern in a region underlain by homogeneous crystalline rock of a batholith?

3. What kind of topography develops in regions of belted metamorphic rocks such as gneiss, schist, slate, marble, and quartzite? Which of these rock types would form valleys? What would form narrow ridges; which broad ridges?

4. What are some of the varieties of rocks and structure that might be found in a region of complex structure? From the standpoint of geologic time would a complex region be ancient or comparatively recent in development? Would it be a likely region for mineral deposits of economic value?

5. What types of volcanoes are recognized? How do they differ?

6. Describe a cinder cone. Of what material is it formed? What size is normally attained by cinder cones? How fast do they form? How are groups of cinder cones arranged in plan?

7. How is a composite type of volcano formed? Name several famous large composite volcanoes. Along what belts are most of the world's active, or recently active, large volcanoes located?

8. What is a caldera? What volcanic activity occurred at Krakatoa (1883) and at Katmai (1912)? Describe Crater Lake as an illustration of a caldera.

9. Describe the stages of youth, maturity, and old age in the erosion of a large volcano. What form of drainage pattern is typically present on volcanoes?

10. Describe a volcanic neck with radial dikes. Give an example.

11. Discuss the form and development of large lava domes, or shield volcanoes, as exemplified by the Hawaiian Islands. What feature of a lava dome corresponds to the crater of a composite volcano?

12. Discuss the geographical aspects of volcanic landforms. In what way are soils and vegetation affected by volcanic forms?

Exercises

Exercise 1. *Volcano*. (Source: Dunsmuir, Calif., U.S. Geological Survey topographic map; scale 1:125,000.)

Explanatory Note: This map shows Mount Shasta, a great composite volcano of the Cascade Range. Figure 31.13 is a photograph of the same volcano, taken from the southwest. The main part of the volcano is dissected by streams and glaciers, and no longer shows a crater. Several small glaciers, shown by the cross-hatched pattern, remain on the mountain. Shastina, a subsidiary cone, is seen on the western slope of the main cone. Shastina is relatively young in date of formation and still shows a crater rim. Compare Shasta with Mt. Rainier, shown on a topographic map reproduced as one of the endpapers of this book.

QUESTIONS

1. (a) Determine the summit elevation of Mt. Shasta. **(b)** Determine the summit elevation of Shastina (13.5–17.5). **(c)** How wide is the volcano at its base, assuming the 5000-foot contour to represent the base?

2. Make a topographic profile across this volcano, from 30.0–28.0 to 0.0–4.0, using a vertical scale twice that of the horizontal scale of the map.

3. Compute the angle of the volcano slopes between the 10,000- and 12,500-foot contours. Use the map for this purpose.

4. The serrate, or sawtooth, contours near 9.0–26.0 mean that a rough, blocky lava flow of recent date is present. **(a)** Give grid coordinates of the source of this lava, as closely as you can locate it from the contour indications. **(b)** Locate by grid coordinates two similar lava flows.

5. What is the origin of the round hill at 2.0–12.0?

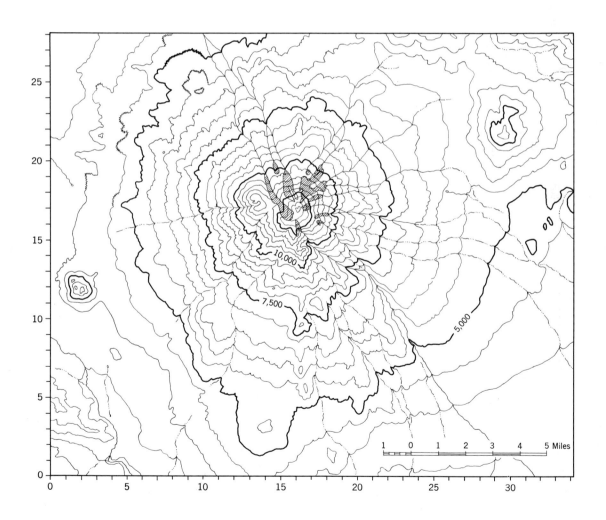

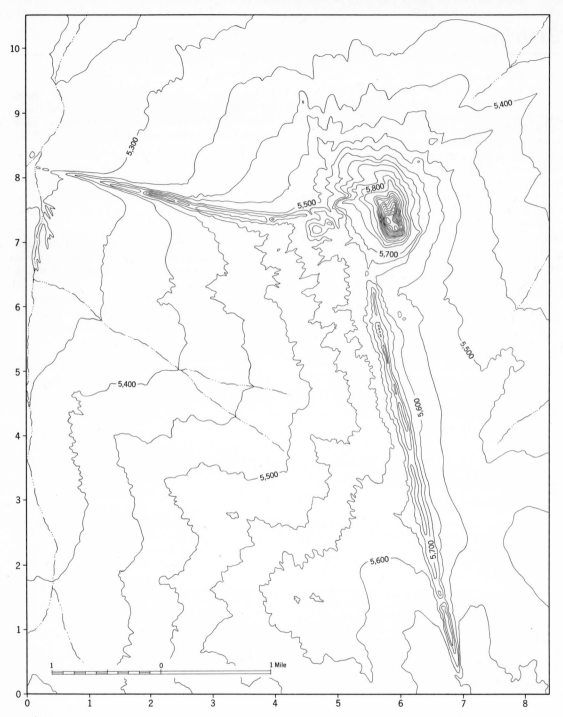

Exercise 2. *Volcanic Neck and Dikes.* (Source: Ship Rock, N.M., U.S. Geological Survey topographic map; sacle 1:62,500.)

Explanatory Note: Ship Rock, a steep-sided volcanic neck, rises above a broad plain, underlain by soft shales which have been easily removed by running water, leaving the harder volcanic rocks standing in bold relief. Figure 31.14 is a photograph of the map area taken from the northeast. Details shown on the photograph can easily be found on the map. Two great dikes extend radially outward, southward and westward from the neck.

QUESTIONS

1. (*a*) What contour interval is used on this map? **(*b*)** What is the summit elevation of Ship Rock (5.8–7.3)? **(*c*)** How high is the dike at 6.7–1.2?

2. On a sheet of thin tracing paper laid over this map, color red all volcanic rock on this map. The dikes should be shown as thin red lines. In addition to the two great dikes, at least two small dikes are indicated by sharply pointed contours. Locate three small pipes of volcanic rock which show on the photograph (Figure 31.14).

Bibliography

CHAPTER 1

FORM OF THE EARTH; GEOGRAPHIC GRID

Johnson, W. E. (1907), *Mathematical geography*, American Book Co., New York, 336 pp. See Chapters 1 and 2.

Bowie, W. (1916), The contributions of geodesy to geography, *Geog. Rev.*, 2:342–353.

Gannett, S. S. (1916), Geographic tables and formulas, *U.S. Geol. Survey Bull.* 650, 388 pp.

National Research Council (1931), The figure of the earth, *Bull.* 78, Nat. Acad. Sci., Washington, D. C.

Pratt, J. H. (1942), American prime meridians, *Geog. Rev.*, 32:233–244.

Witchell, W. M. (1947), Greenwich observatory, *Weather*, 2:23–29.

Depts. of the Army and the Air Force (1951), *The Universal Grid Systems*, TM 5–241, TO 16–1–233, U.S. Govt. Printing Office, Washington, D. C., 324 pp.

Heiskanen, W. A. (1955), The earth's gravity, *Scientific American*, 193, No. 3:164–174.

Knox, R. W. (1957), Precise determination of longitude in the United States, *Geog. Rev.*, 47:555–563.

Jacobs, J. A., R. D. Russell, and J. T. Wilson (1959), *Physics and geology*, McGraw-Hill Book Co., New York, 424 pp. See Chapter 4: The figure of the earth and gravity.

CHAPTER 2

PRINCIPLES OF MAP PROJECTION

Leppard, H. M., and L. P. Denoyer (1943), *Map projection studies*, No. P208, Denoyer-Geppert Co., Chicago, 20 pp.

Stewart, John Q. (1943), The use and abuse of map projections, *Geog. Rev.*, 33:589–604.

Marschner, F. J. (1944), Structural properties of medium- and small-scale maps, *Annals A.A.G.*, 34:1–46.

Deetz, C. H., and O. S. Adams (1945), Elements of map projection, *Special Publ.* 68, U.S. Dept. Commerce, U.S. Govt. Printing Office, Washington, D. C., 226 pp.

Powell, L. H. (1945), New uses for globes and spherical maps, *Geog. Rev.*, 35:49–58.

Chamberlin, W. (1947), *The round earth on flat paper*, Nat. Geog. Soc., Washington, D. C., 126 pp.

Raisz, E. (1948), *General cartography*, McGraw-Hill Book Co., 354 pp.

Kellaway, G. P. (1949), *Map projections*, Methuen and Co., London, 127 pp.

Robinson, A. H. (1949), An analytical approach to map projections, *Annals A.A.G.*, 39:283–290.

Robinson, A. H. (1953), Interrupting a map projection; a partial analysis of its value, *Annals A.A.G.*, 43:216–225.

Bailey, H. P. (1956), A grid formed of meridians and parallels for comparison and measurement of area, *Geog. Rev.*, 46:239–245.

Briesemeister, W. A. (1957), Some three-dimensional relief globes, past and present, *Geog. Rev.*, 47:251–260.

SPECIAL PROJECTIONS DESCRIBED

Goode, J. P. (1925), The homolosine projection; a new device for portraying the earth's surface entire, *Annals A.A.G.*, 15:119–125.

Goode, J. P. (1929), The polar equal area: a new projection for the world map, *Annals A.A.G.*, 19:157–161.

Jefferson, M. (1930), The six-six world map, giving larger, better continents, *Annals A.A.G.*, 20:1–6.

Miller, O. M. (1941), A conformal map projection for the Americas, *Geog. Rev.*, 31:100–104.

Miller, O. M. (1942), Notes on cylindrical world map projections, *Geog. Rev.*, 32:424–430.

Spilhaus, A. F. (1942), Maps of the whole world ocean, *Geog. Rev.*, 32:431–435.

Fisher, I. (1943), A world map on a regular icosahedron by gnomonic projection, *Geog. Rev.*, 33:605–619.

Botley, F. V. (1951), A new use for the plate carrée projection, *Geog. Rev.*, 41:604–644.

Philbrick, A. K. (1953), An oblique equal area map for world distributions, *Annals A.A.G.*, 43:202–215.

Leighly, J. (1956), Extended uses of polyconic projection tables, *Annals A.A.G.*, 46:150–173.

CHAPTER 3

MAP MAKING AND MAP READING

Deetz, C. H. (1943), *Cartography*, U.S. Govt. Printing Office, Washington, D. C., 85 pp.

MacLean, N. F., and E. C. Olson (1943), *Manual for instruction in military maps and aerial photographs*, Harper and Bros., New York, 138 pp.

Lobeck, A. K., and W. J. Tellington (1944), *Military maps and air photographs*, McGraw-Hill Book Co., New York, 256 pp.

Musham, H. A. (1944), *The technique of the terrain*, Reinhold Publ. Corp., New York, 228 pp.

Raisz, E. (1948), *General cartography*, McGraw-Hill Book Co., New York, 354 pp.

Thomas, R. I. (1950), Photographic operations of the Royal Canadian Air Force, *Arctic*, 3:150–165.

Espenshade, E. B., Jr. (1951), Mathematical scale problems, *J. Geog.*, 50:107–113.

Greenhouse, D. (1951), *Down to earth: mapping for everybody*, Holiday House, New York, 262 pp.

Monkhouse, F. J., and H. R. Wilkinson (1952), *Maps and diagrams: their compilation and construction*, Methuen and Co., London, 330 pp.

Dept. of the Army (1953), *Topographic surveying*, TM 5–234, U.S. Govt. Printing Office, Washington, D. C., 280 pp.

Robinson, A. H. (1953), *Elements of cartography*, John Wiley and Sons, New York, 254 pp.

Dept. of the Army (1956), *Map reading*, FM 21–26, U.S. Govt. Printing Office, Washington, D. C., 253 pp.

Military Service Publishing Co. (1957), *Map and aerial photograph reading*, Harrisburg, Pa., 177 pp.

Rude, G. T. (1957), Our last frontier: the Coast and Geodetic Survey's work in Alaska, *Geog. Rev.*, 47:349–364.

Dornbach, J. E. (1959), Design problems in aeronautical charting, *Professional Geographer*, 11, No. 2:7–10.

GEOMAGNETISM

Runcorn, S. K. (1955), The earth's magnetism, *Scientific American*, 193, No. 3:152–162.

Jacobs, J. A., R. D. Russell, and J. T. Wilson (1959), *Physics and geology*, McGraw-Hill Book Co., New York, 424 pp. See Chapter 6: Geomagnetism.

MILITARY GRID

Depts. of the Army and the Air Force (1951), *The universal grid systems*, TM 5–241, TO 16–1–233, U.S. Govt. Printing Office, Washington, D. C., 324 pp.

O'Keefe, J. A. (1952), The universal transverse Mercator grid and projection, *Professional Geographer*, 4, No. 5:19–24.

Dept. of the Army (1958), *Grids and grid references*, TM 5–241–1, U.S. Govt. Printing Office, Washington, D. C., 185 pp.

U.S. LAND OFFICE SURVEY

Johnson, W. E. (1907), *Mathematical geography*, American Book Co., New York, 336 pp. See Chapters 11 and 12.

U.S. Govt. Printing Office (1934), *Manual of instructions for the survey of the public lands of the United States*, Washington, D. C., 530 pp.

Johnson, H. B. (1957), Rational and ecological aspects of the quarter section, *Geog. Rev.*, 47:330–348.

CHAPTER 4

ILLUMINATION OF THE GLOBE

Johnson, W. E. (1907), *Mathematical geography*, American Book Co., New York, 336 pp. See Chapters 3 and 8.

Boggs, S. W. (1931), Seasonal variations in daylight, twilight, and darkness, *Geog. Rev.*, 21:656–659.

Wylie, C. C. (1942), *Astronomy, maps, and weather*, Harper and Bros., New York, 449 pp. See Chapters 5 and 6.

Beckinsale, R. P. (1945), The altitude of the zenithal sun: a geographic approach to determination and climatic significance, *Geog. Rev.*, 35:596–600.

Lyttleton, R. A. (1956), *The modern universe*, Harper and Bros., New York, 207 pp.

Mehlin, T. G. (1959), *Astronomy*, John Wiley and Sons, New York, 391 pp.

U.S. Naval Observatory, *The air almanac*, issued annually, U.S. Govt. Printing Office, Washington, D. C. Tables show sunrise and twilight for various latitudes.

CHAPTER 5

TIME

Johnson, W. E. (1907), *Mathematical geography*, American Book Co., New York, 336 pp. Chapters 4, 5, 6, and 7 deal with time.

Marvin, C. F. (1918), Diagrams showing conditions and effects of the Daylight-Savings Act, *Monthly Weather Rev.*, February 1918, pp. 75–76, pl. 19–21.

Strong, H. M. (1935), Universal world time, *Geog. Rev.*, 25:479–484.

Wylie, C. C. (1942), *Astronomy, maps, and weather*, Harper and Bros., New York, 449 pp. See Chapter 11.

Pyne, T. E. (1958), *Standard time*, Interstate Commerce Commission, U.S. Govt. Printing Office, Washington, D. C., 8 pp.

U.S. Naval Observatory, *The air almanac*, issued annually, U.S. Govt. Printing Office, Washington, D. C. Tables give standard times of most countries.

CHAPTER 6

THE MOON

Johnson, W. E. (1907), *Mathematical geography*, American Book Co., New York, 336 pp. See Chapter 9.

Whipple, F. L. (1941), *Earth, moon and planets*, The Blakiston Co., Philadelphia, 293 pp. See Chapters 7, 8, and 9.

Wylie, C. C. (1942), *Astronomy, maps and weather*, Harper and Bros., New York, 449 pp. See Chapter 13.

Mehlin, T. G. (1959), *Astronomy*, John Wiley and Sons, New York, 391 pp.

TIDES

Macgowan, D. J. (1855), On the eagre of the Tsien-Tang, *Am. J. Sci*, 2nd ser., 20:305–314. Eyewitness account of the tidal bore at Hangchow.

Marmer, H. A. (1921), Tide tables, *Geog. Rev.*, 11:406–413.

Marmer, H. A. (1922), Tides in the Bay of Fundy, *Geog. Rev.*, 12:195–205.

Marmer, H. A. (1923), Flood and ebb in New York Harbor, *Geog. Rev.*, 12:413–444.

Marmer, H. A. (1925), Mean sea level and its variations. *Annals A.A.G.*, 15:106–118.

Marmer, H. A. (1925), Tides and currents in New York harbor, U.S. Dept. Commerce, Coast and Geodetic Survey, *Special Publ.* 111, Washington, D. C., 174 pp.

Marmer, H. A. (1926), *The tide*, Appleton and Co., New York, 282 pp. An outstanding book on tides written in simple, non-mathematical style.

Marmer, H. A. (1928), On cotidal maps, *Geog. Rev.*, 18:129–143.

Marmer, H. A. (1932), Tides and tidal currents, Chapter 7 of Physics of the earth, Vol. 5: *Bull. Nat. Research Council* 85, pp. 229–309.

Bauer, H. A. (1933), A world map of tides, *Geog. Rev.*, 23:259–270.

Rappleye, H. S. (1947), Sea level, *Trans, N. Y. Acad. Sci.*, 10, No. 2:33–44.

Marmer, H. A. (1948), Is the Atlantic Coast sinking? The evidence from the tide, *Geog. Rev.*, 38:652–657.

Manning, T. H., and R. W. Rae (1950), Tidal observations in Arctic waters, *Arctic* 3:95–104.

Russell, R. C. H., and D. H. Macmillan (1954) *Waves and tides*, Hutchinson's Sci. and Tech. Publ., London, 348 pp.

CHAPTER 7 ✓

GENERAL DESCRIPTIVE METEOROLOGY

Brooks, C. F. (**1935**), *Why the weather?* Harcourt, Brace and Co., New York, 295 pp.

Kendrew, W. G. (**1938**), *Climate, a treatise on the principles of weather and climate*, Clarendon Press, Oxford, 327 pp.

Shaw, W. N. (**1939**), *The drama of weather*, Cambridge Univ. Press, London, 307 pp.

Haynes, B. C. (**1940**), Meteorology for pilots, *Civil Aeronautics Bull.* 25, U.S. Dept. Commerce, U.S. Govt. Printing Office, Washington, D. C., 167 pp.

Brunt, D. (**1942**), *Weather study*, The Ronald Press Co., New York, 215 pp.

Humphreys, W. J. (**1942**), *Ways of the weather: A cultural survey of meteorology*, Jaques Cattell Press, Lancaster, Pa., 400 pp.

Wenstrom, W. H. (**1942**), *Weather and the ocean of air*, Houghton Mifflin Co., Boston, 484 pp.

Barber, C. W. (**1943**), *An illustrated outline of weather science*, Pitman Publ. Corp., New York, 248 pp.

Kraght, P. E. (**1943**), *Meteorology for ship and aircraft operation*, Cornell Maritime Press, New York, 373 pp.

Trewartha, G. T. (**1943**), *An introduction to weather and climate*, McGraw-Hill Book Co., New York, 545 pp.

Byers, H. R. (**1944**), *General meteorology*, McGraw-Hill Book Co., New York, 645 pp.

Haynes, B. C. (**1947**), *Techniques of observing the weather*, John Wiley and Sons, New York, 272 pp.

Blair, T. A. (**1948**), *Weather elements*, Prentice-Hall, Englewood Cliffs, N. J., 414 pp.

Donn, W. L. (**1951**), *Meteorology with marine applications*, McGraw-Hill Book Co., New York, 465 pp.

U.S. Dept. Commerce (**1955**), Pilot's Weather handbook, Civil Aeronautics Administration, *Tech. Manual* 104, U.S. Govt. Printing Office, Washington, D.C., 143 pp.

Koeppe, C. E., and G. C. DeLong (**1958**), *Weather and Climate*, McGraw-Hill Book Co., New York, 341 pp.

Massey, H. S. W., and R. L. F. Boyd (**1959**), *The upper atmosphere*, Philosophical Library, New York, 333 pp.

AIR TEMPERATURE ✓

Reed, W. G. (**1916**), Protection from damage by frost, *Geog. Rev.*, 1:110–122.

McAdie, A. (**1917**), Saving crops from injury by frost, *Geog. Rev.*, 4:351–358.

Jefferson, M. (**1918**), The real temperatures throughout North and South America, *Geog. Rev.*, 6:240–267.

Cox, H. J. (**1920**), Weather conditions and thermal belts in the North Carolina mountain region and their relation to fruit growing, *Annals A.A.G.*, 10:57–68.

Visher, S. S. (**1922**), Laws of temperature, *Annals A.A.G.*, 13:15–40.

Jefferson, M. (**1926**), Actual temperatures of South America, *Geog. Rev.*, 16:443–466.

Parkins, A. E. (**1926**), The temperature region map, *Annals A.A.G.*, 16:151–165.

Kincer, J. B. (**1928**), Temperature, sunshine and wind, *Atlas of American agriculture*, U.S. Govt. Printing Office, Washington, D. C., 40 pp.

Hartshorne, R. (**1938**), Six standard seasons of the year, *Annals A.A.G.*, 28:165–178.

Jefferson, M. (**1938**), Standard seasons, *Annals A.A.G.*, 28:1–12.

Jones, S. B. (**1942**), Lags and ranges of temperature in Hawaii, *Annals A.A.G.*, 32:68–97.

Hawke, E. L. (**1946**), Frost-hollows, *Weather*, 1:41–45.

Leighly, J. B. (**1947**), Profiles of air temperatures normal to coast lines, *Annals A.A.G.*, 37:75–80.

Court, A. (**1949**), How hot is Death Valley? *Geog Rev.*, 39:214–220.

Geiger, R. (**1950**), *The climate near the ground*, Harvard University Press, Cambridge, Mass., 482 pp.

Court, A. (**1953**), Temperature extremes in the United States, *Geog. Rev.*, 43:39–49.

Sumner, A. R. (**1953**), Standard deviation of mean monthly temperatures in Anglo-America, *Geog. Rev.*, 43:50–59.

Miller, D. H. (**1956**), The influence of open pine forest on daytime temperature in the Sierra Nevada, *Geog. Rev.*, 46:209–218.

Chang, Jen-Hu (**1957**), World patterns of monthly soil temperature distribution, *Annals A.A.G.*, 47:241–249.

CHAPTER 8 ✓

AIR PRESSURE AND WINDS

Ward, R. deC. (**1916**), The prevailing winds of the United States, *Annals A.A.G.*, 6:99–119.

Marmer, H. A. (**1930**), *The sea*, Appleton and Co., New York, 312 pp. See Chapters 17 and 18.

Dobby, E. H. G. (**1945**), Winds and fronts over Southeast Asia, *Geog. Rev.*, 35:204–218.

Priestley, C. H. B. (**1948**), Wind and pressure change, *Weather*, 3:66–72.

Borchert, J. R. (**1953**), Regional differences in world atmospheric circulation, *Annals A.A.G.*, 43:14–26.

Wexler, Harry (**1955**), The circulation of the atmosphere, *Scientific American*, vol. 193, No. 3:114–124.

Lahey, J. F., and others (**1958**), *Atlas of 500 mb wind characteristics for the northern hemisphere*, Univ. of Wisconsin Press, Madison, 97 pp.

CHAPTER 9

GENERAL PHYSICAL OCEANOGRAPHY

Sverdrup, H. V., and M. W. Johnson (**1942**), *The oceans*, Prentice-Hall, Englewood Cliffs, N. J., 1087 pp.

Sverdrup, H. V., (**1950**), Physical oceanography of the North Polar Sea, *Arctic*, 3:178–186.

La Fond, E. C. (**1954**), Physical oceanography and submarine geology of the seas to the west and north of Alaska, *Arctic*, 7:93–102.

Ewing, M., and B. Heezen (**1956**), Oceanographic research programs of the Lamont Geological Observatory, *Geog. Rev.*, 46:508–535.

Walford, L. A. (**1958**), *Living resources of the sea; opportunities for research and expansion*, The Ronald Press Co., New York, 321 pp.

OCEAN CURRENTS

Murphy, R. C. (**1923**), The oceanography of the Peruvian littoral with reference to the abundance and distribution of marine life, *Geog. Rev.*, 13:64–85.

Bigelow, H. B. (1928), Exploration of the waters of the Gulf of Maine, *Geog. Rev.*, 18:232–260.

Marmer, H. A. (1929), The Gulf Stream and its problems, *Geog. Rev.*, 19:457–478.

Pettersson, O. (1929), Changes in oceanic circulation and their climatic consequences, *Geog. Rev.*, 19:121–131.

Church, P. E. (1932), Surface temperatures of the Gulf Stream and its bordering waters, *Geog. Rev.*, 22:286–293.

Isaac, W. E. (1937), South African coastal waters in relation to ocean currents, *Geog. Rev.*, 27:651–664.

Munk, W. (1955), The circulation of the oceans, *Scientific American*, 193, No. 3:96–104.

OCEAN WAVES

Cornish, V. (1910), *Waves of the sea and other waves*, The Open Court Publ. Co., Chicago, 374 pp.

Johnson, D. W. (1919), *Shore processes and shoreline development*, John Wiley and Sons, New York, 584 pp. Out of print.

Cornish, V. (1934), *Ocean waves and kindred geophysical phenomena*, Cambridge Univ. Press, New York, 164 pp.

Bigelow, H. B., and W. T. Edmondson (1947), Wind waves at sea; breakers and surf, *U.S. Navy Hydrographic Office Publ.* 602, Washington, D. C., 177 pp.

Macdonald, G. A., F. P. Shepard, and D. Cox (1947), The tsunami of April 1, 1946, in the Hawaiian Islands, *Pacific Science*, 1:21–37.

Russell, R. C. H., and D. H. Macmillan (1954), *Waves and tides*, Hutchinson's Sci. and Tech. Publ., London, 348 pp.

SEA ICE

Porsild, M. P. (1918), On "savssats": a crowding of Arctic animals at holes in the sea ice, *Geog. Rev.*, 6:215–228.

Ward, R. de C. (1924), A cruise with the International Ice Patrol, *Geog. Rev.*, 14:50–61.

Smith, E. H. (1932), Ice in the sea, Chap. 10 of Physics of the earth, Vol. 5, Oceanography, *Bull. Nat. Research Council* 85, pp. 384–408.

Weaver, J. C. (1946), Ice atlas of the northern hemisphere, *U.S. Navy Hydrographic Office Publ.* 550, Washington, D. C., 105 pp.

Crary, A. P., R. D. Cotell, and T. F. Sexton (1952), Preliminary report on scientific work on "Fletcher's Ice Island, T 3," *Arctic*, 5:211–223.

Koenig, L. S., K. R. Greenaway, M. Dunbar, and G. Hattersley-Smith (1952), Arctic ice islands, *Arctic*, 5:67–103.

Humphrey, P. A. (1955), The voyage of the Atka, *Scientific American*, 193, No. 3:50–55.

U.S. Navy (1957), Oceanographic Atlas of the Polar Seas, Part I: Antarctic, *Hydrographic Office Publication* 705, U.S. Navy Hydrographic Office, Washington, D. C., 70 pp.

CHAPTER 10

CLOUDS, FOG, HUMIDITY, DEW

McAdie, A. (1931), The commercial importance of fog control, *Annals A.A.G.*, 21:91–100.

Stone, R. G. (1935), Fog in the United States and adjacent regions, *Geog. Rev.*, 25:111–134.

Ives, R. L. (1941), Colorado Front Range crest clouds and related phenomena, *Geog. Rev.*, 31:23–45.

Rossby, C. G. (1941), Amateur forecasting from cloud formations, *Yearbook of Agriculture, 1941*, U.S. Dept. Agriculture, pp. 656–661.

Humphreys, W. J. (1943), *Fogs, clouds and aviation*, Williams and Wilkins Co., Baltimore, 199 pp.

Grant, H. D. (1944), *Cloud and weather atlas*, Coward, McCann, New York, 294 pp.

Hewson, E. W. (1946), The wet-bulb thermometer— its meaning and significance, *Weather*, 1:194–197, 226–230.

Ashbel, D. (1949), Frequency and distribution of dew in Palestine, *Geog. Rev.*, 39:291–297.

Went, F. W. (1955), Fog, mist, dew, and other sources of water, *Yearbook of Agriculture, 1955*, U.S. Dept. Agriculture, pp. 103–109.

Patton, C. P. (1956), Climatology of summer fogs in the San Francisco Bay area, *Univ. of California Publ. in Geography*, 10, No. 3:113–200.

World Meteorological Organization (1956), *International cloud atlas*, Geneva, Switzerland, 2 vols., English language edition.

PRECIPITATION

Ward, R. de C. (1917), Rainfall types of the United States, *Geog. Rev.*, 4:131–144.

Kincer, J. B. (1922), Precipitation and humidity, *Atlas of American agriculture*, U.S. Govt. Printing Office, Washington, D. C., 48 pp.

McAdie, Alexander (1922), Monsoon and trade winds as rain makers and desert makers, *Geog. Rev.*, 12:412–419.

Visher, S. S. (1923), The laws of winds and moisture, *Annals A.A.G.*, 13:169–207.

Sykes, G. (1931), Rainfall investigations in Arizona and Sonora by means of long-period rain gauges, *Geog. Rev.*, 21:229–233.

Church, J. E. (1933), Snow surveying, *Geog. Rev.*, 23:529–563.

Leighly, J. (1935), Continental precipitation on a rotating earth, *Geog. Rev.*, 25:657–666.

Visher, S. S. (1938), Rainfall-intensity contrasts in Indiana, *Geog. Rev.*, 28:627–637.

Lemons, H. (1942), Hail as a factor in the regional climatology of the United States, *Geog. Rev.*, 32:471–475.

Tannehill, I. R. (1947), *Drought, its causes and effects*, Princeton Univ. Press, Princeton, N. J., 264 pp.

Thornwaite, C. W. (1947), Climate and moisture conservation, *Annals A.A.G.*, 37:87–100.

Visher, S. S. (1947), Precipitation seasons in the United States, *Geog. Rev.*, 37:106–111.

Gardner, C., Jr., (1955), Hauling down more water from the sky, *Yearbook of Agriculture, 1955*, U.S. Dept. Agriculture, pp. 91–95.

Hiatt, W. E., and R. W. Schloemer (1955), How we measure the variations in precipitation, *Yearbook of agriculture, 1956*, U.S. Dept. Agriculture, pp. 78–84.

Tannehill, I. R. (1955), Is weather subject to cycles? *Yearbook of Agriculture, 1955*, U.S. Dept. Agriculture, pp. 84–90.

Work, R. A. **(1955)**, Measuring snow to forecast water supplies. *Yearbook of Agriculture, 1955*, U.S. Dept.
Agriculture, pp. 94–102.

Schaefer, V. J. **(1956)**, Artificially induced precipitation
and its potentialities, pp. 607–618 of *Man's role in
changing the face of the earth*, Univ. of Chicago
Press, Chicago, 1193 pp.

THUNDERSTORMS

Bannon, J. K. **(1948)**, Rain making, *Weather*, 3:261–266.

Byers, H. R. **(1949)**, Structure and dynamics of the
thunderstorm, *Weather*, 4:220–222, 244–250.

Byers, H. R. **(1949)**, *The thunderstorm*, U.S. Dept. Commerce, Weather Bureau, U.S. Govt. Printing Office,
Washington, D.C., 287 pp.

Langmuir, I. **(1950)**, Control of precipitation from cumulus
clouds by various seeding techniques, *Science*,
112:35–41.

Flora, S. D. **(1956)**, *Hailstorms of the United States*, Univ.
of Oklahoma Press, Norman, 201 pp.

CHAPTER 11

WEATHER ANALYSIS

Thornthwaite, C. W. **(1937)**, The life history of rainstorms,
Geog. Rev., 27:92–111.

Rossby, C. G. **(1941)**, The scientific basis of modern
meteorology, *Yearbook of Agriculture, 1941*, U.S.
Dept. Agriculture, pp. 599–655.

Visher, S. S. **(1944)**, Storms of the world, *Economic
Geog.*, 20:286–295.

Brooks, C. E. P. **(1946)**, Annual recurrences of weather:
"singularities," *Weather*, 1:107–113.

Lander, A. J. **(1946)**, The British radiosonde, *Weather*,
1:21–24.

Smith, K. H. **(1946)**, The analysis of a weather chart,
Weather, 1:66–71.

Belasco, J. E. **(1948)**, The incidence of anticyclonic days
and spells over the British Isles, *Weather* 3:233–242.

Brent, A. E. **(1948)**, Radar detection of precipitation,
Weather, 3:37–41.

Gentilli, J. **(1949)**, Air masses of the southern hemisphere,
Weather, 4:258–261, 292–297.

TROPICAL WEATHER AND CYCLONES

Visher, S. S. **(1925)**, Effects of tropical cyclones upon the
weather of middle latitudes, *Geog. Rev.*, 15:106–114.

Cline, I. M. **(1926)**, *Tropical cyclones*, The Macmillan Co.,
New York, 301 pp.

Brooks, C. F. **(1939)**, Hurricanes into New England,
Geog. Rev., 29:119–127.

James, P. E. **(1939)**, Air masses and fronts of South
America, *Geog. Rev.*, 29:132–134.

Brooks, C. F., and C. Chapman **(1945)**, The New England
hurricane of September, 1944, *Geog. Rev.*, 35:132–
136.

Spink, P. C. **(1946)**, The 1944–45 cyclone season in the
western Indian Ocean, *Weather*, 1:174–179.

Sawyer, J. S., and B. Ilett **(1950)**, When hurricanes come
north, *Weather*, 5:210–217.

Riehl, H. **(1954)**, *Tropical meteorology*, McGraw-Hill
Book Co., New York, 392 pp.

Tannehill, I. R. **(1956)**, *Hurricanes*, Princeton Univ. Press,
Princeton, N. J., 308 pp.

TORNADOES

Carey, J. P. **(1917)**, The central Illinois tornado of May 26,
1917, *Geog. Rev.*, 4:122–130.

Veryard, R. G. **(1946)**, The tornado, *Weather*, 1:89–91.

Simmonds, J. **(1950)**, The English tornadoes of 21 May,
1950, *Weather*, 5:255–257.

Flora, S. D. **(1954)**, *Tornadoes of the United States*, Univ.
of Oklahoma Press, Norman, 221 pp.

CHAPTER 12

GENERAL CLIMATOLOGY, CLIMATE DATA

Huntington, E. **(1924)**, *Civilization and climate*, Yale University Press, New Haven, Conn., 453 pp.

Clayton, H. H. **(1927, 1934)**, World weather records,
Smithsonian Miscellaneous Collections, 79, 1927, and
90, 1934. Data of many stations throughout the world.

U.S. Dept. Agriculture **(1928)**, *Atlas of American agriculture*, U.S. Govt. Printing Office, Washington, D. C.

Russell, R. J. **(1934)**, Climatic years, *Geog. Rev.*, 24:92–
103.

Brooks, C. F., A. J. Connor, and others **(1936)**, *Climatic
maps of North America*, Harvard Univ. Press, Cambridge, Mass.

Visher, S. S. **(1941)**, Climate and geomorphology: some
comparisons between regions, *J. Geomorphology*,
4:54–64.

Blumenstock, D. I., and C. W. Thornthwaite **(1941)**, Climate and the world pattern, *Yearbook of Agriculture,
1941*, pp 98–127.

U.S. Dept. Agriculture **(1941)**, Climate and man, *Yearbook
of Agriculture, 1941*, U.S. Govt. Printing Office,
Washington, D. C. Many papers on climate topics.
United States climate data.

Blair, T. A. **(1942)**, Climatology, general and regional.
Prentice-Hall, Englewood Cliffs, N. J., 484 pp.

Harwood, W. A. **(1947)**, Tree rings and climate through
the centuries, *Weather*, 2:112–120.

Brooks, C. F. **(1948)**, The climatic record: its content,
limitations and geographic value, *Annals A.A.G.*,
38:153–168.

Brooks, C. E. P. **(1949)**, *Climate through the ages*, Mc-
Graw-Hill Book Co., New York, 395 pp.

Conrad, V., and L. W. Pollak **(1950)**, *Methods in climatology*, Harvard Univ. Press, Cambridge, Mass.,
459 pp.

Peltier, L. **(1950)**, The geographic cycle in periglacial
regions as it is related to climatic geomorphology,
Annals A.A.G., 40:214–236.

Kendrew, W. G. **(1953)**, *The climates of the continents*,
Oxford Univ. Press, London, 607 pp.

Lee, D. H. K. **(1953)**, Physiological climatology as a field
of study, *Annals A.A.G.*, 43:127–137.

Miller, A. A. **(1953)**, *Climatology*, 1953 ed., Methuen and
Co., London, 318 pp.

Thomas, M. K. **(1953)**, *Climatological atlas of Canada*,
Nat. Research Council, Ottawa, Canada, 253 pp.

Visher, S. S. **(1954)**, *Climatic atlas of the United States*,
Harvard Univ. Press, Cambridge, Mass., 403 pp.

Hare, F. K. (1955), Dynamic and synoptic climatology, *Annals A.A.G.*, 45:152–162.

Trewartha, G. T. (1955), *An introduction to climate*, McGraw-Hill Book Co., New York, 402 pp.

U.S. Navy (1955 and later), *Marine climatic atlas of the world*, 4 vols., U.S. Govt. Printing Office, Washington, D. C.

Court, A. (1957), Climatology: complex, dynamic, and synoptic, *Annals A.A.G.*, 47:125–136.

Landsberg, Helmut (1958), *Physical climatology*, Gray Printing Co., DuBois, Pa., 446 pp.

Lydolph, P. E. (1959), Fedorov's complex method in climatology, *Annals A.A.G.*, 49:120–144.

KÖPPEN SYSTEM

Köppen, W. (1923), *Die Klimate der Erde; Grundriss der Klimakunde*, Walter de Gruyter Co., Berlin, 369 pp.

Köppen, W., and R. Geiger (1930 and later), *Handbuch der Klimatologie*, 5 vols., Gebrüder Borntraeger, Berlin. See vol. 1, Part C (1936) for general analysis of Köppen system of climatology.

Ackerman, E. A. (1941), The Köppen classification of climates in North America, *Geog. Rev.*, 31:105–111.

Kesseli, J. E. (1942), The climates of California according to the Köppen classification, *Geog. Rev.*, 32:476–480.

Köppen-Geiger (1954), Klima der Erde (map), Justus Perthe, Darmstadt, Germany. American distributor, A. J. Nystrom & Co., Chicago.

THORNTHWAITE SYSTEM

Thornthwaite, C. W. (1931), The climates of North America, according to a new classification, *Geog. Rev.*, 21:633–655.

Thornthwaite, C. W. (1933), The climates of the earth, *Geog. Rev.*, 23:433–440, with world map.

Thornthwaite, C. W. (1943), Problems in the classification of climates, *Geog. Rev.*, 33:233–255.

Thornthwaite, C. W. (1948), An approach toward a rational classification of climate, *Geog. Rev.*, 38:55–94.

Chang, Jen-Hu (1959), An evaluation of the 1948 Thornthwaite classification, *Annals A.A.G.*, 49:24–30.

NATURAL VEGETATION

Campbell, D. H. (1926), *An outline of plant geography*, The Macmillan Co., New York, 392 pp.

Matoon, W. R. (1936), Forest trees and forest regions of the United States, *U.S. Dept. Agriculture Misc. Publ.* 217, 54 pp.

Whittlesey, D. (1936), Major agricultural regions of the earth, *Annals A.A.G.*, 26:199–240. World agriculture map.

Carter, G. F. (1946), The role of plants in geography, *Geog. Rev.*, 36:121–131.

Küchler, A. W. (1947), A geographic system of vegetation, *Geog. Rev.*, 37:233–240.

U.S. Dept. Agriculture (1948), *Grass*, U.S. Govt. Printing Office, Washington, D. C., 892 pp. Papers on the nature and distribution of grass.

Küchler, A. W. (1949), A physiognomic classification of vegetation, *Annals A.A.G.*, 39:201–210.

Küchler, A. W. (1955), A comprehensive method of mapping vegetation, *Annals, A.A.G.*, 45:404–415.

Amer. Geog. Society (1956), *A world geography of forest resources*, edited by Haden-Guest, Wright, and Teclaff, The Ronald Press Co., New York, 736 pp.

Küchler, A. W. (1956), Classification and purpose in vegetation maps, *Geog. Rev.*, 46:155–167.

deLaubenfels, D. J. (1957), The status of "conifers" in vegetation classifications, *Annals A.A.G.*, 47:145–149.

Wagner, P. L. (1957), A contribution to structural vegetation mapping, *Annals A.A.G.*, 47:363–369.

Shantz, H. L., and B. L. Turner (1958), *Photographic documentation of vegetational changes in Africa over a third of a century*, Univ. of Arizona, College of Agriculture, Tucson, 158 pp.

CHAPTER 13

EQUATORIAL RAINFOREST CLIMATE

Miller, L. E. (1916), The descent of the Rio Gy-Paraná, *Geog. Rev.*, 1:169–191.

Miller, L. E. (1917), The land of the Maquiritares, *Geog. Rev.*, 3:356–374.

Ross, E. (1919), The climate of Liberia and its effect on man, *Geog. Rev.*, 7:387–402.

Scrivenor, J. B. (1921), The physical geography of the southern part of the Malay Peninsula, *Geog. Rev.*, 11:351–371.

Barbour, T., and W. S. Brooks (1923), The Sapo Mountains and the Sambu Valley; a biological reconnaissance in southeastern Panama, *Geog. Rev.*, 13:211–222.

van Valkenburg, S. (1925), Java: the economic geography of a tropical island, *Geog. Rev.*, 15:563–583.

Stamp, L. D. (1930), Burma: an undeveloped monsoon country, *Geog. Rev.* 20:86–109.

Harley, G. W. (1939), Roads and trails in Liberia, *Geog. Rev.*, 29:447–460.

Brass, L. J. (1941), Stone age agriculture in New Guinea, *Geog. Rev.*, 31:555–569.

Stone, R. G. (1941), Health in tropical climates, *Yearbook of Agriculture, 1941*, U.S. Dept. Agriculture, pp. 246–261.

Pendleton, R. L. (1942), Land utilization and agriculture of Mindanao, Philippine Islands, *Geog. Rev.*, 32:180–210.

Schneeberger, W. F. (1945), The Kerayan-Kalabit highland of central northeast Borneo, *Geog. Rev.*, 35:544–562.

Pendleton, R. L. (1950), Agricultural and forestry potentialities of the tropics, *Agronomy J.*, 42:115–123.

Lee, D. H. K. (1951), Thoughts on housing for the humid tropics, *Geog. Rev.*, 41:124–147.

Lee, D. H. K. (1957), *Climate and economic development in the tropics*, Harper and Bros., New York, 182 pp.

TRADE WIND LITTORAL CLIMATE

Durland, W. D. (1922), The forests of the Dominican Republic, *Geog. Rev.*, 12:206–222.

James, P. E. (1932), The coffee lands of southeastern Brazil, *Geog. Rev.*, 22:225–244.

van Royen, W. (1938), A geographical reconnaissance of the Cibao of Santo Domingo, *Geog. Rev.*, 28:556–572.

von Hagen, V. W. (1940), The Mosquito Coast of Honduras and its inhabitants, *Geog. Rev.*, 30:238–259.

Hodge, W. B. (1943), The vegetation of Dominica, *Geog. Rev.*, 33:349–375.

TROPICAL DESERT AND STEPPE CLIMATES

Huntington, E. (1910), The Libyan oasis of Kharga, *Am. Geog. Soc. Bull.*, 42:641–661.

MacDougal, D. T. (1912), North American deserts, *Geog. J.*, 39:105–123.

Hobbs, W. H. (1917), A pilgrimage in northeastern Africa, with studies of desert conditions, *Geog. Rev.*, 3:337–355.

MacDougal, D. T. (1917), A decade of the Salton Sea, *Geog. Rev.*, 3:457–473.

West, L. C. (1918), Dongola Province of the Anglo-Egyptian Sudan, *Geog. Rev.*, 5:22–37.

Gautier, E. F. (1925), The trans-Saharan railway, *Geog. Rev.*, 15:51–69.

Clapp, F. G. (1926), In the northwest of the Australian desert, *Geog. Rev.*, 16:206–231.

Taylor, G. (1926), The frontiers of settlement in Australia, *Geog. Rev.*, 16:1–25.

de Martonne, E. (1927), Regions of interior-basin drainage, *Geog. Rev.*, 17:397–414.

Sykes, G. (1927), The Camino del Diablo: with notes on a journey in 1925, *Geog. Rev.*, 17:62–74. Physiological effects of heat and thirst on desert trail.

Hoover, J. W. (1929), The Indian country of southern Arizona, *Geog. Rev.*, 19:38–60.

Wilson, E. D. (1931), New mountains in the Yuma Desert, *Geog. Rev.*, 21:221–228.

Shreve, F. (1934), Rainfall, runoff and soil moisture under desert conditions, *Annals A.A.G.*, 24:131–156.

Gautier, E. F., tr. by D. F. Mayhen (1935), *Sahara, the great desert*, Columbia Univ. Press, New York, 264 pp.

Forbes, R. H. (1942), Egyptian-Libyan borderlands, *Geog. Rev.*, 32:294–302.

Twitchell, K. S. (1944), Water resources of Saudi Arabia, *Geog. Rev.*, 34:365–386.

Capot-Rey, R. (1945), Dry and humid morphology in the western Erg, *Geog. Rev.*, 35:391–407.

Moolman, J. H. (1946), The Orange River, South Africa, *Geog. Rev.*, 36:653–676.

Gorrie, R. M. (1948), Countering desiccation in the Punjab, *Geog. Rev.*, 38:30–40.

Ives, R. L. (1949), Climate of the Sonoran Desert, *Annals A.A.G.*, 39:143–187.

WEST COAST DESERT CLIMATE

Rich, J. L. (1941), The nitrate district of Tarapacá, Chile: An aerial traverse, *Geog. Rev.*, 31:1–22.

Light, M., and R. Light (1946), Atacama revisited: "Desert trails" seen from the air, *Geog. Rev.*, 36:525–545.

Rudolph, W. E. (1951), Chuquicamata revisited twenty years later, *Geog. Rev.*, 41:88–113.

Hammond, E. H. (1954), A geomorphic study of the Cape region of Baja California. *Univ. of California Publ. in Geography*, 10, No. 2:45–111.

Lydolph, P. E. (1957), A comparative analysis of the dry western littorals, *Annals A.A.G.*, 47:211–230.

TROPICAL SAVANNA CLIMATE

deBooy, T. (1918), The western Maracaibo lowland, Venezuela, *Geog. Rev.*, 6:481–500.

Heller, E. (1918), The geographical barriers to the distribution of big game animals in Africa, *Geog. Rev.*, 6:297–319.

Taylor, G. (1919), The settlement of tropical Australia, *Geog. Rev.*, 8:84–115.

Shantz, H. L. (1922), Urundi, territory and people, *Geog. Rev.*, 12:329–357.

Whitbeck, R. H. (1922), Geographical influences in the development of Cuban agriculture, *Geog. Rev.*, 12:223–240. See pp. 228–230, Climate of Cuba.

Bennett, H. H. (1925), Some geographic aspects of western Ecuador, *Annals A.A.G.*, 15:126–147.

Sheppard, G. (1930), Notes on the climate and physiography of southwestern Ecuador, *Geog. Rev.*, 20:445–453.

Cochran-Patrick, C. K. (1931), Aerial reconnaissance mapping in Northern Rhodesia, *Geog. Rev.*, 21:213–220. Good air photographs.

Dainelli, G. (1931), The agricultural possibilities of Italian Somalia, *Geog. Rev.*, 21:56–69.

Darby, H. C. (1931), Settlement in northern Rhodesia, *Geog. Rev.*, 21:559–573.

Williamson, A. V. (1931), Indigenous irrigation works in peninsular India, *Geog. Rev.*, 21:613–626.

Crist, R. (1932), Along the Llanos-Andes border in Zamora, Venezuela, *Geog. Rev.*, 22:411–422.

Forbes, R. H. (1932), The desiccation problem in West Africa: the capture of the Sourou by the Black Volta, *Geog. Rev.*, 22:97–106.

Gautier, E. F. (1933), Climatic and physiographic notes on French Guinea, *Geog. Rev.*, 23:248–258.

Price, A. G. (1933), Pioneer reactions to a poor tropical environment, *Geog. Rev.*, 23:353–371.

Sheppard, G. (1933), The rainy season of 1932 in southwestern Ecuador, *Geog. Rev.*, 23:210–216.

Williams, L. (1941), The Caura Valley and its forests, *Geog. Rev.*, 31:414–429.

Pendleton, R. L. (1943), Land use in northeastern Thailand, *Geog. Rev.*, 33:15–41.

Rudolph, W. E. (1944), Agricultural possibilities in northwestern Venezuela, *Geog. Rev.*, 34:36–56.

Bates, M. (1948), Climate and vegetation in the Villavicencio region of eastern Colombia, *Geog. Rev.*, 38:555–574.

Davis, N. E. (1948), West Indian weather, *Weather*, 3:113–116.

Waibel, L. (1948), Vegetation and land use in the Planalto Central of Brazil, *Geog. Rev.*, 38:529–554.

Gillman, C. (1949), A vegetation-types map of Tanganyika Territory, *Geog. Rev.*, 39:7–31.

James, P. E. (1952), Observations on the physical geography of northeast Brazil, *Annals, A.A.G.*, 42:153–176.

Parsons, J. J. (1955), The Miskito pine savanna of Nicaragua and Honduras, *Annals A.A.G.*, 45:36–63.

Whittlesey, D. (1956), Southern Rhodesia—an African compage, *Annals A.A.G.*, 46:1–97.

CHAPTER 14

HUMID SUBTROPICAL CLIMATE

Tower, W. S. (1918), The Pampa of Argentina, *Geog. Rev.*, 5:293–315.

Emerson, F. V. (1919), The southern long-leaf pine belt, *Geog. Rev.*, 7:81–90.

Durland, W. D. (1924), The quebracho region of Argentina, *Geog. Rev.*, 14:227–241.

Trewartha, G. T. (1928), A geographic study in Shizuoka Prefecture, Japan, *Annals A.A.G.*, 18:127–259.

Frothingham, E. H. (1931), Timber growing and logging practice in the southern Appalachian region, *U.S. Dept. Agriculture Tech. Bull.* 250, 93 pp.

Visher, S. S. (1941), Torrential rains as a serious handicap in the South, *Geog. Rev.*, 31:644–652.

MARINE WEST COAST CLIMATE

Furlong, C. W. (1917), Some effects of environment on the Fuegian tribes, *Geog. Rev.*, 3:1–15.

Brooks, A. H. (1925), The value of Alaska, *Geog. Rev.*, 15:25–50.

Heintzleman, B. F. (1928), Pulp-timber resources of southeastern Alaska, *U.S. Dept. Agriculture Misc. Publ.* 41, 34 pp.

Munday, W. A. (1928), Explorations in the coast range of British Columbia, *Geog. Rev.*, 18:196–214.

Hoover, J. W. (1933), The littoral of northern California as a geographic province, *Geog. Rev.*, 23:217–229.

Bilham, E. G. (1938), *The Climate of the British Isles*, Macmillan and Co., London, 347 pp.

Cumberland, K. B. (1941), A century's change: natural to cultural vegetation in New Zealand, *Geog. Rev.*, 31:529–554.

Küchler, A. W. (1946), The broadleaf deciduous forests of the Pacific Northwest, *Annals A.A.G.*, 36:122–147.

Taylor, J. A., and R. A. Yates (1958), *British weather in maps*, St. Martin's Press, New York, 256 pp.

MEDITERRANEAN CLIMATE

Bowman, I. (1913), The dwarf forests of southern California, *Am. Geog. Soc. Bull.*, 45:13–16.

Smith, J. R. (1916), The oak tree and man's environment, *Geog. Rev.*, 1:3–19.

Semple, E. C. (1919), Climatic and geographic influences on ancient Mediterranean forests and the lumber trade, *Annals A.A.G.*, 9:13–37.

Coulter, J. W. (1930), Land utilization in the Santa Lucia region, *Geog. Rev.*, 20:469–479.

Raup, H. F. (1935), Land use and water-supply problems in southern California: market gardens of the Palos Verdes Hills, *Geog. Rev.*, 25:264–269.

Torbet, E. N. (1935), The specialized commercial agriculture of the northern Santa Clara Valley, *Geog. Rev.*, 25:247–263.

Stotz, C. L. (1939), The Bursa region of Turkey, *Geog. Rev.*, 29:81–100.

Leighly, J. (1941), Settlement and cultivation in the summer-dry climates, *Yearbook of Agriculture, 1941*, U.S. Dept. Agriculture, pp. 197–204.

Fish, W. B. (1944), The Lebanon, *Geog. Rev.*, 34:235–258.

Nuttonson, M. Y. (1947), Agroclimatology and crop ecology of Palestine and Trans-Jordan and climatic analogues in the United States, *Geog. Rev.*, 37:436–456.

Whyte, R. O. (1950), The phytogeographical zones of Palestine, *Geog. Rev.*, 40:600–614.

MIDDLE-LATITUDE DESERT AND STEPPE CLIMATES

Huntington, E. (1906), The border belts of the Tarim Basin, *Am. Geog. Soc. Bull.*, 38:91–96.

Gregory, H. E. (1915), The oasis of Tuba City, Arizona, *Annals A.A.G.*, 5:107–119.

Jefferson, M. (1916), The oasis at the foot of the Wasatch, *Geog. Rev.*, 1:346–358.

Visher, S. S. (1916), The biogeography of the northern great plains, *Geog. Rev.*, 2:89–115.

Smith, J. W. (1920), Rainfall of the Great Plains in relation to cultivation, *Annals A.A.G.*, 10:69–74.

Stein, A. (1920), Explorations in the Lop Desert, *Geog. Rev.*, 9:1–34.

Shantz, H. L. (1923), The natural vegetation of the Great Plains, *Annals A.A.G.*, 13:81–107.

Bryan, K. (1929), Flood-water farming, *Geog. Rev.*, 19:444–456.

Hoover, J. W. (1930), Tusayan: The Hopi Indian country of Arizona, *Geog. Rev.*, 20:425–444.

Bowman, I. (1931), Jordan country, *Geog. Rev.*, 21:22–55. Topography, agriculture, and soils in high plains region of Montana.

Brown, R. H. (1933), Belle Fourche valleys and uplands, *Annals A.A.G.*, 23:127–164.

Brown, R. H. (1934), Irrigation in a dry-farming region, *Geog. Rev.*, 24:596–604. Montana.

Bowman, I. (1935), Our expanding and contracting desert, *Geog. Rev.*, 25:43–61.

Crowe, P. R. (1936), The rainfall regime of the Western Plains, *Geog. Rev.*, 26:463–484.

Lackey, E. E. (1937), Annual-variability rainfall maps of the Great Plains, *Geog. Rev.*, 27:665–670.

Thornthwaite, C. W. (1941), Climate and settlement in the Great Plains, *Yearbook of Agriculture, 1941*, U.S. Dept. Agriculture, pp. 177–196.

Bryan, K., and C. C. Albritton (1943), Soil phenomena as evidence of climate change, *Am. J. Sci.*, 241:469–490.

Nuttonson, M. Y. (1947), Agroclimatology and crop ecology of the Ukraine and climatic analogues in North America, *Geog. Rev.*, 37:216–232.

Bretz, J. H., and L. Horberg (1949), Caliche in southeastern New Mexico, *J. Geol.*, 57:491–511.

Borchert, J. R. (1950), The climate of the central North American grassland, *Annals A.A.G.*, 40, pp. 1–39.

Leopold, L. B. (1951), Vegetation of southwestern watersheds in the nineteenth century, *Geog. Rev.*, 41:295–316.

Villmow, J. R. (1956), The nature and origin of the Canadian dry belt, *Annals A.A.G.*, 46:211–232.

White, G. F., ed. (1956), The future of arid lands, *Am. Assoc. Advancement of Sci. Publ.* 43, Washington, D. C., 453 pp.

Zierer, C. M., ed. (1956), *California and the southwest*, John Wiley and Sons, New York, 376 pp.

Jaeger, E. C. (1957), *The North American deserts*, Stanford Univ. Press, 308 pp.

Weaver, J. E., and F. W. Albertson (1957), *Grasslands of the Great Plains*, Johnsen Publishing Co., Lincoln, Nebr., 395 pp.

HUMID CONTINENTAL CLIMATE

Brooks, C. F. (1917), New England snowfall, *Geog. Rev.*, 2:222–240.

Kindle, E. M. (1922), Notes on the forests of southeastern Labrador, *Geog. Rev.*, 12:57–71.

Kincer, J. B. (1923), The climate of the Great Plains as a factor in their utilization, *Annals A.A.G.*, 13:67–80.

Durand, L., Jr., and K. Bertrand (1935), The forest and woodland regions of Wisconsin, *Geog. Rev.*, 25:264–271.

Church, P. E. (1936), A geographical study of New England temperatures, *Geog. Rev.*, 26:283–292.

Rose, J. K. (1936), Corn yield and climate in the corn belt, *Geog. Rev.*, 26:88–102.

McCune, S. (1941), Climatic regions of Korea and their economy, *Geog. Rev.*, 31:95–99.

Sauer, C. O. (1941), The settlement of the humid East, *Yearbook of Agriculture, 1941*, U.S. Dept. Agriculture, pp. 157–176.

Forbes, C. B. (1942), Snowfall in Maine, *Geog. Rev.*, 32:245–251.

Manley, G. (1945), The effective rate of altitudinal change in temperate Atlantic climates, *Geog. Rev.*, 35:408–417.

Calef, W. (1950), The winter of 1948–49 in the Great Plains, *Annals, A.A.G.*, 40:267–292.

CHAPTER 15

SUBARCTIC CLIMATE

Alcock, F. J. (1916), The Churchill River, *Geog. Rev.*, 2:433–448.

Kindle, E. M. (1920), Arrival and departure of winter conditions in the Mackenzie River basin, *Geog. Rev.*, 10:388–399.

Novakovsky, S. (1922), Climatic provinces of the Russian far East in relation to human activities, *Geog. Rev.*, 12:100–115.

Kindle, E. M. (1925), The James Bay coastal plain, *Geog. Rev.*, 15:226–236.

Bell, J. M. (1929), Great Slave Lake, *Geog. Rev.*, 19:556–580.

Albright, W. D. (1933), Crop growth at high latitudes, *Geog. Rev.*, 23:608–620.

Albright, W. D. (1933), Gardens of the Mackenzie, *Geog. Rev.*, 23:1–22.

Soper, J. D. (1939), Wood Buffalo Park, *Geog. Rev.*, 29:383–399.

Rockie, W. A. (1942), A picture of Matanuska, *Geog. Rev.*, 32:353–371.

Raup, H. M. (1945), Forests and gardens along the Alaska Highway, *Geog. Rev.*, 35:22–48.

Sanderson, M. (1948), Drought in the Canadian Northwest, *Geog. Rev.*, 38:289–299.

Hare, F. K. (1950), Climate and zonal divisions of the boreal forest formation in eastern Canada, *Geog. Rev.*, 40:615–635.

Imanishi, K. (1950) Ecological observations on the Great Khingan expedition, *Geog. Rev.*, 40:236–253.

Smeds, H. (1950), The Replot Skerry Guard: emerging islands in the northern Baltic, *Geog. Rev.*, 40:103–133.

Benninghoff, W. S. (1952), Interaction of vegetation and soil frost pehnomena, *Arctic*, 5:34–44.

Hare, F. K. (1952), The Labrador frontier, *Geog. Rev.*, 42:405–424.

TUNDRA CLIMATE

Flaherty, R. J. (1918), Two traverses across Ungava Peninsula, Labrador, *Geog. Rev.*, 6:116–132.

Hall, H. U. (1918), A Siberian wilderness: native life on the Lower Yenisei, *Geog. Rev.*, 5:1–21.

Rabot, Chas. (1919), The Norwegians in Spitsbergen, *Geog. Rev.*, 8:209–226.

Holtedahl, O. (1922), Novaya Zemlya, a Russian arctic land, *Geog. Rev.*, 12:521–531.

Smith, P. S. (1925), Explorations in northwestern Alaska, *Geog. Rev.*, 15:237–254.

Transehe, N. A. (1925), The Siberian Sea road, *Geog. Rev.*, 15:367–398.

Hobbs, W. H. (1927), The first Greenland expedition of the University of Michigan, *Geog. Rev.*, 17:1–35.

Ekblaw, W. E. (1927, 1928), The material response of the polar Eskimo to their far arctic environment, *Annals A.A.G.*, 17:147–198; 18:1–24.

Putnam, G. P. (1928), The Putnam Baffin Island expedition, *Geog. Rev.*, 18:1–40.

Soper, J. D. (1930), Explorations in Foxe Peninsula and along the west coast of Baffin Island, *Geog. Rev.*, 20:397–424.

Wheeler, E. P. (1935), The Nain-Okak section of Labrador, *Geog. Rev.*, 25:240–254.

Porsild, A. E. (1938), Earth mounds in unglaciated arctic northwestern America, *Geog. Rev.*, 28:46–58.

Adams, J. Q. (1941), Settlements of the northeastern Canadian arctic, *Geog. Rev.*, 31:112–126.

Sharp, R. P. (1942), Ground-ice mounds in tundra, *Geog. Rev.*, 32:417–423.

Sharp, R. P. (1942), Soil structures in the St. Elias Range, Yukon Territory, *J. Geomorphology*, 5:274–301.

Taber, S. (1943), Perennially frozen ground in Alaska: its origin and history, *Geol. Soc. Am. Bull.*, 54:1433–1548.

Department of Transport, Air Services Branch, Meteorological Division (1944), *Meteorology of the Canadian arctic*, Ottawa, Canada, 85 pp.

Cabot, E. C. (1947), The northern Alaska coastal plain interpreted from aerial photographs, *Geog. Rev.*, 37:639–648.

Washburn, A. L. (1947), Reconnaissance geology of portions of Victoria Island and adjacent regions, arctic Canada, *Geol. Soc. Am. Memoir* 22, 142 pp.

Jenness, J. L. (1949), Permafrost in Canada, *Arctic*, 2:13–27.

Black, R. F. (1950), Permafrost, Chapter 14 of *Applied sedimentation*, edited by P. D. Trask, John Wiley and Sons, New York, pp. 247–275.

Rae, R. W. (1951), Joint arctic weather project, *Arctic*, 4:18–26.

Ray, L. L. (1951), Permafrost, *Arctic*, 4:196–203.

Flint, R. F. (1952), The Ice Age in the North American arctic, *Arctic*, 3:135–152.

Jenness, J. L. (1952), Erosive forces in the physiography of western arctic Canada, *Geog. Rev.*, 42:238–252.

Black, R. F. (1954), Permafrost—a review, *Geol. Soc. Am. Bull.*, 65:839–856.

Hopkins, D. M., and T. N. V. Karlstrom (1954), Permafrost and ground water in Alaska, *U.S. Geol. Survey Prof. Paper* 264–F, 34 pp.

Mercer, J. H. (1956), Geomorphology and glacial history of southernmost Baffin Island, *Geol. Soc. Am. Bull.*, 67:553–570.

Washburn, A. L. (1956), Classification of patterned ground and review of suggested origins, *Geol. Soc. Am. Bull.*, 67:823–866.

Jenness, J. L. (1957), *Dawn in arctic Alaska*, University of Minnesota Press, Minneapolis, 222 pp.

ICECAP CLIMATE

Isachsen, G. (1929), Modern whaling in the antarctic, *Geog. Rev.*, 19:387–403.

Wilkins, H. (1929), The Wilkins-Hearst antarctic expedition, 1928–1929, *Geog. Rev.*, 19:353–376.

Mawson, D. (1930), The antarctic cruise of the "Discovery," *Geog. Rev.*, 20:535–554.

Wilkins, H. (1930), Further antarctic explorations, *Geog. Rev.*, 20:357–388.

Gould, L. M. (1931), Some geographical results of the Byrd antarctic expedition, *Geog. Rev.*, 21:177–200.

Byrd, R. E., and H. E. Saunders (1933), The flight to Marie Byrd Land, *Geog. Rev.*, 23:177–209.

Zubov, N. N., (1933), The circumnavigation of Franz Josef Land, *Geog. Rev.*, 23:394–401.

Wade, F. A. (1937), Some geographical results of the second Byrd antarctic expedition, 1933–1935. Part II. Northeastern borderlands of the Ross Sea, *Geog. Rev.*, 27:584–597.

Wade, F. A. (1946), Wartime investigation of the Greenland ice cap and its possibilities, *Geog. Rev.*, 36:452–473.

Ronne, F. (1948), Ronne antarctic research expedition, 1946–1948, *Geog. Rev.*, 38:355–391.

Ronne, F. (1949), *Antarctic conquest*, G. P. Putnam's Sons, New York, 299 pp.

Arctic Institute of North America (1955), Arctic research, edited by D. Rowley, *Arctic*, 7:117–375; also reprinted as *Special Publ.* 2. Status of research in the North America arctic and subarctic, including physical, biological, and social sciences.

Giaever, J. (1955), *The white desert*, E. P. Dutton and Co., New York, 256 pp.

American Geophysical Union (1956), Antarctica in the International Geophysical Year, Nat. Acad. Sci., Nat. Research Council, Washington, D. C., *Publ.* 462, 133 pp.

Dufek, G. J. (1957), *Operation Deepfreeze*, Harcourt, Brace and Co., New York, 243 pp.

Gould, L. M. (1957), Antarctic prospect, *Geog. Rev.*, 47:1–28.

Petrov, V. P. (1959), Soviet expeditions in Antarctica, *Professional Geographer*, 11, No. 3:6–10.

HIGHLAND CLIMATES, EFFECTS OF ALTITUDE

Huntington, E. (1905), The mountains of Turkestan, *Geog. J.*, 25:139–158.

Bowman, I. (1916), *The Andes of Peru*, Henry Holt and Co., New York, 336 pp.

Bowman, I. (1916), The country of the shepherds, *Geog. Rev.*, 1:419–442.

Harshberger, J. W. (1919), Alpine fell-fields of eastern North America, *Geog. Rev.*, 7:233–255.

Atwood, W. W. (1927), Utilization of the rugged San Juans, *Econ. Geog.*, 3:193–209.

Miller, O. M. (1929), The 1927–28 Peruvian expedition of the American Geographic Society, *Geog. Rev.*, 19:1–37.

Peattie, R. (1929), Andorra: A study in mountain geography, *Geog. Rev.*, 19:218–233.

Troll, K. (1929), An expedition to the Central Andes, *Geog. Rev.*, 19:234–247.

Anon. (1930), Forest and range resources of Utah: their protection and use, *U.S. Dept. Agriculture Misc. Publ.* 90, 101 pp.

Pearson, G. A. (1931), Forest types in the southwest as determined by climate and soil, *U.S. Dept. Agriculture Tech. Bull.* 247, 144 pp.

Antevs, E. (1932), *Alpine zone of Mt. Washington Range*, Merrill and Webber Co., Auburn, Maine, 118 pp.

Platt, R. S. (1932), Six farms in the Central Andes, *Geog. Rev.*, 22:245–259.

Monahan, R. S. (1933), *Mt. Washington reoccupied*, Stephen Daye Press, Brattleboro, Vt., 270 pp.

Garnett, A. (1935), Insolation, topography, and settlement in the Alps, *Geog. Rev.*, 25:601–617.

Peattie, R. (1936), *Mountain geography. A critique and field study*, Harvard Univ. Press, Cambridge, Mass., 257 pp.

Seifriz, W. (1936), Vegetation zones in the Caucasus, *Geog. Rev.*, 26:59–66.

Deffontaines, P. (1937), Mountain settlement in the central Brazilian Plateau, *Geog. Rev.*, 27:394–413.

Hanson-Lowe, J. (1941), Notes on the climate of the South Chinese-Tibetan borderland, *Geog. Rev.*, 31:444–453.

Ives, R. L. (1942), The beaver-meadow complex, *J. Geomorphology*, 5:191–203.

Hunt, T. L. (1947), Weather conditions on Kilimanjaro, *Weather*, 2:338–344.

Spencer, J. E., and W. L. Thomas (1948), The hill stations and summer resorts of the Orient, *Geog. Rev.*, 38:637–651.

Miller, D. H. (1955), Snow cover and climate in the Sierra Nevada, California, *Univ. of California Publ. in Geography*, Vol. 11, Berkeley, 218 pp.

Drewes, W. U., and A. T. Drewes (1957), *Climate and related phenomena of the eastern Andean slopes of central Peru*, Syracuse Univ. Research Institute, Syracuse, 85 pp.

CHAPTER 16

SOIL SCIENCE

Ramann, E. (1928), *The evolution and classification of soils*, W. Heffer and Sons, Cambridge, England, 125 pp.

Joffe, J. S. (1936), *Pedology*, Rutgers Univ. Press, New Brunswick, N. J., 575 pp.

Robinson, G. W. (1936), *Soils; their origin, constitution, and classification*, 3rd ed. (1950), John Wiley and Sons, New York, 573 pp. Out of print.

U.S. Dept. Agriculture (1938), Soils and man, *Department of Agriculture Yearbook, 1938*, U.S. Govt. Printing Office, Washington, D. C., 1232 pp. Contains many papers of interest on various phases of soil science.

Nikiforoff, C. C. (1939), Weathering and soil evolution, *Soil Science*, 67:219–230.

Jenny, H. (1941), *Factors of soil formation*, McGraw-Hill Book Co., New York, 281 pp.

Kellogg, C. E. (1941), *The soils that support us*, The Macmillan Co., New York, 370 pp.

Bryan, K., and C. Albritton, Jr. (1943), Soil phenomena as evidence of climatic changes, *Am. J. Sci.*, 241:469–490.

Lyon, T. L., and H. O. Buckman (1943), *The nature and properties of soils*, 4th ed., The Macmillan Co., New York, 499 pp.

Nikiforoff, C. C. (1943), Introduction to paleopedology, *Am. J. Sci.*, 241:194–200.

Kelley, W. P. (1946), Modern concepts of soil science, *Soil Science*, 62:469–476.

Kirkaldy, J. F. (1948), Soil and weather, *Weather*, 3:225–231.

Nikiforoff, C. C. (1948), Stony soils and their classification, *Soil Science*, 66:347–363.

Muckenhirn, R. J., E. P. Whiteside, E. H. Templin, R. F. Chandler, Jr., and L. T. Alexander (1949), Soil classification and the genetic factors of soil formation, *Soil Science*, 67:93–106.

Kellogg, C. E. (1950), Soil, *Scientific American*, 185:30–39.

Carter, G. F., and Pendleton, R. L. (1956), The humid soil: process and time, *Geog. Rev.*, 46:488–507.

Albrecht, W. A. (1957), Soil fertility and biotic geography, *Geog. Rev.*, 47:86–105.

CHAPTER 17

SOIL GROUPS

Marbut, C. F. (1925), The rise, decline and revival of Malthusianism in relation to geography and character of soils, *Annals A.A.G.*, 15:1–29.

Glinka, K. D. (1927), *The great soil groups of the world and their development* (tr. by C. F. Marbut), Edwards Brothers, Ann Arbor, Mich., 235 pp.

Wolfanger, L. A. (1929), Major soil groups and some of their geographic implications, *Geog. Rev.*, 19:94–113.

Dachnowski-Stokes, A. P. (1934), Peat-land utilization, *Geog. Rev.*, 24:238–250.

Kellogg, C. E. (1941), Climate and soil, *Yearbook of Agriculture, 1941*, U.S. Dept. Agriculture, pp. 265–291.

Thorp, J. (1948), How soils develop under grass, *Yearbook of American Agriculture, 1948*, U.S. Dept. Agriculture, pp. 55–66.

Thorp, J., and G. D. Smith (1949), Higher categories of soil classification: order, suborder and great soil groups, *Soil Science*, 67:117–126.

GREAT SOIL GROUPS OF THE UNITED STATES

Marbut, C. F. (1923), Soils of the Great Plains, *Annals A.A.G.*, 13:41–66.

Wolfanger, L. A. (1930), *The major soil divisions of the United States*, John Wiley and Sons, New York, 150 pp. Out of print.

Marbut, C. F. (1931), Russia and the United States in the world's wheat market, *Geog. Rev.*, 21:1–21. Chernozem and chestnut soils.

Thorp, J. (1931), The effects of vegetation and climate upon soil profiles in northern and northeastern Wyoming, *Soil Science*, 32:283–302.

Wolfanger, L. A. (1931), Economic geography of the gray-brownerths of the eastern United States, *Geog. Rev.*, 21:276–296.

Marbut, C. F. (1935), Soils of the United States. Part III of *Atlas of American Agriculture*, U.S. Govt. Printing Office, Washington, D. C., 29 pp.

Kellogg, C. E. (1936), Development and significance of the great soil groups of the United States, *U.S. Dept. Agriculture Misc. Publ.* 229, 40 pp.

Nikiforoff, C. C. (1937), The inversion of great soil zones in western Washington, *Geog. Rev.*, 27:200–213.

Foscue, F. J. (1938), Influence of contrasted soil types upon changing land values near Grapevine, Texas, *Annals A.A.G.*, 28:137–144.

Strong, H. M. (1938), A land use record in blackland prairies of Texas, *Annals A.A.G.*, 28:128–136.

Thorp, J., and M. Baldwin (1940), Laterite in relation to soils of the tropics, *Annals A.A.G.*, 30:163–194.

GREAT SOIL GROUPS OF FOREIGN COUNTRIES

Harrison, J. B. (1910), The residual earths of British Guiana commonly termed "laterite," *Geol. Mag.*, 7:553–562.

Marbut, C. F., and C. B. Manifold (1926), The soils of the Amazon Basin in relation to agricultural possibilities, *Geog. Rev.*, 16:414–442.

Bennett, H. H. (1928), Some geographic aspects of Cuban soils, *Geog. Rev.*, 18:62–82.

Strahorn, A. T. (1929), Agriculture and soils of Palestine, *Geog. Rev.*, 19:581–602.

Taylor, G. (1933), The soils of Australia in relation to topography and climate, *Geog. Rev.*, 23:108–113.

Moyer, R. T. (1936), Agricultural soils in a loess region of North China, *Geog. Rev.*, 26:414–425.

Pendleton, R. L. (1941), Laterite and its structural uses in Thailand and Cambodia, *Geog. Rev.*, 31:177–202.

Powers, W. L. (1945), Soil development and land use in northern Venezuela, *Geog. Rev.*, 35:273–285.

Goldich, S. S., and H. R. Bergquist (1948), Aluminous lateritic soil of the Republic of Haiti, W. I., *U.S. Geol. Survey Bull.* 954-C, pp. 99–109.

Smith, R. (1949), A comparison of the reddish chestnut soils of the United States with the redbrown earth of Australia, *Soil Science*, 67:209–218.

CHAPTER 18

GENERAL GEOMORPHOLOGY

Davis, W. M. (1909), *Geographical essays*, Ginn and Co., Boston, 777 pp. Reprinted in 1954, Dover Publications, New York.

Geikie, J. (1909), *Earth sculpture, or the origin of landforms*, 2nd ed., John Murray, London, 320 pp.

Davis, W. M. (1915), The principles of geographical description, *Annals A.A.G.*, 5:61–105.

deMartonne, E. (1927), *A shorter physical geography*, A. A. Knopf, New York, 338 pp.

Hobbs, W. H. (1931), *Earth features and their meaning*, The Macmillan Co., New York, 517 pp.

Wooldridge, S. W., and R. S. Morgan (1937), *The physical*

basis of geography, Longmans, Green and Co., London, 445 pp.

Lobeck, A. K. **(1939)**, *Geomorphology*, McGraw-Hill Book Co., New York, 731 pp.

Worcester, P. G. **(1939)**, *A textbook of geomorphology*, D. Van Nostrand Co., New York, 565 pp.

Cotton, C. A. **(1941)**, *Landscape as developed by processes of normal erosion*, Cambridge Univ. Press, Cambridge, England, 301 pp.

Cotton, C. A. **(1942)**, *Climatic accidents in landscape-making*, Whitcombe and Tombs, Christchurch, New Zealand, 354 pp.

von Engeln, O. D. **(1942)**, *Geomorphology*, The Macmillan Co., New York, 655 pp.

Hinds, N. E. A. **(1943)**, *Geomorphology, the evolution of landscape*, Prentice-Hall, Englewood Cliffs, N. J., 894 pp.

Cotton, C. A. **(1949)**, *Geomorphology*, John Wiley and Sons, New York, 505 pp. Out of print.

Thornbury, W. D. **(1954)**, *Principles of geomorphology*, John Wiley and Sons, New York, 618 pp.

Shimer, J. A. **(1959)**, *The sculptured earth: the landscape of America*, Columbia Univ. Press, New York, 255 pp.

TOPOGRAPHIC MAPS

Salisbury, R. D., and W. W. Atwood **(1908)**, The interpretation of topographic maps, *U.S. Geol. Survey Prof. Paper* 60, U.S. Govt. Printing Office, Washington, D. C.

Birdseye, C. H. **(1928)**, *Topographic instructions of the U.S. Geological Survey*, U.S. Govt. Printing Office, Washington, D. C., 432 pp.

Raisz, E., and J. Henry **(1937)**, An average slope map of southern New England, *Geog. Rev.*, 27:467–472.

Cozzens, A. B. **(1940)**, An angle of slope scale, *J. Geomorphology*, 3:52–56.

Brown, C. B. **(1941)**, Mapping Lake Mead, *Geog. Rev.*, 31:385–405.

Wright, J. K. **(1942)**, Map makers are human, *Geog. Rev.*, 32:527–544.

Lobeck, A. K., and W. J. Tellington **(1944)**, *Military maps and air photographs*, McGraw-Hill Book Co., New York, 256 pp.

Platt, R. R. **(1945)**, Official topographic maps: a world index, *Geog. Rev.*, 35:175–181.

Am. Geog. Soc. **(1946)**, The Map of Hispanic America on the scale of 1:1,000,000, *Geog. Rev.*, 36:1–28.

Tanaka **(1950)**, The relief contour method of representing topography on maps, *Geog. Rev.*, 40:444–456.

Low, J. W. **(1952)**, *Plane table mapping*, Harper and Bros., New York, 365 pp.

Calef, W., and R. Newcomb **(1953)**, An average slope map of Illinois, *Annals A.A.G.*, 43:305–316.

Lobeck, A. K. **(1956)**, *Things maps don't tell us*, The Macmillan Co., New York, 159 pp.

Robinson, A. H. **(1956)**, mapping the land, *Scientific Monthly*, 82, No. 6:294–303.

PERSPECTIVE DIAGRAMS, RELIEF MODELS

Lobeck, A. K. **(1924)**, *Block diagrams*, John Wiley and Sons, New York, 206 pp. Reprinted 1958, with revisions, by Emerson Trussell Book Co., Amherst, Mass.

Raisz, E. **(1931)**, The physiographic method of representing scenery on maps, *Geog. Rev.*, 21:297–304.

Reed, H. P. **(1946)**, The development of the terrain model in the war, *Geog. Rev.*, 36:632–652.

King, P. B., and E. M. McKee **(1949)**, Terrain diagrams of the Philippine Islands, *Geol. Soc. Am. Bull.*, 60:1829–1836.

Hammond, E. H. **(1954)**, Small-scale continental landform maps, *Annals A.A.G.*, 44:33–42.

Robinson, A. H., and N. J. W. Thrower **(1957)**, A new method of terrain representation, *Geog. Rev.*, 47:507–520.

Stacy, J. R. **(1958)**, Terrain diagrams in isometric projection—simplified, *Annals A.A.G.*, 48:232–236.

AIR PHOTOGRAPHS, AERIAL MAPPING

Matthes, G. H. **(1926)**, Oblique aerial surveying in Canada, *Geog. Rev.*, 16:568–582.

Birdseye, C. H. **(1940)**, Stereoscopic phototopographic mapping, *Annals A.A.G.*, 30:1–24.

Smith, H. T. U. **(1941)**, Aerial photographs in geomorphic studies, *J. Geomorphology*, 4:172–205.

Smith, H. T. U. **(1943)**, *Aerial photographs and their applications*, Appleton-Century Co., New York, 372 pp.

Raisz, E. **(1951)**, The use of air photos for landform maps, *Annals A.A.G.*, 41:324–330.

MacFadden, C. H. **(1952)**, The uses of aerial photographs in geographic research, *Photogrammetric Engineering*, Sept. 1952, pp. 732–737. Also in *Outside readings in geography*, Crowell Co., New York, 1955, pp. 49–57.

Walker, F. **(1953)**, *Geography from the air*, Methuen and Co., London, 111 pp.

Institut Géographique National **(1956)**, *Relief form atlas*, Paris, France, 179 pp. Maps and air photographs of representative geomorphic types in France and North Africa.

Monkhouse, F. J. **(1959)**, *Landscape from the air*. Cambridge Univ. Press, New York, 53 pp.

Stone, K. H. **(1959)**, World air photo coverage, *Professional Geographer*, 11; No. 3:2–6.

CHAPTER 19

ROCKS

Shand, S. J. **(1931)**, *The study of rocks*, Thomas Murby and Co., London, 236 pp.

Davison, E. H. **(1938)**, *Field determination of rocks*, Chapman and Hall, London, 87 pp.

Fenton, C. L., and M. A. Fenton **(1940)**, *The rock book*, Doubleday, Doran and Co., New York, 357 pp.

Loomis, F. B. **(1948)**, *Field book of common rocks and minerals*, G. P. Putnam's Sons, New York, 352 pp.

Spock, L. E. **(1953)**, *Guide to the study of rocks*, Harper and Bros., New York, 256 pp.

Fritzen, D. K. **(1959)**, *The rock-hunter's field manual*, Harper and Bros., New York, 200 pp.

GENERAL GEOLOGY

Mather, K. F. **(1932)**, *Old mother earth*, Harvard Univ. Press, Cambridge, Mass., 177 pp.

Croneis, C. G., and W. C. Krumbein **(1936)**, *Down to earth*, Univ. Chicago Press, Chicago, 501 pp.

Shand, S. J. (1938), *Earth-lore*, E. P. Dutton and Co., New York, 144 pp.

Mather, K. F., and S. L. Mason (1939), *A source book in geology*, McGraw-Hill Book Co., New York, 702 pp.

Garrels, R. M. (1951), *A textbook of geology*, Harper and Bros., New York, 511 pp.

Leet, L. D., and S. Judson (1954), *Physical geology*, Prentice-Hall, Englewood Cliffs, N. J., 466 pp.

Emmons, W. H., G. A. Thiel, C. R. Stauffer, and J. S. Allison (1955), *Geology, principles and processes*, McGraw-Hill Book Co., New York, 638 pp.

Longwell, C. R., and R. F. Flint (1955), *Introduction to physical geology*, John Wiley and Sons, New York, 432 pp.

Dunbar, C. O., and J. Rodgers (1957), *Principles of stratigraphy*, John Wiley and Sons, New York, 356 pp.

Low, J. W. (1957), *Geologic field methods*, Harper and Bros., New York, 489 pp.

Gilluly, J., A. Waters, and A. O. Woodford (1958), *Principles of geology*, Freeman and Co., San Francisco, 631 pp.

CHAPTER 20

EARTH'S INTERIOR AND CRUST

Bowie, W. (1922), The earth's crust and isostasy, *Geog. Rev.*, 12:613–627.

Jeffreys, H. (1950), *Earthquakes and mountains*, Methuen and Co., London, 191 pp.

Bullen, K. E. (1955), The interior of the earth, *Scientific American*, 193, No. 3:56–61.

Kay, M. (1955), The origin of continents, *Scientific American*, 193, No. 3:62–66.

Jacobs, J. A., R. D. Russell, and J. T. Wilson (1959), *Physics and geology*, McGraw-Hill Book Co., New York, 424 pp.

SUBMARINE GEOLOGY AND TOPOGRAPHY

Shepard, F. P. (1933), Submarine valleys, *Geog. Rev.*, 23:77–89.

Davis, W. M. (1934), Submarine mock valleys, *Geog. Rev.*, 24:297–308.

Shepard, F. P., and C. N. Beard (1938), Submarine canyons: distribution and longitudinal profiles, *Geog. Rev.*, 28:439–451.

Johnson, D. (1939), *The origin of submarine canyons*, Columbia Univ. Press, New York, 126 pp.

Smith, P. A. (1939), Atlantic submarine valleys of the United States, *Geog. Rev.*, 29:648–652.

Stetson, H. C. (1940), Depositional environments of sedimentary rocks, *Geog. Rev.*, 30:480–484.

Murray, H. W. (1941), Submarine mountains in the Gulf of Alaska, *Geol. Soc. Am. Bull.*, 52:333–362.

Betz, F., and H. H. Hess (1942), The floor of the North Pacific Ocean, *Geog. Rev.*, 32:99–116.

Murray, H. W. (1945), Profiles of the Aleutian trench, *Geol. Soc. Am. Bull.*, 56:757–782.

Hess, H. H. (1946), Drowned ancient islands of the Pacific basin, *Am. J. Sci.*, 244:772–791.

Shepard, F. P. (1948), *Submarine geology*, Harper and Bros., New York, 348 pp.

Emery, K. O. (1949), Topography and sediments of the Arctic basin, *J. Geol.* 57:512–521.

Kuenen, Ph. H. (1950), *Marine geology*, John Wiley and Sons, New York, 568 pp.

Ericson, D. B., M. Ewing, and B. C. Heezen (1951), Deep-sea sands and submarine canyons, *Geol. Soc. Am. Bull.*, 62:961–966.

Tolstoy, I., (1951), Submarine topography in the North Atlantic, *Geol. Soc. Am. Bull.*, 62:441–450.

Shepard, F. P. (1952), Composite origin of submarine canyons, *J. Geol.*, 60:84–96.

Dietz, R. S. (1953), Possible deep-sea turbidity current channels in the Indian Ocean, *Geol. Soc. Am. Bull.*, 64:375–377.

Hamilton, E. L. (1956), Sunken islands of the mid-Pacific mountains, *Geol. Soc. Am. Bull.*, Memoir 64, 97 pp.

Hamilton, E. L. (1957), The last geographic frontier: the sea floor, *Scientific Monthly*, 85:294–314.

Guilcher, A. (1958), *Coastal and submarine morphology*, John Wiley and Sons, New York, 274 pp.

Heezen, B. C., M. Tharp, and M. Ewing (1959), The floors of the oceans, Geol. Soc. Am., *Special Paper* 65, 122 pp.

Shepard, F. P. (1959), *The earth beneath the sea*, The Johns Hopkins Press, Baltimore, 288 pp.

HISTORICAL GEOLOGY

Dunbar, C. O. (1949), *Historical geology*, John Wiley and Sons, New York, 567 pp.

Moore, R. C. (1958), *Introduction to historical geology*, 2nd ed., McGraw-Hill Book Co., New York, 656 pp.

CHAPTER 21

GENERAL HYDROLOGY; HYDROLOGIC CYCLE

Holzman, B. (1937), Sources of moisture for precipitation for the United States, *U.S. Dept. Agriculture Tech. Bull.* 589, U.S. Govt. Printing Office, Washington, D. C., 41 pp.

Meinzer, O. E., ed. (1942), Hydrology, Vol. IX of *Physics of the earth*, McGraw-Hill Book Co., New York, 712 pp.

Foster, E. E. (1949), *Rainfall and runoff*, The Macmillan Co., New York, 487 pp.

Johnstone, D., and W. P. Cross (1949), *Elements of applied hydrology*, The Ronald Press Co., New York, 276 pp.

Wisler, C. O., and E. F. Brater (1949), *Hydrology*, John Wiley and Sons, New York, 419 pp.

Colman, E. A. (1953), *Vegetation and watershed management*, The Ronald Press Co., New York, 412 pp.

Ackerman, W. C., E. A. Colman, and H. O. Ogrosky (1955), From ocean to sky to land to ocean, *Yearbook of Agriculture, 1955*, U.S. Dept. Agriculture, pp. 41–51.

Thornthwaite, C. W., and J. R. Mather (1955), The water balance, *Publications in climatology*, 8, No. 1, Laboratory of Climatology, Centerton, N. J., 104 pp.

Subrahmanyam, V. P. (1956), The water balance of India according to Thornthwaite's concept of evapotranspiration, *Annals A.A.G.*, 46:300–311.

SOIL WATER

Bernstein, L. (1955), The needs and uses of water by plants, *Yearbook of Agriculture, 1955*, U.S. Dept. Agriculture, pp. 18–25.

Fletcher, H. C., and H. B. Elmendorf (1955), Phreatophytes —a serious problem in the West, *Yearbook of Agriculture, 1955*. U.S. Dept. Agriculture, pp. 423–429.

Haise, H. R. (1955), How to measure the moisture in the soil, *Yearbook of Agriculture, 1955*, U.S. Dept. Agriculture, pp. 362–371.

Musgrave, G. W. (1955), How much rain enters the soil? *Yearbook of Agriculture, 1955*, U.S. Dept. Agriculture, pp. 151–159.

Richards, L. A. (1955), Retention and transmission of water in soil, *Yearbook of Agriculture, 1955*, U.S. Dept. of Agriculture, pp. 144–151.

Thornthwaite, C. W., and J. R. Mather (1955), The water budget and its use in irrigation, *Yearbook of Agriculture, 1955*, U.S. Dept. Agriculture, pp. 346–358.

Wadleigh, C. H. (1955), Soil moisture in relation to plant growth, *Yearbook of Agriculture, 1955*, U.S. Dept. Agriculture, pp. 358–361.

GROUND WATER

Bryan, Kirk (1919), Classification of springs, *J. Geol.*, 27:522–561.

Meinzer, O. E. (1923), The occurrence of ground water in the United States with a discussion of principles, U.S. Geol. Survey, *Water Supply Paper* 489, 321 pp.

Stearns, H. T. (1936), Origin of large springs and their alcoves along the Snake River in southern Idaho, *J. Geol.*, 44:429–450.

Tolman, C. F. (1937), *Ground water*, McGraw-Hill Book Co., New York, 593 pp.

Hubbert, M. K. (1940), Theory of ground water motion, *J. Geol.*, 43:708–728.

Guyton, W. F. (1946), Artificial recharge of glacial sand and gravel with filtered river water at Louisville, Kentucky, *Econ. Geol.*, 41:644–658.

Thomas, H. E. (1951), *The conservation of ground water*, McGraw-Hill Book Co., New York, 321 pp.

Gregor, H. F. (1952), The Southern California water problem in the Oxnard area, *Geog. Rev.*, 42:16–36.

Halpenny, L. C., et al (1952), *Ground water in the Gila River basin and adjacent areas, Arizona; a summary*, U.S. Geol. Survey, Washington, D. C., 224 pp.

Meigs, P. (1952), Water problems in the United States, *Geog. Rev.*, 42:346–366.

Garver, H. L. (1955), Water supplies for homes in the country, *Yearbook of Agriculture, 1955*, U.S. Dept. Agriculture, pp. 655–663.

Muckel, D. C. (1955), Pumping ground water so as to avoid overdraft, *Yearbook of Agriculture*, 1955, U.S. Dept. Agriculture, pp. 294–301.

Muckel, D. C. and L. Schiff (1955), Replenishing ground water by spreading, *Yearbook of Agriculture, 1955*, U.S. Dept. Agriculture, pp. 302–310.

Parker, G. G. (1955), The encroachment of salt water into fresh, *Yearbook of Agriculture, 1955*, U.S. Dept. Agriculture, pp. 615–635.

Rohwer, C. (1955), Wells and pumps for irrigated lands, *Yearbook of Agriculture, 1955*, U.S. Dept. Agriculture, pp. 285–295.

Thomas, H. E. (1956), Changes in quantities and qualities of ground and surface waters, pp. 542–563 of *Man's role in changing the face of the earth*, Univ. of Chicago Press, Chicago, 1193 pp.

Cressey, G. B. (1957), Water in the desert, *Annals A.A.G.*, 47:105–124.

Todd, D. K. (1959), *Ground water hydrology*, John Wiley and Sons, New York, 336 pp.

CHAPTER 22

WEATHERING PROCESSES AND FORMS

Gilbert, G. K. (1904), Domes and dome structures of the High Sierras, *Geol. Soc. Am. Bull.*, 15:29–36.

Barton, D. C. (1916), Notes on the disintegration of granite in Egypt, *J. Geol.*, 24:382–393.

Cvijić, J. (1924), The evolution of lapiés, *Geog. Rev.*, 14:26–49.

Blackwelder, E. (1925), Exfoliation as a phase of rock weathering, *J. Geol.*, 33:793–806.

Blackwelder, E. (1927), Fire as an agent in rock weathering, *J. Geol.*, 35:134–140.

Blackwelder, E. (1929), Cavernous rock surfaces of the desert, *Am. J. Sci.*, 17:393–399.

Taber, S. F. (1929), Frost heaving, *J. Geol.*, 37:428–461.

Matthes, F. E. (1930), Geologic history of Yosemite Valley, *U.S. Geol. Survey Prof. Paper* 160, 137 pp. See pp. 114–116.

Taber, S. (1930), The mechanics of frost heaving, *J. Geol.*, 38:303–317.

Blackwelder, E. (1933), The insolation hypothesis of rock weathering, *Am. J. Sci.*, 26:97–113.

Crickmay, G. F. (1935), Granite pedestal rocks in the southern Appalachian Piedmont, *J. Geol.*, 43:745–758.

Balk, R. (1939), Disintegration of glaciated cliffs, *J. Geomorphology*, 2:305–334.

Chapman, R. W. (1940), Monoliths in the White Mountains of New Hampshire, *J. Geomorphology*, 3:302–310.

Smith, L. L. (1941), Weather pits in granite of the southern Piedmont, *J. Geomorphology*, 4:117–127.

Jahns, R. H. (1943), Sheet structure in granites: its origin and uses as a measure of glacial erosion, *J. Geol.*, 51:71–98.

White, W. A. (1945), Origin of granite domes in the southeastern Piedmont, *J. Geol.*, 53:276–282.

Reiche, P. (1950), *A survey of weathering processes and products*, Univ. of New Mexico Press, 95 pp.

MASS WASTING

Dawson, G. M. (1899), Remarkable landslip in Portneuf County, Quebec, *Geol. Soc. Am. Bull.*, 10:484–490.

Andersson, J. G. (1906), Solifluction, a component of subaerial denudation, *J. Geol.*, 14:91–112.

Howe, E. (1909), Landslides in the San Juan Mountains. *U.S. Geol. Survey Prof. Paper* 67; 58 pp.

Capps, S. R., Jr. (1910), Rock glaciers in Alaska, *J. Geol.*, 18:359–375.

Blackwelder, E. (1912), The Gros Ventre slide, an active earth-flow, *Geol. Soc. Am. Bull.*, 23:487–492.

Daly, R. A., W. G. Miller, and G. S. Rice (1912), Report of the Commission appointed to investigate Turtle Mountain, Frank, Alberta, Canada; Dept. Mines, Geol. Survey Branch, Ottawa, *Memoir 27*, 34 pp.

Allix, A. (1924), Avalanches, *Geog. Rev.*, 14:519–560.

Blackwelder, E. (1928), Mudflows as a geologic agent in semi-arid mountains, *Geol. Soc. Am. Bull.*, 39:465–480.

Sharpe, C. F. S. (1938), *Landslides and related phenomena*, Columbia Univ. Press, New York, 137 pp. A general treatise on all forms of mass wasting.

Putnam, W. C., and R. P. Sharp (1940), Landslides and earthflows near Ventura, Southern California, *Geog. Rev.*, 30:591–600.

Strahler, A. N. (1940), Landslides of the Vermilion and Echo Cliffs, northern Arizona, *J. Geomorphology*, 3:285–296.

Ives, R. L. (1941), Vegetative indications of solifluction, *J. Geomorphology*, 4:128–132.

Kesseli, J. E. (1941), Rock streams in the Sierra Nevada, California, *Geog. Rev.*, 31:203–227.

Blackwelder, E. (1942), The process of mountain sculpture by rolling debris, *J. Geomorphology*, 5:325–328.

Sharp, R. P. (1942), Mudflow levees, *J. Geomorphology*, 5:222–227.

Sharpe, C. F. S. (1942), Relation of soil-creep to earthflow in the Appalachian Plateaus, *J. Geomorphology*, 5:312–324.

Wentworth, C. K. (1943), Soil avalanches on Oahu, Hawaii, *Geol. Soc. Am. Bull.*, 54:53–64.

Wagner, W. T. (1944), A landslide area in the Little Salmon River Canyon, Idaho, *Econ. Geol.*, 39:349–358.

Terzaghi, K. (1950), Mechanism of landslides, Geol. Soc. Am., *Berkey Vol.*, pp. 83–123.

Sharp, R. P., and L. H. Nobles (1953), Mudflow of 1941 at Wrightwood, Southern California, *Geol. Soc. Am. Bull.*, 64:547–560.

CHAPTER 23

RUNOFF

Goldthwait, J. W. (1928), The gathering of floods in the Connecticut River system, *Geog. Rev.*, 18:428–445.

Hoyt, W. G. (1936), Rainfall and runoff in the United States, *U.S. Geol. Survey Prof. Paper* 772, Washington, D. C., 301 pp.

Corbett, D. M., and others (1943), Stream-gaging procedure, U.S. Geol. Survey, *Water Supply Paper*, 888, 245 pp.

Hoover, M. D. (1944), Effect of removal of forest vegetation upon water yields, *Trans. Am. Geophysical Union*, 25:969–977.

Foster, E. E. (1948), *Rainfall and runoff*, the Macmillan Co., New York, 487 pp.

Wilm, H. G., and E. G. Dunford (1948), Effect of timber cutting on water available for stream flow from a lodgepole pine forest, *U.S. Dept. Agriculture Tech. Bull.*, 968, U.S. Govt. Printing Office, Washington, D. C., 43 pp.

Langbein, W., and others (1949), Annual runoff in the United States, *U.S. Geol. Survey Circular* 52.

Linsley, R. K., M. A. Kohler, and J. L. H. Paulhus (1949), *Applied hydrology*, McGraw-Hill Book Co., New York, 698 pp.

Fowler, F. J. (1950), Some problems of water distribution between East and West Punjab, *Geog. Rev.*, 40:583–599.

Colman, E. A. (1953), Vegetation and watershed management, The Ronald Press Co., New York, 412 pp.

Borchert, J. R. (1954), The surface water supply of American municipalities, *Annals A.A.G.*, 44:15–32.

Langbein, W. B., and J. V. B. Wells (1955), The water in the rivers and creeks, *Yearbook of Agriculture, 1955*, U.S. Dept. Agriculture, pp. 52–62.

Van Burkalow, A. (1959), The geography of New York City's water supply: a study of interactions, *Geog. Rev.*, 49:369–386.

SOIL EROSION, SOIL CONSERVATION

Lowdermilk, W. C., and J. R. Smith (1927), Notes on the problem of field erosion, *Geog. Rev.*, 17:226–235.

Bennett, H. H. (1928), The geographical relation of soil erosion to land productivity, *Geog. Rev.*, 18:579–605.

Shaw, C. F. (1929), Erosion pavement, *Geog. Rev.*, 19:638–641.

Reeds, C. A. (1930), Land erosion, *Nat. Hist.*, 30:131–149.

Bennett, H. H. (1931), The problem of soil erosion in the United States, *Annals A.A.G.*, 21:147–170.

Forsling, C. L. (1932), Erosion on uncultivated lands in the intermountain region, *Scientific Monthly*, 34:311–321.

Bennett, H. H. (1933), The quantitative study of erosion technique and some preliminary results, *Geog. Rev.*, 23:423–432.

Sharpe, C. F. S. (1938), What is soil erosion? *U.S. Dept. Agriculture Misc. Publ.* 286, 85 pp.

Rockie, W. A. (1939), Man's effects on the Palouse, *Geog. Rev.*, 29:34–45.

Tieh, T. M. (1941), Soil erosion in China, *Geog. Rev.*, 31:570–590.

Bennett, H. H. (1943), Adjustment of agriculture to its environment, *Annals A.A.G.*, 33:163–198.

Bennett, H. H. (1944), Food comes from soil, *Geog. Rev.*, 34:57–76.

Cumberland, K. B. (1944), Contrasting regional morphology of soil erosion in New Zealand, *Geog. Rev.*, 34:77–95.

Gottschalk, L. C., and V. H. Jones (1955), Valleys and hills, erosion and sedimentation, *Yearbook of Agriculture, 1955*, U.S. Dept. Agriculture, pp. 135–143.

Osborn, B. (1955), How rainfall and runoff erode soil, *Yearbook of Agriculture, 1955*, U.S. Dept. Agriculture, pp. 127–135.

Leopold, L. B. (1956), Land use and sediment yield, pp. 639–647 of *Man's role in changing the face of the earth*, Univ. of Chicago Press, Chicago, 1193 pp.

Strahler, A. N. (1956), The nature of induced erosion and aggradation, pp. 621–638 of *Man's role in changing the face of the earth*, Univ. of Chicago Press, Chicago, 1193 pp.

FLOODS

Brooks, C. F., and A. H. Thiessen (1937), The meteorology of the great floods in the eastern United States, *Geog. Rev.*, 27:269–290.

Barrows, H. K. (1948), *Floods, their hydrology and control*, McGraw-Hill Co., New York, 432 pp.

Leopold, L. B., and T. Maddock, Jr. (1954), *Big dams, little dams, and land management*, The Ronald Press Co., New York, 278 pp.

Leopold, L., and T. Maddock, Jr. (1954), The flood control controversy. The Ronald Press Co., New York, 255 pp.

Brown, C. B., and W. T. Murphy (1955), Conservation begins on the watersheds, *Yearbook of Agriculture, 1955*, U.S. Dept. Agriculture, pp. 161–165.

Ford, E. C., W. L. Cowan, and H. N. Holtan (1955), Floods—and a program to alleviate them, *Yearbook of Agriculture, 1955*, U.S. Dept. Agriculture, pp. 170–176.

Heard, W. L., and V. B. MacNaughton (1955), The Yazoo-Little Tallahatchie flood prevention project, *Yearbook of Agriculture, 1955*, U.S. Dept. Agriculture, pp. 199–205.

Hoyt, W. G., and W. B. Langbein (1955), *Floods*, Princeton Univ. Press, Princeton, N. J., 469 pp.

Kautz, H. M. (1955), The story of Sandstone Creek watershed, *Yearbook of Agriculture, 1955*, U.S. Dept. Agriculture, pp. 210–218.

Matson, H. O., W. L. Heard, G. E. Lamp, and D. M. Ilch (1955), The possibilities of land treatment in flood prevention, *Yearbook of Agriculture, 1955*, U.S. Dept. Agriculture, pp. 176–179.

Storey, H. C. (1955), Frozen soil and spring and winter floods, *Yearbook of Agriculture, 1955*, U.S. Dept. Agriculture, pp. 179–184.

Bordne, E. (1957), Some hydrologic aspects of the flood of August, 1955, in a Connecticut valley, *Geog. Rev.*, 47:211–223.

CHAPTER 24

STREAM CHANNELS; EQUILIBRIUM PROFILES

Gilbert, G. K. (1914), The transportation of debris by running water, *U.S. Geol. Survey Prof. Paper* 86, 263 pp.

Johnson, D. (1929), Baselevel, *J. Geol.*, 37:575–582.

Johnson, D. (1932), Streams and their significance, *J. Geol.*, 40:481–497.

Mackin, J. H. (1948), Concept of the graded river, *Geol. Soc. Am. Bull.*, 59:463–512.

Holmes, C. D. (1952), Stream competence and the graded stream profile, *Am. J. Sci.*, 250:899–906.

Leopold, L. B., and T. Maddock, Jr. (1953), The hydraulic geometry of stream channels and some physiographic implications, *U.S. Geol. Survey Prof. Paper* 252, 57 pp.

Wolman, M. G. (1955), The natural channel of Brandywine Creek, Pa., *U.S. Geol. Survey Prof. Paper* 271, 56 pp.

Leopold, L. B., and J. P. Miller (1956), Ephemeral streams—hydraulic factors and their relation to the drainage net, *U.S. Geol. Survey Prof. Paper* 282-A, 37 pp.

Hack, J. T. (1957), Studies of longitudinal stream profiles in Virginia and Maryland, *U.S. Geol. Survey Prof. Paper* 294-B, 97 pp.

Miller, J. P. (1958), *High mountain streams: effects of geology on channel characteristics and bed materials*, State Bureau Mines and Mineral Technology, N. M. Inst. Mining and Tech., Socorro, N. M., 53 pp.

GORGES, CANYONS, FALLS

Powell, J. W. (1875), *Exploration of the Colorado River of the West and its tributaries*, U.S. Govt. Printing Office, Washington, D. C., 291 pp.

Gilbert, G. K. (1895), Niagara Falls and their history, *Nat. Geog. Mag.*, Monograph 1, pp. 203–236. Also in *The Physiography of the United States* (1896), American Book Co., New York, pp. 203–236.

Darton, N. H. (1896), Examples of stream robbing in the Catskill Mountains, *Geol. Soc. Am. Bull.*, 7:505–507.

Davis, W. M. (1903), The stream contest along the Blue Ridge, *Geog. Soc. Phila. Bull.*, 3:213–244.

Dellenbaugh, F. S. (1908), *A canyon voyage*, G. P. Putnam's Sons, New York, 277 pp.

Bowman, I. (1912), The canyon of the Urubamba, *Am. Geog. Soc. Bull.*, 44:881–897.

Freeman, O. W. (1938), The Snake River Canyon, *Geog. Rev.*, 28:597–608.

ALLUVIAL RIVERS; FLOOD PLAINS

Brown, R. M. (1906), The protection of the alluvial basin of the Mississippi, *Pop. Sci. Monthly*, 69:248–256.

Davis, W. M. (1913), Meandering valleys and underfit rivers, *Annals A.A.G.*, 3:3–28.

Macar, P. F. (1934), Effects of cut-off meanders on the longitudinal profiles of streams, *J. Geol.* 42:523–536.

Melton, F. A. (1936), An empirical classification of floodplain streams, *Geog. Rev.*, 26:593–609.

Happ, S. C., G. Rittenhouse, and G. C. Dobson (1940), Some principles of accelerated stream and valley sedimentation, *U.S. Dept. Agriculture Tech. Bull.* 695, 134 pp.

Fisk, H. N. (1944), *Geological investigation of the alluvial valley of the lower Mississippi*, U.S. Army Corps of Engineers (Mississippi River Commission), 78 pp.

Fisk, H. N. (1947), *Fine-grained alluvial deposits and their effects on Mississippi River activity*, U.S. Army Corps of Engineers, Waterways Experiment Station, Vicksburg, Miss., 82 pp.

Matthes, G. H. (1951), Paradoxes of the Mississippi, *Scientific American*, 184, No. 4:19–23.

Dury, G. H. (1954), Contribution to the general theory of meandering valleys, *Am. J. Sci.*, 252:193–224.

Russell, R. J. (1954), Alluvial morphology of Anatolian rivers, *Annals A.A.G.*, 44:363–391.

Leopold, L. B., and M. G. Wolman (1957), River channel patterns: braided, meandering and straight, *U.S. Geol. Survey, Prof. Paper* 282-B, Washington, D. C., 47 pp.

Wolman, M. G., and L. B. Leopold (1957), River flood plains: some observations on their formation, *U.S. Geol. Survey Prof. Paper* 282-C, 109 pp.

ALLUVIAL FANS

Eckis, R. (1928), Alluvial fans of the Cucamonga district, southern California, *J. Geol.*, 36:224–247. Describes the area shown in Exercise 6, Chapter 24.

Chawner, W. D. (1955), Alluvial fan flooding. The Montrose, California, flood of 1934, *Geog. Rev.*, 25:255–263.

TERRACES

Davis, W. M. (1902), River terraces in New England,

Museum Comp. Zool. Bull., 38:281–346. Also in *Geographical essays* (1909), Ginn and Co., Boston, pp 514–586.

Trewartha, G. T. (1932), The Prairie du Chien Terrace: geography of a confluence site, *Annals A.A.G.*, 22:119–158.

Cotton, C. A. (1940), Classification and correlation of river terraces, *J. Geomorphology*, 3:27–37.

DELTAS

Sykes, G. (1926), The delta and estuary of the Colorado River, *Geog. Rev.*, 16:232–255.

Cressey, G. B. (1935), The Fenghsien landscape: a fragment of the Yangtze delta, *Geog. Rev.*, 25:396–413.

Russell, R. J. (1936), Physiography of the Lower Mississippi delta, Louisiana Conservation Dept., *Bull.* 8; 3–199.

Sykes, G. (1937), The Colorado delta, *Am. Geog. Soc. Special Publ.* 19, 193 pp.

Russell, R. J. (1942), Flotant, *Geog. Rev.*, 32:74–98. Floating marshes of Mississippi delta region.

Russell, R. J. (1942), Geomorphology of the Rhône delta, *Annals A.A.G.*, 32:149–254.

Dobby, E. H. G. (1951), The Kelantan delta, *Geog. Rev.*, 41:226–255.

INTRENCHED MEANDERS AND NATURAL BRIDGES

Cleland, H. F. (1910–11), The formation of North American natural bridges, *Pop. Sci. Monthly*, 78:417–427; *Geol. Soc. Am. Bull.*, 21:313–338.

Rich, J. L. (1914), Certain types of stream valleys and their meaning, *J. Geol.*, 22:469–497.

Miser, H. D., K. W. Trimble, and S. Paige (1923), Rainbow Bridge, Utah, *Geog. Rev.*, 13:518–531.

Mahard, R. H. (1942), Origin and significance of intrenched meanders, *J. Geomorphology*, 5:32–44.

Strahler, A. N. (1946), Elongate intrenched meanders of Conodoguinet Creek, Pa., *Am. J. Sci.*, 244:31–40.

CHAPTER 25

CYCLE IN HUMID CLIMATE

Gilbert, G. K. (1877), *Geology of the Henry Mountains*, U.S. Geog. and Geol. Survey, Rocky Mt. Region (Powell). See land sculpture, pp. 99–150.

Davis, W. M. (1899), The geographical cycle, *J. Geog.*, 14:481–504. Also in *Geographical essays* (1909), Ginn and Co., Boston, pp. 249–278.

Rich, J. L. (1917), Cultural features and the physiographic cycle, *Geog. Rev.*, 4:297–308.

Davis, W. M. (1923), The scheme of the erosion cycle, *J. Geol.*, 31:10–25.

Johnson, D. W. (1929), Baselevel, *J. Geol.*, 37:775–782.

Glock, W. S. (1931), The development of drainage systems; a synoptic view, *Geog. Rev.*, 21:475–482.

Johnson, D. (1933), Development of drainage systems and the dynamic cycle, *Geog. Rev.*, 23:114–121.

Fenneman, N. M. (1936), Cyclic and non-cyclic aspects of erosion, *Geol. Soc. Am. Bull.*, 47:173–186.

Bryan, K. (1940), The retreat of slopes, *Annals A.A.G.*, 30:254–268.

Peltier, L. (1950), The geographic cycle in periglacial

regions as it is related to climatic geomorphology, *Annals A.A.G.*, 40:214–236.

Strahler, A. N. (1950), Equilibrium theory of erosional slopes approached by frequency distribution analysis, *Am. J. Sci.*, 248:673–696, 800–814.

Penck, W. (1953), *Morphological analysis of land forms*, Macmillan and Co., London, 429 pp.

PENEPLAINS

Davis, W. M. (1896), Plains of marine and subaerial denudation, *Geol. Soc. Am. Bull.*, 7:377–398. Also in *Geographical essays* (1909), Ginn and Co., Boston, pp. 323–349.

Davis, W. M. (1899), The peneplain, *Am. Geologist*, 23:207–239. Also in *Geographical essays* (1909), Ginn and Co., Boston, pp. 350–380.

Davis, W. M. (1902), Base-level, grade, and peneplain, *J. Geol.*, 10:77–111. Also in *Geographical essays* (1909), Ginn and Co., Boston, pp. 381–412.

Davis, W. M. (1911), The Colorado Front Range, *Annals A.A.G.*, 1:21–83.

Johnson, D. (1916), Plains, planes, and peneplanes, *Geog. Rev.*, 1:443–447.

Davis, W. M. (1922), Peneplains and the geographic cycle, *Geol. Soc. Am. Bull.*, 23:587–598.

Ward, F. (1930), The role of solution in peneplanation, *J. Geol.* 38:262–270.

Rich, J. L. (1938), Recognition and significance of multiple erosion surfaces, *Geol. Soc. Am. Bull.*, 49:1695–1722.

Meyerhoff, H. A. (1940), Migration of erosion surfaces, *Annals A.A.G.*, 30:247–254.

Dixey, F. (1944), African landscape, *Geog. Rev.*, 34:457–465. Erosion surfaces and peneplains of Africa.

QUANTITATIVE ANALYSIS OF FLUVIALLY ERODED LANDSCAPES

Horton, R. E. (1945), Erosional development of streams and their drainage basins; hydrophysical approach to quantitative morphology, *Geol. Soc. Am. Bull.*, 56:275–370.

Langbein, W. B., and others (1947), Topographic characteristics of drainage basins, U.S. Geol. Survey, *Water Supply Paper* 968-C, 157 pp.

Smith, K. G. (1950), Standards of grading texture of erosional topography, *Am. Jour. Sci.*, 248:655–668.

Strahler, A. N. (1952), Hypsometric (area-altitude) analysis of erosional topography, *Geol. Soc. Am. Bull.*, 63:1117–1142.

Strahler, A. N. (1954), Statistical analysis in geomorphic research, *J. Geol.*, 62:1–25.

Schumm, S. A. (1956), Evolution of drainage systems and slopes in badlands at Perth Amboy, N. J., *Geol. Soc. Am. Bull.*, 67:597–646.

Strahler, A. N. (1956), Quantitative slope analysis, *Geol. Soc. Am. Bull.*, 67:571–596.

Chorley, R. J. (1957), Climate and morphometry, *J. Geol.* 65:628–638.

Melton, M. A. (1957), Geometric properties of mature drainage basins and their representation in a E_4 phase space, *J. Geol.*, 66:35–54.

Strahler, A. N. (1957), Quantitative analysis of watershed

geomorphology, *Trans. Am. Geophysical Union*, 38:913–920.

Morisawa, M. **(1958)**, Measurement of drainage-basin outline form, *J. Geol.*, 66:587–591.

Strahler, A. N. **(1958)**, Dimensional analysis applied to fluvially eroded landforms, *Geol. Soc. Am. Bull.*, 69:279–300.

CYCLE IN ARID CLIMATE; PEDIMENTS

McGee, W J **(1897)**, Sheetflood erosion, *Geol. Soc. Am. Bull.*, 8:87–112.

Davis, W. M. **(1905)**, The geographical cycle in an arid climate, *J. Geol.*, 13:381–407. Also in *Geographical essays* **(1909)**, Ginn and Co., Boston, pp. 296–322.

Paige, S. **(1912)**, Rock-cut surfaces of the desert ranges, *J. Geol.*, 20:442–450.

Lawson, A. C. **(1915)**, The epigene profiles of the desert, Univ. of Calif. Publ., *Geology*, 9:23–48.

Davis, W. M. **(1930)**, Rock floors in arid and humid climates, *J. Geol.*, 38:1–27, 136–158.

Blackwelder, E. **(1931)**, Desert plains, *J. Geol.*, 39:133–140.

Fenneman, N. M. **(1931)**, *Physiography of Western United States*, McGraw-Hill Book Co., New York. See pp. 326–333, 340–348.

Johnson, D. **(1931)**, Planes of lateral corrasion, *Science*, n. ser., 73:174–177.

Johnson, D. **(1932)**, Rock plains of arid regions, *Geog. Rev.*, 22:656–665.

Bagnold, R. A. **(1933)**, A further journey through the Libyan Desert, *Geog. J.*, 82:103–129, 211–235.

Willis, B. **(1934)**, Inselbergs, *Annals A.A.G.*, 24:123–129.

Rich, J. L. **(1935)**, Origin and evolution of rock fans and pediments, *Geol. Soc. Am. Bull.*, 46:999–1024.

Davis, W. M. **(1938)**, Sheetfloods and streamfloods, *Geol. Soc. Am. Bull.*, 49:1337–1416.

Peel, R. F. **(1941)**, Denudational landforms of the central Libyan Desert, *J. Geomorphology*, 4:3–23.

Howard, A. D. **(1942)**, Pediments and the pediment pass problem, *J. Geomorphology*, 5:3–31, 95–136.

Childs, O. E. **(1948)**, Geomorphology of the Little Colorado River, Arizona, *Geol. Soc. Am. Bull.*, 59:353–388.

Tator, B. A. **(1952)**, Pediment characteristics and terminology, *Annals A.A.G.*, 42:295–317 and 43:47–53.

CHAPTER 26

ALPINE GLACIERS

Russell, I. C. **(1897)**, *Glaciers of North America*, Ginn and Co., Boston, 210 pp.

Hobbs, W. H. **(1911)**, *Characteristics of existing glaciers*, The Macmillan Co., New York, 289 pp.

Tarr, R. S. **(1912)**, Glaciers and glaciation of Alaska, *Annals A.A.G.*, 2:3–24.

Boyd, L. A. **(1932)**, Fiords of East Greenland, *Geog. Rev.*, 22:529–561.

Field, W. O., Jr. **(1932)**, The glaciers of the northern part of Prince William Sound, Alaska, *Geog. Rev.*, 22:361–388.

Cooper, W. S. **(1937)**, The problem of Glacier Bay, Alaska, a study of glacier variations, *Geog. Rev.*, 27:37–62.

Field, W. O., Jr. **(1937)**, Observations on Alaskan coastal glaciers in 1935, *Geog. Rev.*, 27:63–81.

Lewis, W. V. **(1940)**, The function of meltwater in cirque formation, *Geog. Rev.*, 30:64–83.

Sharp, R. P. **(1947)**, The Wolf Creek glaciers, St. Elias Range, Yukon Territory, *Geog. Rev.*, 37:26–52.

Dyson, J. L. **(1948)**, Shrinkage of Sperry and Grinnell glaciers, Glacier National Park, Montana, *Geog. Rev.*, 38:95–103.

Sharp, R. P. **(1948)**, The constitution of valley glaciers, *J. Glaciology*, 1:182–189.

Matthes, F. E. **(1949)**, Glaciers, Chapter 5, in Hydrology, Vol. IX of *Physics of the earth*, Dover Publ. Co., New York, pp. 149–219.

Field, W. O., Jr., and M. M. Miller **(1950)**, The Juneau Ice Field research project, *Geog. Rev.* 40:179–190.

Lawrence, D. B. **(1950)**, Glacier fluctuation for six centuries in southeastern Alaska and its relation to solar activity, *Geog. Rev.*, 40:191–223.

Sharp, R. P. **(1951)**, Accumulation and ablation on the Seward-Malaspina glacier system, Canada-Alaska, *Geol. Soc. Am. Bull.*, 62:725–744.

Field, W. O., Jr., and C. J. Heusser **(1952)**, Glaciers—historians of climate, *Geog. Rev.* 42:337–345.

Nye, J. F. **(1952)**, The mechanics of glacier flow, *J. Glaciology*, 2:81–93.

Sharp, R. P. **(1954)**, Glacier flow: a review, *Geol. Soc. Am. Bull.*, 65:821–838.

Field, W. O., Jr., **(1955)**, *Scientific American*, 193, No. 3:84–92.

Sharp, R. P. **(1958)**, The latest major advance of Malaspina Glacier, Alaska, *Geog. Rev.*, 48:16–26.

LANDFORMS OF ALPINE GLACIATION

Davis, W. M. **(1906)**, The sculpture of mountains by glaciers, *Scot. Geog. Mag.*, 22:76–89. Also in *Geographical essays* **(1909)**, Ginn and Co., Boston, pp. 617–634.

Atwood, W. W. **(1907)**, The glaciation of the Uinta Mountains, *J. Geol.*, 15:790–804.

Atwood, W. W. **(1909)**, Glaciation of the Uinta and Wasatch Mountains, *U.S. Geol. Survey Prof. Paper* 61, 96 pp. Describes the area shown in Exercise 2.

Davis, W. M. **(1920)**, Features of glacial origin in Montana and Idaho, *Annals A.A.G.*, 10:75–148.

Martin, L., and F. E. Williams **(1924)**, An ice-eroded fiord, *Geog. Rev.*, 14:576–596.

Matthes, F. E. **(1930)**, Geologic history of the Yosemite Valley, *U.S. Geol. Survey Prof. Paper* 160. See pp. 45–97.

Forbes, A. **(1932)**, Surveying in northern Labrador, *Geog. Rev.*, 22:30–60.

Hubbard, G. D. **(1932)**, The geography of residence in Norway fiord areas, *Annals A.A.G.*, 22:109–118.

Matthes, F. E. **(1950)**, *The incomparable valley; a geological interpretation of the Yosemite*, edited by F. Fryxell, Univ. of California Press, Berkeley, 160 pp.

Nichols, R. L., and M. M. Miller **(1951)**, Glacial geology of the Ameghino Valley, Lago Argentino, Patagonia, *Geog. Rev.*, 41:274–294.

Dyson, J. L. **(1952)**, Ice-ridged moraines and their relation to glaciers, *Am. J. Sci.*, 250:204–211.

ICECAPS

Gould, L. M. (1935), The Ross Ice Shelf, *Geol. Soc. Am. Bull.*, 46:1367–1394.

Demorest, M. (1943), Ice sheets, *Geol. Soc. Am. Bull.*, 54:363–400.

Katz, H. R. (1953), Journey across the Nunataks of central East Greenland, *Arctic* 6:3–14.

Neuburg, H. A. C., et al (1959), The Filchner Ice Shelf, *Annals A.A.G.*, 49:110–119.

PLEISTOCENE GLACIATION

Meinzer, O. E. (1922), Map of Pleistocene lakes of the Basin-and-Range Province and its significance, *Geol. Soc. Am. Bull.*, 33:541–552.

Coleman, A. P. (1926), *Ice ages recent and ancient*, The Macmillan Co., New York, 296 pp.

Reeds, C. A. (1929), Weather and glaciation, *Geol. Soc. Am. Bull.*, 40:597–629.

Wright, W. B. (1937), *The Quaternary Ice Age*, Macmillan and Co., London, 478 pp.

Flint, R. F. (1943), Origin of the former North American ice sheet, *Geog. Rev.*, 33:479–481.

Flint, R. F., and others (1945), Glacial map of North America, Geol. Soc. Am., *Special Paper* 60, 37 pp. Pt. 1, Glacial map; Pt. 2, Explanatory notes.

Colbert, E. H., and others (1948), Pleistocene of the Great Plains, *Geol. Soc. Am. Bull.*, 59:541–630.

Upson, J. E. (1949), Late Pleistocene and recent changes of sea level along the coast of Santa Barbara County, California, *Am. J. Sci.* 247:94–115.

Carter, G. F. (1950), Evidence for Pleistocene man in Southern California, *Geog. Rev.*, 40:84–102.

Menard, H. W. (1953), Pleistocene and Recent sediment from the floor of the northeastern Pacific Ocean, *Geol. Soc. Am. Bull.*, 64:1279–1294.

Emiliani, C. (1955), Pleistocene temperatures, *J. Geol.*, 63:538–578.

Ewing, M., and W. L. Donn (1956), A theory of ice ages, *Science*, 123:1061–1066.

Plass, G. N. (1956), Carbon dioxide and the climate, *American Scientist*, 4:302–316.

Carter, G. F. (1957), *Pleistocene man at San Diego*, The Johns Hopkins Press, Baltimore, 400 pp.

Flint, R. F. (1957), *Glacial and Pleistocene geology*, John Wiley and Sons, New York, 553 pp.

Sauer, C. O. (1957), The end of the ice age and its witnesses, *Geog. Rev.*, 47:29–43.

Geol. Assn. of Canada (1958), Glacial map of Canada, Toronto, Ontario. Scale 1:3,801,600. 50 × 62 inches.

Hough, J. L. (1958), *Geology of the Great Lakes*, Univ. of Illinois Press, Urbana, 313 pp.

LANDFORMS OF CONTINENTAL GLACIATION

Chamberlin, T. C. (1888), Rock-scorings of the great ice invasion, U.S. Geol. Survey, *7th Ann. Rept.*, pp. 147–248.

Alden, W. C. (1905), The drumlins of southeastern Wisconsin, *U.S. Geol. Survey Bull.*, 273, 46 pp.

Davis, C. A. (1907), Peat, Mich. State Board of Geol. Survey, *Rept. of 1906*, Lansing, 395 pp.

Fairchild, H. L. (1907), Drumlins of central western New York, *N. Y. State Museum Bull.*, 111:391–443.

Whitbeck, R. H. (1913), Economic aspects of glaciation in Wisconsin, *Annals A.A.G.*, 3:62–87.

von Engeln, O. D. (1914), Effects of continental glaciation on agriculture, *Am. Geog. Soc. Bull.*, 46:241–264, 336–355.

Thwaites, F. T. (1926), The origin and significance of pitted outwash, *J. Geol.*, 34:308–319.

Flint, R. F. (1928), Eskers and crevasse fillings, *Am. J. Sci.*, 5th ser., 15:410–416.

Flint, R. F. (1929), The stagnation and dissipation of the last ice sheet, *Geog. Rev.*, 19:256–289.

Flint, R. F. (1930), The classification of glacial deposits, *Am. J. Sci.*, 19:169–176.

Flint, R. F. (1930), The origin of the Irish "eskers," *Geog. Rev.*, 20:615–630.

Brown, T. C. (1931), Kames and kame terraces of central Massachusetts, *Geol. Soc. Am. Bull.*, 42:467–479.

Cotton, C. A. (1942), *Climatic accidents in landscape making*, Whitcombe & Tombs, Christchurch, N. Z., 354 pp.

von Engeln, O. D. (1945), Glacial diversion of drainage, *Annals A.A.G.*, 35:79–120.

Gravenor, C. P. (1951), Bedrock source of tills in southwestern Ontario, *Am. J. Sci.*, 249:66–71.

Gravenor, C. P. (1953), The origin of drumlins, *Am. J. Sci.*, 251:674–681.

Horberg, L. and R. C. Anderson (1956), Bedrock topography and Pleistocene glacial lobes in central United States, *J. Geol.* 64:101–116.

CHAPTER 27

GENERAL PRINCIPLES AND CLASSIFICATION

Gilbert, G. K. (1890), Lake Bonneville, *U.S. Geol. Survey Monograph* 1. See pp. 29–65.

Cotton, C. A. (1916), Fault coasts of New Zealand, *Geog. Rev.*, 1:20–33.

Cotton, C. A. (1918), The outline of New Zealand, *Geog. Rev.*, 6:320–340.

Johnson, D. W. (1919), *Shore processes and shoreline development*, John Wiley and Sons, New York, 584 pp. Out of print.

Sharp, H. S. (1929), The physical history of the Connecticut shoreline, State of Connecticut, Geol. and Nat. Hist. Survey, *Bull.* 46, 97 pp.

Putnam, W. C. (1937), The marine cycle of erosion for a steeply sloping shoreline of emergence, *J. Geol.*, 45:844–850.

Shepard, F. P. (1937), Revised classification of marine shorelines, *J. Geol.*, 45:602–624.

Lucke, J. (1938), Marine shorelines reviewed, *J. Geol.* 46:985–995.

Steers, J. A. (1946), *The coastline of England and Wales*, Cambridge Univ. Press, New York, 644 pp.

Shepard, F. P. (1948), *Submarine geology*, Harper and Bros., New York, 348 pp.

Kuenen, Ph. H. (1950), *Marine geology*, John Wiley and Sons, New York, 568 pp.

Davis, J. H. (1956), Influences of man upon coast lines, pp. 504–521 of *Man's role in changing the face of the earth*, Univ. of Chicago Press, Chicago, 1193 pp.

Guilcher, A. (1958), *Coastal and submarine morphology*, John Wiley and Sons, New York, 274 pp.

McGill, J. T. (1958), Map of coastal landforms of the world (with separate map), *Geog. Rev.*, 48:402–405.

WAVE EROSION

Davis, W. M. (1923), The Halligs, vanishing islands of the North Sea, *Geog. Rev.*, 13:99–106.

Howard, A. D. (1939), Hurricane modification of the offshore bar of Long Island, New York, *Geog. Rev.*, 29:400–415.

Jutson, J. T. (1939), Shore platforms near Sydney, N.S.W., *J. Geomorphology*, 2:236–250.

Brown, C. W. (1939), Hurricanes and shore-line changes in Rhode Island, *Geog. Rev.*, 29:416–430.

Edwards, A. B. (1941), Storm-wave platforms, *J. Geomorphology*, 4:223–236.

Munk, W. H., and M. A. Traylor (1947), Refraction of ocean waves: a process linking underwater topography to beach erosion, *J. Geol.*, 40:1–26.

Wengerd, S. (1951), Elevated strandlines of Frobisher Bay, Baffin Island, Canadian Arctic, *Geog. Rev.*, 41:622–637.

BEACHES, BARS, SPITS

Shaler, N. S. (1895), Beaches and tidal marshes of the Atlantic coast, *Nat. Geog. Soc. Monograph* 1, pp. 137–168.

Davis, W. M. (1896), The outline of Cape Cod, *Am. Acad. Arts and Sci. Proc.*, 31:303–332. Also in *Geographical essays* (1909), Ginn and Co., Boston, pp. 690–724.

Johnson, D. W., and W. G. Reed (1910), The form of Nantasket Beach, Mass., *J. Geol.*, 18:162–189.

Patton, R. S. (1931), Moriches Inlet: a problem in beach evolution, *Geog. Rev.*, 21:627–632.

Hitchcock, C. B. (1934), The evolution of tidal inlets, *Geog. Rev.*, 24:653–654.

Russell, R. J., and H. V. Howe (1935), Cheniers of southwestern Louisiana, *Geog. Rev.*, 25:449–461.

Evans, O. F. (1942), The origin of spits, bars, and related structures, *J. Geol.*, 50:846–865.

Grant, U. S. (1943), Waves as a sand-transporting agent, *Am. J. Sci.*, 241:117–123.

Krumbein, W. C. (1950), Geological aspects of beach engineering, Geol. Soc. Am., *Berkey Vol.*, pp. 195–223.

Zeigler, J. M., C. R. Hayes, and S. D. Tuttle (1959), Beach changes on outer Cape Cod, Massachusetts, *J. Geol.*, 67:318–336.

CORAL REEFS, ATOLLS, MANGROVE COASTS

Dana, J. D. (1874), *Corals and coral islands*, Dodd and Mead, New York, 406 pp.

Darwin, C. (1898), *The structure and distribution of coral reefs*, 3rd ed., Appleton and Co., New York, 344 pp.

Davis, W. M. (1916), Problems associated with the study of coral reefs, *Scientific Monthly*, 2:313–333, 479–501, 557–572.

Davis, W. M. (1922), The barren reef of Tagula, New Guinea, *Annals A.A.G.*, 12:97–151.

Davis, W. M. (1928), The coral reef problem, *Am. Geog. Soc. Special Publ.* 9, 596 pp.

Stearns, H. T. (1946), An integration of coral-reef hypotheses, *Am. J. Sci.*, 244:772–791.

Emery, K. O. (1948), Submarine geology of Bikini atoll, *Geol. Soc. Am. Bull.*, 59:855–860.

Teichert, C., and R. W. Fairbridge (1948), Some coral reefs of the Sahul Shelf, *Geog. Rev.*, 38:222–249.

Murphy, R. E. (1950), The economic geography of a Micronesian atoll, *Annals A.A.G.*, 40:58–83.

West, C. (1956), Mangrove swamps of the Pacific coast of Colombia, *Annals A.A.G.*, 46:98–121.

Wiens, H. J. (1959), Atoll development and morphology, *Annals A.A.G.*, 49:31–54.

CHAPTER 28

DEFLATION, ABRASION

Udden, J. A. (1896), Dust and sand storms in the West, *Pop. Sci. Monthly*, 49:656–664.

Hobbs, W. H. (1917), The erosional and degradational processes of desert depressions, *Annals A.A.G.*, 7:25–60.

Bryan, K. (1923), Wind erosion near Lee's Ferry, *Am. J. Sci.*, 5th ser., 6:291–307.

Blackwelder, E. (1931), The lowering of playas by deflation, *Am. J. Sci.*, 5th ser., 21:140–144.

Page, L. R., and R. W. Chapman (1933), The dust fall of Dec. 15–16, 1933, *Am. J. Sci.*, 5th ser., 28:288–297.

Blackwelder, E. (1934), Yardangs, *Geol. Soc. Am. Bull.*, 45:159–166.

Kellogg, C. E. (1935), Soil blowing and dust storms, *U.S. Dept. Agriculture Misc. Publ.* 221, 11 pp.

King, L. C. (1936), Wind-faceted stones from Marlborough, New Zealand, *J. Geol.* 44:201–213.

Sharp, R. P. (1949), Pleistocene ventifacts east of the Big Horn Mountains, Wyoming, *J. Geol.*, 57:175–195.

Higgins, C. G. (1956), Formation of small ventifacts, *J. Geol.*, 64:506–516.

DUNES

Bradwell, H. J. L. (1910), The sand dunes of the Libyan Desert, *Geog. J.*, 35:379–395.

Cressey, G. B. (1928), The Indian sand dunes and shore lines of the Lake Michigan Basin, *Geog. Soc. Chicago Bull.* 8, 80 pp.

Madigan, C. T. (1936), The Australian sand-ridge deserts, *Geog. Rev.*, 26:205–227.

Smith, H. T. U. (1939), Sand dune cycle in western Kansas, *Geol. Soc. Am. Bull.*, 50:1934–1935.

Melton, F. A. (1940), A tentative classification of dunes, *J. Geol.*, 48:113–173.

Bagnold, R. A. (1941), *The physics of blown sand and desert dunes*, Methuen and Co., London, 265 pp.

Hack, J. T. (1941), Dunes of the Navajo country, *Geog. Rev.*, 31:240–263.

Capot-Rey, R. (1945), Dry and humid morphology in the western Erg, *Geog. Rev.*, 35:391–407.

Black, R. F. (1951), Eolian deposits of Alaska, *Arctic*, 3:89–111.

Cooper, W. S. (1958), Coastal sand dunes of Oregon and Washington, *Geol. Soc. Am. Memoir* 72, 169 pp.

Olson, J. S. (1958), Lake Michigan dune development, *J. Geol.*, 66:254–263, 345–351, 473–483.

LOESS

Fuller, M. L. (1922), Some unusual features of the loess of China, *Geog. Rev.*, 12:570–584.

Fuller, M. L., and F. G. Clapp (1924), Loess and rock dwellings of Shensi, China, *Geog. Rev.*, 14:215–226.

Barbour, G. B. (1935), Recent observations on the loess of North China, *Geog. J.*, 86:54–64.

Moyer, R. T. (1936), Agricultural soils in a loess region of North China, *Geog. Rev.*, 26:414–425.

Russell, R. J. (1940), Lower Mississippi Valley loess, *Geol. Soc. Am. Bull.*, 55:1–40.

Bryan, K. (1945), Glacial versus desert origin of loess, *Am. J. Sci.*, 243:245–248.

Symposium on Loess (1945), *Am. J. Sci.*, 243:225–303. Ten papers on loess.

Leighton, M. M., and H. B. Willman (1950), Loess formations of the Mississippi Valley, *J. Geol.*, 58:599–623.

Fisk, H. N. (1951), Loess and Quaternary geology of the lower Mississippi Valley, *J. Geol.*, 59:333–356.

Frye, J. C., and A. B. Leonard (1951), Stratigraphy of the late Pleistocene loess of Kansas, *J. Geol.*, 59:287–305.

Péwé, T. L. (1951), An observation on wind-blown silt, *J. Geol.*, 59:399–401.

Thorp, J., and others (1952), Map of Pleistocene eolian deposits of the United States, Alaska, and parts of Canada. Scale 1:2,500,000, Geol. Soc. Am., New York.

Flint, R. F. (1957), *Glacial and Pleistocene geology*, John Wiley and Sons, New York, 553 pp. See Eolian features, pp. 176–194.

CHAPTER 29

REGIONAL LANDFORM CLASSIFICATION AND DESCRIPTION

Powell, J. W., and others (1896), *The physiography of the United States*, American Book Co., New York, 345 pp.

Bowman, I. (1911), *Forest physiography*, John Wiley and Sons, New York, 759 pp. Out of print.

Fenneman, N. M. (1928), Physiographic divisions of the United States, *Annals A.A.G.*, 18:261–353.

Fenneman, N. M. (1931), *Physiography of the Western United States*, McGraw-Hill Book Co., New York, 534 pp.

Zernitz, E. R. (1932), Drainage patterns and their significance, *J. Geol.*, 40:498–521.

Fenneman, N. M. (1938), *Physiography of the Eastern United States*, McGraw-Hill Book Co., New York, 691 pp.

Atwood, W. W. (1940), *The physiographic provinces of North America*, Ginn and Co., Boston, 536 pp.

Strahler, A. N. (1946), Geomorphic terminology and classification of landmasses, *J. Geol.*, 54:32–42.

King, L. C. (1951), *South African scenery*, Oliver and Boyd, Edinburgh, 379 pp.

COASTAL PLAINS

Davis, W. M. (1895), The development of certain English rivers, *Geog. J.*, 5:127–146.

Davis, W. M. (1896), The Seine, the Meuse, and the Moselle, *Nat. Geog. Mag.*, 7:180–202, 228–238.

Also in *Geographical essays* (1909), Ginn and Co., Boston, pp. 587–616.

Davis, W. M. (1918), *Handbook of northern France*, Harvard Univ. Press, Cambridge, Mass., 174 pp.

Cleland, H. F. (1920), The Black Belt of Alabama, *Geog. Rev.*, 10:375–387.

Grabau, A. W. (1920), The Niagara cuesta from a new viewpoint, *Geog. Rev.*, 9:264–276.

Johnson, D. W. (1921), Battlefields of the World War, *Am. Geog. Soc. Research Ser.*, No. 3, 648 pp.

Renner, G. T., Jr. (1927), The physiographic interpretation of the Fall Line, *Geog. Rev.*, 17:278–286.

Johnson, D. W. (1931), A theory of Appalachian geomorphic evolution, *J. Geol.*, 39:497–508.

Lobeck, A. K. (1939), *Geomorphology*, McGraw-Hill Book Co., New York, 731 pp. Chapter 13, Coastal plains, pp. 439–468.

Stokes, G. A. (1957), Lumbering and western Louisiana cultural landscapes, *Annals A.A.G.*, 47:250–266.

HORIZONTAL STRATA

Dutton, C. E. (1882), Tertiary history of the Grand Canyon district, *U.S. Geol. Survey Monograph* 2, 264 pp.

Atwood, W. W. (1911), A geographic study of the Mesa Verde, *Annals A.A.G.*, 1:95–100.

Lee, W. T. (1921), The Raton mesas of New Mexico and Colorado, *Geog. Rev.*, 11:384–397.

Birdseye, C., and R. C. Moore (1924), A boat voyage through the Grand Canyon of the Colorado, *Geog. Rev.*, 14:177–196.

Haas, W. H. (1926), The cliff-dweller and his habitat, *Annals A.A.G.*, 16:167–215.

Pike, R. W. (1940), Land and peoples of the Hadhramaut, Aden Protectorate, *Geog. Rev.*, 30:627–648. Plateau of horizontal strata in a dry climate.

Smith, G.-H. (1935), The relative relief of Ohio, *Geog. Rev.*, 25:272–284.

Lobeck, A. K. (1939), *Geomorphology*, McGraw-Hill Book Co., New York, 731 pp. Chapter 14, Plains and plateaus, pp. 469–502.

Ives, R. (1947), Reconnaissance of the Zion hinterland, *Geog. Rev.*, 37:618–638.

Koons, D. (1955), Cliff retreat in the southwestern United States, *Am. J. Sci.*, 253:53–60.

Doerr, A., and L. Guernsey (1956), Man as a geomorphological agent: the example of coal mining, *Annals A.A.G.*, 46:197–210.

Schumm, S. A. (1956), The role of creep and rainwash on the retreat of badland slopes, *Am. J. Sci.*, 254:693–706.

Deasy, G. F., and P. R. Griess (1957), Some new maps of the underground bituminous coal mining industry of Pennsylvania, *Annals A.A.G.*, 47:336–349.

Smith, K. G. (1958), Erosional processes and landforms in Badlands National Monument, South Dakota, *Geol. Soc. Am. Bull.*, 69:975–1008.

CAVERNS, KARST

Eigenmann, C. H. (1917), The homes of blindfishes, *Geog. Rev.*, 4:171–182.

Sanders, E. M. (1921), The cycle of erosion in a karst region (after Cvijić), *Geog. Rev.*, 11:593–604.

Lee, W. T. (1925), Carlsbad cavern, New Mexico, *Scientific Monthly*, 21:186–190.

Lobeck, A. K. (1929), The geology and physiography of the Mammoth Cave National Park, *Ky. Geol. Survey*, 6th ser., 31:327–399.

Davis, W. M. (1930), Origin of limestone caverns, *Geol. Soc. Am. Bull.*, 41:475–628.

Thorp, J. (1934), The asymmetry of the "Pepino Hills" of Puerto Rico in relation to the trade winds, *J. Geol.*, 42:537–545.

Dicken, S. N. (1935), Kentucky karst landscapes, *J. Geol.*, 43:708–728.

Bretz, J. H. (1938), Caves of the Galena formation, *J. Geol.*, 46:828–841.

Meyerhoff, H. A. (1938), The texture of karst topography in Cuba and Puerto Rico, *J. Geomorphology*, 1:279–295.

Bretz, J. H. (1942), Vadose and phreatic features of limestone caverns, *J. Geol.*, 50:675–811.

Bretz, J. H. (1949), Carlsbad Caverns and other caves of the Guadalupe block, New Mexico, *J. Geol.*, 57:447–463.

Jordan, R. H. (1950), An interpretation of Floridan karst, *J. Geol.*, 58:261–268.

DOMES

Gilbert, G. K. (1877), *Report on the geology of the Henry Mountains*, U.S. Geog. and Geol. Survey Rocky Mt. Region (Powell), pp. 18–98.

Newton, H., and W. P. Jenny (1880), *Geology of the Black Hills*, U.S. Geog. and Geol. Survey Rocky Mt. Region (Powell), 566 pp.

Cross, C. W. (1894), The laccolithic mountain groups of Colorado, Utah and Arizona, U.S. Geol. Survey, *14th Ann. Rept.*, Part 2, pp. 157–241.

Darton, N. H., and S. Paige (1925), *Central Black Hills*, U.S. Geol. Survey, Folio 219.

Lobeck, A. K. (1939), *Geomorphology*, McGraw-Hill Book Co., New York, 731 pp. Chapter 15, Dome mountains, pp. 503–542.

CHAPTER 30

FOLDS

Davis, W. M. (1889), The rivers and valleys of Pennsylvania, *Nat. Geog. Mag.*, 1:183–253. Also in *Geographical essays* (1909), Ginn and Co., Boston, pp. 413–484.

Willis, B. (1895), The northern Appalachians, *Nat. Geog. Soc. Monograph*, 1:169–202.

Davis, W. M. (1906), The mountains of southernmost Africa, *Am. Geog. Soc. Bull.*, 38:593–623.

Chamberlin, R. T. (1910), The Appalachian folds of central Pennsylvania, *J. Geol.*, 18:228–251.

ver Steeg, K. (1930), Wind gaps and water gaps of the northern Appalachians, *Annals N. Y. Acad. Sci.*, 32:87–220.

Johnson, D. (1931), *Stream sculpture on the Atlantic slope*, Columbia Univ. Press, New York, 142 pp.

Johnson, D. (1934), How rivers cut gateways through mountains, *Scientific Monthly*, 38:129–135.

Meyerhoff, H. A., and E. W. Olmsted (1936), The origins of Appalachian drainage, *Am. J. Sci.*, 232:21–41.

Fenneman, N. M. (1938), *Physiography of the Eastern United States*, McGraw-Hill Book Co., New York, pp. 195–278.

Mackin, J. H. (1938), The origin of Appalachian drainage—a reply, *Am. J. Sci.*, 236:27–53.

Lobeck, A. K. (1939), *Geomorphology*, McGraw-Hill Book Co., New York, 731 pp. Chapter 17, Folded mountains, pp. 581–612.

Rich, J. L. (1939), A bird's-eye cross section of the central Appalachian Mountains and Plateau: Washington to Cincinnati, *Geog. Rev.*, 29:561–586.

Thompson, H. D. (1939), Drainage evolution in the southern Appalachians, *Geol. Soc. Am. Bull.*, 50:1323-1356.

Strahler, A. N. (1925), Hypotheses of stream development in the folded Appalachians of Pennsylvania, *Geol. Soc. Am. Bull.*, 56:45–88.

Bethune, P. de (1948), Geomorphic studies in the Appalachians of Pennsylvania, *Am. J. Sci.*, 246:1-22.

FAULTING AND EARTHQUAKES

Davis, W. M. (1934), The Long Beach earthquake, *Geog. Rev.*, 24:1–11.

Reeds, C. A. (1934), Earthquakes, *Nat. Hist.*, 34:733–747.

Heck, N. H. (1935), A new map of earthquake distribution, *Geog. Rev.*, 25:125–130.

Page, B. M. (1935), Basin-range faulting of 1915 in Pleasant Valley, Nevada, *J. Geol.*, 43:690–707.

Lynch, J. (1940), *Our trembling earth*, Dodd, Mead and Co., New York, 202 pp.

Macelwane, J. B. (1947), *When the earth quakes*, The Bruce Publ. Co., Milwaukee, 288 pp.

FAULT FORMS AND BLOCK MOUNTAINS

Davis, W. M. (1903), Mountain ranges of the Great Basin, *Museum Comp. Zool. Bull.*, 42:129–177. Also in *Geographical essays* (1909), Ginn and Co., Boston, pp. 725–772.

Johnson, D. W. (1903), Block mountains in New Mexico, *Am. Geol.*, 31:135–139.

Cushing, S. W. (1913), Coastal plains and block mountains in Japan, *Annals A.A.G.*, 3:43–61.

Johnson, D. W. (1918), Block faulting in the Klamath Lakes region, *J. Geol.*, 26:229–236.

Blackwelder, E. (1928), The recognition of fault scarps, *J. Geol.*, 36:289–311.

Fuller, R. E., and A. A. Waters (1929), The nature and origin of the horst and graben structure of southern Oregon, *J. Geol.*, 37:204–338.

Davis, W. M. (1930), The Peacock Range, Arizona, *Geol. Soc. Am. Bull.*, 41:293–313.

Longwell, C. R. (1930), Faulted fans west of the Sheep Range, southern Nevada, *Am. J. Sci.*, 220:1–13.

Fenneman, N. M. (1931), *Physiography of the Western United States*, McGraw-Hill Book Co., New York, 691 pp. See pp. 326–395.

Teale, E. O., and Harvey E. Teale (1933), A physiographical map of Tanganiyka Territory, *Geog. Rev.*, 23:402–413.

Willis, B. (1938), San Andreas Rift, California, *J. Geol.*, 46:793–827.

Johnson, D. (1939), Fault scarps and fault-line scarps, *J. Geomorphology*, 2:174–177.

Lobeck, A. K. (1939), *Geomorphology*, McGraw-Hill Book Co., New York, 731 pp. Chapter 16, Block mountains, pp. 543–580.

Sharp, R. P. (1939), Basin-range structure of the Ruby-East Humboldt Range, northeastern Nevada, *Geol. Soc. Am. Bull.*, 50:881–920.

Dixey, F. (1941), Geomorphic development of the Shire Valley, Nyasaland, *J. Geomorphology*, 4:97–116.

Gardner, L. S. (1941), The Hurricane fault in southwestern Utah and northwestern Arizona, *Am. J. Sci.*, 239:241–260.

Strahler, A. N. (1948), Geomorphology and structure of the West Kaibab fault zone and Kaibab Plateau, Arizona, *Geol. Soc. Am. Bull.*, 59:513–540.

Cotton, C. A. (1950), Tectonic scarps and fault valleys, *Geol. Soc. Am. Bull.*, 61:717–757.

CHAPTER 31

CRYSTALLINE AND COMPLEX MASSES

Davis, W. M. (1896), Physical geography of southern New England, *Nat. Geog. Soc. Monograph*, 1:269–304.

Davis, W. M. (1911), Colorado Front Range, *Annals A.A.G.*, 1:21–83.

Martin, L. (1911), Physical geography of the Lake Superior region, *U.S. Geol. Survey Monograph*, 52:85–117.

Lobeck, A. K. (1917), Position of the New England peneplain in the White Mountains region, *Geog. Rev.*, 3:53–60.

Fenneman, N. M. (1931), *Physiography of Western United States*, McGraw-Hill Book Co., New York, 534 pp. Chapters 2, 4, 5, and 9.

Fenneman, N. M. (1938), *Physiography of the Eastern United States*, McGraw-Hill Book Co., New York, 691 pp. Chapters 3, 6, 7, and 13.

Taylor, G. (1942), British Columbia. A study in topographic control, *Geog. Rev.*, 32:372–402.

Woodruff, J. F., and E. J. Parizek (1956), Influence of underlying rock structures on stream courses and valley profiles in the Georgia Piedmont, *Annals A.A.G.*, 46:129–139.

VOLCANOES

Russell, I. C. (1897), *Volcanoes of North America*, The Macmillan Co., New York, 346 pp.

Atwood, W. W. (1906), Red mountain: a dissected volcanic cone, *J. Geol.*, 14:138–146.

Hobbs, W. H. (1906), The grand eruption of Vesuvius in 1906, *J. Geol.*, 14:636–655.

Johnson, D. W. (1907), Volcanic necks of the Mount Taylor region, New Mexico, *Geol. Soc. Am. Bull.*, 18:303–324.

Martin, G. C. (1913), The recent eruption of Katmai Volcano in Alaska, *Nat. Geog. Mag.*, 24:131–181.

Stearns, H. T. (1924), Craters of the Moon National Monument, Idaho, *Geog. Rev.*, 14:362–372.

Stearns, H. T. (1928), Lava beds National Monument, California. *Geog. Soc. Phila. Bull.*, 26:239–253.

Peacock, M. A. (1931), The Modoc Lava field, northern California, *Geog. Rev.*, 21:68–82.

Tyrrell, G. W. (1931), *Volcanoes*, T. Butterworth, London, 252 pp.

Colton, H. S. (1932), Sunset Crater: the effects of a volcanic eruption on an ancient Pueblo people, *Geog. Rev.*, 22:582–590.

Shippee, R. (1932), Lost valleys of Peru, *Geog. Rev.*, 22:562–581. Photographs of cinder cones, flows.

Atwood, W. W., Jr., (1935), The glacial history of an extinct volcano, Crater Lake National Park, *J. Geol.*, 43:142–168.

Putnam, W. C. (1938), The Mono Crater, California, *Geog. Rev.*, 28:68–82.

Lobeck, A. K. (1939), *Geomorphology*, McGraw-Hill Book Co., New York, 731 pp. Chapter 19, Volcanoes, pp. 647–704.

Williams, H. (1941), *Crater Lake, the story of its origin*, Univ. of California Press, Berkeley and Los Angeles, 97 pp.

Stearns, H. T., and G. A. Macdonald (1942), Geology and ground-water resources of the island of Maui, Hawaii, *Bull.* 7, Div. of Hydrography, Terr. of Hawaii, Honolulu, 344 pp.

Cotton, C. A. (1944), *Volcanoes as landscape forms*, Whitcombe and Tombs, 416 pp.

Jaggar, T. A. (1945), *Volcanoes declare war*, Paradise of the Pacific, Honolulu, 166 pp.

Nichols, R. L. (1946), McCartys basalt flow, Valencia County, New Mexico, *Geol. Soc. Am. Bull.*, 57:1049–1086.

Index

Elevated shorelines, 425
Elevation, bench marks, 267
　map determination, 266
Ellesmere Island, 147
Ellipse, 8
　foci, 66
　focus, 66
　major axis, 66
　minor axis, 66
　radius vector, 89
Ellipsoid, axes, 14, 15
　of revolution, 8
Eluviation, 240
Empirical classification, 260
Epeirogenic warping, 292
Epochs of geologic time, 294
Equation of time, 87
Equatorial belt of winds and calms, 131
Equatorial map projections, 21
Equatorial trough, 125
Equatorial wave, 172
Equilibrium of streams, 352
Equinox, 68
　autumnal, 68
　conditions at, 71
　vernal, 68
Era of geologic time, 294
Eratosthenes, 6
Erg, 438
Erosion, accelerated, 333, 334
　agents, 261
　geologic norm, 333
　glacial, 390
　rill, 334
　sheet, 334
　splash, 333
　stream, 347
　wind, 434
Eskers, 401, 404
Esplanade, 455
Establishment of port, 98
Estuaries, 101
Evaporation, 300
　annual, 198, 299
　as change of state, 148
　of precipitation, 331
Evaporites, 282, 316
Evapotranspiration, 301
　actual, 301, 304
　potential, 301, 304
　cycle, 304
Everest spheroid, 13, 14
Exaggeration of profiles, 268
Exfoliation, 312
Exfoliation dome, 314
Extended consequent stream, 450

Fahrenheit scale, 113
Fan, alluvial, 357
Fault-block mountains, 478
　development, 478
　geographical aspects, 478
　lifted, 478
　tilted, 478
Fault blocks, 448
Fault line, 474
Fault-line scarp, 477
　obsequent, 477
　resequent, 478
Fault plane, 475
Fault scarp, 476
　erosional development, 477
　mature, 477
　young, 477
Fault splinter, 476
Faulting, block, 295
Faults, 284, 474
　active, 479

Faults, control of streams, 484
　downthrown side, 476
　mineralization along, 478
　normal, 475
　overthrust, 294, 476
　reverse, 476
　shoreline, 420
　upthrown side, 476
Feldspar, plagioclase, 278
　potash, 277
Felsenmeer, 313
Fenno-Scandian Shield, 292, 488
Ferrel's law, 128
Ferro, meridian of, 50
Fetch of ocean waves, 143
Field capacity, 302
Finger lakes, 393
　of New York State, 400
Fiord shoreline, 417
Fiords, 211, 393
Firn, 392
First-order accuracy, of base-lines, 42
　of triangulation, 43
Fissures, volcanic, 278, 489, 495
Flatiron, 463
Flattening of poles, 8, 14, 15
Flexing, monoclinal, 476
Floes of ice, 146
Flood plains, 341
　development, 353
　utilization, 356
Flood stage, 342
Floods, 341
　channel changes, 349
　control, 343
　crest, 342
　debris, 357
　desert streams, 380
　expectancies, 343
　prediction, 343
　progress, 342
　wave, 342
Florida Stream, 140
Flow of streams, 335
　overland, 299
Flowage, of earth, 319
　of mud, 319
　of soil, 319
Foehn winds, 158
Fog, 153
　advection, 153
　on west coasts, 202
　radiation, 153
Folding of strata, 294
Folds of strata, 284, 294, 448
　anticlinal, 471
　axis, 473
　erosional development, 471
　geographical aspects, 474
　plunge, 473
　synclinal, 471
Foliation in rocks, 283
Foredeeps, 291
Foreland, cuspate, 423
Forest, boreal, 224, 226
　broadleaf, 183, 210, 218
　coniferous, 183, 219, 226, 246
　deciduous, 246
　Mediterranean, 183
　mixed broadleaf-coniferous, 183, 210,
　　219
　scrub and thorn, 183
　tropical, 183
　yellow pine, 496
Forest Service, 330
Form ratio of stream channels, 334
Formations of rock, 280
Fort Hamilton, N. Y., tide, 98

Foucault pendulum, 65
Frank, Alberta, landslide, 322, 328
Freezing point of sea water, 139
Friagems, 173
Frigid zone, 182
Fringing reefs, 426
Fronts of weather, 166
　cold, 166
　occluded, 168
　warm, 166
Frost, killing, 121
Frost action on rocks, 312

Gabbro, 278
Gage for streams, 336
Gaging of streams, 336
Gall's projection, 31
Gamma rays from sun, 111
Garnet, 283
Gas, volcanic, 279
Gaseous state of water, 148
Gases in sea water, 138
Gauss conformal projection, 34
Genetic description, 260
Geodesist, 9
Geodesy, 1, 8
Geographic grid, 10
Geoid, 9
Geologic time scale, 292
Geology, 2
　historical, 292, 293
Geomorphology, definition, 2, 259
　quantitative, 379
Geophysics, 138, 287
Geostrophic wind, 128
Geosyncline, 294
Glacial drift, 400
Glacial trough, 392, 393
Glaciation, causes, 398
　continental, effects, 226, 244
Glaciers, 389
　ablation, 389
　abrasion by, 390
　alpine, 389
　　cycle of erosion, 392
　　geographical aspects, 393
　　landforms, 391
　　névé, 392
　continental, 389
　　calving, 395
　　deposits, 400
　　glaciofluvial, 401
　　glaciolacustrine, 405
　　erosion, 399
　　geographical aspects, 405
　　ice shelves, 395
　　landforms made by, 400
　　moraines, 401
　　of Pleistocene epoch, 395
　　of North America, 395
　　of Europe, 395
　　outlet, 394
　　stages, 396
　erosion, 390
　of rock, 319
　rate of flow, 390
　valley, 389
Glaciofluvial deposits, 401
Glaciolacustrine deposits, 405
Glass, volcanic, 278
Glaze of ice, 155
Gley horizon, 248
Globes, as scale models, 18
　disadvantages, 17
　use, 17
Gneiss, 283
Gnomonic projection, 25
Goode's homolosine projection, 38

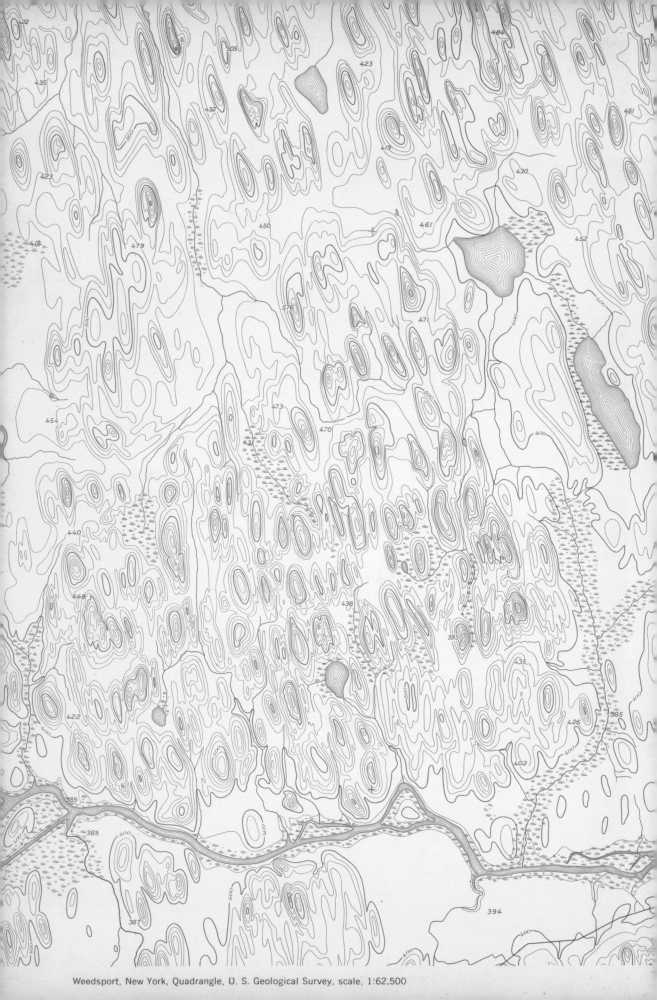

Weedsport, New York, Quadrangle, U. S. Geological Survey, scale, 1:62,500